Part
5

The Plant World

Acknowledgments

Consultant Editor   Ruth Binney

Consultants and Contributors

Ruth Binney
M. E. Cain
Louise Egerton
Margy Fischer
Malcolm Hart
Rosanne Hooper
Ginny Johnson

Nicholas Law
Gordon Leedale
Michael Lock
Keith Lye
Peter Moore
Hellen Pellant
T. C. Whitmore

Artists and Designers

Mick Gillah
Nicki Kemball
Aziz Khan

Mick Saunders
Charlotte Styles
Stuart Worker

Bull Publishing Consultants Ltd

Wendy Allen
Harold Bull
John Clark
Kate Duffy

Martyn Page
Polly Powell
Hal Robinson
Sandy Shepherd

The World Book
Encyclopedia of Science

Volume
II

World Book, Inc.

a Scott Fetzer company

Chicago

Volume II Contents

The following have provided photographs for this book's cover: (left) Stone Associates, London, 2; (middle) R. Clark/M. Goff/Science Photo Library; (right) Heather Angel

© Verlagsgruppe Bertelsmann International, GmbH, Munich 1984, 1989.
Published by World Book, Inc., Chicago 1989

ISBN: 0-7166-6053-9
A/HI

Part 5 Contents

Preface

The Plant World, like the other parts in this publication, deals with a specific scientific area—botany. It begins with the various approaches to the science and introduces the basic life processes of plants. The categories of plants from the simplest to the most highly evolved are described, as well as how these plants have adapted to their environmental conditions. The economic uses of the plant kingdom are also included in the text and lead to a final discussion of the exploitation and threatened extinction of plants and the consequent need for their conservation.

The editorial approach

The object of the content is to explain for an average family readership the many aspects of science that are fascinating and vitally important for an understanding of the world today. The material has therefore been made straightforward, concise, and accurate, and is clearly and attractively presented. It is also a readily accessible source of scientific information.

The often forbidding appearance of traditional science publications has been avoided. Approximately equal proportions of illustrations and text make the most unfamiliar subjects interesting and attractive. Even more important, all the drawings have been created specially to complement the text, each explaining a topic that can be difficult to understand through the printed word alone.

The thorough application of these principles has created a publication that encapsulates its subject in a stimulating way and that will prove to be an invaluable work of reference and education for many years to come.

The advance of science

One of the most exciting and challenging aspects of science is that its frontiers are constantly being revised and extended, and new developments are occurring all the time. Its advance depends largely on observation, experiment, dispute, and debate, which generate theories that have to be tested and even then stand only until they are replaced by better concepts. For this reason it is difficult for any science publication to be completely comprehensive. It is possible, however, to provide a thorough foundation that ensures any such advances can be comprehended—and it is the purpose of each part in this series to create such a foundation by providing all the basic knowledge in the particular area of science it describes.

How to use this material

This material can be used in two ways.

The first, and more conventional way, is to start at the beginning and to read through to the end, which gives a coherent and thorough picture of the subject and opens a resource of basic information that can be returned to for rereading and reference.

The second allows this set to be used as a library of information presented subject by subject, which the reader can consult piece by piece, as required.

All articles are presented so that the subject is equally accessible by either method. Topics are arranged in a logical sequence, outlined in the contents list. The indexes allow access to more specific points.

Within an article scientific terms are explained in the main text where an understanding of them is central to the understanding of the subject as a whole. Fact entries giving technical, mathematical, or biographical details are included, where appropriate, at the end of the article to which they relate. There is also an alphabetical glossary of terms at the end of each part, so that the reader's memory can be refreshed and so that the material can be used for quick reference whenever necessary.

All articles are relatively short, but none has been condensed artificially. Most articles occupy two pages, but some are four, or occasionally, six to twelve pages long.

The sample two-page article *(right)* shows the important elements of this editorial plan and illustrates the way in which this organization permits maximum flexibility of use.

(A) **Article title** gives the reader an immediate reference point.

(B) **Section title** shows the section in which a particular article falls.

(C) **Main text** consists of approximately 850 words of narrative information set out in a logical manner, avoiding biographical and technical details that might interrupt the story line and hamper the reader's progress.

(D) **Illustrations** include specially commissioned drawings and diagrams and carefully selected photographs that expand and clarify the main text.

(E) **Captions** explain the illustrations and connect the textual and visual elements of the article.

(F) **Annotation** of the drawings allows the reader to identify the various elements referred to in the captions.

(G) **Theme images,** where appropriate, are included in the top left-hand corner of the left-hand page, to emphasize a central element of information or to create a visual link between different but related articles. In place of a theme image, certain articles have a list of terms, units, and abbreviations relevant to the article concerned.

(H) **Fact entries** are added at the foot of the last page of certain articles to give biographical details, physical laws and equations, or additional information relating to the article but not essential to an understanding of the main text itself.

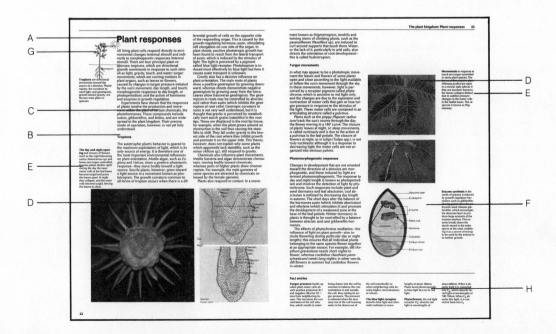

Introduction

Ferns are some of the oldest plants on earth, their fossils dating back to the late Devonian period, more than 350 million years ago. They grow in a large range of habitats, but predominantly in shady, damp environments.

It is undoubtedly true to say that plants do not receive the attention that they deserve. Perhaps it is because they are rather static and, therefore, do not display the interesting behavior patterns that make bird- and mammal-watching so appealing. For the same reason, plants are not particularly appropriate subjects for popular films and do not feature promi-nently in wildlife programs on television. They have a photogenic beauty, certainly, but not the charisma of furry animals, such as rac-coons and pandas. Or is it, perhaps, the evolu-tionary gulf that separates us from plants that makes them so unapproachable? We can iden-tify with a fox and anthropomorphize a mouse, but a plant is alien to us and any attempt to hu-

manize it may result in the creation of a monster.

Needless to say, this attitude is hardly a fair one, for plants really do form the basic support of almost all the life on this planet. All living things need energy, and nearly all the energy required by the earth's inhabitants—including ourselves—is produced from sunlight by green plants during photosynthesis. There are no animals that can perform this task for themselves, although some, such as the microscopic fresh water *Hydra* and the saltwater corals, have entered into very close relationships with single-celled algae in order to satisfy some of their energy needs.

Some microbes, such as the photosynthetic bacteria and the blue-green algae, or Cyanobacteria, are able to fix the energy of sunlight, but most, including the majority of bacteria and all fungi, are not. They resemble animals in that they can obtain their energy second-hand only, from the green plants. But there are some other, rather unusual, microbes that have a purely inorganic chemical source for their energy; these go by the rather daunting name of chemosynthetic autotrophs. They often derive their energy from an oxidation process, which may involve elements like iron or sulfur. These elements are very important in habitats such as the vast thermal vents in the abyssal depths of the ocean, where they form the basic energy resource for almost all the animals present.

But it is green plants that constitute the major source of energy on land and in the upper layers of water, wherever light penetrates. Their capacity to tap this inexhaustible source of energy must be regarded as one of the most critical steps in the evolution of life. Without it, the primitive life forms, with their vast potential for development, would have soon met with extinction as the energy-rich compounds contained in the earth's primeval broth became exhausted.

We know now that the entire process of photosynthesis, from the trapping of light to the construction of sugars, takes place within the chloroplasts, the little, green-pigmented organelles that are suspended within the photosynthetic cells of leaf and stem tissues. It has been found that isolated chloroplasts in a test tube are able to perform the whole process outside the plant cell. But perhaps even more remarkable a discovery is that each chloroplast contains some genetic material of the type normally associated with the nucleus of cells. This implies that chloroplasts may once have been independent living organisms that were captured by, or developed a very close association with, other primitive creatures that lacked the photosynthetic capacity. The outcome was the first plant cells.

The evolutionary gulf between plants and animals began to form at a very early stage when one major line of energy-fixing organisms branched off and began to exploit all the opportunities that the aquatic environment offered them. The plant kingdom had been born.

Most scientists believe that the earth is about 4.5 billion years old and that life, including photosynthetic organisms, evolved by about 3.5 billion years ago. We know very little about these primitive plants and the equally primitive animals that fed off them, but we do know that they dominated the seas for billions of years. They were so simple that they even lacked a nucleus in their single cell, and this structure (the center of cellular organization) did not appear until 1 billion years ago, which led to a very rapid diversification of both plant and animal life. It was not until about 435 million years ago that plant life began to colonize the land, so for about 90 per cent of the history of life on earth, that life was restricted to the seas.

Throughout this immense period of time, the photosynthetic activity of the primitive plants was beginning to alter the entire chemistry of the globe. Plants were starting to make their presence felt. When life first began to evolve, there probably was no oxygen in the atmosphere. Indeed, if there had been oxygen present it would probably have reacted very quickly with the organic molecules and destroyed them. But one of the by-products of the plants' photosynthesis was oxygen, generated from the splitting of water molecules, and over the course of billions of years this gas began to build up in the atmosphere. The atmospheric oxygen and ozone formed from it filtered off some of the lethal ultraviolet light that had previously made life on land impossible. So by producing oxygen (perhaps about 1 per cent of the earth's atmosphere 600 million years ago, compared with about 21 per cent today), plants paved the way for the colonization of the land.

There are two reasons why plants are worthy of respect and attention. Without them there would be no sustainable source of energy for the life of the planet; without them there would also be no oxygen to shield life from harmful radiation and to provide a means

The brightly colored fly agaric *(Amanita muscaria)* appears to be the stuff of fairy tales but in fact is what nightmares are made of, being highly poisonous. Nevertheless, such mushrooms and other fungi have a beneficial role—that is, by living off dead and decaying matter, they recycle nutrients for higher organisms. Their color warns predatory animals of their poison, which has been used to kill flies and from which the fungus gets its name.

for respiration, the process whereby we liberate the energy that plants have stored for us.

If there is one thing more remarkable than the vast period of time in which evolution seemed to make little or no progress, it is the explosive rate of evolutionary development in the last 10 per cent of the history of life on earth. Once multicellular land plants had evolved, almost all possible strategies of structural developments were soon exploited.

The flower was the next great step in plant evolution, for it led to a fascinating spiral of elaborate development in concert with the evolution of insects. Here is an area of botany that is attracting much research attention today; over the relatively short period of 125 million years, the great diversity of floral forms came into being largely because of the coevolution of insects, which acted as pollen carriers. For billions of years animals had been exploiting the energy-fixing properties of plants, but here at last was a group of plants that could turn the tables of evolution and begin to make use of the mobility of those animals that had lived a life of semiparasitism at their expense. But this about-face had its costs, for the animals still had to be attracted by and rewarded with food. Thus came the remarkable development of floral forms that comprise such a conspicuous and colorful feature of modern vegetation.

Humans are a very recent addition to the world's biota, but it is evident that even our early ancestors were aware of the value of plants as an energy source. A whole new way of life opened for us, however, when we began to store some of the grain from useful annual grasses through a climatically unfavorable period, such as drought, and then sowed the seeds when conditions were suitable again. The greater reliability and productivity of the resulting food supply allowed rapid population expansion, and man effectively entered into a symbiotic relationship with the plants he had adopted as a food resource. As he selected plant variants with larger grains more easily detached from the main stem, so he was directing and speeding up their evolution. But in doing so he was also creating species that were increasingly dependent upon his attentions for their survival. No longer could they hope to compete with the leaner, hardier wild wheats and barleys. Man, too, was becoming more vulnerable, for he depended more and more upon the cultivated plants for his food supply. His ecology and way of life became adapted to the needs of cultivated plants, as well as domesticated animals.

The scientific breeding and selection of productive plant strains is a very recent development in human activities. Only when Gregor Mendel had conducted his genetic researches in the 1860's, and when his long-lost work had come to the notice of science in 1900, was the scene set for the systematic and thorough modification of domestic plants. With a knowledge of genetics available, we have been able to improve productivity beyond recognition and have also bred for resistance to certain pests and diseases.

There have been times, however, when breeders have placed high productivity above all other considerations, with disastrous results. An example is the so-called Green Revolution, when new, high-yielding varieties of crop plants, such as rice, were introduced widely in developing countries and made considerable impact upon food shortage problems, for a while. The weakness of these new varieties was that they demanded high inputs of fertilizers and pesticides, and when these became expensive as a result of rising world oil prices, farmers were left in the unfortunate position of having lost many of their old, less productive but pest-resistant varieties of crop plants. The last state was often worse than the first.

It is a surprising fact that we rely largely upon a very small number of crop species for

Venus's-flytraps *(Dionaea muscipula)* are an example of the highly adaptive nature of plants. These insectivorous plants grow in acid bogs, which lack nitrogen in the soil. To supplement their nitrogen supply they trap insects, which they dissolve by means of a digestive enzyme so that they can absorb them more easily.

our food. Nine-tenths of the world's population is fed largely on only 20 species of plant. But there are still great opportunities for bringing new species into cultivation. For example, in the pea and bean family (Leguminosae), there are many species that might prove valuable, especially those capable of growing in dry soil. Careful, chemical screening is required first, however, because many members of this family have poisonous seeds, such as the laburnum.

Many botanists are now looking to wild plants as a source of new genetic material to improve domesticated varieties. For instance, the wild barleys of the Middle East are both more drought-tolerant and more salt-tolerant than the domesticated varieties. If these tolerances could be added to the crop plants without decreasing yields substantially, then they could permit the growth of plants, such as barley, in many semiarid areas where their cultivation is not possible at present.

Plants have many other uses besides their value as food. They provide us with lumber, fibers, rubber, and dyes. They also supply us with a large range of drugs, which have been instrumental in saving many human lives. The list of valuable plants is constantly growing as pharmacologists and plant biochemists work their way through the world's flora. Only recently the leguminous plant *Mucuma* has been found to be a rich source of dopamine, which can be used in the treatment of Parkinson's disease, and the feverfew *(Chrysanthemum parthenium)* is being examined as a possible agent for the relief of migraine.

Not only is the plant kingdom the source of our energy, it is also a repository of information about the course of evolution on our planet, the origin of the oxygen which we breathe, and the sponge for the carbon dioxide that we, our cars, and our factories exhale. Apart from the many essential materials we obtain from plants, their esthetic value has been an inspiration for centuries to authors, artists, and poets.

There can be only two reasonable conclusions when one considers the numerous ways in which plants have contributed to our well-being. One is that we should care for our plants and conserve them. It may take decades to assess their value to us and even then we cannot predict their unseen future uses. Conservation of our flora and of the habitats which support it is one of the most pressing needs of our day.

The second conclusion is that if we have neglected the study of botany, then we are missing a great deal. It is to remedy this last situation that this book has been written, and we trust that it may generate a renewed interest in and respect for the remarkable world of plants.

Insect pollination has been an important feature in plant evolution and has meant that the ovule could develop deep within the flower where the embryonic seed would be protected. The bright colors of the petals and the sticky nectar attract insects to the flowers. The insects pick up pollen grains and, in moving about, transfer them to the female stigmas. The pollen grain then travels down the style, or extends a tube, to the ovule where the male gamete fertilizes the female one.

The plant kingdom

Of the more advanced living organisms on earth, the plants evolved before the animals. The oldest plant fossils date from the Precambrian era, over 3 billion years ago. It was not until the Cambrian period almost 600 million years ago, however, that animals evolved, by which time plants had prepared the conditions in which animal life could exist. The green plants manufactured starch and sugar by photosynthesis and in doing so released oxygen, which revolutionized the atmosphere of the planet. Only then could the air be utilized by animals.

Since the first appearance on earth of plant life, millions of plant species have populated the planet, many of which are now extinct. Today about 350,000 species of plants are known, although the true number is probably considerably more, because new species are constantly being discovered and identified. Traditionally, the plants are divided into the lower, or nonflowering plants, and those that produce seeds and flowers.

What is a plant?

Plant cell structure usually distinguishes these organisms from animals. The cell has a rigid, cellulose wall, rather than a flexible membrane. Large, permanent vacuoles occur in the center of the cytoplasm, whereas animal cells have small temporary ones, or none at all. Plant cells have chloroplasts that contain chlorophyll; animal cells do not.

A plant is generally considered to be a living organism that manufactures its own food (it is autotrophic). There are some, however, that are parasitic, and others that are saprophytes, processing food outside their bodies and then absorbing it. Plants are usually immobile, feeding on the spot.

Even so, there is some overlap between lower animals and simple plants, and the distinction between them is not always clear. Many unicellular and some multicellular algae move around like animals, but are autotrophic; some surround and ingest their food (they are phagotrophic) like protozoa, but do not have a true cell wall, only a membrane; slime molds are also phagotrophic but have a cell membrane during their feeding stage only and, unlike protozoa, reproduce by spores (they are sporophytic).

The most primitive lower plants have no root structures, conducting or supporting tissues. Vascular plants, in contrast, have a system of vessels that transport water and photosynthetic products. These higher plants are differentiated into stems, leaves, and, often, roots and flowers; they also have supporting tissues. Most lower plants are spore-producing, or sporophytic, whereas the higher plants are seed-producing, or spermatophytic.

Lower plants

The simplest organisms are the bacteria and blue-green algae, which are called procaryotes because they have no distinct nucleus in their cells. All other plants are called eucaryotes—that is, each cell has a true nucleus. Bacteria are single-celled but contain no chlorophyll and, rather than surviving by photosynthesis, use a variety of biochemical means to obtain energy. Some manufacture their energy supplies from chemicals in their immediate environment whereas others rely on finding it ready-made. These bacteria in-

Animal cells *(below)* and plant cells *(below right)* differ in several respects but also contain some of the same organelles. The main distinctions between them are that the animal cell wall is plastic while that of the plant is rigid and contains cellulose; plant cells have large sap vacuoles, but animal cells have none; chloroplasts containing chlorophyll are present in many plant cells, but not in animal cells.

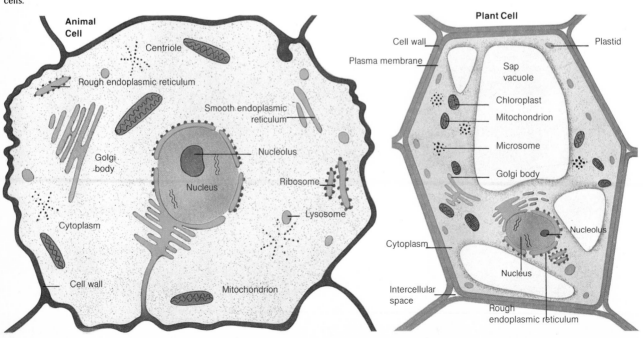

Animal Cell
- Centriole
- Rough endoplasmic reticulum
- Smooth endoplasmic reticulum
- Nucleolus
- Ribosome
- Golgi body
- Nucleus
- Lysosome
- Cytoplasm
- Cell wall
- Mitochondrion

Plant Cell
- Cell wall
- Plasma membrane
- Plastid
- Sap vacuole
- Chloroplast
- Mitochondrion
- Microsome
- Golgi body
- Nucleolus
- Cytoplasm
- Nucleus
- Intercellular space
- Rough endoplasmic reticulum

clude the disease-forming types that inhabit the bodies of humans and other animals. They reproduce simply by splitting in two (binary fission) and, occasionally, by spores. Bacteria comprise thousands of species.

The blue-green algae are grouped with the bacteria because they share some structural features: for example, their DNA is not arranged into chromosomes; and they do not have a nuclear membrane. The rest of the algae are more closely related to the higher plants in their cell structure. Many, such as *Euglena,* consist of single cells capable of independent existence. Others are composed of chains (filaments) of cells, and the large seaweeds are made up of thousands of cells. They also vary widely in their pigmentation, cell wall composition, and the kind of foodstuff they store. Algal reproduction may be asexual—by binary fission—or sexual, by conjugation. There are approximately 21,000 species of algae.

In common with the bacteria, the fungi do not contain chlorophyll and, therefore, do not photosynthesize. Instead, they live either as parasites on other plants or animals, obtaining food ready-processed or as saprophytes. Like the bacteria, they function as decomposers, releasing nutrients that support higher organisms. Fungi include molds, yeasts, rusts, smuts, mushrooms, and toadstools. This group comprises more than 100,000 species. Most reproduce sexually and asexually, the typical mushroom-shaped fruiting body producing spores by sexual means.

The lichens are compound organisms of fungi and algae, which have a symbiotic relationship. This successful group is autotrophic and survives in almost every habitat; it contains about 18,000 species.

Mosses and liverworts (the bryophytes) are represented by more or less the same number of species as lichens are. They photosynthesize but are nevertheless regarded as primitive land-dwelling plants because they do not have roots or a truly differentiated vascular system. These green plants typically have an alternation of sexual and asexual generations (gametophyte and sporophyte respectively).

The ferns, club mosses, and horsetails—the pteridophytes—do have a vascular system. Like the mosses, these plants also display alternation of generations, but the mature plant (the sporophyte) is much more complex than that of the bryophytes, with differentiated growing and conducting tissues. There are about 12,000 known species of pteridophyte, which are distributed worldwide; this is, however, a tiny fraction of the number that dominated the earth about 400 million years ago.

Higher plants

The higher plants are distinguished from the lower ones by the development of the seed and with it the restriction of the gametophyte (sexual) generation to a fusion of cells within the sporophyte. This development reduced the risks of the reproductive process and (except in primitive forms such as cycads and ginkgos) lessened the need for water as an essential medium for the completion of fertilization.

About 250,000 species of seed-producing

plants are recognized today. Of these some 500 species are gymnosperms (conifers and cycads). Typically, the seeds of gymnosperms are naked, compared with those of angiosperms, whose seeds are enclosed in a tissue coating called an ovary. The angiosperms, or flowering plants, now dominate the earth's vegetation, having adapted to survive in almost every habitat.

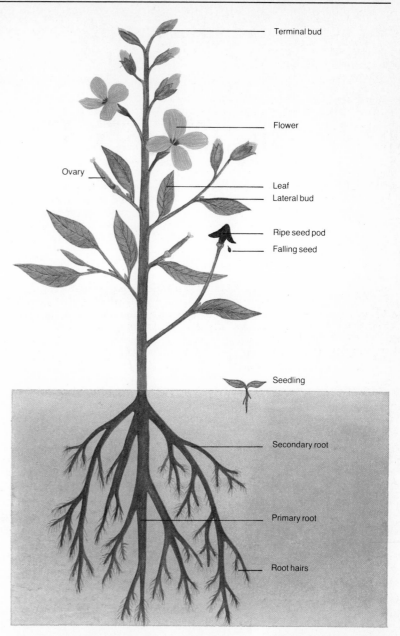

Terminal bud

Flower

Ovary

Leaf
Lateral bud

Ripe seed pod
Falling seed

Seedling

Secondary root

Primary root

Root hairs

The basic structures of many flowering plants include a primary root, which bears secondary roots; a main, woody stem; lateral branches from which grow photosynthetic leaves; and flowers. Lateral buds in the angles between the branches and the leaves, or the main stem, are suppressed regions of growth, which may later develop into branches themselves. After blooming, when fertilization occurs, the flower petals drop off, leaving the ovary in which the seeds develop. The seeds are shed when they are ripe and later grow into seedlings.

Plant classification

Field rose
(*Rosa arvensis*)

Kingdom
Eucaryota
Phylum
Spermatophyta
Subphylum
Magnoliophytina
(Angiospermae)
Class
Magnoliopsida
Subclass
Rosidae
Order
Rosales
Family
Rosaceae
Genus
Rosa
Species
arvensis

Scientific classification is the system most commonly used in describing plants. Using this method, a common field rose could first be grouped into those organisms that are eucaryotes—that is, they have nuclei in their cells. This group embraces most animals and plants and is considered to be a kingdom by some botanists. The grouping can then be broken down in stages to the basic unit—the plant's species name, *Rosa arvensis*.

The classification of plants and animals provides a logical system by which living organisms can be accurately identified. But in its widest sense, plant classification means more than just giving a name to each of the more than 50,000 or so species of which the plant kingdom is composed. It consists of grouping plants in categories of ever-increasing size—a process known as scientific classification. If a classification also takes account of the relationships that exist between plants then it is described as systematic. The entire process of classifying organisms, and the study of classifications past and present, is embraced by the blanket term taxonomy.

The foundations of modern taxonomy were laid in the mid-eighteenth century with the work of the Swedish naturalist Carl von Linné (1707-1778), better known by the Latinized version of his name—Linnaeus. It was Linnaeus who, with the publication of his *Species Plantarum* in 1753, established the system of binomial nomenclature for plants—such as *Rosa arvensis* for the field rose.

Naming and grouping

Today the naming of plants and their placement in a standard, accepted hierarchical system of classification is governed by strict rules laid down in *The International Code of Botanical Nomenclature* (ICBN). This rule book recognizes 12 principal ranks of diminishing size,

ranging from kingdom through phylum and species to form, with subcategories that can be designated for each category. Of these, the basic "unit" of classification is generally considered to be the species.

A species is a group of individuals that are so similar as to be more or less identical and that can interbreed. Similar species are grouped into genera, similar genera into families, and so on.

Despite the fact that plants are grouped and named in such a rigid way, they are not classified using just one system. Scientific classification is an interpretation of facts. It is based on the opinion and judgment a biologist forms after studying specimens of animals and plants. Most biologists use the same basic framework for classification. But not all biologists agree on how individual animals and plants fit into this scheme, and so classifications often differ in details. The system used here differs slightly from that discussed in *The World Book Encyclopedia*. For more information on scientific classification, see the *World Book* articles CLASSIFICATION, SCIENTIFIC and PLANT (A classification of the plant kingdom).

Any system of classification that takes into account only one or a few plant (or animal) characteristics is described as artificial. Such an artificial system could group plants, for example, according to their color, petal number, or edibility. While they are useful for specific

Scanning electron micrographs are often used to study pollen grains and spores. Such microscopic examination of these bodies reveals their structural characteristics, which can be used as a means of grouping together species of plants.

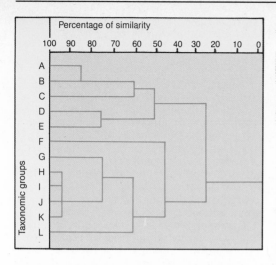

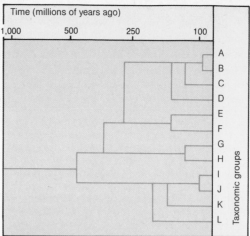

Dendrograms are a graphic means of showing the relationships between groups of plants. A phenogram *(far left)* charts the percentage of phenotypic similarities between a number of taxonomic groups. A cladogram *(left)* indicates the evolutionary pathways of species over the past millions of years to reveal their lineage relationships.

Fossils of plant organs such as leaves are an important source of material for the evolutionary classification of plants.

Illustrated herbals played a significant role in the early description and subsequent classification of plants. Many portrayed the whole plant and its individual parts.

purposes, such systems do not have great worth in the wider botanical context. By comparison natural systems, based on the analysis of a great many characteristics shared (or not shared) by plants, are very useful.

In some aspects of botanical study, however, demands are made that are not necessarily met by a natural system of classification; notable among these is the study of the evolutionary relationships between plants. This system is designed to reflect in particular the evolutionary pathways along which plants have progressed over millions of years of development.

Gathering information

Any system of classification relies on the accumulation of vast amounts of data about plants. This information includes the gross structure of a plant (its morphology), often with special reference to flowers and other organs involved in reproduction. Plants are measured and examined microscopically in every detail with light and electron microscopes. The development of each plant is studied macro- and microscopically, and its chromosomes, breeding systems, geographical distribution, and ecology are all considered. Chemistry can be significant, and the fossil record can also provide valuable insight into the way in which plants should be grouped together.

The practice of numerical taxonomy is based on the construction of similarity tables or data matrices between species, genera, and other classifications. It relies on computers to store and analyze information and to calculate the degrees of similarity between plants. By this means, plants are evaluated and grouped according to the degree of similarity they possess.

Plant classification is a means by which we can keep track of the changing nature of the plant kingdom, for example by monitoring plants that are in danger of extinction, particularly now that many of our traditional natural resources are in short supply or running out. At the laboratory level, experimental taxonomy, which is designed to discover more about the nature and genetic basis of the diversity of species, could hold the key to the preservation of that diversity and its use in such tasks as the improvement of crop plants.

Plant structure and photosynthesis

Two factors that make plants as living organisms different from animals are their structure and their method of obtaining the energy to "power" their life processes. Structurally most plants are based largely on cellulose, a natural polymer made up of atoms of carbon, hydrogen, and oxygen (cellulose is a complex carbohydrate). Plants derive their energy from sunlight, which they use in the process called photosynthesis to bring about the chemical combination of carbon dioxide (from the air) and water (from the soil) to make simple sugars. In addition, for healthy growth plants need various other elements—particularly nitrogen and phosphorus—which they must also obtain from the soil. Transport of the various elements and compounds through the tissues of the plant is carried out by water, and so water plays a key role both in photosynthesis and in running the biochemical factory of which every plant consists. Water is the chief constituent of the fluid within the plant cells that make up the various tissues and structures of a plant.

Cell structure

In 1665, when the British scientist Robert Hooke first turned his simple microscope onto a thin slice of cork (the outermost layer of a woody plant stem), he described what he saw as resembling a collection of "little boxes." Later he coined the word "cell" for the units of plant tissue (later to be applied to animal tissue as well).

Plant cells are "packets" of living protoplasm surrounded by a dead cell wall composed mostly of cellulose, a carbohydrate manufactured by a plant cell's cytoplasm. Cellulose fibers give strength to plant stems, roots, and leaves. It is the substance that makes plant stems stiff.

The cell wall surrounds a central mass of living cytoplasm, which in turn encloses a large vacuole containing cell sap, a mixture of various chemicals in a watery solution. The cytoplasm, which is bounded by a thin cell membrane, is not uniform in appearance or texture but contains various structures called organelles. These include mitochondria, the cell's energy-producers; chloroplasts, which conduct the process of photosynthesis; and lysosomes, which contain digestive enzymes to break down any substances that enter the cell. Also in the cytoplasm is the many-folded endoplasmic reticulum, which produces fats and proteins, and the nucleus, the center for nucleic acids and the genetic material of the cell.

The cells of a plant begin as small units produced at growing points, called meristems. Those at the growing tips of shoots or roots are known as apical meristems; those in the body of a plant include cambium, which produces vascular tissue, and cork cambium, which produces the outer tissue called cork.

Plant tissues

As cells grow they differentiate into the various tissues of the plant. For instance the outermost covering of cells known as the epidermis forms a continuous layer around the plant. The characteristics of epidermal cells depend on their position on the plant, but most of them are flat, platelike cells. Modified versions include the guard cells of stomata (the "breathing holes" in a leaf) and the fine hairs on roots and rootlets. Epidermal cells secrete a waxy cuticle onto their surface and have cell walls containing a great deal of a fatty water-repellent substance called cutin, both of which help to protect the plant.

In older stems and roots the epidermis is frequently replaced by the cork, which is bet-

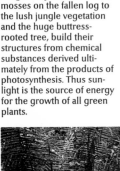

All green plants, from the mosses on the fallen log to the lush jungle vegetation and the huge buttress-rooted tree, build their structures from chemical substances derived ultimately from the products of photosynthesis. Thus sunlight is the source of energy for the growth of all green plants.

ter at withstanding damage. It contains three different kinds of cells: the cork cambium (phellogen), a typical meristematic tissue that divides to produce cork cells (phellem) to the outside and cortical cells (phelloderm) to the inside. The cork cells include a layer of water-repellent suberin.

The water-conducting tissues (the xylem) are long tubes running the length of the plant and form part of the vascular bundle in angiosperms. There are two types—the tracheids and the vessels—with walls that characteristically show spiral, annular, scalariform (ladderlike), or reticulate (netlike) thickening. Tracheids are long narrow cells about .5 to 3 inches (1 to 7.5 centimeters) long and 0.04 to 0.06 millimeter across, which join at their ends with a very slanting wall. Vessel cells are small but some of the walls between them break down to form a long tube; those walls that remain are perforated by pores. The vessels may be as narrow as only 0.006 millimeter across or up to 0.7 millimeter wide, but in trees they may be as long as 16 feet (5 meters).

The conducting tissues—the xylem and phloem—are produced by a layer of meristematic tissue called the cambium. This vascular tissue is formed primarily in discrete bundles, but the cambium may extend to form a complete ring of tissue within the plant stem. Cells produced by the cambium differentiate into xylem on the inner side and phloem on the outer side. Both occur throughout the plant.

Xylem's main function concerns the movement of water around the plant (by the tracheids and vessels), although it is also a supporting tissue (by means of sclereid and fiber cells) and has some storage functions (using its parenchyma cells). Phloem is concerned with the movement and storage of food, and it also acts as a supporting tissue. Food movement is achieved by sieve tubes. The surrounding tissue, the parenchyma, is again the food store, and phloem fibers are the supporting elements.

Parenchyma consists of living cells capable of growth and division. They have various shapes from stellate (star-shaped in cross section) to the more common polyhedral conformation. Some have thickened walls, and some may be specialized for secretion or excretion. Their general functions are in photosynthesis, storage, and repair. The type specialized as a supporting tissue—with unevenly thickened walls—is called collenchyma. It occurs as strands or bundles in stems, leafstalks, and leaf veins.

Sclereids and fibers occurring as mechanical tissue in both xylem and phloem are examples of sclerenchyma. To fulfill their function as support and strengthening cells they have thickened and often lignified walls. The two types vary in shape: fibers are long and thin, whereas sclereids may vary between polyhedral and elongated and are sometimes branched.

Water conduction

Most herbaceous plants contain from 70 to 95 per cent water, and some algae may contain as much as 98 per cent. The water has a number of functions. One is to act as a hydrostatic skel-

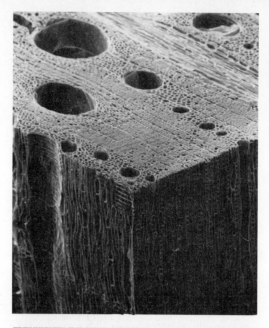

The water-conducting vessels, consisting of joined-up long narrow cells, can be clearly seen in the scanning electron micrograph of a piece of wood *(above left).* Xylem vessels may have various structures, with the walls thickened in a characteristic way *(above).* Common forms, shown here in longitudinal section, are spiral (A), annular (B), and the ladderlike scalariform (C). Like the blood vessels in an animal, the vessels become increasingly finer toward a plant's extremities, until eventually they form the threadlike veins of the leaves *(left).*

eton that helps to support the plant (most plants deprived of water soon wilt). Another role of water is as a medium in which biochemical processes take place. But one of its most important functions is to transport various materials—dissolved gases, minerals, and nutrients—around the plant's tissues.

The continual movement of water through a plant is known as the transpiration stream. Water from the soil enters root hairs by osmosis (that is, it crosses the semipermeable membranes surrounding the cells) and thus dilutes the cell contents. This causes water to flow through the membranes into the next cell, and an osmotic chain is set up through the cells to the water-conducting tissues. A similar chain is set up in the leaves. Cells surrounding the air spaces lose water by evaporation, which concentrates the cell sap. Water from surrounding cells passes in, establishing a chain back to the water-conducting tissues.

The transpiration stream therefore comprises the movement of water into and through the roots, along the xylem vessels, and through the leaf cells to be evaporated or transpired through the stomata of the leaves.

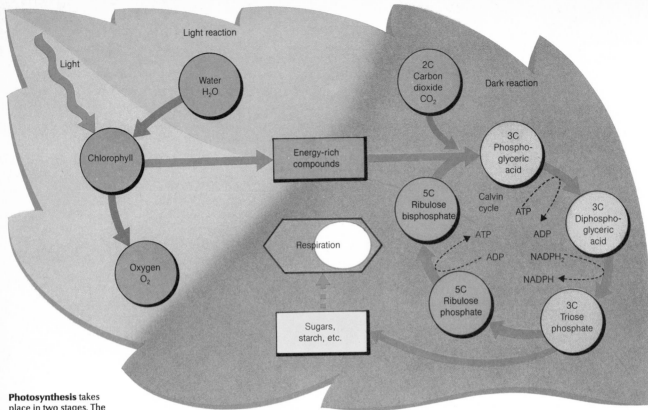

Light reaction

Light

Water
H₂O

Chlorophyll

2C
Carbon
dioxide
CO₂

Dark reaction

Energy-rich
compounds

3C
Phospho-
glyceric
acid

Oxygen
O₂

5C
Ribulose
bisphosphate

Calvin
cycle

ATP

3C
Diphospho-
glyceric
acid

Respiration

ATP

ADP

ADP

NADPH₂

NADPH

5C
Ribulose
phosphate

3C
Triose
phosphate

Sugars,
starch, etc.

Photosynthesis takes place in two stages. The overall outcome of the light reaction is the splitting of water molecules—using the energy of sunlight absorbed by chlorophyll—to release oxygen and generate energy-rich compounds such as ATP. A cycle of reactions (the Calvin cycle) in the dark reaction converts carbon dioxide into carbohydrates.

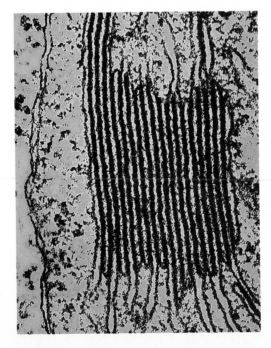

The closely packed layers called thylakoids, or granae, are the sites within chloroplasts in which the light reaction of photosynthesis takes place.

The water in the conducting tissues passes up the plant partly because of the osmotic "root pressure," partly because of the capillary effect of the narrow tubes, and partly because of the osmotic "suction pressure" from the leaves. The rate of movement in the conducting tissues varies, but rates of 10 inches and 13 feet (25 and 400 centimeters) per hour have been recorded. The amount of water loss per plant also varies. A corn plant *(Zea mays)*, for example, may lose nearly a gallon (3.8 liters) of water per day, or approximately 325,000 gallons of water per acre (3,040,000 liters per hectare) in a growing season.

Photosynthesis

Apart from a few bacteria, plants are the only living organisms that are capable of manufacturing their own food. It is the energy of sunlight that powers this process, which is appropriately called photosynthesis. Animals cannot make their own food but rely—directly or indirectly—on plants to produce it.

This is the fundamental difference between plants and animals. All other differences follow on. Since an animal cannot make its own food it must go out and find it—hence it must be mobile. Animals must be able to recognize food when they meet it—hence the sensory and nervous systems that plants lack. Movement entails cells that are flexible—not stiffened with strong walls of cellulose, as plant cells are. Since animals eat plants, or eat other animals that eat plants, it can be said that nearly all the biosphere derives its energy directly from the sun. The only exceptions are in volcanic areas in the dark ocean depths, where the energy to power life is obtained from the erupting chemicals.

The raw materials for photosynthesis are carbon dioxide from the air (taken in through the leaves) and water, usually from the soil (taken in through the roots). The two combine initially to produce simple sugars and oxygen. Sunlight is the energy source, and the green pigment chlorophyll is the means whereby the sunlight can be used. In biochemical terms, the whole process is the reduction of carbon dioxide (to simple sugars) by hydrogen obtained from the photolysis of water mediated by chlorophyll. Photosynthesis takes place as a large number of interrelated stages, but can be summed up overall by the simple equation:

$$6CO_2 + 6H_2O + (light + chlorophyll) \rightarrow C_6H_{12}O_6 + 6O_2$$

The green color of plants is due to the presence of pigments in the chloroplasts. Chief of these pigments is chlorophyll *a*, which is found in all green plants and converts light energy in the red and blue wavelengths into chemical form. Most plants also contain other pigments—chlorophyll *b*, xanthophyll, carotene, and pheophytin—each of which absorbs light of different wavelengths. The process generates a reducing agent (which is later used for converting carbon dioxide to organic materials), whose production consumes electrons from the chlorophyll itself. These electrons are replaced by splitting molecules of water into hydrogen and oxygen. The oxygen is lost from the plant by simple diffusion into air spaces in the leaves and out to the atmosphere through the stomata. The hydrogen that is released combines with a hydrogen-carrier (NADP, reducing it to NADPH$_2$). This entire process, which releases energy stored as ATP (adenosine triphosphate), is called the "light reaction."

The next stage, the "dark reaction" (so called because it does not require light), is a cyclic process known as the Calvin cycle in which ATP and NADPH$_2$ reduce carbon dioxide to carbohydrate. The cycle begins when carbon dioxide combines with a 5-carbon sugar (RUBP or ribulose biphosphate), which splits into two 3-carbon molecules: PGA, or phosphoglyceric acid, and a triose phosphate (phosphoglyceraldehyde). The reducing agent NADPH$_2$ is used up and so is some ATP; RUBP is regenerated using the remaining ATP. The rest of the triose phosphate is employed to make carbohydrates, proteins, fats, and other similar substances needed by the plant.

In many tropical grasses and plants that grow in arid areas the cycle is modified so that the first photosynthetic product is not a 3-carbon molecule but a 4-carbon one (a dicarboxylic acid). This alternative method, the so-called C4 pathway, is more efficient than the C3 pathway.

The rate at which photosynthesis takes place is affected by various external factors. The most obvious of these is the availability of light. At low light levels the rate of photosynthesis is proportional to the light intensity. At higher light levels, a point of light saturation is reached beyond which any increase in light does not increase the rate of photosynthesis. Then other factors become limiting. One of these limiting factors is the carbon dioxide concentration of the air; an increase in carbon dioxide speeds up photosynthesis. Temperature is a limiting factor only to the dark reaction, because it is a chemical process (the light reaction is photochemical, and therefore largely independent of temperature). Water is a limiting factor in that lack of it causes the stomata of the leaves to close, thereby preventing carbon dioxide from entering.

Plant respiration

Photosynthesis effectively traps the energy of sunlight and stores it (as food materials) for fu-

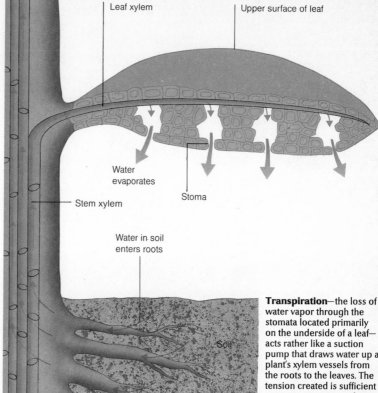

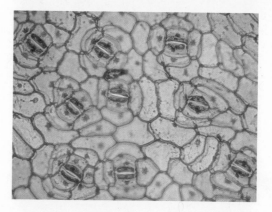

Transpiration—the loss of water vapor through the stomata located primarily on the underside of a leaf—acts rather like a suction pump that draws water up a plant's xylem vessels from the roots to the leaves. The tension created is sufficient to transport water to the top of the tallest tree. Stomata (shown close-up, *below left*) are pores, each one edged with two guard cells that enable them to open and close, depending on external conditions such as humidity and temperature.

ture use. The stored energy is released in the process of respiration, which chemically is an oxidation reaction in which sugars, for example, are converted to carbon dioxide and water. Like photosynthesis, respiration is a stepwise process that can be summed up by the simple equation:

$$C_6H_{12}O_2 + 6O_2 \rightarrow 6CO_2 + 6H_2O + energy$$

which is the exact opposite of the photosynthesis equation. At a certain light level, the rates of photosynthesis and respiration balance and no carbon dioxide or oxygen enter or leave the plant—this is known as the light compensation point.

Respiration takes place in the cytoplasm of the cell, principally in the mitochondria. The major sequence of reactions follows a cyclic path known as the Krebs cycle (or citric acid cycle), which is preceded by a shorter metabolic pathway called glycolysis. Using glucose as an example, the first stages involve the splitting of the 6-carbon glucose molecule (by hydrolysis) in a series of reactions to produce pyruvic acid. Next, carbon dioxide is lost from the 4-carbon pyruvic acid, and the resultant

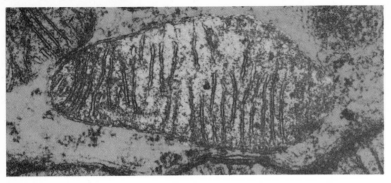

A mitochondrion *(yellow)* is the microscopic body most concerned with cell respiration, as explained in the diagram below.

Cell respiration is a complex process that begins with glycolysis, the breakdown of carbohydrates with the release of carbon dioxide. The 2-carbon compound acetyl coenzyme A is produced, which then initiates a series of reactions within a mitochondrion. In this series, called the Krebs cycle, more carbon dioxide is released and energy stored in the form of ATP (adenosine triphosphate), 12 molecules of which are produced during each cycle.

2-carbon acetyl group combines with a carrier enzyme to form acetyl coenzyme A. Then at the start of the Krebs cycle the acetyl group is transferred to a 4-carbon molecule (oxaloacetic acid) to produce the 6-carbon citric acid. Finally this acid is broken down in a series of steps to regenerate oxaloacetic acid. Some steps involve the release of carbon dioxide and hydrogen, which is passed via a hydrogen acceptor such as NAD in another series of stages to cytochrome. In the presence of an enzyme (cytochrome oxidase), cytochrome converts hydrogen and oxygen into water. Energy is released during hydrogen transfer, and some of it converts ADP into ATP.

Some organisms such as yeasts and bacteria can derive their energy in the absence of oxygen, by anaerobic respiration or fermentation, from glycolysis. The route is pyruvic acid to carbon dioxide and acetaldehyde, which is converted to ethyl alcohol (as in winemaking), which in turn may be oxidized to acetic acid. Only a small amount of energy is released, and some of the products are toxic. When oxygen is in short supply—for example, in water-logged roots—plants may be forced to use anaerobic respiration. Some have developed systems to convert the poisonous product alcohol into less toxic substances (such as or-

ganic acids) so that they can employ anaerobic respiration to get through difficult times.

Synthesis of complex compounds

The energy released by respiration is used by plants for various purposes, including the build-up of complex compounds such as carbohydrates, fats, and proteins and to power energy-consuming processes that take place within the cells. A simple sugar, such as glucose, is a basic end product of photosynthesis and is the starting material for a large number of different chemicals. Chemically, glucose is a monosaccharide whose molecules contain six carbon atoms, five of which together with an oxygen atom are arranged in a ring—it is termed a hexose. Each carbon has a hydrogen atom and a hydroxyl group attached to it. It is the replacement of the attached groups or one of the carbon atoms that alters the chemistry of the molecule and creates new compounds. Other important plant monosaccharides include 3-carbon (triose) and 5-carbon (pentose) sugars.

When two hexose molecules join together they form a disaccharide such as sucrose (table sugar), which is formed and stored in plants such as sugar beet and sugar cane. When large numbers of hexose molecules join together, a polysaccharide results. Polysaccharides may be structural, such as the natural polymer—and valuable raw material—cellulose, formed from glucose units. Other structural polysaccharides include mannan from yeast (mannose units), xylan (xylose units), and pectin, materials that form cell walls.

Other groups of polysaccharides have nutrient functions, acting as food stores in plants. Among the most important are starches and inulins. Starch in a storage organ such as a potato tuber, for example, occurs as grains containing two different molecules, amylose and amylopectin. Amylose consists of long chains

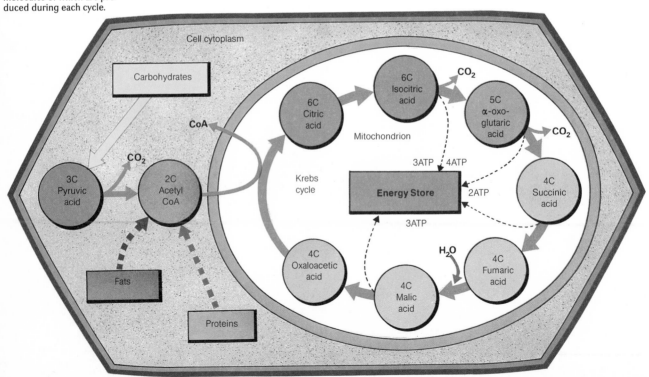

of glucose units, whereas amylopectin has a very branched structure. Inulin is made up mainly of fructose units, with some glucose.

Many seeds have fats and oils as storage material rather than carbohydrates such as saccharides and polysaccharides. The fats are esters of a high molecular weight fatty acid (such as stearic or oleic acid) and an alcohol (usually glycerol). Many plant oils are of economic importance: examples include the oils from olives and groundnuts.

The living parts of cell protoplasm consist of proteins, rather complex molecules containing nitrogen and built up from amino acids. There are about 20 naturally occurring amino acids in proteins, and any given protein depends on the number and arrangement of some of these. Important proteins include enzymes, the biological catalysts that bring about and control most of the chemical processes in the cells; some work only in conjunction with a (nonprotein) coenzyme. There are various types of enzymes. Carbohydrases, for example, break down carbohydrates; transferase enzymes transfer various groups—for instance, carboxylases add or subtract carbon dioxide. The synthesis of enzymes and other proteins, and the passing on of hereditary information, is controlled by nucleic acids. There are two kinds found in the nuclei of cells: the complex DNA (deoxyribonucleic acid) and the simpler RNA (ribonucleic acid).

Secondary plant products

In addition to carbohydrates, fats, and proteins, there are several other classes of chemicals produced by plants, many of commercial value. The nitrogen-containing alkaloids, for instance, are toxic compounds used as drugs. Their function in plants is probably to deter grazing animals. Most occur in members of three families: the poppies (Papaveraceae), buttercups (Ranunculaceae), and the nightshade family (Solanaceae). Examples of alkaloids include atropine, colchicine, morphine, nicotine, opium, and strychnine.

Tannins are a group of substances frequently found in the vacuoles of cells. Most are polymers of carbohydrates and phenolic acids and have a bitter, astringent taste. Their function, like alkaloids, may be to deter herbivores. Cultivated plants containing them include tea, coffee, and bilberries.

Terpenes are aromatic chemicals that are important constituents of essential oils. Together with aldehydes, ketones, and alcohols they form the scents of plants and give rise to resins and balsams. They are often produced in response to an injury from special cells and have a protective function.

Sugar (sucrose) is a carbohydrate made and stored by plants, from which it is extracted for human consumption. In temperate regions farmers grow sugar beets, seen being harvested *(below)*; sugar cane is the equivalent crop in tropical areas.

Belladonna *(Atropa belladonna)* is the source of the alkaloid atropine. Like other such compounds it is highly poisonous and is prescribed as a drug in carefully controlled doses.

Fact entries

Chlorophyll exists in several related forms, all with a structure based on the chemical porphyrin (as is hemin, a component of the red blood pigment hemoglobin). It is present in the chloroplasts in the leaves of green plants, where it mediates the utilization of light energy in the synthesis of carbohydrates from carbon dioxide and water (photosynthesis).

Calvin, Melvin, an American chemist, was awarded the 1961 Nobel Prize in Chemistry for discovering the series of stages involved in the dark reaction of photosynthesis. Working at the University of California, he used compounds "labeled" with radioactive carbon-14 to trace the complex pathway of what has become known as the Calvin cycle.

Krebs, Hans Adolf (1900-1981), a German-born British biochemist, shared the 1953 Nobel Prize in Physiology and Medicine for determining the energy-generating cyclic pathway involved in cell respiration. Known also as the citric, or tricarboxylic, acid cycle, it is now generally called the Krebs cycle after him. It takes place in mitochondria, tiny structures found within plant and animal cells.

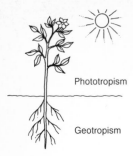

Plant responses

Tropisms are directional movements toward the source of a stimulus. Phototropism, the curvature toward light, and geotropism, growth toward gravity, are the two main plant responses.

The day and night opening and closure of flowers (such as the night-blooming cactus *Selenicereus* sp.) and leaves are turgor-controlled. In some plants *(below right)* during the day the inner motor cells at the leaf bases become turgid and press the leaves apart. At night they collapse, and the outer cells become turgid, forcing the leaves to close.

All living plant cells respond directly to environmental changes (external stimuli) and indirectly to morphogenetic responses (internal stimuli). There are four principal plant responses: tropisms, which are directional growth movements in response to such stimuli as light, gravity, touch, and water; turgor movements, which are curving motions in plant organs, such as leaves or flowers, caused by changes in turgor pressure initiated by the sun's movement, day length, and touch; morphogenetic responses to day length, or photoperiodism; and the action of hormones and enzymes in growth regulation.

Experiments have shown that the responses of plants involve the production and movement within the plant of certain chemicals, the phytohormones. These compounds include auxins, gibberellins, and kinins, and are widespread in the plant kingdom. Their precise mode of operation, however, is not yet fully understood.

Tropisms

The autotrophic plant's behavior is geared to the maximum exploitation of light, which is its only source of energy. It is therefore one of the most important environmental influences on plant orientation. Motile algae, such as *Euglena* and *Volvox*, show a positive phototactic response—they move bodily toward a light source. Sessile plants, however, grow toward a light source in a movement known as phototropism. The growth curvature common to all forms of tropism occurs when there is a dif-ferential growth of cells on the opposite side of the responding organ. This is caused by the growth-regulating hormone, auxin, stimulating cell elongation on one side of the organ. In plant shoots, positive phototropic growth has been found to result from the lateral transport of auxin, which is induced by the stimulus of light. The light is perceived by a pigment called blue light receptor. Phototropism is induced most effectively by blue light but how it causes auxin transport is unknown.

Gravity also has a decisive influence on plant orientation. The main roots of plants show a positive geotropism by growing downward, whereas shoots demonstrate negative geotropism by growing away from the force. Leaves show transverse geotropism. The geotropism in roots may be controlled by abscisic acid rather than auxin (which inhibits the geotropism of root cells). Geotropic curvature in roots is not very well understood, but it is thought that gravity is perceived by metabolically inert starch grains (statoliths) in the root tips. These are displaced in the root tip tissue, for example, when the plant grows around an obstruction in the soil thus causing the statoliths to shift. They fall under gravity to the lowest side of the root where they inhibit growth and promote it on the upper side. This theory, however, does not explain why some plants which apparently lack statoliths, such as the onion (*Allium* sp.), still respond to gravity.

Chemicals also influence plant movements. Motile bacteria and algae demonstrate chemotaxis, moving bodily toward chemicals, whereas parts of higher plants show chemotropism. For example, the male gametes of some species are attracted by chemicals released by the female gametes.

Plants also respond to contact. In a move-

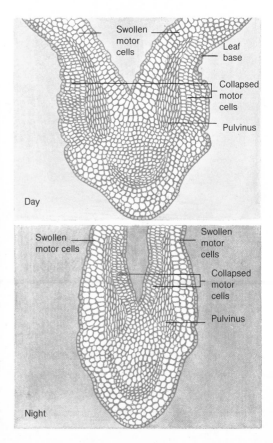

ment known as thigmotropism, tendrils and twining stems of climbing plants, such as the passionflower (*Passiflora* sp.), are induced to curl around supports that touch them. Water, or the lack of it, particularly in arid soils, also directs the orientation of root development—this is called hydrotropism.

Turgor movements

In what may appear to be a phototropic movement the leaves and flowers of some plants open and close according to the light available or follow the sun's movement through the sky. In these movements, however, light is perceived by a receptor pigment called phytochrome, which is sensitive to red light only, and the changes are due to the expansion and contraction of motor cells that gain or lose turgor pressure in response to the stimulus of the light. These motor cells are contained in an articulating structure called a pulvinus.

Plants such as the poppy *(Papaver radicatum)* track the sun's course through the day, the flower moving in a 180° curve. The closure of plants' leaves at night, or sleep movements, is called nyctinasty and is due to the action of a pulvinus in the leaf petiole. The closure of flowers at night, as in tulips (*Tulipa* spp.), is not truly nyctinastic although it is a response to decreasing light; the motor cells are not organized into obvious pulvini.

Photomorphogenetic responses

Changes in development that are not oriented toward the direction of a stimulus are morphogenetic, and those induced by light are termed photomorphogenetic. The response to day and night length is known as photoperiodism and involves the detection of light by phytochrome. Such responses include plant and seed dormancy and leaf abscission. Leaf abscission is initiated by decreasing day length in autumn. The short days alter the balance of the hormones auxin (which inhibits abscission) and ethylene (which stimulates it) and promote the development of a weakened zone at the base of the leaf petiole. Winter dormancy in plants is thought to be controlled by a balance between abscisic acid and gibberellin hormones.

The effects of phytochrome mediation—the influence of light on plant growth—also include flowering during particular day or night lengths; this ensures that all individual plants belonging to the same species flower together at an appropriate season. For example, dill *(Anethum graveolens)* needs short nights to flower, whereas cocklebur *(Xanthium pennsylvanicum)* needs long nights; in other words, dill flowers in summer but cocklebur flowers in winter.

Movements in response to touch are turgor-controlled in some plant species. The leaves of the sensitive plant *(Mimosa pudica)* are open in a normal state *(above)*. If they are touched, however, the leaves collapse *(below)*, due to sudden pressure changes in the motor cells in the leaflet bases. This response is known as thigmonasty.

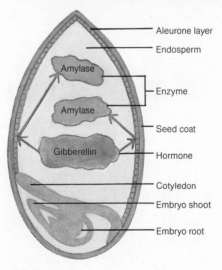

Aleurone layer
Endosperm

Amylase

Enzyme

Amylase

Seed coat

Gibberellin

Hormone

Cotyledon
Embryo shoot

Embryo root

Enzyme synthesis in the seeds of grasses is induced by growth-regulatory hormones, such as gibberellin. During germination the embryonic seed releases gibberellin, which encourages the aleurone layer to produce large amounts of the enzyme amylase. This enzyme breaks down the starch stored in the endosperm of the seed, mobilizing it as a source of energy to be used by the embryo in its further growth.

Fact entries

Turgor pressure builds up when plant motor cells absorb positive potassium (K+) and negative chlorine (Cl−) ions from neighboring tissues. This increases the concentration of the cell solution, which results in water being drawn into the cell by osmosis to balance the concentrations in and outside the cell, thus raising its turgor pressure. The pressure is released when the ions seep out of the cell (causing water to be drawn out of the cell osmotically) or when neighboring cells develop higher concentrations of solutes.

The blue light receptor absorbs blue light and ultraviolet radiation at wavelengths of about 360nm. Plants bend phototropically to blue light but not to red light.

Phytochrome, the red light receptor (P_R), absorbs red light at wavelengths of about 680nm. When it absorbs light it is converted into P_{FR}, which absorbs farred light at wavelengths of 700-730nm. When P_{FR} absorbs this light, it is converted back into P_R.

Nonflowering plants

The nonflowering plants, that is, those which reproduce without the means of seeds, include a wide range of organisms, from the simplest unicellular bacterium to complex cone-bearing trees. Most of the groups have little more than this one reproductive feature in common. Instead of seeds they employ such diverse methods of reproduction as binary fission, conjugation, and spore formation. But despite the success and reduced risks of asexual and nonspermatophytic reproduction, most plants are spermatophytes.

The primary division of living organisms in modern classification systems is into procaryotes and eucaryotes. Procaryotes have relatively simple cells without true nuclei and other cell bodies, whereas eucaryotes have complex cells with nuclei and organelles, such as mitochondria and Golgi bodies. The procaryotes consist of bacteria and blue-green algae; eucaryotes comprise all other cellular organisms. Blue-green algae are the earliest identifiable living organisms, having been found in schist that is about 3.5 billion years old.

Bacteria

Most bacteria (class Schizomycetes) are unicellular microscopic organisms. Almost all of them are heterotrophic, which means that they feed off living and decaying organisms as parasites and saprophytes, rather than autotrophic, which means that they manufacture their own food by the process of photosynthesis, as many other plants do. They occur in every possible environment and in large quantities—one drop of liquid can contain 50 million bacteria, one ounce of average soil contains more than 30 billion.

Heterotrophic bacteria include the parasitic pathogens that cause cholera, syphilis, botulism, and many other diseases. The pathogens are, however, outnumbered by the bacteria that are beneficial to us. Most nonpathogenic bacteria are saprophytes and are responsible for the decomposition of dead plants and animals, restoring essential mineral elements to the ecosystem, and preventing waste accumulation and pollution. Some live inside our bodies and assist digestion. Others are used in such industrial processes as the fermentation of alcohol to acetic acid in vinegar production, the fermentation of sugars to lactic acid in green fodder silos, and the making of yogurt and cheese.

Some saprophytic bacteria play an important role in the production of nitrogen. In well-aerated soil that is not very acid, bacteria such as *Nitrosomonas* convert ammonium to nitrite, which is itself converted by another bacterium, *Nitrobacter,* to nitrate. Nitrate is taken up by plant roots more easily than is ammonium. Nitrogen is also fixed in the root nodules of certain plants (such as legumes: pea, bean, and other pod-bearing plants) by the bacterium *Rhizobium,* which is of vital importance to agriculture. Other bacteria, such as *Pseudomonas,* reduce the nitrates in the soil to nitrogen and nitrous oxide, which are released into the atmosphere.

Autotrophic bacteria include those that photosynthesize, using light to split hydrogen sulfide rather than water. These bacteria, examples of which are *Chlorobium* and *Rhodomicrobium,* do not evolve oxygen as other photosynthetic organisms do. Other autotrophic bacteria are chemosynthetic; they are found, for example, near submarine fumaroles on the Mid-Atlantic Ridge and in areas of the Pacific Ocean Ridge near the Galapagos Islands, where they oxidize hydrogen sulfide to obtain energy.

Bacteria are usually identified and classified by cell shape, size, grouping, and flagellar arrangement. *Streptococcus* and *Staphylococcus* are spherical and occur in groups; *Bacillus* can occur singly or in chains of rodlike cells; *Spirillum* is found singly and, as its name sug-

Bacilli are rod-shaped bacteria, shown here *(below left)* magnified 700 times; each individual microorganism is only about 5 micrometers long. The diagram *(below right)* illustrates the main features of a generalized bacterium. Not all bacteria have flagella, but in those that do it is the whiplike lashing of this appendage that propels the organism.

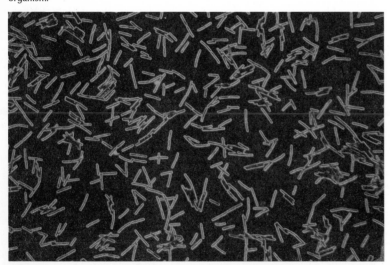

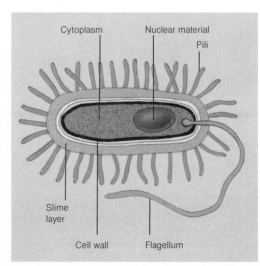

Cytoplasm

Nuclear material

Pili

Slime layer

Cell wall

Flagellum

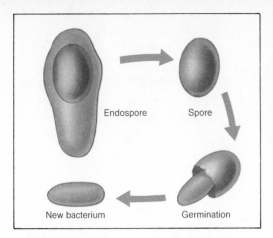

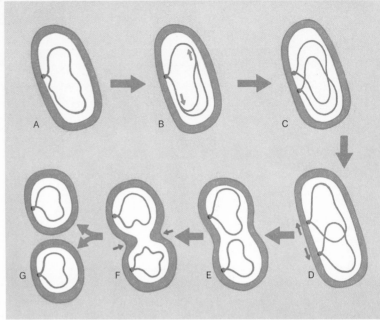

Reproduction in bacteria takes various forms. Some develop into endospores, which contain a "resting" cell called a spore. Most spores can withstand extreme changes in their environment, such as heating, freezing, or drying. They germinate when conditions again become favorable.

gests, is spiral in shape.

Bacterial cell structure

A generalized bacterial cell consists of a cell bounded by a cell wall and moved by the whiplike action of flagella. The cell wall contains polysaccharides, proteins, and lipids, but not cellulose. Gram-positive bacteria (so-called because they retain the purple color of Gram's stain) have weak walls with few amino acids. Examples are *Staphylococcus* (which causes boils) and *Streptococcus* (which, among other things, causes sore throats). They are, therefore, sensitive to certain antibiotics such as penicillin. Fortunately, most pathogens are of this type. Gram-negative forms have strong walls—they include *Salmonella* (a species of which causes typhoid) and *Escherichia* (the source of gastroenteritis).

Inside the cell, the hereditary material consists of a single loop molecule of DNA (the genophore) attached to the cell membrane, but not bounded by an envelope to form a nucleus, as in eucaryotes. Other tiny DNA fragments known as plasmids also occur in the cell and can become incorporated into the genophore when they are concerned with sexual conjugation. Plasmids can be used to transfer genes from one species to another (even from a bacterium to a higher plant or animal cell) for genetic engineering. The cytoplasm contains ribosomes for protein synthesis, and storage inclusions. These organelles are much smaller than those of eucaryotic cells. Procaryotes also do not contain chloroplasts, as do most other plant cells.

Bacterial reproduction

Some bacteria multiply by very rapid cell fission (*Pseudomonas,* for example)—one fission can take place every 20 minutes. Others, such as *Clostridium,* produce dormant survival spores called endospores, which resist boiling and can cause food poisoning, such as botulism. Sexual reproduction in the form of conjugation is also exhibited by some bacteria. In this process, DNA passes in one direction from one bacterial cell to another via filamen-

Cell division is another method of bacterial reproduction. The organism's DNA consists of a closed chromosome loop anchored to the cell wall (A). Replication of the DNA (B) results in two loops (C). The cell then elongates at the middle (D) until the loops are separated (E), and then forms a "neck" (F), which eventually divides the original cell into two new ones (G).

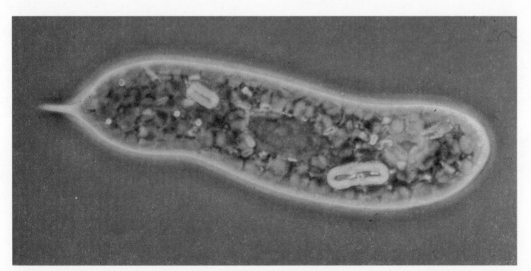

Euglena spirogyra is a photosynthetic microorganism, which propels itself using a long flagellum (at left side of the cell in this photograph). This organism, whose characteristics lie between those of plant and animal, swims toward light, which it detects with a photoreceptor located near the base of the flagellum.

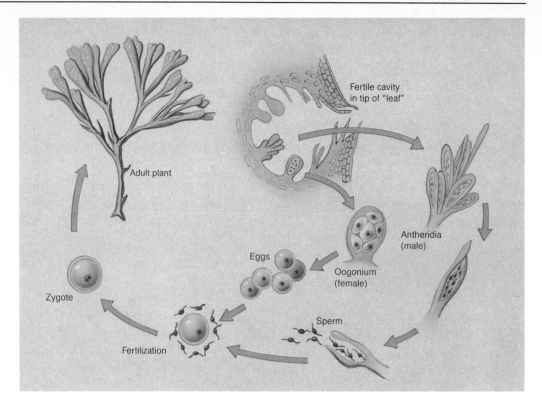

Rockweed *(Fucus)* is a common seaweed that grows on the shore between high- and low-water marks. The leathery leaflike blades *(below)* contain small cavities, in which antheridia produce male sperm and oogonia produce female eggs *(right)*. As these sex cells are released into the water, the flagellate sperm swim to the eggs and combine with them to form zygotes, from which new mature plants grow.

tous structures on the cell wall called pili. Foreign DNA can also enter a cell from the environment (transformation) or when transferred by a bacterial virus (transduction).

Blue-green algae

The blue-green algae (class Schizophyceae) are a successful and ubiquitous group of photosynthetic procaryotes. They occur in all freshwater habitats and in the sea, in the soil, as slime and gelatinous growths on rocks and manmade surfaces, as the algal partner in lichens, and in extreme environments such as hot springs with temperatures up to 185° F. (85° C).

The blue-green algal cell is typically procaryotic; it differs, however, from a bacterial cell in that photosynthetic pigments occur on the internal membranes, although they are not delimited into chlorophyll *a* (which is green), the yellow xanthophylls, blue phycocyanin, and red phycoerythrin. Different combinations

of these pigments result in organisms that are blue-green, blue, black, purple, brown, red, and yellow.

Blue-green algae usually form groups of spherical or coccoid cells, or filaments. Some filaments have complex cell types and specialized morphology, such as branching, aggregation into colonies, and three-dimensional cell division to produce simple tissues. The three main cell types are vegetative cells, akinetes, and heterocysts. Vegetative cells multiply by fission, and no sexual process is known. Akinetes are thick-walled resting spores. Heterocysts are concerned with nitrogen-fixation, a procaryotic attribute of vital ecological and economic importance; for example, the fertility of rice paddyfields depends upon the fixation of nitrogen by blue-green algae rather than the application of nitrogenous fertilizers.

A recently discovered procaryotic alga is *Prochloron,* which lives symbiotically inside marine tunicates (animals like the sea-squirt) on reefs. *Prochloron's* cell structure is similar to that of a blue-green alga, but its photosynthetic pigments include chlorophyll *b* as in green algae and higher plants. *Prochloron* could, therefore, be a key organism in the evolutionary history of land plants.

Eucaryotic algae

Algae (superphylum Phycophyta) form a heterogeneous collection of photosynthetic lower organisms ranging from single cells, multicellular colonies, and filaments to highly organized plant bodies such as seaweeds. Algae are mainly aquatic but also occur on soil, moist rocks, trees, and snow; they also occur as epiphytes and zoophytes.

In most species cellulose is contained in the cell walls. Almost all of them have no true vascular system, little tissue differentiation, and no morphological parts, such as stems, roots, or leaves. The exceptions are giant sea-weeds, such as giant kelp (*Macrocystis* sp.). This plant has a vascular system composed of sieve and trumpet cells, which form tubes down the stems that transport synthesized sugar alcohols and other foods, much like the phloem system of higher plants.

The sexual reproduction of algae is unique in that the whole organism may form the gamete, or the gametes are reproduced in uni- or multicellular gametangia in which every cell becomes a gamete. The number of algal phyla varies depending on the classification system used, but in all there are at least nine phyla. Among these groups, the green algae (Chlorophyta) contain motile single cells with two or four equal smooth flagella (*Chlamydomonas*, for example), colonial forms such as *Volvox*, microscopic filaments such as *Spirogyra*, and macroscopic seaweeds like *Ulva*, the sea lettuce. The pigments of this phylum are identical to those of mosses, ferns, and flowering plants—not surprisingly, because the land plants certainly evolved from the green algae. Sexual reproduction in chlorophytes varies from simple fusion of identical swimming gametes (isogamy) to advanced systems involving eggs and sperm (oogamy). Several genera have complex life cycles involving alternation of generations and are the forerunners of such systems in land plants.

The chrysomonads of the phylum Chrysophyta are golden-brown algae. These cells each have two unequal flagella (one with stiff hairs, the other smooth and bearing a photoreceptor), and an eyespot within a chloroplast. This arrangement is called heterokont organization. The cells are naked or are covered in siliceous scales or live inside cases (loricas) of cellulose or chitin. In many species the cells join together to form elaborate spherical or dendroid motile colonies.

In contrast, Prymnesiophytes, which are also members of the phylum, have two equal smooth flagella and a unique third coiling appendage (the haptonema), which may function as a chemoreceptor; the cells are covered with delicate organic scales that may become calcified to form disks and spines. Vast deposits of such flagellates in prehistoric seas have resulted in the formation of deep layers of chalk as in the White Cliffs near Dover, England, and on the French coast of the English Channel, as well as the vast Niobrara Chalk formations of Kansas.

Diatoms (Bacillariophyta) are characterized by a boxlike covering composed of richly patterned silica; they are either elongate or circular, and the cells may be single or joined in chains, stars, or zigzags. Fossil deposits of diatom skeletons (diatomaceous earth) form the basis of household scouring powders and toothpaste, as well as industrial filters and insulation material. One particular type—kieselguhr—absorbs about three times its own weight of the explosive nitroglycerin to form the more easily handled explosive dynamite.

Dinoflagellates (Pyrrophyta) are brown and have a complex symmetry and an armored cuticle (periplast) of cellulose plates; some are bioluminescent and give off flashes of light when disturbed. *Gonyaulax*, for example, blooms to produce red tides; shellfish that eat these blooms accumulate a nerve toxin, which

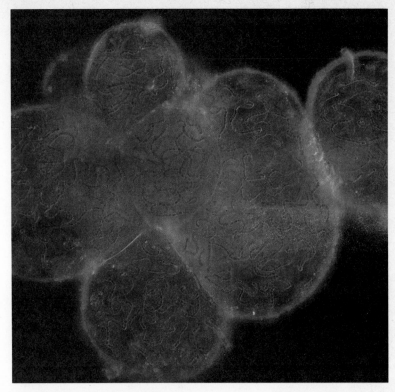

can be lethal to anyone who eats it.

Most of the other main algal divisions consist of the macroscopic thalli—the seaweeds. The red algae (Rhodophyta), which are feathery and leafy seaweeds, have no flagella or motile stages and only one chlorophyll pigment, *a*. They have, however, a predominance of the red pigment, phycoerythrin. The brown algae (Phaeophyta) comprise the bulk of the intertidal and coastal seaweeds, including the wrack *Fucus* and the giant kelps. Most of the vast array of species of brown and red seaweeds have complicated life cycles involving two or three phases.

Many of these algal species constitute the marine and freshwater phytoplankton that serve as a primary food source for zooplankton and larger filter-feeders, such as sponges, mollusks, and certain fish. Their potential and value in food and energy production is tremendous. Together the algal groups, and phytoplankton in particular, are responsible for almost half of the annual global fixation of carbon (estimated at about 23×10^9 tons of carbon per year).

Algae are not very important economically, compared with the higher plants. Certain kinds are eaten as food, especially in Wales where it is called laver bread, and in Japan, where *nori*, as it is called, is specially cultivated, dried, and eaten wrapped around rice. However, red algae provide agar and brown algae produce alginates. These jellylike substances are extracted and used in food canning; for making emulsions for use in paint, cosmetics, ice cream, medicines, and photographic film; and as a medium for growing microorganisms in the laboratory.

Nostoc is a blue-green alga, here enlarged about 200 times, whose filamentous strands are held in fluid-filled sacs. It belongs to the group called Cyanophyta and, despite its name, may be black or red, as well as blue or green.

Fungi

The fungi, which make up the phylum Mycota, embrace a wide variety of organisms. Nevertheless, they have several characteristics in common: they have no chlorophyll and, therefore, cannot photosynthesize, but obtain food by absorbing soluble materials as saprophytes (feeding on decaying matter) or parasites (feeding on living organisms); they reproduce by spores sexually or asexually; and they usually have cell walls that contain chitin or cellulose. Scientists now believe there are more than 100,000 species of fungi.

This broad group is divided into the subphyla Myxomycotina, which contains the slime molds (related to protozoa), and Eumycotina, the "true fungi." Unlike slime molds, eumycotes are typically nonmobile and composed of branching filaments called hyphae. They include the aquatic molds and downy mildews (Phycomycetes, regarded by many botanists as colorless algae) and three other groups of fungi: the so-called bread molds (Aplanatae); the powdery mildews, flask fungi, cup fungi, yeasts, and truffles (Ascomycetes); and the rusts, smuts, mushrooms, and toadstools (Basidiomycetes). In addition, there is a group of fungi—the "fungi imperfecti"—that have never been observed to have a sexual stage in their life cycle, so are difficult to classify precisely, but are usually classed as Deuteromycetes.

Myxomycetes—the slime molds

These protozoalike organisms live on land in moist environments, growing on damp soil, rotting logs, and leaf mold.

The true slime molds consist of a white, yellow, or red ameboid slime called a plasmodium. An inch or so across, it moves imperceptibly, feeding on bacteria and particles of organic matter. The molds feed by engulfing their food (phagocytosis), a method which is atypical of fungi. They also differ from most other fungi by lacking a hyphal structure at any stage of their life cycle. Eventually movement ceases and the organism develops fruiting bodies known as sporangia, which produce spores. When the spores germinate, they release naked flagellated sex cells (gametes),

which fuse in pairs to produce ameboid zygotes. The ameba grows into a plasmodium by feeding and nuclear division.

In cellular slime molds, the spores give rise to free-living soil amebas. When there is a large population of amebas they aggregate (but do not fuse) to form a "slug," which finally produces a sporangium. The cellular slime mold *Dictyostelium* is a common laboratory organism and has been used extensively in

Fungi, classified botanically as the phylum Mycota, include a range of outwardly dissimilar organisms, from yeasts and molds to mushrooms. The major classes are shown in the diagram *(far right)*. (Remember that this system of classification may differ somewhat from systems used elsewhere.)

Major Classes

Basidiomycetes (mushrooms, etc.)

Oomycetes (water molds)

Ascomycetes (yeasts etc.)

Phycomycetes (aquatic fungi)

Zygomycetes (bread molds)

Subphyla

Eumycotina ("true fungi")

Myxomycotina (slime molds)

Phylum

Mycota (fungi)

Resembling the antlers of a deer, a club fungus *(Xylaria hypoxylon)* grows from a rotting log in the leaf litter of a woodland floor. Mosses also take advantage of the nutrients readily available in this damp environment.

research on the physiology of ameboid movement.

Phycomycetes—the algal fungi

This group includes aquatic single-celled and filamentous forms and the downy mildews which attack some land plants. The spores or gametes are the only motile stage in the life cycles of these plants. Like the rest of the eumycotes (but unlike slime molds) they have cell walls at every phase.

Many species of those fungi known as chytrids are parasitic on algae, other fungi, aquatic angiosperms, and even fish. Among this group asexual reproduction is by uniflagellate swimming cells (zoospores), whereas sexual reproduction is by the fusion of two flagellated gametes to form a thick-walled survival spore.

Unlike most other aquatic fungi the water molds (class Oomycetes) develop an extensive branching system of hyphae, known as a mycelium. The hyphae usually contain several nuclei not separated by cell walls and are termed coenocytic. The water molds grow in water or damp soil, on seeds, dead insects, frogs, fish, and fish eggs. The downy mildews (Peronosporales) are devastating plant pathogens; *Phytophthora infestans,* for example, causes potato blight and *Pythium* attacks plant seedlings.

The oomycetes are also characterized by having cellulose only in their cell walls, asexual reproduction by biflagellated zoospores, and sexual reproduction by oogamy. This process involves the fertilization of eggs in the female sexual organs (oogonia) by male nuclei from antheridia. These and other features—typical of some algae—suggest that the oomycetes derive from algae that have lost their chlorophyll.

Aplanatae—the bread molds

These fungi are composed of the classes Zygomycetes and Trichomycetes, both of which reproduce sexually by conjugation of gametes attached to a mycelium. They form extensive molds in terrestrial habitats, occurring as bread molds, plant parasites, fungal parasites, insect parasites (the trichomycetes are parasites in the gut of arthropods only), and dung fungi; those in the order Zoopagales prey on amebae and nematodes.

The reproductive processes of the common bread molds *Rhizopus* and *Mucor* exemplify the group. In asexual reproduction, the hyphae, which grow on damp bread, produce globular sporangia that release thousands of nonmotile spores into the air. The spores land and germinate on a suitable surface to produce new, haploid mycelia. In sexual reproduction, short branches from two hyphae touch at the tips and each separates off a haploid gamete by a cross wall. The gametes fuse (conjugate) to form a diploid zygote that develops a thick protective coat, and is then known as a zygospore. After dormancy for several months the zygospore undergoes meiosis (reduction division) and germinates to produce a haploid sporangium. The spores from this structure grow into new mycelia, and thus complete the sexual cycle. The many different species of these molds are classified by the

Despite its attractive appearance the fly agaric *(Amanita muscaria, above)* contains a toxin that is deadly poisonous to human beings. Like the club fungus illustrated on the opposite page, a yellow slime fungus *(left)* has colonized a fallen branch as its food supply.

shapes and patterns of their sporangia.

Ascomycetes—cup and flask fungi

The class Ascomycetes is the largest group of fungi, with more than 30,000 named species. They are mainly terrestrial and are saprophytic or parasitic. They include edible fungi, such as morels and truffles; some of the yeasts; plant parasites, such as those that cause Dutch elm disease; ergot; powdery mildews; animal parasites such as ringworm; most of the fungal components of lichens; and most marine fungi.

The unique characteristic of the ascomycetes is the ascus—a saclike cell. This structure produces eight haploid spores (ascospores) internally by "free cell formation," which involves the spores being cut out from the substance of the cell. The ascus is formed during sexual reproduction after fusion of male and female gametes. The asci may be surrounded by a large mycelium of tightly packed hyphae that are able to form macroscopic fruiting bodies of various forms. Typical fruiting ascomycetes are the morels (*Morchella* sp.), truffles (Tuberales), and such common woodland forms as the orange-peel fungus *(Aleuria aurantia).* In these forms the asci are produced by disk-, cup-, or flask-shaped ascocarps.

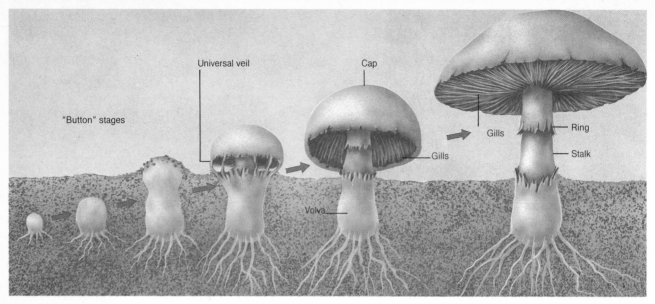

Universal veil · Cap · "Button" stages · Gills · Ring · Gills · Stalk · Volva

The edible field mushroom *(Agaricus campestris)* is a typical member of the class Basidiomycetes. The fruiting body—the part we eat—consists of a cap lined underneath with gills, in which the spores are formed. The development of the fruiting body, from the underground "button" stages, is illustrated above.

Yeasts, in the class Ascomycetes, consist of microscopic single-celled organisms. They reproduce asexually by budding, as explained in the diagram below. Yeast was probably the first plant to be domesticated, and it is still used in making bread, beer, and wine, as well as for other fermentation processes.

Aspergillus is an important ascomycete, which has a moldlike form and reproduces asexually by single-spored sporangia (conidia). It causes considerable damage to stored grain, cloth, and other goods. It also produces aflatoxin, one of the most potent of the poisons and carcinogens.

Most yeasts are specialized ascomycetes that grow as single oval cells. Some multiply by fission, but most undergo budding, as do baker's and brewer's yeast *(Saccharomyces cereviseae).* In the sexual phase, two haploid yeast cells fuse to form a diploid colony in which individual cells act as asci and cleave out four or eight haploid ascospores. Yeasts can ferment sugars to produce alcohol and carbon dioxide, a property that is exploited in brewing beer, making wine, and raising bread.

Imperfect fungi

The 17,000 fungi in the class Deuteromycetes are known as imperfect fungi because they only reproduce asexually. Reproduction usually involves the production of conidia (on conidiophores) or by budding. Many of these fungi probably represent the asexual stages of ascomycetes and basidiomycetes.

The deuteromycetes include yeastlike and mycelial forms, many of which cause diseases. A typical deuteromycete genus is *Penicillium,* which grows as a gray-green mold on rotting fruit. It reproduces asexually by the erect conidiophores producing chains of conidia. Spe-

cies of this genus are well known for their commercial use in the production of the antibiotic penicillin.

Basidiomycetes

Most of the large conspicuous fungi—mushrooms, toadstools, puffballs, and brackets—are grouped in the class Basidiomycetes, of which there are more than 38,000 species. The vegetative mycelium of these fungi is an extensive, usually underground, system of septate (rather than coenocytic) hyphae. The aerial structures, such as those of toadstools, are composed of interwoven hyphae and are the spore-bearing portions of the fungus. These fruiting bodies are often brightly colored due to pigments in their cell walls.

The common characteristic of the basidiomycetes is the basidium, a club-shaped reproductive cell from which four hornlike prongs are formed and from each of which a single basidiospore is produced. The basidium is the end product of sexual reproduction in cells that contain two haploid nuclei derived from the fusion of two different mycelia. The mycelium, with genetically different nuclei, is biologically very important because, with two different nuclei present, "complementation" can occur, and the fungus can grow in a greater variety of situations that would not support either parent fungus on its own.

In the basidium, the two nuclei fuse and the resulting zygote undergoes meiosis, forming

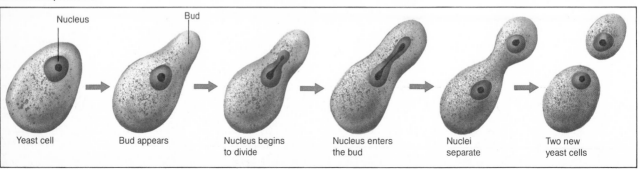

Nucleus · Bud · Yeast cell · Bud appears · Nucleus begins to divide · Nucleus enters the bud · Nuclei separate · Two new yeast cells

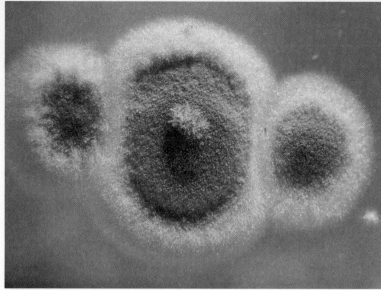

four haploid spores. The basidia may be borne on gills, in tubes, or in fleshy masses inside the fruiting bodies as in puffballs (Lycoperdales) or outside as in stinkhorns (Phallales). A typical mushroom discharges 10 million spores per hour for several days. These are usually dispersed by wind or insects. The basidia discharge their spores by means of a little explosion that carries them a distance of 1 millimeter or so. They then drop down the space between the gills or the inside of the tubes until they reach the open air and are wafted away.

Mushrooms are often found in "fairy rings." As the underground mycelium uses up all the nutrients in the soil, it grows outward to find fresh food. This results in a ring of hyphae, enlarging all the time, producing fruiting bodies as it goes.

Rust (Uredinales) and smut fungi (Ustilaginales) are characterized by a variety of spore types and complex life cycles involving parasitism of several host plants. There are about 6,000 species of rusts and 1,000 species of smuts. Many live as parasites on cereals, vegetables, and flowers.

Basidiomycetes are of immense ecological and industrial importance in their mycorrhizal associations with forest trees and many other plants. Mycorrhiza is a symbiotic association between fungi and plant roots, from which both benefit. The advantages for the fungi are that the plants with which they are associated pass on photosynthetic products to them, and in turn the fungi provide the plants with mineral nutrients, which they can extract more efficiently from the soil. Many pioneer plants of poor soils are extremely dependent on these mycorrhizal fungi. Plants may form mycorrhizal associations with many fungal species; birch, for example, has a large number of basidiomycetes with which it will grow.

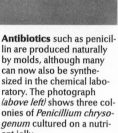

Antibiotics such as penicillin are produced naturally by molds, although many can now also be synthesized in the chemical laboratory. The photograph *(above left)* shows three colonies of *Penicillium chrysogenum* cultured on a nutrient jelly.

When a single raindrop falls on top of an earth star fungus *(Geastrum triplex, above right)* it explosively ejects a cloud containing many thousands of spores that are dispersed by the wind, before germinating to produce new plants.

A bracket fungus is named after its horizontal fruiting bodies, which stick out from the bark of a tree. The yellow, or sulfur, bracket fungus *Laetipurus sulphurus (below)* forms a cascade of brackets that grow up to 1 foot (30 centimeters) across.

Mosses and liverworts

The mosses and liverworts are a group of simple green plants found throughout the world—they are among the most primitive of land plants. Classified botanically as bryophytes, the species number more than 9,000 for mosses and about 8,000 for liverworts. They require water to complete their life cycles; for this reason most of them frequent damp, shady habitats. Some bryophytes (such as the moss *Sphagnum*) can, however, withstand periods of drought.

Plant structure

Most bryophytes form cushions or layers of vegetation no more than 6 inches (15 centimeters) high for mosses and less than .5 inch (1.4 centimeters) high for liverworts. But the larg-

est moss, the Australian species *Dawsonia,* grows up to 3 feet (91 centimeters) tall. All are attached to the ground or to a substratum, such as tree bark, by rootlike threads called rhizoids. In liverworts rhizoids generally comprise one cell each, whereas in mosses they are made up of several cells.

Nearly all bryophyte structures that grow above ground contain chlorophyll, as well as other pigments, and are green; the chlorophyll is located in disk-shaped chloroplasts clustered in certain cells. The moss plant consists of a system of shoots along which leaves are arranged alternately. In most moss species the leaves have a characteristic central midrib, but otherwise vary enormously in shape and size, from the pointed, tooth-edged leaves of *Mnium* to the broad leaves of *Orthotrichum,* which have unbroken edges and long hairlike extensions at their tips.

Liverworts are more diverse in appearance than mosses and are described as either thalloid or leafy. A thalloid liverwort consists of a flat, platelike structure (the thallus) with rhizoids on its underside. The thallus may have a scalloped edge, as in *Lunularia,* or may be deeply divided into lobes, as in *Conocephalum.* In leafy liverworts, which comprise more than 80 per cent of the total number of species, the thallus is divided into leaflike structures arranged up the "stem" in ranks of two or three. Most liverwort leaves have no midrib.

Alternation of generations

Bryophytes are of considerable botanical interest because they are the most primitive plants to display alternation of generations. According to this system, the plant's life cycle takes place in two stages or generations: the gametophyte generation, which is responsible for producing sex cells, and the sporophyte generation, whose function is to make and

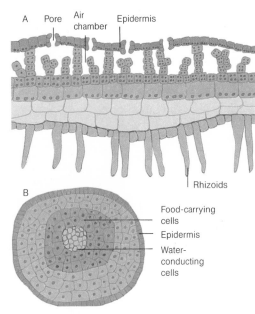

A **liverwort thallus** (A) has no leaves, stem, or roots. It is simply arranged into upper layers of chloroplast-containing cells and lower, empty ones. Fine rhizoids attach it to the soil. A moss stem (B) has a primitive vascular arrangement of non-nucleated, water-conducting cells, surrounded by nucleated ones which carry organic compounds.

A Pore Air chamber Epidermis

Rhizoids

B

Food-carrying cells

Epidermis

Water-conducting cells

The spore-filled capsules at the tip of the stalks of mosses *(below)* form the sporophyte generation.

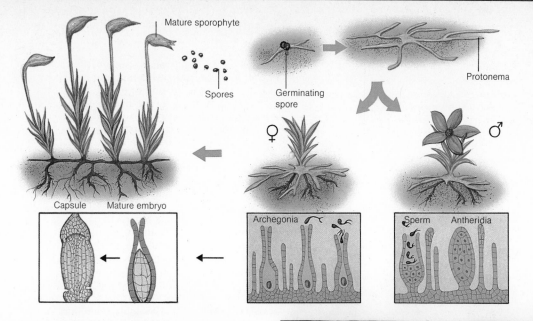

Mature sporophyte

Spores

Germinating spore

Protonema

♀ ♂

Capsule Mature embryo

Archegonia

Sperm Antheridia

The capsules on a mature moss plant release spores. A spore develops into a threaded mesh (protonema), which, from a bud, gives rise to a male or female gametophyte plant. The male gametophyte has a pink flowerlike structure when it is mature. Club-shaped spermatozoids are released from its antheridia and swim to the archegonia on the female plant where they fertilize the ova. Each ovum develops into an embryo that eventually becomes the spore-producing capsule.

disperse large numbers of asexual spores. In flowering plants the gametophyte generation is confined to specific parts of the flower, but in bryophytes it takes the form of the obvious main green "body" of the plant.

Anatomically, bryophyte sex organs vary little between species. Male sex cells (spermatozoids) are made in antheridia, and female sex cells (called ova, or oospheres) in archegonia. The antheridia are thin-walled sacs, which, when mature, contain spermatozoids, each of which bears a pair of long whiplike flagella. The fully developed archegonium containing the ovum is usually flask-shaped with a long neck.

For sexual reproduction to take place, a spermatozoid must swim to an ovum in an archegonium and fuse with it. Water is thus essential to the process of fertilization. The journey of the male cells is facilitated by a "spreading agent," which when released from the antheridium, lowers the surface tension of the water and thus aids the flow of the spermatozoids. The fertilized ovum develops into a sporophyte, which is incapable of an independent existence. Instead it grows as a semi-parasite on the gametophyte, although in some bryophytes, such as the unusual *Anthoceros,* it contains chlorophyll and so is capable of photosynthesis. The typical sporophyte of a moss or liverwort consists of a flattened foot, a long stalk or seta, and a capsule containing thousands of spores. The methods of spore release from the capsule vary, but most depend on the drying of the capsule and an inbuilt spore-ejector mechanism.

Spores that fall on a suitable environment germinate and develop into a new gametophyte generation. As well as reproducing sexually, this gametophyte also has the capacity for asexual reproduction—that is, leaves or other parts broken off the plant may develop into new, independent gametophytes.

Evolution and ecology

The evolution of bryophytes is not well understood. Botanists are still not certain whether

bryophytes evolved from a kind of alga or whether they represent a retrograde evolution from pteridophytes—the ferns and their allies.

Ecologically, bryophytes are important because they can survive in inhospitable conditions and because they are often among the pioneer species that colonize land that has been laid waste by catastrophes such as fire or earthquake. Once established, bryophyte colonies inhibit soil erosion and promote the retention of soil moisture. In swamps, the *Sphagnum* moss plays a leading role, stabilizing wet ground and eventually making it sufficiently firm and nutrient-rich to support tree species.

Because many bryophytes have specific nutrient requirements, it is possible to tell whether habitats are acid or alkaline, or contain high levels of nitrogen or phosphorus, by the types of bryophytes that inhabit them. Similarly, bryophyte species can, by their presence or absence, indicate whether there is a high level of sulfur dioxide in the atmosphere.

Cup-shaped structures found commonly on liverworts contain fruitlike bodies, called gemmae. These structures are organs of vegetative reproduction. The gemmae are distributed to new habitats by splashes of water into the cups, or by attaching to the feet or fur of passing animals. In a suitable environment they develop into a new gametophyte plant.

Club mosses and horsetails

Club mosses and horsetails, together with quillworts, ferns, and whisk-ferns, are known as pteridophytes (fern plants). These primitive plants were much more abundant at least 300 million years ago in the Pennsylvanian period than they are today. Their ancestors reached an enormous height—more than 100 feet (30 meters)—and were dominant over large areas of land. Superficially, many of them resemble mosses, and they are sporophytic—that is, they reproduce from spores instead of seeds—but they differ from mosses in that they have a vascular system.

Club mosses and quillworts

The members of the class Lycopsida are grouped into three living orders: Lycopodiales (with about 200 species) and Selaginellales (more than 700 species) both contain the club mosses, and Isoetales (about 70 species) contains the quillworts. Most lycopsids are found in the tropics and subtropics but some occur in temperate, desert, arctic, and alpine regions. They usually grow on the ground, although a few species live on other plants commensally (when they are known as epiphytes). The quillworts are found worldwide, and most live largely below the ground level, with only the tips of their sporophylls (fertile leaves) showing.

Most club mosses creep or trail although some have erect stems. The roots generally grow directly from the stem, and some species produce rhizophores, which grow down from the stem to the soil with true roots issuing from their tips. The leaves, which photosynthesize, are small with an unbranched midrib—those of *Lycopodium* are needlelike. In most species the leaves are spirally arranged, but in some species of *Selaginella* they are attached in four rows—two on the upper side and two laterally. The leaves may all be the same size or there may be a regular pattern of large and small leaves. In *Selaginella,* a membranous scale (ligule) grows at the base of each leaf, the function of which is not known. Ligules are also found in quillworts during the development of the sporophylls.

In addition to the ordinary green leaves, club mosses have fertile leaves (sporophylls). In contrast to the club mosses all the leaves of the quillworts are sporophylls. These leaves, which project above the soil level, are the only photosynthetic part of the plant; the rest survives as a corm (a condensed stem) underground.

In most species of club mosses the sporophylls are grouped at the top of the stem to form a cone (strobilus). Each sporophyll has a single large spore receptacle, or sporangium, on its upper surface near the base of the leaf.

Stag's horn club moss (*Lycopodium clavatum*) is named after its long white stalks, which usually have two fertile cones (strobili). Its trailing stems, which are often 10 feet (3 meters) long, give rise to fertile and sterile branches. The stalks grow from the fertile branches. Their spore leaves (sporophylls) are smaller than those of the sterile and fertile branches and grow more closely against the stem. This club moss is homosporous—its spores are all identical.

Alternation of generations in some club mosses involves the underground germination of a spore. The resulting prothallus (the gametophyte) has female sex organs (archegonia) and male ones (antheridia) on its upper surface. When the sex cells (gametes) mature, the necks of the archegonia open and the antheridia release the sperm cells whose walls rupture. The sperm "swim" to the archegonia where they fertilize the ova. The developing embryo begins the sporophyte phase.

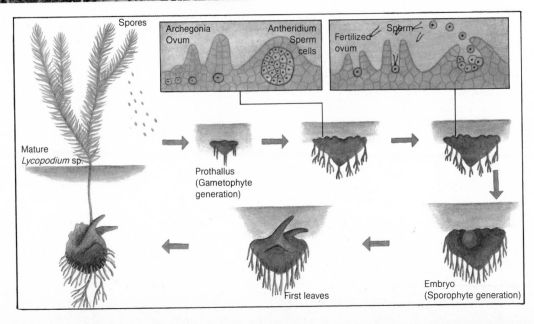

Spores

Archegonia
Ovum

Antheridium
Sperm
cells

Sperm

Fertilized
ovum

Mature
Lycopodium sp.

Prothallus
(Gametophyte
generation)

First leaves

Embryo
(Sporophyte generation)

The sporangium may be globular or kidney-shaped. *Lycopodium* bears sporangia that are identical and produce one type of spore only. It is, therefore, described as homosporous. *Selaginella* and the quillworts, however, are heterosporous, having both small microsporangia and larger megasporangia.

In club mosses the spores are released when they are ripe—the sporangium splits open and the spores are dispersed by the wind. In quillworts the spores have to wait until the sporangia decay before they can be released. In suitable conditions, each spore germinates in the ground to form a tiny prothallus. In some species, the prothallus lives underground in a symbiotic association with mycorrhizal fungi from which it gets its food. In other species the prothalli are surface-dwelling and photosynthetic. In *Selaginella* and the quillworts, the prothalli are endosporic—that is, they develop within the spores.

The life cycle of club mosses consists of two alternating phases—the gametophyte generation and the sporophyte generation. The gametophyte phase begins with spores that germinate into prothalli and ends with the fertilization of the female gametes by the male sperm.

The sporophyte generation begins with the fertilized egg (zygote), which develops into the spore-producing plant. In *Lycopodium* the male and female gametes are produced in the same prothalli. *Selaginella* and quillworts, however, have minute microprothalli, which have a single male organ (antheridium) and much larger megaprothalli, which are produced by the megaspores and which have several female organs (archegonia). Sperm and ova are thus produced on separate prothalli. To achieve fertilization the sperm must swim through a film of water from the microprothallus to the archegonia on the megaprothallus.

Reproduction among the club mosses is, however, not always sexual—in some species of *Lycopodium,* leafy stem structures called bulbils detach themselves from the plant and develop into new plants.

Horsetails

The horsetails (class Sphenopsida) are today represented by a single genus—*Equisetum*—with about 25 species. They are found worldwide, except in Australia and New Zealand, and in a varied range of habitats. These plants have long underground rhizomes that give rise to aerial stems that are usually 4 to 24 inches (10 to 61 centimeters) in height. The stems normally contain chlorophyll, but some species alternate the growth of special fertile stems without chlorophyll with green sterile ones.

The stems are grooved and have thick silicified walls. They are simple (unbranched) and carry whorls of slender branches, which are simple or have further whorls of branches. The small leaves, too, are produced in whorls, each cluster being fused into a tubular sheath, except for the tips, which form a serrated edge around the margin of the sheath. Most of the leaves have no chlorophyll, and photosynthesis is carried out by the green stems.

The reproductive organs of horsetails are grouped together to form a terminal cone, or

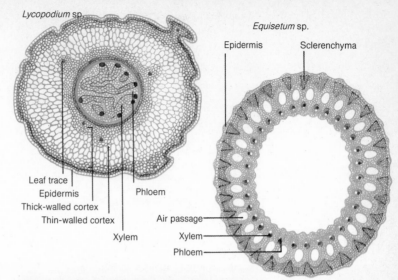

Lycopodium sp.

Leaf trace
Epidermis
Thick-walled cortex
Thin-walled cortex
Xylem
Phloem

Equisetum sp.
Epidermis   Sclerenchyma
Air passage
Xylem
Phloem

A cross section through the stems of club mosses and horsetails reveals their primitive vascular systems. *Lycopodium* has a central cylinder which contains lobes of xylem interspersed with phloem. *Equisetum* has a hollow stem ringed by small xylem and phloem bundles.

The great horsetail *(Equisetum telmateia)* produces pale photosynthetic fertile stems with strobili at their tips in early spring. Later in the year sterile stems with green leaves develop, which are seen here. This plant grows in damp woods and on hedge banks.

strobilus. Each strobilus consists of a central axis bearing whorls of mushroom-shaped (peltate) sporangiophores, each with several sporangia on the lower surface. The sporangia split to release the spores. Each spore has four long strips called elaters, which coil and uncoil in response to humidity changes and assist its dispersal in water and wind. Some of the spores germinate to form male prothalli, which bear antheridia, whereas others produce female prothalli with archegonia. In others still, antheridia and archegonia may be borne successively on the same prothallus. Fertilization is achieved in the same way as in the club mosses; the horsetails also develop by an alternation of generations.

A young fern, the sporophyte generation of its reproductive cycle, develops from a prothallus, the gametophyte generation. The new fern is nourished by the photosynthesizing prothallus, but when it can photosynthesize for itself, the prothallus dies.

Ferns

The ferns (class Filicopsida) first appeared in the Devonian period, more than 350 million years ago, and have flourished ever since, particularly in forests. They are a large group of plants, containing approximately 10,000 species, which now inhabit a variety of environments. Most are ground-dwelling, preferring damp, shady habitats, but some are epiphytic, growing attached to the stems or leaves of other plants; others can survive in more exposed situations, and a few have an entirely aquatic life style.

Ferns vary widely also in their appearance, ranging from the giant, treelike ferns, which can reach a height of 65 feet (20 meters), to tiny, mosslike species that grow on rocks. They all belong to the phylum Pteridophyta and are, therefore, closely related to club mosses, horsetails, and quillworts. Like them, ferns have alternating sporophyte (asexual) and gametophyte (sexual) generations. The class is roughly divided into the "primitive" eusporangiates, such as adder's tongue *(Ophioglossum vulgatum)* and moonwort *(Botrychium lunaria),* and the "higher" leptosporangiates (which contain the most common ferns, such as maidenhair fern, *Adiantum* sp.); the subclass between, Osmundidae, shares features of both groups. The class Osmunda includes the complex-leaved royal fern,

The sporangia on most species of ferns are borne on the underside of the fronds, grouped into sori. On buckler fern, each sorus is partly covered by a kidney-shaped indusium. On lady fern the indusium forms a flap, whereas on holly fern it is reduced, forming a dimpled disk which barely covers the sorus. The sori of common polypody have no indusium. The sporangia of maidenhair fern develop on the margins of the leaves and are protected by the leaf curling over them. Those of tree ferns are contained in cuplike receptacles sometimes covered by an indusium which splits to uncover the sporangia.

Osmunda regalis. (Remember that there are several classification systems; the system used here may differ slightly from others.)

Structure

In most ferns the stem is usually a short, thick stock, as in the common male fern *(Dryopteris filix-mas),* or a long rhizome, as in bracken *(Pteridium aquilinum)* and epiphytic ferns. The stock grows almost completely buried in the ground, with an ascending growing point above ground surrounded by a close spiral of leaves, resembling a whorl, and often forming a basketlike tuft. Roots usually grow from the backs of the leaf-bases and on the lower surface of rhizomes, which grow horizontally above or below the ground, bearing single leaves at intervals along the upper surface. The growing point of rhizomes is surrounded not by leaves, but by scales or hairs, which are usually brown and sometimes glandular.

The leaves (fronds) of most ferns are spirally arranged and known as megaphylls. When they are in bud, in most species, they are rolled up like a shepherd's crook, or crozier. Like the stems, they are normally covered (at least when young) with scales or hairs. They contain chlorophyll and photosynthesize. Small adjustable pores called stomata, through which gas exchange takes place, are located in the epidermis of the leaf, and water and nutrients in solution are carried through the leaves and stems by xylem and phloem tissue.

Spore production

Some ferns are able to reproduce vegetatively (asexually) by means of creeping rhizomes or by bulbils produced on the leaves, but propagation is usually by spores formed in sporangia. In most species, the sporangia are located on the lower surface of ordinary leaves; others bear them on the axis of the leaves or at their tips. Still others have separate fertile leaves, such as the royal fern.

Usually, many sporangia are grouped together to form a sorus, many sori occurring

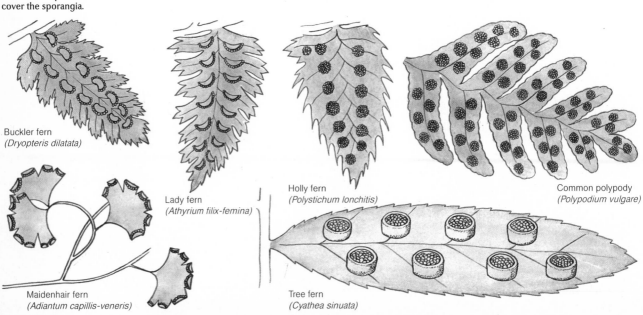

Buckler fern
(Dryopteris dilatata)

Maidenhair fern
(Adiantum capillis-veneris)

Lady fern
(Athyrium filix-femina)

Holly fern
(Polystichum lonchitis)

Tree fern
(Cyathea sinuata)

Common polypody
(Polypodium vulgare)

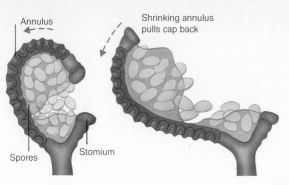

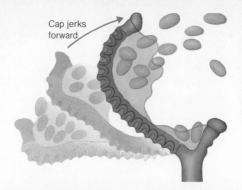

The sporangium of a fern splits at a point called the stomium when the spores are ripe. The surrounding ring of cells (the annulus) shrinks, pulling the cap back. When the tension reaches a maximum point, the cap jerks back to its original position, shooting the spores into the air.

on each leaf or leaf-segment. Each sorus is normally situated on a cushion-shaped structure, called the receptacle, directly above a vein that supplies it with nourishment. In some species, such as common polypody *(Polypodium vulgare),* the sori are not protected, but in most ferns each sorus has a cover (the indusium), which is most commonly linear, kidney-shaped (reniform), or mushroom-shaped (peltate).

The sporangium is usually stalked and has a head that is often shaped like a biconvex lens, with a ring or annulus of thickened cells almost completely surrounding the margin. Thin-walled cells occupy the remainder of the margin, flanking a weak point called the stomium, which eventually ruptures to release the spores. The sporangia contain a large number of spores; *Christensenia,* for example, releases about 7,000 spores from each sporangium, and adder's tongue more than 15,000. These spores contain chlorophyll.

Sexual reproduction

If a spore lands in favorable conditions it germinates a few days after it is released, forming a tiny green prothallium (the gametophyte). Hairlike roots (rhizoids), which form on the lower surface of the prothallium, supply the plant with water and nutrients, and in some species the prothallia photosynthesize. Most prothallia, however, are also mycorrhizal.

On the underside of this cushion of cells are the female reproductive organs (archegonia), each one consisting of an egg cell and a narrow, cylindrical neck that projects from the surface of the prothallium and is filled with neck canal cells. The male reproductive organs (antheridia) are normally located on the same prothallium, toward its base. Inside the spherical wall of each antheridium is a cavity containing sperm cells, each producing a single sperm with several long whiplike hairs (cilia or flagella) with which it propels itself through water.

Because the only way the sperm can reach the archegonia is by swimming, fertilization takes place only when the prothallium is covered with a film of water. This moisture causes the antheridia to split open, releasing the sperm cells whose walls dissolve, setting the sperm free. Simultaneously, the canal cells of the archegonia disintegrate, releasing a chemical that attracts the sperm and leaves the neck open. The sperm travel up the neck canal where one enters the egg and fuses with the nucleus.

Following fertilization, the resulting zygote begins its development attached to the prothallium and is nourished by it. But when it has formed its first root stem and leaf and is able to photosynthesize and thus manufacture food itself, the prothallium dies.

Most ferns are termed homosporous, which means that their spores are all alike. But the water ferns (those belonging to the orders Marsileales and Salviniales) are termed heterosporous, which means that they produce two different types of spores from different sporangia—micro- and megasporangia—on the same plant. In these ferns, the tiny microspores germinate to form the male prothallia, which bear antheridia, and the larger megaspores give rise to female prothallia, with archegonia.

Tree ferns (families Cyatheaceae and Dicksoniaceae) are found in mountain forests in tropical areas such as the South Pacific, Malaysia, and parts of Australasia. They can reach 65 feet (20 meters) in height and usually have unbranched stems that end in a crown of leaves. They first appeared in the Jurassic period about 170 million years ago.

Seed ferns and cycads

The seed ferns (order Pteridospermales) and the cycads (Cycadales) are both very ancient groups. The seed ferns are known only from fossils dating from the mid-Devonian to early Cretaceous periods, 360 to 130 million years ago, when they had a worldwide distribution. About seven families can be identified, but the number of species is not known due to the fragmentary nature of the fossil record. The cycads, however, have living representatives, although they date back to the late Triassic period, 180 million years ago. They comprise 9 genera and about 75 species, all of which are now confined to the New and Old World tropics, whereas once they too were widespread.

Together the seed ferns and cycads make up the class Cycadopsida and are grouped as gymnosperms along with the other cone-bearing plants. They both have manoxylic wood—it is soft and spongy with wide parenchyma rays. Their leaves are large and frondlike and tend to branch pinnately (like a feather). In addition, their seeds are radially symmetrical (the same on all sides).

The seed ferns

The fossils of seed ferns are relatively common although incomplete. They reveal, nonetheless, that the leaves of these plants were large and fernlike (and consequently became broken at some stage during fossilization). It has also been found that the cambium in the stems formed large amounts of secondary xylem, unlike the cycads.

The plant parts have all been found but have not been joined together and consequently have been given separate scientific names. This has to a certain extent obscured the relationship between the various organs and made it even more difficult to build up a complete picture of the plants. This problem is compounded by the existence of a large number of different species. Enough has been discovered, however, to suggest that the appearance of seed ferns ranged from *Lyginopteris,* a scrambling plant with long thin stems and equally branched fertile fronds (sporophylls), to *Sphenopteris,* a large upright plant that resembled a tree fern.

Seed ferns evidently had neither cones nor flowers but produced seeds that were naked and not enclosed in an ovary. The presence of seeds places these plants among the gymnosperms and sets them apart from the ferns that they resemble so closely in appearance. The seeds were contained in leafy cupules on the ends of leaves or on special nonleafy branches (much like those on tree ferns). The seeds occurred either singly or in numbers up to about 70 in one cupule. These containers were shaped rather like a modern tulip flower, with the seeds on stalks inside them. It is thought that as each seed matured, the stalk elongated and carried the seed upwards to the mouth of the cupule, where it could more easily be dispersed.

Pollen sacs were also borne on the fronds. Without evidence, however, the method of pollination can only be guessed at, but it has been suggested that the female gametes were wind-pollinated. Nothing has been learned from any fossils of details of fertilization or embryo development.

Cycads

From what can be seen of their structure it is thought that the seed ferns formed an intermediate evolutionary stage between the true ferns and the conifers. Despite the fact that cycads show many primitive features, which suggest a close relationship with the seed ferns, they are considered to be intermediate between the seed ferns and the flowering plants, and some botanists believe that the flowering plants may have originated from the early cycads.

Most species of cycad are similar in appearance. The stem, or trunk, resembles that of a palm and can vary in height between species, up to about 60 feet (18 meters), as in the Australasian cycad *Macrozamia hopei.* Most, however, are only about 3 feet (91 centimeters) high and some species even have an underground stem, or tuber, such as *Stangeria* spp., from South Africa. The stem develops little secondary xylem but contains large amounts of parenchyma mixed with other conducting cells. It is usually unbranched and scarred with the bases of fallen leaves. The leaves, which grow in a crown at the top of the trunk, resemble fern or palm fronds and may vary in length from 10 feet (3 meters) in *Cycas* sp. to 2 inches (5 centimeters), as in *Zamia pygmaea.*

Male and female flowers occur on separate plants (they are dioecious) in the form of a cone at the top of the plant, up to about 3 feet (91 centimeters) long and 10 inches (25 centimeters) thick. The cones are formed in a spiral

The male cones of the cycad *Encephalartos frederici-guilelmii,* of southern Africa, are formed from tight spirals of microsporophylls.

from fertile leaves (sporophylls). In the male flower the sporophylls are known as microsporophylls because pollen sacs containing the microspores, or pollen, grow on their underside. The microsporophylls may be up to 20 inches (50 centimeters) in length.

The sporophylls of the female cone are known as megasporophylls and are much smaller than the microsporophylls, being only 6 to 8 inches (15 to 20 centimeters) long. They are also conelike, except in *Cycas*, when they form a loose aggregation of sporophylls. The ovules, which may grow to the size of a hen's egg, or larger, are formed in numbers from two to eight on the lower half of the megasporophyll (as in *Cycas*) or may hang from under the sporophylls. Pollen released from the microsporangia is transferred to the ovules by the wind or by insects. Up to six months may pass before fertilization occurs, and the seed may take a year to mature.

Because the flowers are terminal, growth in male plants continues from an axillary bud at the base of the cone. The female flowers of most species of cycads are similar except in the case of *Cycas*, in which the apical meristem is unaffected by the flower and it continues its normal growth through the middle of the flower.

Cycads have adapted to survival in a dry climate by being xeromorphic—the long-lived ones live up to 1,000 years. The leaves have a thickened epidermis with sunken stomata. Apart from a long taproot, the roots are short and grow as coralloid masses (groups of short, thickened interwined roots), which contain symbiotic blue-green algae, such as *Anabaena*.

The cycads have little economic value, although several species are grown as ornamental garden or house plants.

The cycad *Encephalartos latifrondia* indicates how palmlike these primitive plants are, except for their small stature—3 feet (91 centimeters) high at the most.

Microsporophyll

Microspores

Megasporophyll

Megaspores

Pollen grains being dispersed

Pollen grain

Gametophyte

Nucellus

Pollen chamber

Archegonia

Sperm

New plant

Cotyledons

Cotyledons

Gametophyte

Seed coat

Cotyledons   Roots

Pollen tube

Pollination of cycads occurs when microspores, which have developed into pollen grains, are carried by the wind to the female megasporophyll. This body contains a gametophyte with two archegonia. The pollen grows a tube that fertilizes a gamete in one of the archegonia (this may take six months). The developing seed may take a year to germinate and is nourished by the starchy foodstore of the gametophyte.

Cone-bearing plants

The cone-bearing plants comprise the biggest group of nonflowering plants—the subphylum Gymnospermae (the gymnosperms). This group bridges the gap between the ferns and the angiosperms—the flowering plants. The structure of gymnosperm cones and the details of their reproduction may indicate how angiosperm flowers evolved; both groups may have had a common ancestor at some stage in their evolution—gymnosperms are known to date from the Permian period, about 275 million years ago.

Gymnosperm characteristics

The name gymnosperm applies to the seed (*gymnos* is the Greek word for naked), which is not enclosed within an ovary. This means that the extensions of the ovary wall found in angiosperms—the style and stigma—are absent. In most gymnosperms the fertile leaves (sporophylls) grow in tightly grouped formations called strobili, which in many species are conelike.

The gymnosperms can be divided into three orders, based on the anatomy of their wood, the shape of their leaves, and the structure of their seeds: the Cycadopsida, the Gnetopsida, and the Coniferopsida.

The Cycadopsida comprises the seedferns and cycads, together with other fossil orders. These fern- and palmlike plants are described in the previous article.

The class Gnetopsida contains three odd groups—the welwitschias, the ephedras, and the genus *Gnetum*. Despite being gymnosperms these plants have close affinities to the angiosperms, particularly in their wood structure.

The Coniferopsida consists of the ginkgos, the conifers, and the yews. These plants have pycnoxylic wood—that is, the secondary wood is relatively dense with small parenchyma rays. The wood is simpler than angiosperm wood and contains the elongated cells called tracheids but does not in most gymnosperms have true vessels. Pith rays found in the phloem and xylem tissues transport food from the leaves to the trunk for storage and carry water away from the trunk. Some conifers, such as spruce (*Picea* sp.), have no fibers.

The wood parenchyma of gymnosperms is usually associated with resin. These cells may form a network from the resin canals, as in pines (*Pinus* spp.), or a column of cells that fill with resin. The leaves are usually needle- or scalelike, but may be fan- or paddle-shaped. The leaves or veins branch dichotomously—that is, they branch equally into two and then two again, and so on.

A cross section through coniferous wood shows that its structure is much simpler than that of angiosperm wood. It is composed mostly of tracheid vessels. The vessels formed in the spring are large and thin-walled, to allow as much water to course through the plant as possible. In the summer, the tracheids formed are smaller and thick-walled, which slows down the rate of water flow. Interspersed between the vessels are large resin canals.

Resin canal

Summer tracheids

Ray

Spring tracheids

The welwitschia *(Welwitschia mirabilis)* of the Namib Desert appears at first sight to be an unlikely relation of the cone-bearing plants. But the dark patches on top of the plant centrally placed between its two leaves are groups of cones. These cones are similar to those of conifers in that those of the male plants bear pollen grains and those of the female plants carry an ovule. Pollination is mainly by means of insects.

The odd group

The plants in the class Gnetopsida differ widely in appearance but all share some features—for example, they are all woody and contain conducting vessels. Also, the male flowers have a perianth surrounding them, as may the female flowers. The flowers themselves are arranged in compound strobili, or inflorescences. No fossils (apart from pollen grains) of any of the three living genera have been found, so relationships between them cannot be determined.

The presence of vessels in the secondary xylem may be a characteristic shared with angiosperms but does not indicate a close relationship with them—it is, rather, an example of convergent evolution. They have evolved from pitted tracheids, whereas angiosperm vessels are derived from tracheids with ladderlike (scalariform) thickening.

Found only in the deserts of southwestern Africa is the unique welwitschia *(Welwitschia mirabilis),* the only species of the order Welwitschiales. This peculiar plant has a large, globe-shaped, underground stem, or taproot, with two strap-shaped leaves that can be 2 to 3 feet (61 to 91 centimeters) wide and often twice as long. The leaves continue to grow throughout the life of the plant (more than 100 years), and are continually split into ribbons by the hot, desert winds. Male and female strobili grow on different plants in the form of a cone covered by scales or bracts. The female cones are larger than the male cones and are scarlet when mature. Pollination is mainly by insects.

The small, thin xerophytic shrubs that comprise the order Ephedrales are found in North and South America and from the Mediterranean eastward to China. The plants have small, scalelike leaves and are dioecious (with male and female organs on different plants). The male strobili are solitary and form a conelike inflorescence. The female strobili grow in groups of two or three and are wind-pollinated. Depending on the species, the seeds are either dry and winged or brightly colored and fleshy; they are wind- or animal-dispersed, respectively.

The species of the genus *Gnetum* are usually found in tropical rain forests. Most are woody climbers (lianas) although some species grow as shrubs or trees, such as *Gnetum gnemon,* which grows in Malaysia. The leaves are remarkable in that they look just like dicotyledon leaves with a central midrib, net venation, and a broad blade (lamina). The flowers resemble small upright catkins and are generally dioecious. The female flowers are wind-pollinated and produce seeds in which the embryo is covered with a protective stony layer and surrounded by a fleshy outer layer. The seeds are dispersed by birds.

The ginkgo

The ginkgo *(Ginkgo biloba),* or maidenhair tree, has distinctive two-lobed, fan-shaped leaves. The leaves are identical to those that fell from ginkgos millions of years ago, probably in the Triassic period, when some were preserved in mud and fossilized. Then it had a worldwide distribution, whereas now the

The joint pine, or ephedra (*Ephedra* sp.), is another unexpected conifer. The small groups of yellow-green cones on this shrub mark it as a conifer and also identify it as a female plant—the male strobili are solitary and borne on a separate plant.

ginkgo is found naturally only in Asia. It remains the sole representative of the order Ginkgoales.

The mature tree has a broad spreading crown that reaches a height of about 80 feet (24 meters), with deciduous leaves. Male and female reproductive organs are found on separate trees. The male microstrobili, which bear pendulous microsporangia, are like catkins produced at the end of short shoots. The pollen is transferred by the wind to the ovules, which are also produced at the ends of short shoots. The sperm released from the pollen is large with a spiral band of flagella—a primitive feature. Unlike all other members of the class Coniferopsida, the sperm is motile and swims to the female gamete. The mature ovule falls from the tree in autumn and fertilization may take place while it is on the ground. The seed develops a stony inner layer and an outer fleshy one, which gives off a smell like rancid butter. This smell may be attractive to the animals that are potential dispersers of the seeds.

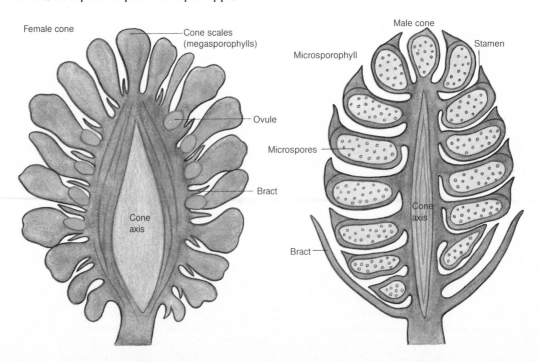

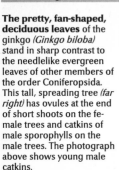

The pretty, fan-shaped, deciduous leaves of the ginkgo *(Ginkgo biloba)* stand in sharp contrast to the needlelike evergreen leaves of other members of the order Coniferopsida. This tall, spreading tree *(far right)* has ovules at the end of short shoots on the female trees and catkins of male sporophylls on the male trees. The photograph above shows young male catkins.

Conifers

The true cone-bearers belong to the order Coniferales. Most living species are trees, and only a few can properly be described as shrubs. Some of the tallest of living trees are included in the order—the Californian redwood *(Sequoia sempervirens),* for example.

The wood of conifer trunks has tracheids with large pits in their walls, but no vessels or pores. Resin canals are common, found sometimes in the wood but mostly in the leaves and cortex. The branches are generally regularly arranged up the trunk to give most conifers their distinctive pyramidal appearance.

Most conifers are evergreen and in some species, notably the monkey puzzle tree *(Araucaria araucana),* the leaves may remain on the tree for up to 15 years. A few species drop their leaves every autumn—larch *(Larix* sp.), for example. The leaves are usually needle-shaped, scalelike, and small, but may be broad, as in podocarps *(Podocarpus* spp.),

whose leaves are 12 inches (30 centimeters) long and 2 inches (5 centimeters) wide.

Conifers are adapted to growing in boreal zones and on mountains, where there may be a lack of water when the ground is frozen in winter, although there are exceptions—such as the swamp cypress *(Taxodium* sp.) of the southern United States. In addition, their pyramidal shape ensures that snow is more likely to slide off the branches than collect on them, possibly breaking them. The conifer leaves are constructed to resist drying out, with a thick, waxy cuticle and, usually, a small size. The needle shape is most resistant to frost. The xeromorphic characters equally help those conifers that live in arid places such as sand dunes, as do many species of pine *(Pinus* sp.). The stone pine *(Pinus pinea),* for example, is a familiar sight on bare stony Mediterranean hills where water is in short supply.

Conifers can be monoecious or dioecious. In all species, however, the cones are unisex-

A cross section through a female cone from a conifer *(right)* reveals the cone scales, or megasporophylls, each containing one ovule. In these ovules one megaspore develops into a gametophyte. In the male cones *(far right)* the microsporophylls each contain several microsporangia, which develop two or three microspores; these eventually become pollen grains.

Female cone — Cone scales (megasporophylls)

Ovule

Bract

Cone axis

Male cone

Microsporophyll

Stamen

Microspores

Cone axis

Bract

ual. The female cones, or megastrobili, contain two ovules. In some species of podocarp, however, there is only one ovule in the cone. The cones usually consist of a central axis with large woody bract scales attached to them, each scale carrying a seed. But not all cones take this form; in some species, such as juniper, the bract scales are so reduced that the cones resemble berries (which are used for flavoring gin), whereas in the podocarps the cones look like small plums.

The male cones, or microstrobili, tend to be smaller than the female ones and simpler. In the larch the male cones turn from bright red to dark red to chestnut-brown when ripe. They contain microsporophylls with pollen sacs—each cone may produce up to 10 million pollen grains. Pollination is by means of the wind in all conifers. The pollen grains that land on the ovule develop a pollen tube with one male nucleus, which fertilizes the female gamete.

The roots of conifers are inhabited by mycorrhizal fungi. The fungal hyphae grow either between the cells of the cortex (when the association is known as ectotrophic mycorrhiza) or inside the cells (endotrophic mycorrhiza). In the podocarps the fungi grow in special root nodules. These fungi supply the trees with minerals, especially nitrogen.

The order contains six families, the largest one being the pines (Pinaceae). The others are the cypresses (Cupressaceae), the plum yews (Cephalotaxaceae), the redwoods and swamp cypresses (Taxodiaceae), the araucarias (Araucariaceae), and the podocarps (Podocarpaceae). Most are found in the Northern Hemisphere, although the last two families occur predominantly in the south.

The pine family (Pinaceae) is found naturally in the Northern Hemisphere. Its members are essentially part of the "cold flora," found at the polar forest limits, and compose most of the northern boreal forests. In the south they are mainly found on mountains. The family contains 10 genera and about 100 species; these include silver firs (*Abies* spp.), spruces (*Picea*

spp.), hemlocks (*Tsuga* spp.), Douglas firs (*Pseudotsuga* spp.), cedars (*Cedrus* spp.), larches, and pines.

The leaves of this family are characteristically spirally arranged on short or long shoots (or both) in the form of needles or scale-leaves. Two ovules occur on each bract of the female cone. They are wind-pollinated by pollen grains that are kept buoyant by two air bladders. Fertilization takes place within a month, except in pines, where it may take up to 12 months. The ovules develop into winged seeds. This family is of great economic importance because it supplies about 75 per cent of the world's lumber requirements.

Growth in many pines is rapid, and trees reach maturity in 15 to 20 years. But some desert pines, such as the bristlecone pine *(P. aristata)* of North America, are very long-lived; some are estimated to be more than 4,000 years old.

Redwoods (*Sequoia* spp.) are among the largest trees in the world, generally reaching a height of about 200 to 275 feet (61 to 84 meters) and a diameter of 8 to 12 feet (2.4 to 3.6 meters).

The life cycle of a typical conifer involves the transportation of pollen grains from a microsporophyll to a megasporophyll. The pollen grain grows a tube that contains a male gamete; this fuses with the female gamete in one of the archegonia. The developing seed is winged and is dispersed by wind.

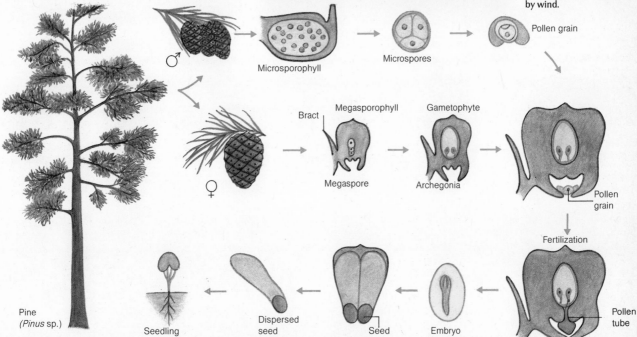

Pine
(*Pinus* sp.)

Microsporophyll

Microspores

Pollen grain

Bract

Megasporophyll

Gametophyte

Megaspore

Archegonia

Pollen grain

Fertilization

Pollen tube

Seedling

Dispersed seed

Seed

Embryo

Pines (*Pinus* spp.), along with most other conifers, are well adapted to living in cold environments. The pyramidal shape of these trees means that heavy snow will slip off the branches, preventing them from breaking.

The sexual organs of cone-bearing plants all differ slightly from species to species, as does the arrangement of their leaves. The spruces, firs, plum yews, and yews have branches with leaves growing singly on them. Cedars, larches, and pines bear sprays of grouped needles. The "cones," which contain the sex cells, range in shape and form from elongated strobili with cone scales, to berries, as in the junipers, and fleshy arils, as in the yews.

Most of the cypress family (Cupressaceae) grow in North America, Europe, and Asia. These include cypresses (*Cupressus* spp.), and juniper, false cypress (*Chamaecyparis* sp.), and arborvitae (*Thuja* spp.). Cypress pines, such as *Callitris, Libocedrus,* and *Papuacedrus,* are confined to Australasia.

The family Cephalotaxaceae contains six species of plum yews, all belonging to the single genus *Cephalotaxus.* They are found in eastern Asia where they grow as shrubs or trees up to 49 feet (15 meters) high, with long yewlike leaves. The secondary wood of these plants resembles that of the yews, but because the ovules grow as cones they are grouped with the conifers. The male and female cones grow on separate plants. The pollen grains do not fertilize the ovule after pollination until the following season. The female cones contain two ovules, but only one normally develops. It produces a seed that resembles a large olive.

The family Taxodiaceae contains the dawn redwood (*Metasequoia glyptostroboides*),

which was identified from Miocene fossils and thought to be extinct until 1944, when living trees were found in central China. The redwoods and giant redwood *(Sequoia giganteum)* also belong to this family, as do the deciduous swamp cypresses of southern North America.

Naturally growing species of the family Araucariaceae are confined to the Southern Hemisphere, although the monkeypuzzle tree is widely planted in gardens, and the Norfolk Island pine *(A. heterophylla)* is a common indoor plant. Of the two genera in the family, *Araucaria* is found in South America and Australasia, whereas the Kauri pines (*Agathis* spp.) are found from southeastern Asia to New Zealand. *Araucaria* provides lumber (parane pine), and Kauri pines are the source of copal, a resin used in the production of a hard varnish.

The seven genera of podocarps (Podocarpaceae) grow in the countries and islands within and surrounding the southern Pacific Ocean. The family shows an amazing diversity of form, ranging from trees 200 feet (61 me-

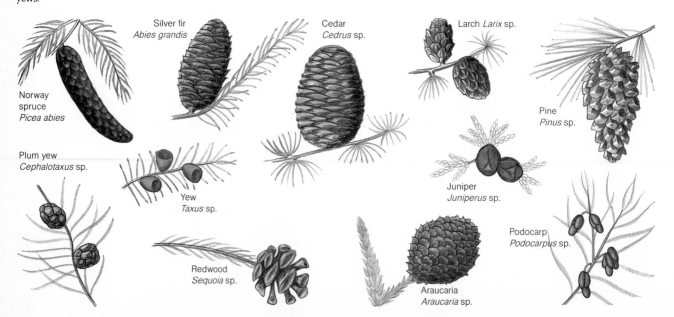

Norway spruce
Picea abies

Silver fir
Abies grandis

Cedar
Cedrus sp.

Larch *Larix* sp.

Pine
Pinus sp.

Plum yew
Cephalotaxus sp.

Yew
Taxus sp.

Juniper
Juniperus sp.

Podocarp
Podocarpus sp.

Redwood
Sequoia sp.

Araucaria
Araucaria sp.

ters) high to small shrubs. The shrub *Podocarpus ustus,* from New Caledonia, may be a unique conifer because it is thought to be a hemiparasite on the roots of another podocarp, *Dacrydium taxaoides.* The genus *Phyllocladus* has no leaves, photosynthesis being carried out instead by flattened stems, or cladodes. The female flowers of this family range from cones to a swollen receptacle bearing a terminal ovule. In *Phyllocladus* the ovules are partly covered by an outgrowth called an aril—this is unique among conifers. Some species of *Podocarpus* have a single ovule that is supported on a receptacle that swells and becomes bright red. It is eaten by birds and animals and is the means whereby the seeds are dispersed.

The yews and associated species

The evergreen shrubs and small trees that make up the order Taxales grow only in the Northern Hemisphere, except for the monospecific genus *Austrotaxus,* which is confined to the island of New Caledonia in the South Pacific. There are five living genera, the sixth (extinct) genus *Palaeotaxus* having provided the basis upon which the order was separated from the true conifers (its seeds were not present in cones, but attached to part of a branch). The yews belong to the genus *Taxus,* and other genera include the torreyas (*Torreya* spp.), *Amentotaxus,* and *Pseudotaxus.*

The plants vary in size from a height of 100 feet (30 meters) with a diameter of only 10 feet (3 meters) as in *Torreya* to a height of 65 feet (20 meters) and a diameter of 22 feet (7 meters) as in the yews. The massive trunk of yews may not be a single trunk but represents several fused smaller ones.

Yew leaves are flattened and shaped rather like a Roman sword. They are usually about 1 inch (2.5 centimeters) in length, but reach about 3 inches (8 centimeters) in the Californian nutmeg *(Torreya californica).* The leaves contain one vascular bundle only, which has special transfusion tissue on each side of it that facilitates the movement of materials between the leaf and the bundle. The leaves spread apart in two rows along the stem. The branches grow out horizontally from the main trunk and form a rather dense umbrella under which little will grow.

Unlike the wood produced by conifers, the wood of these plants does not contain resin canals or wood parenchyma cells. The yew leaves do not have resin canals, but in the other genera resin sacs occur in the leaves and flowers. The tracheids of the secondary wood have abundant spiral thickening and may account for the elasticity of the wood, which made it so popular for bows.

Whereas the ovules of most of the other gymnosperms, except *Podocarpus,* are grouped, the ovules of these plants are solitary, growing at the end of a small branch and not in a cone. They are surrounded by stony integuments and a succulent cup, or aril. The red fleshy aril is eaten by birds, which consequently disperse the seeds. The aril is the only part of the plant that does not contain the poisonous alkaloid taxin.

Yews are dioecious. Pollen is produced by microstrobili that take the form of cones or

Cypresses (*Cupressus* spp.) are a familiar sight among the olive groves of the Mediterranean countries and are one of the few examples of conifers that do not grow in cold, mountainous regions.

The bright red cups, or arils, of yew trees (*Taxus* spp.) surround the ovules. The color attracts birds that eat the aril and later disperse the seed.

scales. It is transmitted to the female flowers by the wind, and the seeds are produced a few months later. The seeds have two cotyledons that persist after germination for about three years; they are similar in shape to the true leaves, but somewhat larger.

Flowering plants

The development of the flowering plants is possibly the greatest success story in the evolution of the earth. From the time of their appearance in the middle of the Cretaceous period, about 100 million years ago, they have flourished and diversified so that today they dominate nearly all the terrestrial plant communities, from tropical forests to temperate deciduous woodlands, and from grasslands to deserts. Even the sea has flowering plants of some kind. They are also the prime producers of food for the animals of the earth (but not the sea), not least for humans who rely on them as food for themselves and domesticated livestock.

Flowering plants are grouped into the Angiospermae, or Magnoliophytina, about 250,000 species of which have been named and described. These plants are further arranged in 2 groups—the dicotyledons, or Magnoliopsida, with about 190,000 species, and the monocotyledons, or Liliopsida, with about 60,000 species. (There are, however, several systems of classification; the system described in this book may differ slightly from systems used elsewhere. For examples, *see The World Book Encyclopedia* articles PLANT [A classification of the plant kingdom] and CLASSIFICATION, SCIENTIFIC.) In addition to the thousands of "natural" species, million of forms, varieties, and cultivars have been artificially created by plant breeding programs, to decorate gardens and homes, and to increase the abundance and extent of crops.

The appearance of angiosperms

The first fossils with rudimentary angiosperm characteristics, such as pollen grains, date from the Triassic period, which began about 245 million years ago. The first true angiosperms, which possibly evolved from an ancestral cycad, were most likely to have been tropical trees with flowers—possibly similar to those of a present-day magnolia—and with large, fleshy edible fruits that were attractive to birds and other animals.

These appeared in the early part of the Cretaceous period, about 100 million years ago. During this period—the climax of the Age of Dinosaurs—the land flora underwent a great change, and many of the new plants would be recognizable today. As well as the magnolias, there were willows, oaks, poplars, and sycamores. The ubiquitous grasses that make up such a familiar part of the modern landscape did not develop until Cenozoic times, when grasslands, and their accompanying running mammals, spread at the expense of the forests.

But the exact way in which the angiosperms evolved and the steps that occurred between the appearance of the first flowering plants and the production of the diversity that exists today remains a mystery. The answer lies in the huge gaps in the fossil record—possibly due to the fact that flowering plants evolved in

The flowering parts of plants vary, from the primitive plants in which they are complex and many, to the advanced plants in which they are simple and reduced. Sunflowers *(Helianthus annuus)*, like all members of the Compositae family, are higher dicotyledonous plants with only their central disk florets capable of forming seeds. The yellow, outer, petallike florets serve to attract pollinating insects and birds.

parts of the world that were subsequently submerged—and until these gaps are filled, the precursors of the angiosperm plants will remain unknown.

The characters of success

The whole design and life of the angiosperm flower, whether it is a showy bloom or an inconspicuous grass flower, is devoted to the production of viable seed from which the next generation can grow. Flowering plants differ from the other major class of plants—Gymnospermae—by having their female sex cells (ovules) enclosed in an ovary; the gymnosperms have naked seeds. In addition, the seeds that develop from angiosperm ovules are enclosed in a fruit. But the most important feature of the angiosperm life style is that the generation of gametophytes, on which the insurance of genetic diversity depends, is reduced to the activities of a few cells only, and confined to the safe depths of the flower.

The first flowering plants were hermaphroditic—that is, they contained male pollen-producing anthers and female ovule-containing ovaries in the same flower. This arrangement is still found in most modern angiosperms, but it seems likely that the primitive plants possessed genes that induced a state of self-sterility—the pollen from one flower was not capable of fertilizing the ovules of the same flower—which made a transfer of pollen between the flowers of different individuals of the same species essential.

Animals were originally responsible for this necessary process of the transfer of pollen from flower to flower—a role they have now played for millions of years. Only in specialized advanced states of angiosperm development has animal help been replaced by obligatory self-pollination, seed production without the need for fertilization, or by wind-pollinating mechanisms. Insects were the first pollinators to aid plants in their need—they were tempted by the pollen produced by the plants, which is rich in nutrients. In time they turned to the sugary nectar and, as the insects entered the flower in search of the nectar, they brushed against the rough-surfaced pollen, which stuck to them. On the next visit to a flower of the same species, the pollen was transferred to the receptive stigma and carried to the ovule, where fertilization was effected.

As the plants' systems evolved, petals became brightly colored and patterned to attract birds and guide insects to the nectar. Many of these patterns are visible only in the ultraviolet wavelength, a part of the light spectrum in which insect vision can operate. Flowers also developed scents that were attractive to insects and birds. The opening of flowers and scent production became synchronized to the active periods of pollinators, and as the reliance of specific pollinators increased, so the structure of the flower became more complex. Those flowers that do not rely on animal associations for pollination do not have color, nectar, or scent because they do not need to attract animals.

Wind, animals, the explosive mechanisms of the seeds, and occasionally water, are the prime dispersers of angiosperm seed. Because the seeds have a self-contained food supply, they are also freed from the necessity of an external food source when they start to germinate; they can also remain dormant for long periods if they need to. Nevertheless, angiosperm seeds develop extremely quickly in comparison to, say, gymnosperms. A dandelion, for example, takes six weeks from seed germination to seed dispersal from a mature plant. A conifer, on the other hand, can take up to two years. These characteristics have made angiosperms highly adaptable and able to diversify, and account for their enormous success on this planet.

Frangipani (*Plumeria* sp.) is a simple tropical flower. It attracts pollinating insects with its bright pink or white and yellow flowers, and also with its distinctive scent.

Tiger lilies (*Lilium tigrinum*) are monocotyledonous flowers, and, like many others, have exposed flowering parts. The six, pendulous, lobed structures are the stamens (male). There are three stigmas (female) and three compartments in the ovary. The large, showy flowers are pollinated by insects that push past the protruding stamens to reach the nectar, picking up pollen as they move, and transferring it to the stigmas.

The flower is the organ of sexual reproduction in plants. The most obvious parts are the petals, which form the corolla, and sepals, which form the calyx; together these two constitute the perianth, mounted on the receptacle. The female pistil is made up of the stigma on its style above the ovule-containing ovary. The male stamens consist of pollen-bearing anthers on supporting filaments.

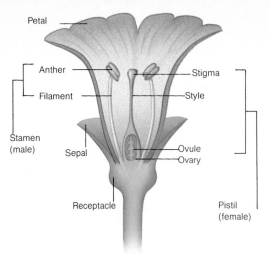

Petal

Anther

Filament

Stamen (male)

Sepal

Stigma

Style

Ovule

Ovary

Receptacle

Pistil (female)

Sexual reproduction

If plants increased by vegetative means only—through budding, runners, and so on—the processes of evolution and adaptation could not take place, because each new plant would have exactly the same genetic makeup as its parent. The element of change relies on sexual reproduction, in which each new individual inherits genetic material from both of its parents. Sexual reproduction has the additional advantage of enabling the individual embryos to be carried away from the parents and to

grow some distance away, perhaps in a more favorable environment. This system helps to prevent the plants from becoming over-crowded and assists the spread of the species.

Flowers

The part of a plant specialized for sexual reproduction is the flower. Here the male and female gametes—pollen (male) and ovules (female)—are produced and come together to produce seeds, each containing an embryo plant. In some species, such as buttercup (*Ranunculus* spp.), all the flowers are hermaphrodite, having both male organs (stamens) and female organs (carpels). Other plants have unisexual flowers, producing either male or female gametes, but not both. Separate male and female flowers may both be borne on the same plant (monoecious), as in hazel (*Corylus avellana)*, or male flowers may be produced on some plants and female flowers on others (dioecious), as in willows (*Salix* spp.). Species with male, female, and hermaphrodite flowers, either on the same plant or on different plants, are known as polygamous.

Flowers may be borne singly or may be grouped together to form an inflorescence. Solitary flowers are seen in anemone (*Anemone patens)*, whereas the flowers of Virginia cowslip (*Mertensia virginica)* form an inflorescence. In some species, such as oxeye daisy (*Chrysanthemum leucanthemum)*, what appear to be single flowers are in fact inflorescences made up of many tiny individual flowers closely grouped together.

Carpels

The top of a flower stem is often enlarged and forms a platform (the receptacle) upon which the other floral organs are located, arranged in whorls, spirals, or both. In the center are the carpels, collectively forming the pistil. Each carpel consists of a sticky stigma at the top of a stalk (the style), which joins a hollow ovary containing one or more ovules. Buttercups have a single ovule in each carpel; some orchid carpels contain half a million ovules each.

Species with only one carpel in each flower are rare; they include the members of the pea family. Sometimes the carpels are separate as in buttercup, but in most species two or more carpels are fused together, having a common ovary. The edges of the fused carpels may project into the ovary but not reach the center, producing a unilocular ovary; however, more frequently, the carpel edges meet at the center of the ovary, dividing it into as many loculi (chambers) as there are carpels. The styles and stigmas may also be entirely or partly fused together, or they may remain separate.

Each ovule consists of an ovoid mass of cells called the nucellus, which is attached to the ovary wall by a short stalk (the funicle). Protective layers (integuments) cover the entire nucellus except for a small opening called the micropyle. Inside the nucellus is the embryo sac, usually containing eight nuclei. Three are situated near the micropyle, the middle one of these forming the ovum (egg); three are at the opposite end to the micropyle; and two are in the center of the embryo sac. These two central nuclei sometimes fuse together to form

Male and female structures show up well in the flower of a hybrid fuchsia. The female stigma protrudes beyond a cluster of five stamens, some of which bear powdery pollen.

the endosperm nucleus or secondary nucleus.

Stamens

Surrounding the carpels are the stamens. They may be separate, or all or some may be joined. Their number is constant in some species, but variable in others. Each stamen has a swollen head (the anther) and usually a stalk (the filament), which carries nutrients from the plant to the anther. The central part of the anther is called the connective, and attached to this are pollen sacs containing pollen mother cells, each of which divides twice (by meiosis) to form a tetrad of four pollen grains. In some species the grains are dispersed in these groups of four, but usually they separate within the pollen sacs. When ripe, the anther opens, generally by means of two longitudinal slits, and the pollen sacs are ruptured, releasing the pollen grains.

The shape of pollen grains varies, but often they are round or oblong. The outer wall has distinctive pores and may also possess spines, ridges, or other features. These characteristics are remarkably constant in any individual species so that it is usually possible to identify a plant by examining its pollen grains. Each grain has two nuclei, one of which forms the generative cell, and the other is the tube nucleus. The generative cell usually divides to form two male gametes or sperm cells; therefore the mature pollen grain contains three nuclei, one vegetative and two generative (gametes).

Petals and sepals

The stamens are usually surrounded by a corolla, formed of petals. These are not directly involved in the reproductive process, but can be of great assistance to the plant because large, brightly colored petals attract insects that may carry out pollination, transferring pollen grains from stamens to stigmas. In some species the petals are joined to form a corolla tube or trumpet shape.

A calyx, composed of sepals, normally forms the outermost part of the flower, protecting the other organs, especially before the bud opens. The sepals may be joined into a calyx tube. Both petals and sepals are of constant number in some species, and variable in others. Usually the sepals are green, but some flowers, such as those of bluebell and crocus, have sepals that are petaloid—they are just like the petals in size, shape, and color, and the two whorls are known collectively as the perianth. Sometimes, as in Christmas rose *(Helleborus niger)*, the parts that appear to be petals are in fact large, showy sepals. Some plants, particularly those pollinated by the wind, have neither corolla nor calyx, because they do not need to attract insects. These "naked flowers" grow in plain, tassel-like inflorescences, called catkins, and can be found on plants such as alders, poplars, and willows.

Before the male and female gametes can unite the pollen grains must be carried from the stamens to the carpels (pollination). Pollen may be deposited on the stigma of the same flower or on the stigma of a different flower on the same plant. Both these processes are forms of self-pollination. When the pollen is transported to the stigma of a flower on a different plant, cross-pollination occurs. Self-pollination perpetuates the characteristics of the parent plant, whereas cross-pollination introduces new genetic combinations, bringing the possibility of better, stronger plants.

Self-pollination

In plants where self-pollination normally occurs, the stamens are usually located so that the anthers are above the stigma, and stamens and stigma ripen simultaneously. The ripe pollen often simply falls onto the receptive stigma below, although sometimes the process is more complex, involving movement of the

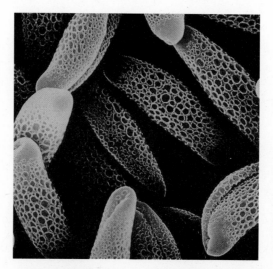

Pollen grains vary in texture and shape—depending on the plant species—from smooth and spherical to pitted and slipper-shaped *(left)*. For fertilization to take place, pollen from the male anther has to get to the female stigma. If this takes place in the same flower (A) or between two flowers on the same plant (B), self-pollination occurs. Transfer of pollen to a flower on another plant (C) leads to cross-pollination.

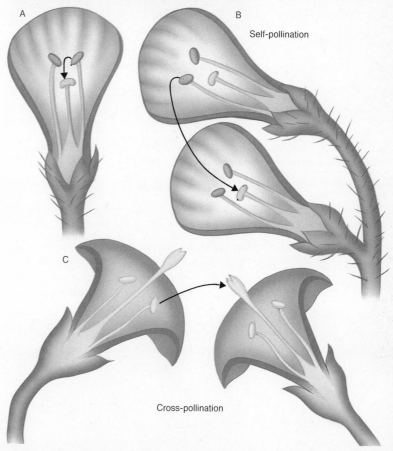

Two different designs of flowers of the same species is termed heterostyly. The "pin" form *(left)* has a long stigma and anthers deep in the flower's corolla, whereas in the "thrum" form *(right)* the positions of the organs are reversed. When an insect visits either flower to feed, pollen left on it by the anthers of one type is transferred to the stigma of the other type.

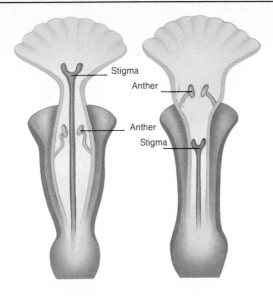

stamens or stigma.

To prevent self-pollination taking place, many plants are dichogamous—that is, their stamens and stigmas do not ripen at the same time. Self-pollination is impossible in dioecious plants, because male and female flowers are borne on separate plants. Sometimes pollen may fall onto a ripe stigma of the same flower but then fail to bring about fertilization, because its genes are incompatible with those of the ovule. Such plants are described as self-sterile.

Another device discouraging self-pollination is called heterostyly, which can be seen in the primrose *(Primula vulgaris)*. The flowers of this species are usually of two types (dimorphic): a "pin-eyed" form, with the stigma at the mouth of the corolla tube on a long style and the stamens halfway up the corolla tube, and a "thrum-eyed" form, with the stigma halfway up the tube on a short style and the stamens located at the top of the corolla tube. The pollen from one form sticks to an insect visitor and is then deposited on a stigma of the other form, as the stamens of one type are at the same level as the stigma of the other. The pollen grains of the two types are different and the plants are self-sterile, a fact which suggests that heterostyly is, by itself, a rather inadequate method of discouraging self-pollination.

Cross-pollination

Cross-pollination is brought about by the wind, by insects (or birds, bats, or other animals), or, in a few aquatic plants, by water. Wind pollination, the simplest method, is also the most wasteful: vast amounts of pollen are produced in an attempt to ensure that some of it lands on a ripe stigma. The male flowers are often borne on dangling catkins, where they are shaken by the slightest breeze. This form of pollination is particularly common among trees, grasses, rushes, and sedges. The flowers are usually small and inconspicuous, with large anthers exposed to the wind on long, slender filaments, and exposed feathery stigmas to catch airborne pollen. The flowers produce neither nectar nor scent.

Insect pollination is less wasteful, but often much more complex. The flowers attract pollinators by means of large, brightly colored petals, and often by a strong scent. This is not

The main kinds of fruits can be divided among simple, aggregate, and multiple types. Simple fruits may be fleshy, as in drupes, pomes, and berries, or dry, as in nuts and the "seeds" (actually fruits) of grasses and some trees. An aggregate fruit, like blackberry, has separated seeds in a pulpy flesh (carpel), all derived from one flower. Multiple fruits, like pineapple, derive from several flowers that condense during development to form a single seed-bearing structure. Figs are another example of multiple fruits.

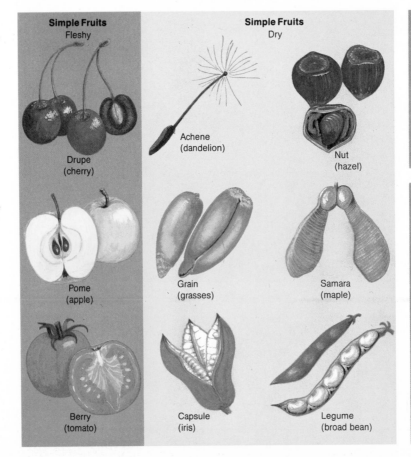

Simple Fruits
Fleshy

Drupe
(cherry)

Pome
(apple)

Berry
(tomato)

Simple Fruits
Dry

Achene
(dandelion)

Grain
(grasses)

Capsule
(iris)

Nut
(hazel)

Samara
(maple)

Legume
(broad bean)

Aggregate Fruits

(blackberry)

Multiple Fruits

(pineapple)

always a sweet perfume; some flowers produce a stench like that of rotting flesh or dung and, thus, attract carrion-feeding or dung-feeding insects. A supply of nectar frequently serves as an invitation to insects, or the visitors may come for the pollen itself. The petals often have bright spots or lines pointing the way to the flower's nectar-store; such markings are known as nectar-guides. Nectar located deep within the flower can only be reached by insects with a long proboscis, such as bees, butterflies, and moths; flies and beetles, which have short tongues, can take nectar from flowers only where it is easily accessible. Thus different flowers are visited by different types of insects. Pollen becomes attached to the hairy legs and body of a feeding insect and is then brushed onto the stigma of the next flower visited.

Some more complex pollination systems include mechanical traps that actually hold the pollinating animal long enough for the pollen to be transferred. The jack-in-the-pulpit *(Arisaema triphyllum)* attracts flies into an enclosed chamber by the smell of carrion. The flies can escape only when the structures at the mouth of the chamber wither, by which time the flies are thoroughly dusted by pollen during their struggles. A similar device makes sure that the pollen is shaken onto the female structures on another plant. Some orchids, such as the early purple orchid *(Orchis mascula)*, have spring-loaded anthers that snap shut on a visiting bee. The bee's struggle to escape dislodges the pollen onto its back.

Water pollination is rare, even among plants that grow in water. Most pollen becomes ineffective when wet, and even in aquatic species that are pollinated by water, it is often the male flowers, and not the individual pollen grains, that are carried by the current to the female flowers, the pollen thus remaining dry.

Fertilization

When a pollen grain lands on a ripe stigma it swells as it absorbs water, sugar, and other materials from the stigma. The pollen then germinates or grows a tube down the style toward the ovary. The pollen tube, containing two male gametes, grows through the canal and enters an ovule by way of the micropyle. The tip of the pollen tube penetrates the embryo sac and releases the two male gametes. One enters the ovum and fuses with its nucleus, forming a zygote from which an embryo plant develops. The other usually fuses with the central nuclei of the embryo-sac, producing nutritive tissue called endosperm, which nourishes the embryo. Fertilization is thus achieved.

A hoverfly feeds on nectar and has grains of yellow pollen on the hairs of its head and body. By this means, the pollen will be transferred to another flower of the same species and will fertilize it.

Oranges ripen on a tree in Australia. The fruit, which develops from the ovary of a fertilized flower, contains several seeds, although horticulturalists have also created seedless varieties of oranges and other fruits.

Fruit and seeds

Following fertilization, many changes take place in the carpel. Each ovule becomes a seed, its integuments forming the protective seed coat (testa), and the ovary becomes a fruit, its three layers of wall forming the pericarp. Sepals, petals, and stamens usually wither, although their dry remains often persist, sometimes attached to the fruit.

There are three main kinds of fruits, classified as simple (that is, single), aggregate (clusters), and multiple, with various types within these categories as illustrated on the opposite page.

Fact entries

Cell division in plants, as in animals, takes two forms. The duplication of cells in normal growth takes place by mitosis. The special type of cell division that gives rise to sex cells (gametes) is termed meiosis.

Mitosis produces two daughter cells, each of which has a full complement of genetic material (chromosomes) similar to that of the parent cell. The new cells are described as being diploid.

Meiosis also produces two cells but in each of them the chromosomes are reduced in number to half of that in the parent cell. The new cells are haploid, and may be a male gamete (pollen in the case of a plant) or a female gamete (ovule). At fertilization, male and female gametes combine to form a fertilized ovum (zygote) with a full complement of chromosomes, half from each gamete. If the two gametes derive from different parents—as in cross-pollination—genetic material from two different individuals is combined in the offspring, although normally both parents belong to the same species.

Seed dispersal

Plant seeds are the product of sexual reproduction, and their dispersal determines where succeeding generations will grow. Seed dispersal is the process that enables a species to expand its territory and helps to reduce the competition for resources between the parent plants and the seedlings.

The seed is often contained in a unit of dispersal, such as a fruit. The embryo inside the seed lies dormant while dispersal takes place, a factor that is as important to the embryo's survival as the protective structures of the seed or fruit. In many cases, the seed, fruit, partial, or whole plant is structurally adapted for dispersal by animals, wind, or water, or for self-dispersal.

Animal dispersal

The dispersal of plant seeds by insects, birds, and mammals may be carried out in various ways, all equally haphazard. The fruits or seeds may be eaten for their nutritional content and the undigested seeds may subsequently be voided elsewhere. Many fruits and seeds have some edible part, whether it is the fleshy outer part of a seed, as in the peony (*Paeonia* sp.), or more commonly of a fleshy fruit, such as a tomato.

Birds feed largely on fleshy fruits retained on the plant. They are attracted primarily by color (they are particularly sensitive to red) because they have little or no sense of smell. The different colorations of immature fruit, reinforced by an unpleasant taste, warn the birds of unripe fruit. This allows the young seed embryo more time to develop. The red currant (*Ribes rubrum*) is an example of this type, as is the mistletoe (*Phoradendron flavescens*), the seeds of which stick to birds' bills and are later scraped off.

The fruit of wild mangoes (*Mangifera* spp.) are eaten by the biggest fruit-eating bats, and the trees are adapted for dispersal by them. The mangoes hang away from the dense foliage and often have a strong rancid smell. These adaptations are necessary because the bats are less maneuverable than birds, are nocturnal and color-blind, and have relatively unsophisticated sonar systems for their species. They do, however, have teeth and a good sense of smell. They suck the fruit dry, spitting out the hard seeds.

Fruit enclosing seeds dispersed primarily by terrestrial mammals are often shed and are easily eaten on the ground. An example is the spiny durian (*Durio zibethinus*), which also has an exceptionally powerful smell. Its oily fruit is eaten not only by humans but also by rhinoceroses, orangutans, elephants, and even carnivorous cats. Its seeds, however, are toxic, which encourages the animals to excrete them as quickly as possible.

Some birds and some of the smaller mammals collect and store nuts for consumption at a later stage. Squirrels and rats store beechnuts and hazelnuts underground, and jays cache acorns in tree hollows. Where hoards are forgotten, seeds are left to grow.

Ants disperse seeds of some *Datura, Euphorbia, Cyclamen,* and *Primula* species and are drawn to them by attractant oils. Small structures (elaiosomes) impregnated with these oil food-substances are appended to the seeds and are easily detached. Alternatively, the oils may be generally distributed in the outer layers of the seeds, which are borne close to the ground. The ants eat the oil substance and leave the rest.

Another way in which seeds are dispersed is when seeds and fruits become attached to animals. They may be transported in pieces of mud that cling to the animal, as are the seeds of sweet grass (*Glyceria* sp.), which stick to the feet of passing waterbirds. Some plants produce a sticky mucilage that helps them to adhere to passing animals. Mistletoe berries eaten by birds also stick to their beaks and plumage, eventually falling off or being removed when the bird preens itself some distance away from the parent plant. Other plants produce fruits and seeds that bear hooks by which they become attached to animals. Stickseed (*Hachelia* sp.) has a small nutlike fruit with barbed prickles that catch in fur. Burdock (*Arctium* sp.) has hooked bracts below the flower, which remain on the fruit.

Wind, water, and self-dispersal

Wind is another important way in which seeds are scattered; it operates best on the outer edges of plant communities and in fairly open environments. The dustlike seeds of some orchids can weigh as little as 0.001 mg and are released in quantities of hundreds of thousands; a single fruit capsule of the *Cynorchis* orchid may release 4 million seeds of similar weight. Some of the heavier fruits and seeds have specific adaptations to increase their surface area relative to their weight and assist in flight. Such adaptations include the "parachute" of the dandelion (*Taraxacum officinale*)—actually a ring of fine hairs, called a pappus, attached to the seed—the downy fruit and style of virgin's-bower (*Clematis* sp.), and the hairy tufts of poplar (*Populus* sp.) and willow (*Salix*

The structure of seeds determines the way in which they will be dispersed. Winged seeds, such as those of the maple, are light and can be carried by the wind. So too can clematis and milkweed seeds, aided by their light hairy tufts, which act as a parachute mechanism. Other seeds are contained in edible fruits and rely on animal consumption for them to be released and dispersed. The barbs and spikes on some seeds also depend on animals for their dissemination, becoming attached to fur or clothing. Some fruits, such as the squirting cucumber, blow their seeds out when they release internal turgor pressure.

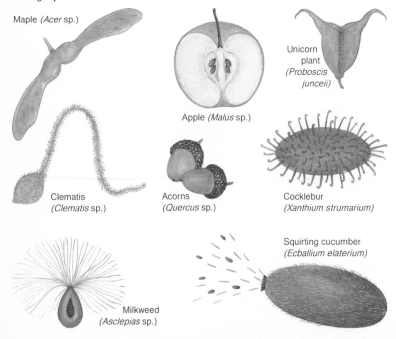

Maple (*Acer* sp.)

Clematis (*Clematis* sp.)

Apple (*Malus* sp.)

Unicorn plant (*Proboscis junceii*)

Acorns (*Quercus* sp.)

Cocklebur (*Xanthium strumarium*)

Squirting cucumber (*Ecballium elaterium*)

Milkweed (*Asclepias* sp.)

sp.) seeds. The fruits of ash *(Fraxinus excelsior)* and maple (*Acer* sp.) have wings that slow their fall and help to widen their distribution. Tumbleweeds *(Salsola kali)* are more radical seed dispersers. The whole plant is blown about, scattering its seeds as it rolls. The poppy (*Papaver* sp.) ripens its fruit on long stalks; when these dry out they are caught by the wind, and the seeds are catapulted out through holes in the fruit.

Some plants rely on water to disperse their seeds. The coco-de-mer *(Lodoicea maldivica)* produces seeds that can weigh up to 45 pounds (20 kilograms) and that float with the help of trapped air. Water-repellent oils and chemicals also enhance buoyancy. But water can also assist a plant's self-dispersal of seeds. The impact of a raindrop on the calyx of the sage, *Salvia lyrata,* flexes the delicate flower stalk, which, on regaining its undisturbed position, throws off the attached nutlets.

Specially weakened tissues in plants can be ruptured by high local water pressures, throwing the seeds in all directions. For example, the touch-me-not (*Impatiens biflora*) has pods that burst open at the slightest touch, scattering seeds everywhere. Excessive water absorption can also create torsions sufficient to release seeds, as in *Vicia* and *Lupinus* species. Torsions in the awns of storkbills (*Erodium* spp.) provide enough force for the attached seeds to bore themselves down into the ground. Certain plants have explosive fruits that, when ripe, rupture and release their seeds in a high-pressure jet of fruit pulp, as does the squirting cucumber (*Ecballium elaterium).*

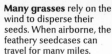

Many grasses rely on the wind to disperse their seeds. When airborne, the feathery seedcases can travel for many miles.

The bright colors of fleshy fruits attract birds to them. Their seeds have a hard casing that may need the animal's digestive juices to act on them and change the structure of the seed coat so that germination is induced.

Coconuts are the seed carriers of the tropical seashore palm tree *Cocos nucifera.* These fruits can weigh several pounds but are dispersed by the sea, floating on the water by means of the air trapped inside the shell. The seed's germination may be delayed for up to two years, allowing enough time for the coconut to reach land.

Vegetative propagation

Most higher plants reproduce by seeds or spores or develop a new plant from part of themselves asexually by vegetative propagation. There are only a few annual plants that reproduce vegetatively, but most herbaceous perennials do reproduce in this way, as well as relying on seeds for propagation.

Most plants that reproduce vegetatively are outstandingly successful in terms of numbers and areas colonized.

Plantlets growing from the edge of *Bryophyllum* sp. *(right)* drop to the ground and root to form new plants. In the same way, the purple bulbils developing in the papery bracts of crow garlic or *Allium vineale (below)* eventually fall to the ground, where they start growing. By these means the plants can multiply without relying on seed dispersal.

Advantages and disadvantages

Vegetative reproduction involves no exchange of genetic material and consequently every new plant is identical to the parent. The lack of potential variability of the offspring, and the absence of the dispersal mechanisms that operate in seed production, are the two major disadvantages of vegetative propagation.

On the other hand, asexual reproduction uses less energy than sexual, and in a harsh environment this factor may be of vital importance. Whereas seeds must carry their own food supply to provide the developing seedling with sufficient energy to become established, the vegetatively developing plant has abundant resources at its disposal from the parent plant. The new plant is thereby not as vulnerable to the problems of competition as a seedling is.

A seed is also vulnerable during its dispersal and may land in an area unsuitable for its growth—this rarely occurs in vegetative propagation. Seeds and seedlings are further disadvantaged in that any damage to them results in death or, at least, a malformed plant. But the vegetatively produced plantlet can withstand damage more easily because it has adequate supplies from the parent for repair.

Colonization of a wide area by vegetative means is rather slow because these plants tend to form clumps—such as buffalo grass *(Buchloë dactyloides).* But competition within the area is minimized because few other plants can grow within the clumps. Such clumps may be extremely persistent and capable of regrowth even after complete removal of the foliage by feeding animals or fire, and so the chances of survival of the species are increased.

The vegetative mechanism

Vegetative propagation occurs as a plant reproduces itself from a part of its stem or root. The Canadian pondweed *(Elodea canadensis),* for example, can reproduce itself from small fragments of its stem. This ability of a cell or group of cells to produce new ones with a function different from that of the parent cells is called cell totipotency.

In higher plants the totipotent cells are the cambium cells. These are small, undifferentiated cells that have not developed a specific function. When properly stimulated they produce the appropriate new part.

Organs of perennation

In higher plants the totipotent cells are concentrated in special organs, or certain parts of a plant. The organs have two functions—perennation, which allows the plants to survive nongrowing periods such as winter or dry seasons, and propagation. Organs of perennation can be underground food or water stores, but are also the above-ground parts of plants.

Many perennial plants grow from a persistent stem base, such as lupines *(Lupinus* spp.). As the plant ages, the stem base increases in

Flowering plants: Vegetative propagation

diameter, and the older center portions die off, leaving the newer outside parts as independent plants.

Some plants develop thick horizontal underground stems called rhizomes, such as irises (*Iris* spp.), Kentucky bluegrass *(Poa pratensis)*, and some ferns, such as bracken (*Pteridium* sp.). Growth is from a terminal bud, but branches also form at intervals, each of which produces a new root. The older parts of the rhizome then die off, leaving the branches independent. Rhizomes produce photosynthetic leaves that grow up through the soil. These aerial shoots are short-lived and die back after one season. The rhizome then overwinters on its food reserves, allowing the plant to survive.

The flattened compact base of a stem, which grows underground, is called a corm and is found in plants such as crocuses (*Crocus* spp.). These stems reproduce at their tips on the surface where buds produce new corms directly; but in other plants, such as *Montbretia*, the rhizomes underground may develop corms at their tips.

Tubers are the underground swollen parts of plants that serve as food and water stores. They may become separated by the death of the parent plant and grow into a new plant, the shoots and roots of which may develop tubers and may be tuberous. Root tubers may involve the whole root, as in some orchids, or just the root tip, as in dahlias (*Dahlia* spp.). Roots themselves may generate stems if they become damaged or separated from the stem.

Bulbs, which can be likened to underground buds, frequently produce new bulbs by the growth of an axillary bud within the parent bulb. Bulb scales are fleshy leaves found on bulbs such as onions (*Allium* spp.). These scales store sugar or starch for the plant's future use.

Organs of propagation

An organ of perennation may also function as an organ of propagation by producing, for example, two shoots rather than one, each of which behaves as an independent plant. Those organs that have most potential for vegetative reproduction are those nearest the ground, because any new plant needs to be rooted in the soil as soon as possible. These organs are usually stems, although they can take the form of roots.

Many stems creep or arch over the ground, rooting at the leaf nodes and developing into a new plant—strawberry runners, for example. Suckers, or stolons, may be underground runners that behave in the same way as surface runners or may be the shoots produced by root buds. Stolons are elongated rhizomes with permanent aerial shoots. They function specifically as an organ of propagation rather than as a food reserve.

Strawberries (*Fragaria* spp.) propagate by sending out runners from the main stem. These shoots root in the ground and form new plants. The plant has flowers and can reproduce sexually, and they develop into fruit which may be eaten by animals, though it may be some time before the seeds are excreted and can germinate.

The underground stem, or rhizome, of the cowslip *(Primula veris)* acts as a food store throughout winter, but also develops new stems in the spring that bear flowers. After a few years the oldest section of the rhizome dies, and the plants are separated.

The swollen stem base (corm) of the crocus (*Crocus* sp.), *far left,* is a food source for the plant during winter. It lasts one growing season. A new corm is formed by a thickening of the base of the new stem, just above the old corm.

Tulips (*Tulipa* spp.), *left,* reproduce by bulbs as well as by sexual reproduction. Bulbs differ from corms in that they are formed from layers of scale leaves that develop underground around the stem. The stem enlarges at its base to form the new bulb and the outermost scale leaves die off.

In the potato (*Solanum tuberosum*) tubers form at the end of rhizomes that develop from the base of the stem. Shoots from the buds, or "eyes," of an underground tuber also become tuberous themselves. These tubers are underground swollen stems and can bear buds and leaves.

Monocotyledon

Dicotyledon

Monocotyledonous leaves *(above)* usually sheathe the stem of the plant and have parallel veins but do not have a distinct central vein or midrib. The bird-of-paradise flower *(Strelitzia reginae), right,* which is native to southern Africa, is an exceptional example because its blue-green leaves sometimes have a red midrib.

Monocotyledons

Monocotyledons belong to one of the two groups into which the flowering plants (angiosperms) are divided. They are so called because their seedlings have only one seed leaf, or cotyledon, compared with the two seed leaves of the dicotyledons. Monocotyledons are sometimes considered to be more advanced than dicotyledons. They were originally thought to be derived from dicotyledons. Fossil leaves of both groups, however, have been found in rocks of the same age; the earliest that have been positively identified come from the Lower Cretaceous epoch, making them about 130 million years old. As these plants can be placed in families living today, it is reasonable to assume that they must have evolved at a much earlier time. It is more probable that they both evolved from the same un-

known seeded ancestor some time before or during the Jurassic period, from 180 million to 130 million years ago.

Monocotyledons are classified into 9 orders and about 30 families and make up about one-fourth of all flowering plants. They range from small flowers, such as snowdrops *(Galanthus nivalis),* to trees, such as the date palm *(Phoenix dactylifera),* and include the grasses (Gramineae) and the orchids (Orchidaceae). Monocotyledons grow throughout the world, and many are popular garden plants.

One group, the bromeliads (Bromeliaceae), the group to which the pineapple belongs, mostly exists as epiphytes. They grow upon the branches of other trees—not parasitizing them, merely using them as support. They have aerial roots that hang down and soak up the moisture of the humid forest air.

Grasses are particularly successful. Grasslands will develop wherever there is little scrub or forest cover, provided there is enough moisture. Much grassland in the temperate Northern Hemisphere is the result of deforestation.

Stems and roots

The stem structure of monocotyledons is simpler than that of dicotyledons. It is made up of a large number of small parallel, vascular bundles that are closed and are scattered within the stem tissue. Unlike dicotyledons, no true thickening of the stem takes place, although in a few genera dividing cells (cambium) differentiate in the outer part of the stem, forming additional vascular bundles and tissues in which they are embedded.

The core of the trunk of a monocotyledonous "tree" is usually a spongy, fibrous mass of tissue rather than hard wood. The trunks of palms (Palmae) are an exception, their cores being very hard. There are only a few monocotyledon families with species that grow as shrubs or trees. Most belong to the palm family; other woody monocotyledons include

Monocotyledons consist of about 60,000 species of flowering plants. The flower parts are usually arranged in threes and can show a great variety of form from species to species.

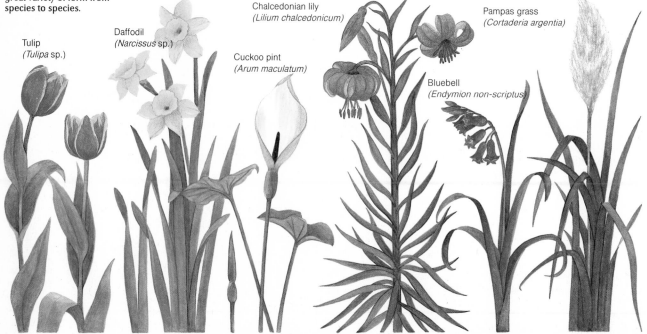

Tulip
(Tulipa sp.)

Daffodil
(Narcissus sp.)

Chalcedonian lily
(Lilium chalcedonicum)

Cuckoo pint
(Arum maculatum)

Pampas grass
(Cortaderia argentia)

Bluebell
(Endymion non-scriptus)

screw-pines (*Pandanus* spp.), dragon trees (*Dracaena* spp.), yuccas (*Yucca* spp.) and some of the aloes (*Aloe* spp.). The banana (*Musa* sp.) is not a true tree because the "stem" is formed out of tightly rolled leaf sheaths and is not woody.

In many monocotyledons, the largest area of growth is underground. The stems grow as rhizomes, corms, bulbs, and tubers, and the aerial projections are only lateral branches or flowering shoots. The roots of monocotyledons differ widely from those of dicotyledons. The primary root, which in a dicotyledon would develop as a taproot, rarely passes the seedling stage before it aborts. In the grasses, the main root disappears soon after germination. The root system of monocotyledons develops from roots growing from the stem. These are simple in structure and do not show any form of secondary thickening. In most species, roots form a fibrous mass, but some large trees, such as several of the palms, have a relatively small root system compared with dicotyledon trees. In some orchids (Orchidaceae), the roots do not branch but remain as simple linear organs. In monocotyledons that have underground stems, such as rhizomes or corms, the roots tend to be annual, dying off at the end of the growing season to be replaced by new ones the following year.

Leaves

The most common type of monocotyledonous leaves are linear or sword-shaped. They have parallel veins—a characteristic of monocotyledons. There are, however, some monocotyledons that have cordate (heart-shaped), ovate, or arrow-shaped leaves, and they generally have a network of veins (reticulate) or ladder-like veined leaves (scalariform). These types of leaves are found mostly in the water plantain family (Alismataceae), yams (Dioscoreaceae), arums (Araceae), and the smilax family (Smilacaceae). The leaves may grow very large, those of the banana (*Musa paradisiaca*) reaching 6 to 10 feet (2 to 3 meters) in length. Generally, the base of the leaf is sheathed, and the leaf stalk (petiole) is frequently absent. But in palms, the petiole is extremely well developed and supports the huge, spreading, hand-shaped (palmate) or feather-shaped (pinnate) leaf.

The leaves of most monocotyledons sheathe the stem and grow alternately on it. The leaf sheath is usually thick and in palms clasps the stem to give the trunk its distinctive ridged appearance. The leaves of aquatic monocotyledons are generally ovate, but the emergent marsh plants may show a variety of leaf shapes. In the arrow-head (*Sagittaria sagittifolia*) the submerged leaves are linear, the floating leaves are ovate, and the aerial leaves are arrow-shaped.

Flowers

In monocotyledon flowers, there are usually five whorls of floral organs: two whorls of perianth segments, two whorls of stamens, and one whorl of carpels. There are normally three parts to each whorl compared with a varied number in dicotyledons. In many species, especially those of the lily family (Liliaceae) and iris family (Iridaceae), the perianth

Date palms *(Phoenix dactylifera)* are monocotyledons that grow in the form of trees. Their stems are like true trunks in that they contain hard woody tissue although the ridges on the stem's surface are not bark but the remnants of dead leaves. They may live for up to 200 years and are found mostly in Africa and southwestern Asia.

Xylem and phloem vessels in monocotyledons are grouped in closed vascular bundles, arranged centrally in the root but scattered in the stem.

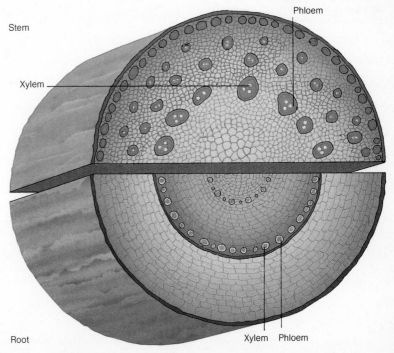

Stem

Phloem

Xylem

Root

Xylem   Phloem

The fly orchid *(Ophrys insectifera)* has flowers that resemble the female tachinid fly. They have "eyes," "feelers," and a blue band of color that looks like the shine on the insect's wings. In addition, the plant is synchronized to bloom at the same time as the male tachinid fly emerges from hibernation. The flowers attract the male fly and are pollinated by it.

There are no perianth whorls, but the flowers are again enclosed in a spathe.

In aquatic plants there is a greater reduction in flower parts. Duckweeds *(Lemna* spp.) have minute flowers that float on the surface of the water. Each flower comprises a spathe surrounding a single stamen. Species of eelgrass *(Zostera* sp.) have further reduced flowers; the male has only one anther and the female one carpel.

Pollination

Monocotyledons are pollinated in a number of ways. Zygomorphic flowers are generally pollinated by animals, such as those of bananas, which rely on bats and birds for the distribution of pollen. The orchids, however, are pollinated by insects, and their flowers show a wide range of adaptations to ensure that the correct insects are attracted to them. In some orchids, such as *Cymbidium*, the flowers twist through 180° as they develop so that they hang upside down when mature, providing a landing place for insects.

Many aquatic monocotyledons are pollinated by water or wind. Canadian pondweed *(Elodea canadensis)* has female flowers that grow at the surface of the water and are pollinated by the submerged male flowers, which break off and float to the surface. In other species of pondweed, submerged flowers are pollinated by water or, if the flowers float on the surface, their pollen is distributed by the wind.

whorls are brightly colored, and flowers in these groups tend to be radially symmetrical (actinomorphic), although there are exceptions. Gladioli *(Gladiolus* spp.) have unequal (zygomorphic) flowers, as do bananas, gingers (Zingiberaceae), cannas (Cannaceae), and orchids.

Many species of monocotyledons show a reduction in flower parts. The flowers of the sweet flag *(Acorus calmus)* have perianth whorls, but these are so reduced as to be inconspicuous; the other flower parts are typically arranged in threes. No perianth whorls are found in the bog arum *(Calla palustris)*, and the flowers are surrounded by a white sheath or spathe (present also in the sweet flag but it is green and does not surround the flower). The number of stamens in the cuckoo pint *(Arum maculatum)* are reduced to three or four, and each ovary contains only one ovule.

Germination and seeds

The food supply of monocotyledon seeds is generally in the form of endosperm or perisperm, which is nutritive tissue formed from the embryo sac. The storage material in the seed may be starch or oil. In some families, notably the orchids, the seeds have neither endosperm nor other stored food because they are too small. In this case, the seeds rely on

Wheat is the staple diet in many countries and is cultivated on a large scale in the United States, Canada, the Soviet Union, and Europe. The grain is ground into flour, which is used to make bread and pasta.

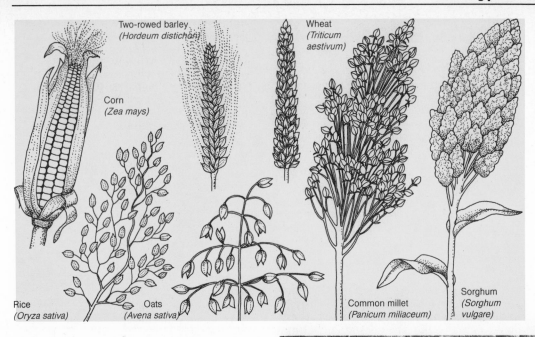

Two-rowed barley
(*Hordeum distichon*)

Corn
(*Zea mays*)

Wheat
(*Triticum
aestivum*)

Rice
(*Oryza sativa*)

Oats
(*Avena sativa*)

Common millet
(*Panicum miliaceum*)

Sorghum
(*Sorghum
vulgare*)

Cereals have provided humans with food for thousands of years. Originally derived from wild grasses, they have been selectively bred to such an extent that some species bear little relation to their ancestors. Grains occupy more than half of the world's harvested land. More than 1.8 billion tons of grain are produced each year. The United States produces about two-fifths of the world's corn, and China more than one-third the rice.

symbiotic fungi, which enter their tissues and supply the seedlings with the necessary nutrients during the early stages of their development. During the germination of a monocotyledonous seed, the radicle (embryo root) emerges from the lower part of the seed followed by a bud called the plumule (upper embryo shoot), which is surrounded by the cotyledon. In some species, the cotyledon remains in the seed where the plumule may be surrounded by a special sheath. In grasses, the plumule is also surrounded by a sheath (coleoptile), a similar sheath (coleorhiza) enclosing the radicle. The plumule develops into an aerial shoot, which is usually herbaceous and which may reach a considerable height.

Many different types of fruit are found in monocotyledon families. In the lily family, plants such as tulips (*Tulipa* spp.) bear capsules containing a number of seeds, whereas Solomon's seal (*Polygonatum* sp.) carries its seeds in juicy berries. The sedges (Cyperaceae) produce fruit in the form of nutlets, and the palm tree *Cocos nucifera* bears one-seeded drupes known as coconuts. Flowering rushes (Butomaceae) contain their seeds in a follicle.

Plant products

Man uses monocotyledons for many purposes but by far the most important is their cultivation as a food source. Grasses and cereals are grown throughout the world, and their grain provides the staple diet in many countries. Wheat (*Triticum* spp.), rye (*Secale cereale*), barley (*Hordeum* spp.), oats (*Avena sativa*), millet (such as *Panicum* spp., *Pennisetum* spp., *Setaria* sp.), corn (*Zea mays*), rice (*Oryza sativa*), and sorghum (*Sorghum* spp.) are notable cereals. Bamboos are grasses whose woody stems have been used for construction for centuries, as have rattans, the flexible stems of climbing palms. The lily family contains many edible species, including onions (*Allium cepa*), leeks (*A. porrum*), garlic (*A. sativum*), and shallots (*A. ascalonicum*). In parts of Africa and Asia, the root tubers of yams provide an important food

source. Some trees of the palm family produce edible fruits, the more familiar of which include the coconut and the date.

Other palms provide valuable fibers. These are extracted from the leaves and are used for brushes and brooms. Another fiber comes from the outer husk of the coconut and is used for matting.

A number of monocotyledon species are cultivated for the fiber that can be extracted from them. Sisal is a strong fiber found in the leaves of some agaves (*Agave* spp.) and when twisted can be made into rope. Other notable fibers obtained from monocotyledons include New Zealand flax (*Phormium tenax*), bowstring hemp (*Sansevieria* spp.), and yuccas.

Many monocotyledons are grown as garden plants, particularly members of the Amaryllidaceae family, including snowdrops and daffodils (*Narcissus* spp.). Irises, freesias, gladioli, and crocuses all belong to the iris family and are popular garden plants.

Bamboos are classified as grasses, but unlike most grasses, some species may reach up to 120 feet (37 meters) in height. They thrive in subtropical to mild temperate climates and are found mainly in southeastern Asia. Young shoots of some species can be eaten, and the hollow stems of mature plants are used for light construction.

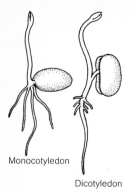

Monocotyledon

Dicotyledon

Dicotyledons are characterized by the presence of two seed leaves (cotyledons) in the embryo contained within the seed. In contrast, most monocotyledons have only one embryonic seed leaf.

Dicotyledons

The angiosperms are a large group of plants that, unlike gymnosperms, bear flowers and have seeds that are completely enclosed. In many modern systems of plant classification, the angiosperms (subphylum Magnoliophytina) are divided again into two classes: the dicotyledons (Magnoliopsida) and the monocotyledons (Liliopsida). (This classification, however, may vary. *See The World Book Encyclopedia* article FLOWER [How flowers are named and classified].) The major basis of these groups, and the one that gives them their names, is their number of seed leaves: dicotyledons have two seed leaves and monocotyledons have one.

There are more than 190,000 species of dicotyledons and all of them, from garden flowers, such as hollyhocks (*Althaea* spp.), to complex trees, such as oaks (*Quercus* spp.), have within their seeds two seed leaves or cotyledons. These may remain underground during the germination process or appear above ground. When visible, the cotyledons have a simple, usually rounded shape.

Leaves, shoots, and roots

Apart from two seed leaves, dicotyledons have other distinctive anatomical features. Their true leaves (those other than the seed leaves) have veins, usually arranged in a netlike pattern with a distinctive central vein, or midrib, and the base of the leaf usually tapers to a point.

The stems of dicotyledons also have characteristics that typify the group: the water-conducting cells (xylem) and those that transport dissolved food substances (phloem) are grouped in open vascular bundles arranged around the perimeter of the stem. Between the xylem and phloem is a growing layer (cambium), which produces new xylem and phloem cells.

Another distinctive feature of most dicotyledon stems is that, as their complement of xylem and phloem cells increases through the activity of the cambium, the stem becomes toughened or thickened. If this process—known as secondary thickening—continues, the stem becomes woody.

Like their stems, the roots of most dicotyledons also contain xylem, phloem, and a cambium capable of creating secondary thickening. Whereas the water-conducting xylem tissues of monocotyledons are commonly arranged in a ring, those of a dicotyledon root take on a characteristic cross or star shape.

Flowers

Monocotyledon flowers, such as tulips (*Tulipa* spp.) and lilies (*Liliaceae*), have their parts arranged in threes, whereas those of the dicotyledons have a different, more varied numerical formula of construction. Most dicotyledons have flowers with their parts—including petals, sepals, the pollen-producing stamens and the pollen-receiving stigmas, and the parts of the ovary in which embryo seeds are contained—grouped in fives or fours. In the dicotyledon flowers, which are thought to have evolved first and which are therefore the most "primitive," the parts are numerous and are arranged in whorls, not joined together. The composites—that is, daisies and their relations—have the most specialized dicotyledon flowers, made up of hundreds of tiny florets.

Dicotyledon flowers are structurally quite varied, the differences in petal structure being one of the most significant features. Plants whose flowers have free (unjoined) petals, such as roses (Rosaceae) and buttercups (*Ranunculus* spp.), and those with no petals, such as those of many trees, including the birch (*Betula* sp.), are placed together in one group, the

Magnolias *(Magnolia* spp., *right)* are considered to be among the most "primitive" (least highly evolved) genera of dicotyledons. The parts of the flower are numerous, unjoined, and arranged in whorls. The wallflower *(Cheiranthus* sp., *far right)* is intermediate in evolutionary development, having flowers with four unjoined petals, four sepals, six stamens, and one stigma.

Archichlamydeae. Those with petals completely or partly fused, such as gentians (*Gentiana* spp.), bluebells (*Campanula* spp.), and heathers (*Erica* spp.), belong to a second group called the Metachlamydeae.

Distribution and diversity

Dicotyledons have evolved to occupy all kinds of habitats, from tropical forests to high mountains, from deserts to fresh or salt water. Only being blanketed with a permanent covering of snow and ice acts as a total deterrent to dicotyledon existence.

In their life styles, dicotyledons show an equal diversity. At the extremes, for example, they may be insect-eaters, such as the sundew (*Drosera* sp.), or pale parasites, for example, the dodder (*Cuscuta* sp.), which sucks its nutrients from the stems of other plants.

Dicotyledons may be perennials, biennials, annuals, or, in some harsh environments, ephemerals, which grow, bloom, and die in the space of a few days or weeks. The perennial species may be herbaceous—dying down to ground level each year—or woody, with a permanent growth structure above the soil level.

The dicotyledons include many of the most prolific wood- and food-producing plants. All the world's hardwoods, from oak to teak, come from dicotyledons. Of the many plant families that provide food for human beings and their domestic animals, the following dicotyledons are among the most significant: the Cruciferae, which includes all of the cabbage family; the Solanaceae, to which potatoes and tomatoes belong; the Rosaceae, from which come apples, pears, and other soft fruits; the Compositae, whose members include the chicories and lettuces; the Cucurbitaceae, the family of melons, marrows, and cucumbers; and the Leguminosae, from which come the beans and peas.

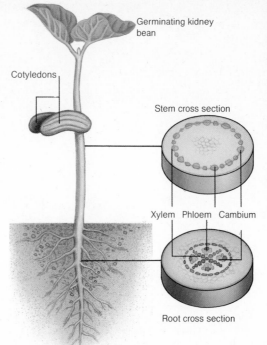

Germinating kidney bean

Cotyledons

Stem cross section

Xylem   Phloem   Cambium

Root cross section

The two cotyledons (seed leaves) of a seedling kidney bean appear above the ground, known as epigeal germination. A cross section of the bean's stem reveals, as in most dicotyledons, vascular bundles (groups of xylem and phloem cells) arranged in a ring around the perimeter of the stem. These cells are separated by a growing layer called the cambium. The pericycle cells outside the phloem often form strengthening fibers. The root of a typical dicotyledon has its xylem and phloem cells grouped at the center—the xylem arranged in a cross or star shape, with the phloem between it.

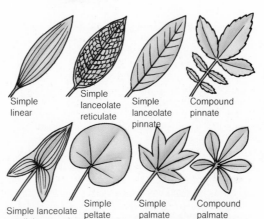

Simple linear

Simple lanceolate reticulate

Simple lanceolate pinnate

Compound pinnate

Simple lanceolate parallel

Simple peltate

Simple palmate

Compound palmate

Leaves of dicotyledons vary widely in shape, size, and complexity. Undivided (simple) leaves include the linear campion, the peltate nasturtium, and the palmate maple leaf. Typical compound leaves (made up of several leaflets) include the pinnate vetch leaf and the palmate horse chestnut leaf.

The inflorescence of the daisy (*Bellis* sp.) consists of many florets. In such a highly evolved flower, only the central disk florets are capable of forming seeds. The purpose of the outer, petallike florets is to attract pollinating insects and birds.

Herbaceous plants

Herbaceous borders are a common feature in cultivated gardens. All garden flowers originated in the wild, but many have been selectively bred to form hybrids. The longer-lasting perennials are generally planted at the back of a herbaceous border where they are allowed to grow tall. Biennials and annuals are usually smaller plants and are planted at the front of the border where they can be easily replaced.

The term herbaceous, in its botanical sense, is applied to plants that usually have no woody parts. In general, the leaves and stems of these plants die back at the end of the growing season. Perennial herbaceous plants overwinter by means of underground storage organs; annual herbaceous plants usually survive winter by means of seeds.

Herbaceous plants do, however, show extremely varied forms. One of the smallest is the aquatic species of duckweed *Wolffia arrhiza,* which is a minute green plant that floats on the surface of fresh water. It has no true roots or stem and is about 0.5 to 1.0 millimeter across. Conversely, herbaceous plants can grow to a large size; the taro *(Colocasia esculenta)* produces leaves 3 feet (91 centimeters) or more in length. Other herbaceous forms include prostrate creepers, such as the creeping jenny *(Lysimachia nummularia),* and matlike

A weed is any plant that grows where it is not wanted. Dandelions are successful weeds because they are fast growers and can survive even when most of their leaves have been removed.

plants, such as the pearlwort (*Sagina* sp.).

Perennials

There are four basic types of herbaceous plant, categorized according to their life cycles: perennials, biennials, annuals, and ephemerals. Herbaceous perennials live for a number of years, surviving from one growing season to another. In temperate climates, perennials must survive a winter between two summers, and in tropical areas they may have to live through a dry season between two wet seasons. This survival is generally achieved by means of a surface-dwelling or underground organ (which is also by a means of vegetative reproduction). These organs lie dormant during the cold season and produce new aerial parts each year, which die back at the end of the growing season.

The life span of perennials varies from species to species. Some plants are generally short-lived and others, such as the peonies (*Paeonia* spp.), may persist for many years. Many familiar garden flowers are herbaceous perennials and include such plants as Michaelmas daisies (*Aster* spp.), pampas grass *(Cortaderia selloana),* dahlias (*Dahlia* spp.), chrysanthemums (*Chrysanthemum* spp.), and numerous plants that have bulbs, corms, and tubers.

Many terrestrial and epiphytic tropical plants—the bromeliads (Bromeliaceae), for example—are also herbaceous perennials although their aerial parts frequently persist from one growing season to another.

Biennials

As their name suggests, biennials live for two years. In the first year, the seedling grows into a rosette of leaves attached to an underground storage organ. This storage organ becomes swollen with food at the end of the growing season and, in the following year, produces a flowering stem with a few sparse leaves. After

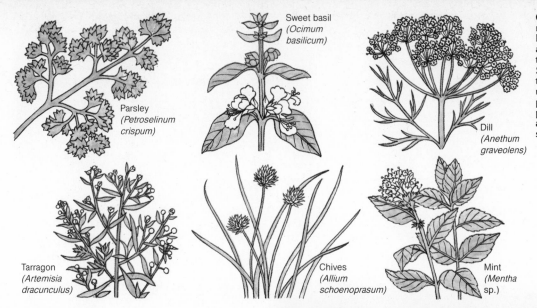

Parsley
(Petroselinum crispum)

Sweet basil
(Ocimum basilicum)

Dill
(Anethum graveolens)

Tarragon
(Artemisia dracunculus)

Chives
(Allium schoenoprasum)

Mint
(Mentha sp.)

Culinary herbs, as their name suggests, are mostly herbaceous perennials and are used in cooking throughout the world. Sweet basil, which is native to India and Iran, is often used in tomato-based recipes, whereas dill is a European herb used in sauces and salads to add an aniseed flavor.

the seeds have been dispersed, the whole plant—including the underground storage organ—dies away.

Occasionally an axillary bud at the base of the stem remains; this will develop as another basal rosette for the following year, with the result that seeds are produced every year rather than every two years. The common foxglove *(Digitalis purpurea)* has axillary buds that persist regularly, as does the garden hollyhock *(Althaea rosea)*.

Many crop species are biennials and include carrots *(Daucus carota)*, parsnips *(Pastinaca sativa)*, and some species of cabbage.

Annuals and ephemerals

Each year, a new crop of annual plants grows from the previous season's seeds. The germinating seedlings mature, flower, scatter their seeds, and die within one growing season. Some of the seeds may survive in a dormant state for several years, until conditions are right for germination. Many culinary herbs are herbaceous annuals and include basil *(Ocimum basilicum)*, caraway *(Carum carvi)*, coriander *(Coriandrum sativum)*, and dill *(Anethum graveolens)*. Annuals grown as crops include peas *(Pisum sativum)*, lentils *(Lens culinaris)*, chick peas *(Cicer arietinum)*, and all the grain crops.

Similar in character to annuals are the ephemerals. These plants, however, have an even shorter life cycle than annuals. They manage to compress the period from germination through seed dispersal to death of the parent plant into a few weeks. If conditions are favorable, several life cycles may take place in the space of one growing season. This group of plants includes many weeds and desert plants. Groundsel *(Senecio vulgaris)* and, in Europe, shepherd's purse *(Capsella bursapastoris)* are typical ephemerals and, as a result, are successful weeds.

Stem structure

All flowering plants, both monocotyledons and dicotyledons, can be separated into two

Passion flowers *(Passiflora* spp.) are herbaceous vines that climb with the help of tendrils. Many species are cultivated for their brightly colored flowers and their edible fruits. This plant grows wild in the Bolivian Andes at an altitude of about 6,000 feet (1,800 meters).

groups on the basis of their stem support structure. Plants such as trees and shrubs have persistent woody aerial parts that survive for a number of years. Nonwoody or herbaceous plants do not have persistent aerial parts although the stems of some species, such as goldenrod *(Solidago* sp.) and sunflower *(Helianthus* sp.), may show some secondary thickening.

The stems of small and short-lived herbaceous plants depend mostly for their support on living tissues with thickened walls (collenchyma) found on the outer areas of the stem and on the veins of the leaf. All herbaceous plants, however, have some strengthening tissues associated with the vascular bundles and, in most species, there is some production of secondary tissue within the bundles. Other herbaceous plants, such as the garden hollyhock, have dead, thick-walled tissue (sclerenchyma), which often contains lignin and helps to support the stem. The distribution of sclerenchyma is often related to the areas of the

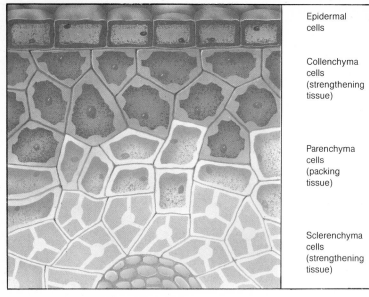

Epidermal cells

Collenchyma cells (strengthening tissue)

Parenchyma cells (packing tissue)

Sclerenchyma cells (strengthening tissue)

A transverse section of a leaf rib *(above)* shows the distribution of strengthening tissue. Small herbaceous plants usually have collenchyma cells only, whereas larger plants may have sclerenchyma cells or both. The sclerenchyma tissue, which is situated next to the vascular bundles, occasionally contains lignin.

plant that are subjected to mechanical stress.

Herbaceous plants also derive support from the tension of water-filled (turgor) cells, which are usually combined with the presence of turgid collenchyma cells.

Roots and storage parts

Herbaceous plants have many different types of root system and underground storage parts. Fibrous root systems are common in herbaceous perennials and grasses, whereas taproots are found in plants such as carrot and dandelion (*Taraxacum* spp.).

In some saprophytic species, the seed germinates and the root grows underground without producing an aerial shoot, except at intervals when the plant is ready to reproduce. The curious-looking bird's nest orchid *(Neottia nidus-avis)* and Indian pipe orchid *(Monotropa uniflora)* produce an aerial stem only when the plant is flowering, with simple yellow or pink leaves and flowers that hang from the end of a

branch. Other species of orchid grow in a similar way, such as the coral root (*Corallorrhiza* sp.) and ghost orchids (*Epipogium* spp.).

Certain species have no roots and produce only shoots. In the case of such species, the plant's stem takes over the water- and mineral-absorbing function of the roots. Typical of these species are the aquatic and terrestrial bladderworts (*Utricularia* spp.), which have modified leaves—known as rhizophylls—that behave like roots.

Rhizomes make up the permanent axis of many herbaceous perennials and are swollen stems (usually partially or totally underground), rather than roots. Whereas aerial shoots may die down at the end of each growing season, rhizomes survive to produce new shoots the following year. Similarly, bulbs are the swollen extensions of perennial stems and are formed from a mass of modified leaf bases. Some perennials rely on underground storage parts called corms, which are also swollen stem bases.

Types of leaves and tendrils

Herbaceous leaves show a great variety of shapes. The most common leaf form is sword-shaped or linear, as produced by the irises (*Iris* spp.), grasses (Graminaceae), and other monocotyledons. Leaf edges can be smooth or have simple serrations or they may have deep regular or irregular incisions—for example, those of the dandelion. A further development of this form is the pinnate leaf, which is a characteristic of poppies (*Papaver* spp.) and many umbellifers (Umbelliferae).

Other sorts of simple leaf form include palmate (as in geraniums, *Geranium* spp.), spear-shaped (as in some arums, *Arum* spp.), heart-shaped (as in the lesser celandine, *Ranunculus ficaria*), and circular (as in penny-wort, *Hydrocotyle* sp.). Leaves like those of the lupine (*Lupinus* sp.) are said to be digitate, and those of hellebores (*Helleborus* spp.) are pedate.

Carnivorous herbaceous plants have a variety of unusual leaf forms that are usually adaptations to their feeding methods. Pitcher plants

The "root" vegetables that we eat are not always true roots in the botanical sense. Potatoes are the swollen extensions of underground stems (tubers) of herbaceous plants, whereas onions are modified storage leaves (bulbs) of herbaceous monocotyledons. Carrots and radishes, however, are the swollen roots of herbaceous plants.

(*Sarracenia purpurea*), as their name suggests, have funnel-like leaves that trap insects that are subsequently digested by enzymes. The leaves of sundews (*Drosera* spp.) are covered with sticky glandular hairs that trap insects. The Venus's-flytrap (*Dionaea muscipula*), another carnivorous plant, has a spring mechanism that allows the leaves to snap shut when the trigger hairs on their surface are touched, thus trapping any insect that may be on the leaves.

Some herbaceous plants have tendrils (modified leaves) for climbing—for example, the legumes (Papilionaceae). In some climbing herbaceous plants, tendrils are entirely separate parts of the plant. The cucumber family (Cucurbitaceae) has tendrils that grow from the leaf base, and in white bryony (*Bryonia dioica*), half of each tendril twists in one direction and half twists in the other direction so as to pull the plant closer to its support. In certain species, it is the plant's branches that are the means of support; in others, it is the stem itself that twines, such as bindweed (*Convolvulus* sp.).

Some species are scramblers, supporting themselves on other, taller vegetation by means of hooks and stiff hairs—for example, goosegrass (*Galium aparine*). Species such as dodder (*Cuscuta* sp.) are parasitic climbers that obtain their nutrients from the host's stem. Others are parasitic on the roots of plants, such as the broomrape (*Lathraea clandestina*). These plants may have no aerial shoots, and their flowers are produced at the soil surface.

Growth rate

Herbaceous plants can produce a phenomenal amount of growth each year. Plants such as rhubarb (*Rheum rhaponticum*) and butterbur (*Petasites hybridus*) produce leaves that often measure 3 feet (91 centimeters) or more in diameter, and some temperate species, such as gunnera (*Gunnera manicata*), can grow leaves that are twice this size.

Perennial climbers such as bindweed (*Convolvulus* sp.) produce many feet of growth each year and are unpopular with gardeners.

Some annuals, such as morning glory (*Ipomoea* sp.), also produce a large quantity of growth in a relatively short space of time. Many biennials and perennials produce stems up to 6 feet (1.8 meters) tall with a similar-sized spread of side-shoots—for example, the teasel and cartwheel flower (*Heracleum mantegazzianum*). These species have perennating organs that allow them to start growing early in spring. Himalayan balsam (*Impatiens glandulifera*), which is an annual plant, produces as much growth starting from seed each year as some perennial species. Its stem may measure up to 2 inches (5 centimeters) at the base and is produced in about 5 months.

Cartwheel flower *(Heracleum mantegazzianum)* is a fast-growing perennial that can reach up to 13 feet (4 meters) in height in one growing season. It is native to the Caucasus but is grown elsewhere as an ornamental plant.

Ephemerals are plants that may condense their growing season into a few weeks. In Central Australia, where rain is scarce, plants take advantage of a summer shower to germinate, flower, and scatter their seeds.

Large periwinkle *(Vinca major)*

Oleaster *(Elaeagnus commutata)*

Common broom *(Cytisus scoparius)*

Shrubs

Shrubs grow naturally in many of the world's floras, from savanna to shrub, from the tundra to the tropical rain forest. Cultivated shrubs are common in gardens throughout the world.

There is no clear line of distinction between shrubs and trees or between semishrubs and subshrubs, but certain generalizations can be made. Plants that grow in the form of shrubs are perennials with woody stems but, unlike trees, have little or no trunk. They may grow as bushes or, in some cases, as climbers. Shrubs branch from near or just below the ground and reach a maximum height at maturity of between 1.5 and 16 feet (0.5 and 5 meters). In addition, they differ from trees in the way in which they allow their lateral buds to grow. A tree prevents these buds from growing except at special branch points, whereas a shrub lets as many grow as is practical. Some shrubs are evergreen and some are deciduous, but almost all are angio-

Shrubs grow in many shapes and sizes, ranging from climbers to small trees. The periwinkle, oleaster, and broom *(shown in silhouette, above)* illustrate three common ways in which shrubs grow: they creep along the ground, branch from just beneath the surface of the ground, or branch from a central "trunk," like trees.

Gorse *(Ulex europaeus), below,* is a spiny evergreen shrub growing up to 4 feet (1.2 meters) in height. Its seeds are contained in hairy pods, which explode loudly when ripe.

sperms—that is, most reproduce sexually by means of flowers.

Types of shrubs

Each group of shrubs is given a name that describes its own particular attributes. Hygromorphic shrubs thrive in hot wet environments such as the tropical forests. Most are evergreen, for example, members of the genus *Philodendron,* which have big, broad leaves—a characteristic that makes them popular house plants.

The tropics and subtropics also support tropophytic shrubs, which are plants able to survive wide variations in rainfall. They are deciduous shrubs, which shed their leaves during a cool or dry season. When the new buds grow, at the arrival of warmth and rain, they are initially protected by scales, sometimes leaflike in form. But tropophytic shrubs are not confined only to the warmer parts of the world. They are also the dominant deciduous shrubs of temperate regions and extend as far as the Arctic and Antarctic. Some, such as the creeping willow *(Salix repens),* also help to mark the boundary between the alpine and subalpine zones of vegetation.

In the warmer parts of the world's temperate regions, conditions favor mesomorphic shrubs. Typically, they have large evergreen leaves, which have a thicker epidermis than most hygromorphic types. The Mediterranean sweet bay *(Laurus nobilis)* is typical, as are the camellias from India, China, and Japan.

Many dwarf species, such as the heathers *(Erica* spp.), are regarded as shrubs because of their woody, branching stems. They inhabit heath and moorland areas and grow to less than 1.5 feet (0.5 meter) tall, extending horizontally because high winds restrict vertical growth. Many leaves grow within the bush where they are protected from grazing animals.

Some groups of shrubs are categorized according to the particular adaptation that allows them to withstand extreme weather conditions, such as heat, drought, and gales. Examples include the scleromorphic shrubs, such as many of the acacias *(Acacia* spp.), which have small, rigid leaves. Because the leaves are small, water loss is minimized during drought, and their rigidity supports the leaf structure in windy conditions.

The heathers are xerophytic; they conserve water by means of leaves that are rolled up at the edges, thereby sealing off the pores (stomata) through which water loss takes place during transpiration. Thorn shrubs—again including many of the acacias—have spiky leaves, which are reduced to needlelike structures. This adaptation helps to conserve water by presenting a smaller surface area from which evaporation can occur. Switch shrubs, such as the brooms *(Cytisus* spp.), prevent excess transpiration by having leaves of many minute, overlapping scales or in some cases by having no leaves at all. Tola shrubs are typified by their needle- or scalelike resinous leaves.

Two other groups of shrubs are also drought-resistant but work on a different principle: they store water as well as prevent its loss. Succulent shrubs of the salt marshes and

salt deserts—halophytes—have fleshy water-re-
tentive leaves borne on their woody stems.
Xylopod shrubs, such as some members of the
genus *Eucalyptus,* store water in swollen, underground stems.

Colonization

In the succession of plant growth that occurs
when terrain is colonized by plants, shrubs
tend to follow annuals and herbaceous perennials, such as the grasses, but precede trees.
When tree growth does occur, it is often at the
expense of shrubs because the trees tend to
starve the shrubs of light and moisture, which
they need for survival. In many forest habitats,
however, both deciduous and coniferous
shrubs benefit from gaps caused by fire or falling trees or from human interference. They
colonize quickly, producing a large quantity of
seed shortly after they start to grow. The cropping of forests, for example, leads to the establishment of shrubs, which dominate the habitat until succeeded by trees that have grown
naturally from seeds or that are planted in re-
forestation programs.

   Only in a few areas are shrubs the dominant form of plant life. Most notable of these
are the shrublands, which are of two kinds—
the chaparral and the scrublands found in continental interiors. Chaparral occurs in coastal
regions of California but is also the generic
term for shrublands in those areas with a
Mediterranean climate, for example, France,
the southwestern Cape of Africa, and southern
and southwestern Australia. Thorny and succulent shrubs are typical of the scrublands of
continental interiors. These areas, which
occur, for example, south of the Sahara Desert
and in the interior of Australia, are usually
bounded by desert and support shrubs such
as acacias and euphorbias.

A

B

C

Yucca plants *(above)* are a
genus of the lily family and
live in arid areas of Central
and South America. Most
yuccas rely on the "yucca"
moth for pollination, which
is attracted by the smell of
the cream-colored flowers.

When land is stripped by
fire or human activity, such
plants as annuals and herbaceous perennials are quick
to colonize it (A). Shrubs
eventually establish themselves (B), but when they are
mature, starve the herba-
ceous plants of light. Similarly, after many years, trees
come to dominate the land
(C) and cut out the light that
reaches shrubs and plants
on the forest floor.

Climbers

There are many species of flowering plants that have developed the ability to climb up other plants or structures. Their stems are not strong enough to be self-supporting and often, instead of using food and energy to build supportive wood, climbers redirect some of this energy into producing structures such as tendrils, which assist them in climbing up their vital supports.

Climbers come from a great range of plant families, from the cucumbers (Cucurbitaceae) and grapevines (Vitaceae) through representatives of tropical families such as the bignonia (Bignoniaceae) and passionflowers (Passifloraceae). Nearly all climbers are dicotyledons, with the exception of the rattans, which are monocotyledons of the palm family (Palmae).

In many habitats, and particularly in dense jungles, climbing is the method these plants use to reach the sunlight that they need for photosynthesis. The energy saved by climbing can be used to grow faster, farther, and higher than neighboring plants, which allows them to stay in the light and gain even more energy. Their flowers are then more likely to be produced in an environment that is conducive to fertilization. Many climbers, however, are also able to reproduce vegetatively by means of organs such as underground stems.

The woody vine, wisteria *(Wisteria sinensis)*, is a popular garden plant for climbing up walls, which it does by twining its stems around a support.

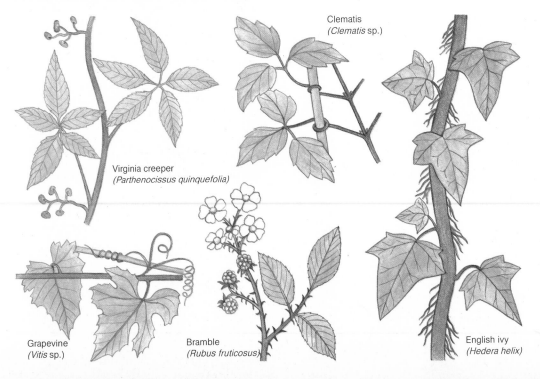

Plants may climb using suckers, as does Virginia creeper, or modified branches that have become tendrils, as on the grapevine. Some plants, for example clematis, wind their whole stem around a support. Adventitious roots on the cablelike stem of ivy attach the plant to a surface. Trailing climbers, such as brambles, hook onto supports with their downward-pointing thorns.

Virginia creeper
(Parthenocissus quinquefolia)

Clematis
(Clematis sp.)

Grapevine
(Vitis sp.)

Bramble
(Rubus fruticosus)

English ivy
(Hedera helix)

Means and methods of climbing

Climbing is accomplished by a variety of methods, and some plants possess special organs for this purpose. The simplest way in which a plant climbs is by twining itself around a support that can be either natural—for example, another plant—or artificial. Most twining climbers are left-handers—that is, the direction in which they twine when viewed from above is counterclockwise. A few—notably the hop *(Humulus lupulus)* and the honeysuckle *(Lonicera periclymenum)*—are right-handers.

Shoots, leaves, and even roots of flowering plants may be modified to assist the climbing process. Shoots may bear sharp down-curved spines, often reinforced with woody tissues, such as those of roses (Rosaceae), which hook onto the surrounding vegetation. Special shoot outgrowths may be equipped with suckers like those of the Virginia creeper *(Parthenocissus quinquefolia)*. Tendrils, which are generally formed as modified leaves, may be a simple spiral or may be armed with hooks. In some species, the tendril bears a leaflike structure, such as that of a vetch *(Vicia* sp.), which may have a simple tendril in place of the uppermost leaflet. The rapidly climbing ivys and their relations produce special roots from cablelike stems, which anchor the plants so that they can grow up the surface of their support. These roots are borne in groups or rows but only on the shaded side of the stem. If the support is a living substrate, such as a tree, the roots may penetrate it and take up nutrients. This process is not likely to kill the support, but its eventual death may be hastened as a result.

How climbers work

The tissues of flowering climbers are often modified in their arrangement to give maximum strength and flexibility. For this purpose, a large number of sclerenchyma fibers may be contained in the stem. Many climbers, particularly the woody jungle lianas, have stems in which rays of phloem-containing pith run through the woody xylem. Liana stems do not cling to their supports, however, but attach themselves more than 330 feet (100 meters) above the ground, with the "trunk" left to hang free.

The xylem vessels contained in the woody tissues of the tallest climbers are very large—in the rattans, for example, they may be 10 to 20 feet (3 to 6 meters) long. These and similar vessels conduct water up the climber at a spectacular rate, sometimes as fast as 6 feet (1.8 meters) per minute. If a section is cut out of a tropical climber and then held upside down, the water in it pours out.

Climbing movements

Apart from their physical structure, climbing plants are largely reliant on innate physiological mechanisms. These mechanisms depend on the plant's ability to sense light, gravity, touch, and temperature, and to respond accordingly by a movement, which generally involves growth. Like those of most plants, the shoots of climbers respond positively to light (phototropism) by growing toward it and neg-

The wild hop *(Humulus* sp.) climbs by twining its stem around anything it can. It is a right-handed climber, climbing in a clockwise direction, unlike most other twining climbers.

The tropical climber balsam pear *(Momordica charantia)* uses spiraling tendrils to attach itself to other plants. This annual plant is a member of the cucumber family, Cucurbitaceae, and grows in the Old World tropics. Its orange fruit splits to reveal an edible pulp and to disperse the seeds.

atively to gravity by growing away from it. The roots behave in an exactly opposite way. There are exceptions, however, such as the wild grape *(Vitis* sp.), the tendrils of which are negatively phototropic. They end in disks which attach themselves to their support.

As a shoot grows it can be seen to move about in circular arcs. This natural tendency, called circumnutation, seems to arise from an inner control on the part of the plant—the stimulus is received at sites in the epidermal cells and is rapidly conducted across the whole tendril. Shoots are also affected by sensitivity to touch (haptotropism). Once a support has been touched by the circumnutating shoot, a growth spurt is triggered on the surface of the shoot directly opposite the point of contact. This surface grows longer and more rapidly than the side of contact, causing the shoot to bend inwards toward the contact and grow around the support. The growth is so rapid that it can be seen over a period of a few hours. Once begun, the shoot continues to grow in the same direction during twining as in circumnutation.

Trees

Most tree species are found among the gymnosperms and angiosperms, the larger part occurring in the latter group. Most are dicotyledons, but a few are monocotyledons, such as palms (Palmae), Joshua trees *(Yucca brevifolia),* which are found in desert areas, and dracaenas (*Dracaena* spp.).

Botanically, trees are plants that usually have a single woody stem (the trunk, or bole) and a crown with woody branches. They may be only a few feet high, as in the undergrowth of tropical rain forests, or very tall—the Australian mountain ash *(Eucalyptus regnans),* for example, may attain a height of more than 300 feet (91 meters).

Only gymnosperms and dicotyledons have proper wood. This substance is a permanent, secondary tissue comprised of cells with lignified walls. Plant cell walls are made mostly of cellulose arranged in microscopic fibrils. In woody plants the cellulose is impregnated with lignin—a material that imparts compressive strength to the cell wall.

Tree growth and form

The apical meristems of a tree—the growing regions at the tips of the trunk, twigs, and roots—are the sources of increase in length in the tree. Auxins (growth hormones) are supplied in greater quantities to the trunk meristems than to the lateral ones, which are often suppressed.

The secondary meristem, in the shape of a thin ring between the wood and the bark, is the vascular cambium. This meristem is the means by which lateral growth, or thickening, takes place in the tree because it forms new wood cells inward, and bark cells on its outer side. Monocotyledon trees do not have wood at all, but numerous vascular bundles set in a matrix of parenchyma, which may become lignified. They either have no secondary thickening (such as palms) or thicken by the formation of extra vascular bundles as do dracaenas, for example.

In some tree species the trunk divides at a low level into two or more trunks. In most trees, a single trunk forms the dominant axis from which lateral branches grow to form a crown, or head, of branches. Those species in which the trunk continues to the tip of the tree as a single axis, with the lateral branches being smaller in size and of secondary importance, have a pyramidal, or excurrent shape, and are described as monopodial (single axis). Trees in which the trunk does not grow to the crown top but is replaced by variously massive limbs, are termed decurrent, or sympodial (many axes), such as oaks (*Quercus* spp.) and limes (*Tilia* spp.). When young, all trees are monopodial. Few dicotyledons retain this form at maturity, although many gymnosperms do. In monopodial trees where the leaves occur only at the top of the trunk, as in palms, the trees may be described as columnar.

The shape of a tree varies partly according to its species and partly in response to its environment. In a specimen tree—a tree grown in the open in isolation—the branches grow, atypically, from low down on the trunk and may spread out, almost sweeping the floor. When trees grow close together, as in a forest, the lower branches receive little light and soon die. The branches forming the crown at the top of the tree are the only ones that survive and the tree grows having a branch-free trunk.

The influence of the environment on the final shape of a tree is well seen in exposed

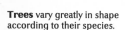

Columnar

Vase-shaped

Multi-trunk

Decurrent

Weeping

Trees vary greatly in shape according to their species.

The growth rings on the trunk of wych elm *(Ulmus glabra)* display the different annual rates of growth. The pale sapwood contains phloem, which transports food, and xylem, which conducts water. The inner dark section is the heartwood. The small rings on the edge of the stem belong to a lateral branch.

windy areas, such as mountaintops or sea cliffs. A tree that manages to grow there develops a distinctive swept-back look with the branches trailing away from the direction of the prevailing wind. As soils in these places tend to be very thin, the tree never grows to such a height as the same species would in a sheltered area with an abundance of rich deep soil.

These shapes can be developed artificially. The art of bonsai, perfected in Japan, involves the development of a shallow root system by growing in a small pot and regular root pruning. This has the same effect as when a tree grows in a shallow pocket on a cliff. The branches are also pruned and trained with wires to grow in the required direction, simulating the effect of the wind. By manipulating the tree's environment in this way, the bonsai master can produce miniature versions of any tree form found in the wild.

Annual rings and wood rays

A cross section of many tree trunks reveals a number of close concentric circles that appear to be split into wedges by raylike lines. These circles are annual growth rings and are apparent in trees that grow in temperate climates only. The rings are formed because the cambium in the trunk produces large conducting cells in the spring and early summer and smaller conducting cells in late summer. The highly porous spring wood conducts water rapidly to the new growing shoots, and the less porous summer wood acts as a strengthening tissue. Because growth ceases in the fall in temperate regions there is a distinct boundary between the ring of one year's growth and the next; but this is not so in trees that grow in equatorial climates, where there are no distinct seasons. Some tropical areas have wet and dry seasons which may form distinctive rings in the wood, but they are not always reliable annual indicators.

Not only does the historical analysis of annual rings (dendrochronology) signify the age of a tree with considerable accuracy, it also indicates good and bad growth seasons, which can give a measure of the rainfall at a certain time in the past. Fossil tree records show that there were temperate regions until the Mesozoic Era, 225 million years ago. Radioactivity levels, the oxygen content of the air, and mineral nutrient levels in the soil, among other things, can be discovered by chemical analysis of a single tree ring.

The rays that divide annual rings into wedges radiate outward from the center of the trunk. They are known as wood rays and are made up of parenchyma cells. As the tree grows in width, the cambium produces new conducting tissues and packing cells of parenchyma. The ray parenchyma cells transport food, waste chemicals, and other materials toward the center of the trunk and carry water away from it. The stored food (often starch) can be mobilized in spring when the buds open and is passed into the vessels to be carried to the areas of growth. In spring the sap consists of a solution of up to 8 per cent sucrose. In the sugar maple *(Acer saccharum)*, for example, this "sugar run" is exploited each year when people tap the vessels for the sugar-rich sap.

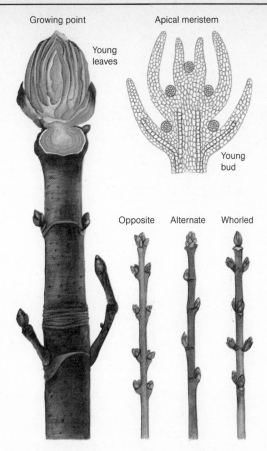

Growing point

Young leaves

Apical meristem

Young bud

Opposite   Alternate   Whorled

The growing point, or apical meristem, on a stem consists of meristem tissue in which new cells are formed by rapid cell division. Buds form in the inner junction of each leaf with the stem and grow on stems in three ways—opposite each other, alternately opposite, or whorled, spiraling up the stem.

Sapwood and heartwood

A transverse section of dicotyledonous wood reveals two types—a light, outer layer of sapwood (alburnum) and an inner, darker layer (the heartwood, or duramen). The sapwood

Maple wood is a diffuse-porous hardwood. The term applies to the vessels in the sapwood, which are more or less the same size and evenly distributed throughout the spring and summer wood.

A longitudinal section
through the sapwood of a
beech tree displays the
wood fibers, running vertically, and the rays, running
horizontally.

has living parenchyma cells and water-conducting xylem cells, tracheids, and vessels, as
well as fibers. Vessels occur in angiosperm
wood and not in that of gymnosperms. In the
latter, the tracheids and fibers are usually not
fully differentiated but exist as fiber-tracheids.

The different cells of the xylem and their arrangement give the wood its characteristics—
the vessels and fibers are often present in different proportions in spring and summer
wood. In some trees—oak, for example—the
broad vessels are confined to the spring wood
whereas in the summer wood there are numerous fibers and fiber-tracheids. This type of
wood is known as ring-porous wood. Diffuse-
porous wood, as found in maples (*Acer* spp.)

and limes, has much smaller vessels, which
are more evenly distributed throughout the
annual rings. A few genera of angiosperms are
exceptional in that, like gymnosperms, they
have no vessels. This feature is believed to be
a primitive one and is found in *Drimys* and
Trochodendron.

In contrast to the sapwood, the cells of the
heartwood are mostly nonconducting and are
not used for storage except at the boundary
with the sapwood where the parenchyma cells
store water. The parenchyma cells of the
newly formed sapwood usually live for several
years. As sapwood ages to form heartwood, its
cell walls undergo a chemical change and become darker and denser. Heartwood also con-

**A dicotyledonous tree
trunk** consists of rings of
several compositions. The
innermost dead section—
the heartwood—is darker
and denser than any other
part of the tree. It is surrounded by the paler, living
sapwood which is sepa-
rated from the next ring, the
phloem, by a thin cambium
layer. Outside the phloem is
the bark-producing cork
layer. Running through the
rings radiating from the
heartwood outward are the
wood rays which are made
up of parenchyma cells.

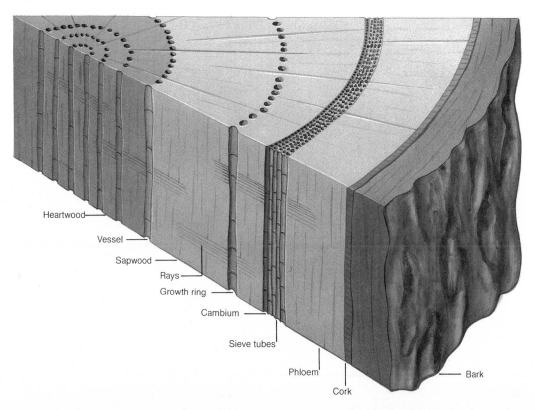

Heartwood

Vessel

Sapwood

Rays

Growth ring

Cambium

Sieve tubes

Phloem

Cork

Bark

Sweet chestnut *(Castanea sativa), far left,* is a rough-barked tree with deep fissures that characteristically spiral around the trunk. The fissures occur as the cork plates in the bark pull apart when the trunk thickens. Smooth-barked trees, such as the Chinese cherry *(Prunus serrula), left,* have a very thin periderm that flakes off as the trunk thickens. The horizontal scars are lenticels, which are specialized structures that contain intercellular spaces that allow oxygen to diffuse through the periderm into the trunk.

tains less moisture than sapwood. The cells often fill with bubblelike inclusions (tyloses) of waste material, such as tannins, resins, dyes, oils, gums, and mineral salts. In the teak tree *(Tectona grandis)* the inclusions are composed of silica, and in satinwood *(Chloroxylon swietenia)* of calcium oxalate.

The altered cell walls and inclusions give the timber its high degree of polish. In some species heartwood is so dense and hard that it is almost impossible to cut. Hematoxylin, which is used as a stain in the study of cells (cytology), comes from the heartwood of the logwood tree of Central and South America *(Haematoxylon campechianum)* and is a typical example of the dyes stored in trees. Tannins act as a protective antibiotic—the more tannin there is in the heartwood (making it a darker color), the more durable it is likely to be, as in, for example, mahogany *(Swietenia mahogoni)* and ebony *(Diospyros* sp.). In some species heartwood does not develop, which is why some trees, such as poplar *(Populus* sp.) and willow *(Salix* sp.), have a tendency to become hollow when they are old.

Phloem and bark

The outermost regions of the trunk, outside the cambium, are comprised of food-con-

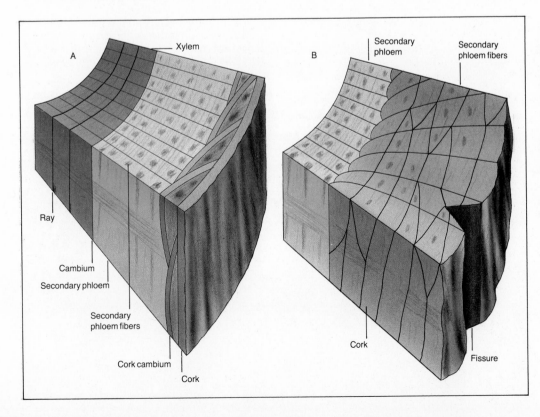

A

Xylem

Ray

Cambium

Secondary phloem

Secondary phloem fibers

Cork cambium

Cork

B

Secondary phloem

Secondary phloem fibers

Cork

Fissure

The formation of rough bark starts in the phloem when the cells differentiate to form cork cambium, which produces the cork cells (A). A second layer of cork cambium cells differentiate from parenchyma cells in the secondary phloem. Successive layers of cork cambium (B) form inside the previous layers, separated from one another by secondary phloem fibers. Each new layer cuts off the connection of the previous layer with the secondary phloem and so the outer bark dies. The cork layers tear as the trunk ages and widens, creating the deep fissures in the bark.

The movement of food and water in a tree occurs in the outer layers of its branches, trunk, and roots. If a tree is stripped of these layers, or they are damaged, it will die. Water movement *(marked in blue)* is upward from the roots, responding to suction pressure from the transpiring leaves. Food, which is manufactured by the leaves, is usually transported downward in the phloem *(indicated in red)*.

Evaporation

ducting phloem tissues. The phloem, like the xylem, consists of a number of different cell types—sieve tubes, each with a companion cell, parenchyma, and fibers. Whereas the flow of water through the xylem is upward, the movement through the phloem just beneath the bark is mainly downward, carrying sap and nutrients from the leaves down to the roots (and up again in the spring in temperate regions).

As the trunk increases in thickness, through cell division in the cambium layers, the phloem often forms wedges that taper toward the periphery (this is very obvious in lime trees). The spaces between the blocks of conducting phloem are filled with wedges of parenchyma cells: greatly widened phloem rays, continuous with the xylem rays in the wood, which function in the storage of starch and tannins. They remain active until cut off from the living part of the plant by a layer of cork cambium, or phellogen.

As a woody stem increases in width, a cork cambium forms in the outer layer of the phloem. On its outer surface it produces small, regular, rectangular cells whose walls become impregnated with a water-repellent material called suberin. These cells are cork cells and form the phellem, or cork—a protective layer around the trunk that prevents evaporation, penetration of pests and disease organisms, and, in some species, is fire-resistant. The phellogen also often develops a layer of cells on its inner face, called the phelloderm. The whole layer of phellem, phellogen, and phelloderm is called the periderm. The cork oak *(Quercus suber)* is unusual because after being damaged it develops a thick cork layer. This can later be stripped off for human use.

The bark of a tree consists of the living inner bark (secondary phloem) and dead outer bark—the part cut off by the periderm. In a smooth-barked tree, the periderm is superficial. In rough-barked trees, however, new periderm forms deeper and eventually cuts off the outside cells from the inner tissue. The outer layer—a mixture of many tissues—then forms a thick, dead, outer bark. As the trunk expands, the bark cracks in a pattern characteristic of the species, while new periderm is continually formed.

The color of bark is due largely to the presence of tannins, which also prevent decay of the bark cells. Spaced out over the bark are tiny pores (lenticels) filled with loosely-packed cells without suberin. They open at the surface and allow the cells of the trunk to breathe.

Transpiration

One of the problems a tree has to overcome is the transportation of water to the top of its crown. This is achieved by "suction pressure" from the leaves. As water is lost from the leaves by evaporation through transpiration, more water is drawn up the stem through the xylem from the roots, and the water in the conducting tissues of the xylem is under considerable tension. The leaf area in a large tree may be sufficient to evaporate many pounds of

Deciduousness is characteristic of many trees growing in temperate regions. The brilliant reds of birch trees *(Betula* spp.) are the result of the disappearance from the leaves of the green pigment chlorophyll, to reveal the secondary pigments carotene, xanthophyll, and anthocyanin.

water in an hour. The amount of water lost during transpiration varies with weather conditions; dry, windy days increase the transpiration rate, and humid, calm days reduce it. The amount of water lost from a transpiring forest is greater than from an open water surface of the same area, such as a lake.

Deciduousness

The leaves, being the main source from which water is lost by the tree, may be shed during periods of water shortage. Some trees regularly shed all their leaves in temperate regions at the beginning of winter, and in tropical regions, at the beginning of the dry season. These trees are said to be deciduous.

There is often a wintertime water shortage in temperate and boreal regions, but that is not the only reason for leaf loss. Low light levels may mean that insufficient photosynthesis can take place, and respiration then exceeds carbon fixation. Low temperatures could damage the leaves and slow down repair, allowing parasites and disease organisms to enter. Leaf fall may be a response to light levels, day length, and temperature, or a combination of these factors. So deciduous trees of temperate regions shed their leaves and remain dormant throughout winter.

The mechanism that causes the leaves to fall involves processes whereby the leaf is separated from the twig on which it is growing without the twig being damaged and at the same time protecting the exposed surface from drying out and infection. Two layers form—the separation and the protective layers. At the leaf base there is a structurally weak zone known as the abscission layer. After food reserves and mineral nutrients have been withdrawn into the woody branches, a periderm grows over this zone at the leaf base, and eventually the leaf falls off, leaving a scar. Sometimes a material called wound gum is also manufactured.

Before the leaf abscises, the chlorophyll in it breaks down, and it loses its green color. Secondary pigments, such as carotene and xanthophyll, become visible and give the leaves their autumnal yellow, orange, and purple colors. Waste products may be translocated to the leaf before it abscises, to prevent their accumulation in the tree.

Evergreen trees retain some of their leaves all year round. Each leaf has a life of about three to four years, and there is a continual exchange of leaves. To conserve water, evergreen leaves are often covered with a thick, waxy cuticle, which gives them a glossy appearance. Deciduous leaves have a much thinner cuticle and tend to be softer and less glossy.

Roots

The crown and trunk of a tree depend on the roots for anchorage, water, and mineral salts. The vascular structure of the roots is much simpler than that of the trunk, and only the bigger roots are surrounded by a periderm. The roots branch laterally, crossing over each other, and may fuse to form a network. There are two types of root—thick, cablelike roots which anchor the tree, and finer, feeding

roots. The anchor roots tend to grow deep below the soil surface and may do so in search of water, especially in arid areas. The feeding roots mostly form a mat just below the soil surface. The finest of these have root hairs near their tips through which water and mineral salts are absorbed. In tropical rain forests the soil is typically very poor in mineral nutrients, and most of the tree roots are very near the surface to take advantage of the nutrients deposited by fallen leaves.

Flowers

Trees may have spectacular, showy flowers, such as those of the horse chestnut *(Aesculus hippo castaneum)* or they may be insignificant, like those of the ash *(Fraxinus excelsior)* or oak. The difference is due to their method of pollination. Large bright flowers attract animals to

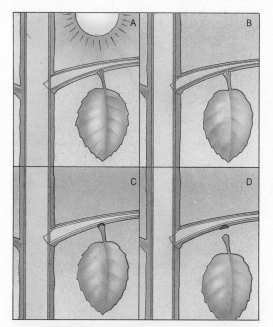

In summer (A) when days are long and warm, the leaves of trees can photosynthesize at a fast rate, drawing vast amounts of water from the roots to replenish the water loss through transpiration. As the days shorten and temperatures drop, food reserves are withdrawn from the leaves, and the chlorophyll breaks down. Secondary pigments become apparent and give the leaves their autumnal colors (B). A layer of periderm grows across the base of the leaf stalk (C) and finally the leaf drops off the branch (D).

Large root systems are needed to anchor trees, which are top-heavy structures. Frequently, more than half a tree's bulk will be in the form of roots underground. These roots also serve to extract water and mineral nutrients from the soil, which are transported by the xylem to other parts of the tree.

The vivid scarlet of the flowers of the flame, or flamboyant tree *(Delonyx regia)*, attracts birds and insects. These animals aid the pollination of the flowers by collecting and transferring pollen as they move from flower to flower.

The catkins of the yellow or silver birch shed pollen as the wind shakes them, releasing from each one 5 million or so grains of pollen. Because they do not rely on animals for pollination the catkins do not have bright colors.

them. In temperate and boreal forests, these animals are insects, such as beetles, moths, and flies. In the tropics, the pollinators also include birds, such as sunbirds and humming-birds, bats, and other mammals, such as the brush-tongued opossum of Australia. The pollinators seek out the nectar that is usually found at the base of the petals inside the flowers, pollen, or the insects that feed in the depth of the flowers. These animals collect pollen grains on them as they brush against the male anthers and transfer them to the female stigmas as they move around.

Wind-pollinated flowers are not as conspicuous as animal-pollinated ones. They are commonly grouped in long, loose clusters or catkins, and have reduced sepals and petals, so that the anthers and stigmas are exposed to the wind. It needs only a gentle rustle when the anthers are ripe for a cloud of free-floating pollen to be released. The pollen grains of these are typically small and smooth, enabling them to be blown easily, whereas those of insect-pollinated flowers are large and ornamental. The anthers in wind-pollinated flowers are frequently on the end of long filaments and are, therefore, shaken with every breeze, shedding pollen. The stigmas are often sticky or hairy to catch the pollen and are carried on the end of long styles. Like other plants, trees can be hermaphrodite (having male and female parts on the same flower), dioecious (with male and female flowers on different trees), or monoecious, the male and female flower occurring on the same tree.

Seeds and fruits

The fruits that are produced by trees also show great variety. Seeds and fruits that are wind-dispersed are quite common because they have the advantage of height from which to drop and be blown. Some trees have winged seeds, the wings of which may be single, as on the jacaranda *(Jacaranda* spp.), or double, as found on some maples. Elms (*Ul-mus* spp.) have seeds rather like a flying saucer. Parachute seeds are also common and are found on trees as diverse as willows (*Salix* spp.) and kapok *(Ceiba pentandra).*

Many trees produce edible fruits, which may be dry or succulent. These are adapted to be carried by animals away from the parent tree. Dry fruits, such as acorns, are often taken away by animals to be buried in the ground and stored for later consumption; there they frequently take root and grow. Succulent fruits usually have hard, resistant seeds, which often need to pass through a gut before they will germinate. The seeds are deposited with their own fertilizer as the animal (usually a bird) defecates. More rarely, tree seeds are designed to be carried by water; alders (*Alnus* spp.) have a float, as do coconuts *(Cocos nucifera),* and many others are capable of floating.

The way in which mangrove trees shed their seeds is remarkable. The seeds of *Rhizophora,* for example, germinate on the parent tree and develop a long heavy cylindrical root. The seed then drops and spears itself into the mud, before the tide can wash it away.

Classification

Most plant classification is based mainly on the structure of the flowers. The flowers of the family Magnoliaceae are among the most primitive of the angiosperms. The trees of this family, such as the tulip trees (*Liriodendron* spp.) and magnolias (*Magnolia* spp.), have large solitary flowers, the sepals and petals of which are in groups of three. The family has a wide distribution in North America and Asia and a number of species are popular as garden trees.

In contrast, the members of the family Loganiaceae, for example, are considered to be some of the least primitive of the dicotyledonous trees. Whereas the petals of magnolias are separate, those of the loganias (such as *Buddleia*) are fused into a symmetrical, tubular, or bell-shaped flower. The family is distributed throughout the tropical and subtropical regions with a few temperate outliers, and includes trees of the genus *Strychnos*, which provide strychnine (from *S. nux-vomica*), curare (from the bark of *S. toxifera*), and edible fruit (from *S. spinosa*).

Many other plant families contain important tree species. The rose family (Rosaceae) comprises most of the commonly cultivated temperate fruit trees, including apple (*Malus* sp.), pear (*Pyrus* sp.), plum, peach, and almond (*Prunus* sp.) trees. In Rosaceae the flowers are usually hermaphrodite, and the sepals and petals are usually five in number. In pear and apple trees the sepals are green, and the petals are generally white or pink. After pollination, the receptacle of the flower becomes fleshy and swollen and encloses the carpels to form the edible fruit.

Whereas the loganias, magnolias, and rosaceous trees are animal-pollinated, those of the beech family (Fagaceae) are wind-pollinated. The male flowers grow in catkins, but the female flowers form a spike of up to three flowers. In both the male and the female flowers, the sepals and petals together form a perianth, which may be green-brown or colorless. The

The brightly colored fleshy fruits produced by some trees attract animals that the trees rely on for the dispersal of their seeds. The animals eat the seeds contained in the fruits and later excrete them away from the parent plant.

flower parts are simple and reduced because of their method of pollination, rather than their advanced stage of development. The pollen is light and copious.

Orange trees (*Citrus* spp.) attract insects with the smell and color of their flowers, which precede the fruit. After the flowers are pollinated the flower receptacles swell and become the fleshy fruit.

Special adaptations

Like all living organisms, plants must in order to survive be able to adapt to the environmental conditions under which they live. These conditions include extremes of temperature, availability of water, and the supply of light. Not only must plants ensure their individual survival but also that of their seeds and spores if the species is to be perpetuated. Successful adaptation is essential for the evolution of new species, because it is the "fittest" or best-adapted species that survive to pass on their genes to subsequent generations. Similarly, those plants that are best adapted to their environments become dominant.

Not all plants, however, are equally well adapted to their environments. There is a great difference in efficiency and effectiveness of adaptation among species. The grasses of the prairies and steppes, for example, have adapted to continuous attacks by grazing animals for whom they provide a staple diet. The growing point of each grass is close to the ground, with the result that the plant survives even when the foliage higher up is cropped. In contrast, the Calabrian primrose *(Dendrobium biggibum)* is an unsuccessful species on the verge of extinction. It is unable to reproduce fast enough to survive being eaten by animals and being picked by people.

Types of adaptation

Plants adapt to their environment in many dif-

ferent ways. In deserts, where high temperatures and lack of water are problems, cacti and other succulents survive by storing fluids in their swollen stems. A waxy cuticle protects the plant against high temperatures by reducing the penetration of heat. Plants that resist such dry conditions are called xerophytes. Some annual herbs in arid areas limit their entire life cycle from seed germination to seed production to the few weeks of the rainy season. These ephemerals, as they are known, include many members of the daisy family (Compositae).

Life in saline environments also requires special adaptations. Plants that live in these conditions are called halophytes. Salt-marsh plants, such as the glasswort *(Salicornia fruticosa),* are regularly covered by seawater; they have adapted in various ways to withstand the build-up of pressure within their cells that results from the influx of water caused by osmotic pressure. In certain freshwater plants, survival is possible only if the leaves are not completely submerged. The giant Amazon waterlily *(Victoria amazonica)* has air-filled honeycomb structures on the underside of its leaves that cause them to float.

Other plant adaptations are specific to food and light requirements. Epiphytes are plants that use other plants as a means of support. In forests they grow on trees in order to be nearer the light, drawing nutrients in solution through their roots from sites such as hollows

The giant Amazonian waterlily *(Victoria amazonica)* survives in fresh water with the aid of air-filled honeycomb structures on the underside of its leaves. These structures help the leaves, which can measure up to 6 feet (1.8 meters) across, to float, and their buoyancy is strong enough to support large birds.

Club mosses and ferns can be epiphytic in forests, living high up on the branches of other plants where they can get at the light that is scarce on the forest floor. These epiphytes obtain mineral nutrients through their roots from their hosts.

in tree bark. The bird's nest fern *(Asplenium nidus)* is an example of an epiphytic plant that relies on its host rather than the soil for its nutritional requirements.

Carnivorous plants, such as sundews *(Drosera* sp.), have adapted to environments with poor nutrient status by catching and "digesting" insects rather than relying on the soil to provide nitrogen and minerals. Parasitic plants have evolved in such a way that they take what they need directly from plants that can provide it. In doing so, however, they often sacrifice their independence. Most have no chlorophyll and, thus, cannot survive on their own by means of ordinary photosynthesis. The pink-stemmed common dodder *(Cuscuta epithymum)*, for example, lives as a parasite on hops and nettles, twining itself around its host's stems and penetrating them with small projections that extract the host's nutrients.

Evolution and adaptation

The Darwinian notion of "the survival of the fittest" operates at different levels in a group of plants. Within a plant community, for example, different species and individuals of the same species have to compete for the available resources. All may succeed by means of different adaptations, or some succeed and others fail. The more severe the "selection" pressure on individuals, the more restricted is the range of possible survivors. Thus, when the selection pressure is reduced, as in a garden, many variations occur.

Selection, and therefore survival, takes three main forms. Directional selection is the process by which plants are directed or "pushed" toward an optimum set of characteristics. Once these have been achieved, by natural selection, that situation as it currently exists is maintained and is known as stabilizing selection—the second form. Any plant not reaching the optimum has a decreased chance of survival unless environmental conditions change, in which case selection again becomes directional.

The third type is known as disruptive selection in which there are two or more sets of optimal characteristics for a particular environment. This occurs where temperature or moisture levels, for example, vary in the environment. Each optimal set stabilizes as before, but the divergence in characteristics may become so great that new subspecies or even new species evolve.

Carnivorous plants feed on insects, getting from them the nitrogen and minerals that are absent from their nutrient-deficient environments. The Venus's-fly-trap *(Dionaea muscipula)* has small hairs on the inside of its leaves that when touched by an insect, induce the leaves to close. Enzymes then digest the insect.

Swamps and marshes

The terms swamp and marsh describe areas on land where the soil is waterlogged because of poor drainage or frequent inundation. These regions can be divided roughly into three categories: saltwater marsh, acid (or nutrient poor) bog, and alkaline freshwater marsh or swamp. Some of these wetlands are immense, covering thousands of acres, such as the African Sudd and the Florida Everglades. They are of great ecological importance because they form carpets of vegetation that protect the soil from being washed away, and the water retained by them speeds up decomposition, which results in a rich soil (except in the acid areas).

Obtaining oxygen

The most constant feature of wetlands is the waterlogged, airless material in which the

Insectivorous plants, such as the common sundew *(Drosera rotundifolia),* obtain the minerals they need from trapped insects, which they digest. This food source is essential for the survival of these plants in the nutrient-poor acid bogs in which they live. The sticky red hairs attached to the leaves of this plant curve inward to trap insects and then secrete a digestive substance onto them.

plants' roots are lodged. Without air, the roots (and therefore the plants) cannot survive. Consequently marsh plants have become modified in various ways to obtain oxygen.

The most important modification is the enlargement of intercellular air spaces in the tissue of the submerged parts of the plants. Such tissue, called aerenchyma (adapted parenchyma), allows oxygen to pass readily through the plant from the exposed stems and leaves to the submerged parts. It also provides buoyancy in the thick mud.

Some plants in coastal swamps have developed special vertical roots, the tips or loops of which project above the surface of the water and allow air to pass into them to be conducted to the parts under water. Known as root knees, or pneumatophores, they are found in some species of mangroves, such as *Rhizophora* spp., and swamp cypresses (*Taxodium* spp.).

Saltwater marshes

Marine marshes are subject to regular flooding by the sea; the plants inhabiting these areas grow in zones corresponding to the frequency of flooding, the depth of water, and length of submergence. Their positions are determined by the degree to which they can cope with inundation and the salinity of the water. These plants often have to cope with a salt concentration as high as 10 per cent.

Salt-tolerant plants, known as halophytes, have difficulty in obtaining water because, as a result of the high salt concentrations in the surrounding water, any "free" water is not easily removed. There is also the problem of osmotic balance—water from the plant cells may be forced out to balance the salt concentrations inside and outside them. In addition, the large amounts of minerals present in sea water are toxic to most plants. Consequently many halophytes, such as glasswort *(Salicornia fruticosa),* have thick, leathery, fleshy leaves that store and retain large amounts of water and slow down transpiration.

The primary colonizers of the mud fringes of temperate marine marshes, such as samphire and seablite (*Suaeda* sp.), are unaffected by frequent inundations and can tolerate high salinity because they have salt glands that excrete excess salt from their shoots. Their roots stabilize the mud and allow the establishment of and replacement by other plants, particularly cord grass *(Spartina townsendii).* This plant spreads its underground stems (stolons) thickly and further stabilizes the mud, which is subsequently colonized by other plants. This colonization of the water is known as hydroseral succession and occurs in bogs and freshwater swamps.

Many of these plants are deciduous, shedding with their leaves excess ions accumulated from the sea water. In some, such as sea lavender (*Limonium* sp.), the chances of survival of the seeds are increased because they germinate only when exposed to seawater.

A zone equivalent to that in temperate saltwater marshes occurs in tropical coastal swamps dominated by mangroves, the various species each having their preferred niches. The bare mud on the seaward edge of some swamps is often colonized by the genus *Sonneratia.* Frequently, the roots of these trees slow the movement of the water sufficiently to cause silt to build up.

The seeds of mangroves such as *Rhizophora* and *Bruguiera* actually germinate on the tree. This adaptation permits the seed to germinate in aerobic conditions, whereas if it were to fall into the airless mud, germination would be difficult. The root grows from the seed on the tree and, when the seed falls, buries itself deep in the mud so that the seedling cannot be washed away.

Acid bogs

Mud and silt are also trapped in freshwater swamps, especially those associated with rivers. Hydroseral succession occurs, the end product of which may be woodland. But in those wetland areas where nutrients are leached out of the soil by moving water, and where the soil is acid, a self-generating bog results, often dominated by a group of mosses of the genus *Sphagnum.* Bog-dwelling plants are called helophytes.

The several species of *Sphagnum* have different water tolerances. Some are aquatic, whereas others prefer dry areas. These preferences can be accommodated because of the hummock-and-hollow nature of the bog. The drier areas of the bogs also maintain heathers (*Erica* spp.), bilberries (*Vaccinium* spp.), and bogcotton (*Eriophorum* sp.). In addition, the surface of the sphagnum supports various species of plants that, because of the soil's low nutrient level, are insectivorous; these include the sundew (*Drosera* sp.), butterwort (*Pinguicula vulgaris),* and pitcher plants (*Sarracenia purpurea).* They are all photosynthetic, but require mineral nutrients, such as potassium, phosphorus, and nitrogen, which they get from insects.

Alkaline freshwater swamps

The number of plant species in most freshwater swamps is low, and most are monocultures. The most obvious of these are the reed swamps that are dominated by a single species of reed, such as papyrus (*Cyperus papyrus)* found in the Sudd of Africa, or Phragmites reed (*Phragmites* sp.). The reason for this dominance is that these plants reproduce vegetatively by rhizomes and form dense clumps in which few other species can survive.

The niches of even these plants varies— reed grass (*Glyceria* sp.) grows in deeper water than flag *(Iris pseudacorus),* for instance, and *Phragmites* reed colonizes even deeper water. The rhizomes form a floating mass on the surface upon which subsequent generations grow.

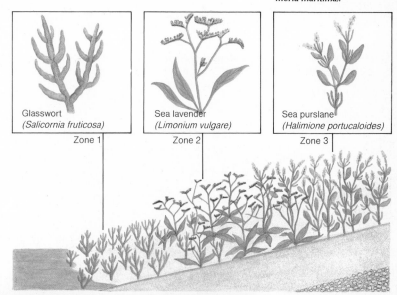

Glasswort
(*Salicornia fruticosa*)
Zone 1

Sea lavender
(*Limonium vulgare*)
Zone 2

Sea purslane
(*Halimione portucaloides*)
Zone 3

The plants on a saltwater marsh grow in zones according to their tolerance of inundation and salinity. On the seaward edges of a temperate marsh grows glasswort and other species of the genus *Salicornia.* Between the low and higher areas are a number of species including sea lavender. The drier, higher areas of the marsh are occupied by sea purslane and thrift *(Armeria maritima).*

Mangrove swamps occur in tropical coastal areas and include several genera, such as *Rhizophora.* In many swamps, this plant grows in the zone immediately behind the most seaward because it cannot tolerate the long periods of inundation that, for example, *Sonneratia* sp. can. These trees grow aerial or looped roots to trap air which is conducted to the parts under water. They also grow prop roots that stabilize the mud, which is then colonized by other species.

Mountains

Mountains are unique habitats because they create a climate of their own. Above sea level, the mean annual temperature falls by approximately 3° or 4° F. per 1,000-foot (2° or 3° C per 300-meter) increase in altitude up to an altitude of 5 to 10 miles (8 to 16 kilometers). These zones have parallels in those that are found with increasing latitude, and the top of a high mountain in the tropics may be similar in average temperature to polar tundra. Averages, however, can be misleading because an alpine climate shows more daily and seasonal variation than an arctic one.

The alpine tundra is the area between the top of a mountain, which is permanently covered in snow and ice, and the point at which trees can grow (the treeline), lower down the slope. Plants in this area show many forms of adaptation to their environmental conditions which include altitude, temperature, wind, rainfall, and snow.

Adaptations to temperature, wind, and snow

At very low temperatures, plant enzymes do not function efficiently and biochemical processes generally slow down. Alpine plants, such as the saxifrages (*Saxifraga* spp.), form dense cushions or tussocks that lie close to the surface of the ground, protecting themselves from the wind and producing their own, relatively warm, microclimate inside. Alpine plants, such as the mountain crowfoot (*Ranunculus glacialis*), protect themselves with concentrated cell fluid that acts like antifreeze.

The Ruwenzori mountains dividing western Uganda and Zaire support many plants that show unusual adaptations to their climate. In the forests in the subalpine zone, temperatures alter sharply between day and night. As the temperature drops, some giant species of lobelia (*Lobelia* spp.) fold in their leaves, creating their own microclimate inside them. Temperatures of 41° F. (5° C) have been recorded inside these leafy spheres, while the temperature outside was below freezing. Rain, which is trapped in the plant's rosette during the day and warmed by the sun, also helps to keep the plant warm during the night.

Other plants, particularly on the tropical mountains, protect themselves from frost with a build-up of dead leaf material around their stems. The species of groundsel (*Senecio* spp.) found in the African equatorial mountains avoid tissue damage in this way. Some alpine plants are sensitive to summer heat, such as the three-leaved rush (*Juncus trifidus*), which cannot survive in conditions where the mean annual maximum temperature exceeds 72° F. (22° C). Occasionally, plants requiring higher average temperatures for growth survive on south-facing slopes but not in the valley below. The reason for this is temperature inversion, in which cold air falls to the valley floor and warm air remains above it.

Strong winds in the alpine tundra, which can travel at speeds of more than 100 miles (161 kilometers) per hour and may carry lacerating ice crystals, restrict plant growth and demand special adaptations. Shrubs, such as the dwarf birch (*Betula nana*), grow close to the ground where they are less likely to be damaged by wind. Some species of willows, such as the violet willow (*Salix daphnoides*) of the Himalayas, have supple branches and stems that yield to wind pressure without breaking.

The growing season in the alpine tundra is short because snow may persist late into the summer and can be a permanent feature of north-facing hollows. Snow patches shrink gradually during the warmer months to reveal a vegetation rich in bryophytes, such as the liverwort *Anthelia juratzkana* and club mosses like the fir club moss (*Lycopodium selago*).

Snow cover can be advantageous to plants, protecting them from very low temperatures and from some wind damage. It also provides a source of water for growth early in the spring, which is necessary where soils

Mountains create unique habitats for plants and demand special adaptations if plants are to survive, reproduce, and evolve there. The great mountain buttercup *(Ranunculus lyalli, below left)* is endemic to Mount Cook in New Zealand and has large showy flowers to attract insects. The llareta *(Azorella glabra, below right)* lives at high altitudes in the Andes and grows as a ground-hugging cushion plant in response to low temperatures and strong winds.

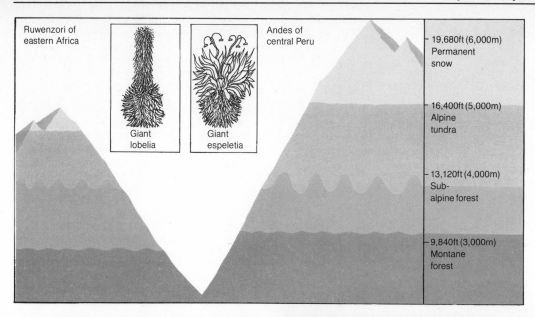

Ruwenzori of eastern Africa

Giant lobelia

Giant espeletia

Andes of central Peru

19,680ft (6,000m) Permanent snow

16,400ft (5,000m) Alpine tundra

13,120ft (4,000m) Sub-alpine forest

9,840ft (3,000m) Montane forest

A mountain can be divided into marked climatic zones, but regional factors dictate which type of zones are present and the levels at which they lie. Vegetation in the Alpine tundra is generally ground-hugging, but in the Ruwenzori mountains, giant species of lobelia (*Lobelia* spp.) grow. In the Andes, some plants, such as the giant espeletia (*Espeletia grandiflora*), grow to a large size.

are shallow and easily drained. Many alpine plants have adaptations normally associated with hot, dry climates, such as succulent leaves, as in the stonecrops (*Sedum* spp.), hairy surfaces, as in the edelweiss (*Leontopodium alpinum*), and thick, waxy cuticles, as in many of the saxifrages. Not only do these adaptations prevent the loss of water, but they also help to reflect the strong light, preventing the plant from overheating. Some species push their buds up through the melting layers to flower—for example, the alpine snowbell (*Soldanella alpina*).

Growth and pollination

In the alpine tundra, annual plants are rare because the growing season is too short for them to complete their life cycle and produce ripe seeds. In the Alps, there are usually less than two months of the year that are frostfree. Most herbaceous plants that grow on mountains are long-lived perennials, which cope with the rigors of the climate by producing only a small amount of growth each year.

Low temperatures may result in a lack of suitable insects for pollination. There is much competition between plants for available pollinators, and flowers have developed adaptations to make themselves particularly attractive. The flowers of many alpine plants are large and showy and some, such as those of the mountain avens (*Dryas octopetala*), take the form of a parabolic reflector that focuses the sun's rays to the central part of the flower, thereby raising its temperature and enabling the insects to work more actively.

Distribution of species

Some alpine plants have a wide global distribution, even though individual populations are isolated. The purple saxifrage (*Saxifraga oppositifolia*), for example, is found in a complete circle around the Arctic and in the mountains of Britain, the Alps, the Hindu Kush, and the Rocky Mountains of North America. Fossil evidence has shown that this species was present in many of the intervening lowlands during the cold conditions of the last glaciation and has become fragmented in its distribution only during the last 10,000 years.

Mountains, particularly in tropical areas, can be regarded as climatic islands, which are centers of independent evolutionary development. The African mountains, such as the Ruwenzori, are rich in endemic species—that is, those species that are restricted in their distribution to one particular area. This area, for example, is known for its giant plants. It is likely that these sites were once in closer contact with one another, perhaps during periods of lower global temperature; subsequent isolation has, thus, allowed evolution to proceed independently, giving rise to new, endemic species. Most alpine species have limited powers of seed dispersal, so the tracts of other vegetation between mountains represent impenetrable barriers to their movement.

Cloud forests occur at cloud level in the montane zone of tropical mountains. This type of forest is characterized by a low, thick canopy of small trees covered with many types of epiphytes—particularly ferns, liverworts, and mosses.

Polar and tundra

The polar and tundra regions lie beyond the areas of normal tree growth, from about 60° N. and 60° S. to the poles; temperatures may be as low as −40° F. (−40° C) in the Arctic and −30° F. (−62° C) in the Antarctic. For part of the year there is continuous night with fre-

quent high winds sweeping across the frigid landscape. During the long daylight hours of summer in the Arctic, temperatures range from an average of 45° to 60° F. (7° to 16° C), but only some of the ice melts—the ground below the surface is permanently frozen. There is little precipitation, at the most 6 to 10 inches (15 to 25 centimeters) in a year, including melted snow.

Low temperatures, wintry blizzards, shallow soil and its scarce nutrients, summer drought, and the absence of tree cover are reflected in the means that the plants that live in these regions have adapted to survive there. Of the few plant species that live in these conditions, most are mosses and lichens, although grasses, sedges, and dwarf shrubs do occur. The vegetation of the Arctic is rich compared with that of Antarctica, where temperatures are lower. In addition, most of the area in the Southern Hemisphere equivalent to that occupied by tundra in the north is ocean.

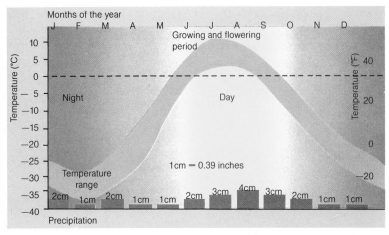

General adaptations

Most tundra flora grow close to the ground because upward growth is inhibited by the harsh winds. But the advantages of this low height are that in the winter, snow can cover the plants and conserve their heat, as well as shield them against wind abrasion and dehydration.

Instead of growing upward, tundra plants spread out; for example, the ground willow (Salix lanata) rarely exceeds 1 inch (2.5 centimeters) in height, but its branches may reach out 16 feet (5 meters) along the ground surface. Their roots also tend to spread out, just beneath the soil surface, because penetration down through the frozen ground—or permafrost—is impossible, and only the top few inches of soil are available for growth.

The North Alaskan woolly lousewort (Pedicularis sylvatica) creates its microclimate by trapping air between the hairs dispersed over its stem and buds. By raising the temperature around the plant in this way, the short reproductive season can be prolonged.

To protect themselves against the desiccating winds, a number of plants, such as some saxifrages (Saxifragaceae), have a leathery cuticle covering their leaves, which retards water loss through evaporation.

Flowering plants

Tundra plants are almost exclusively perennial. This is because the plants' life cycle may be interrupted by the oncoming winter and the entire process suspended until the following summer; annual plants therefore stand little chance of survival.

With a growing season limited to only six to nine weeks, reproduction must be rapid. The green alder (Alnus viridis), for example, unfurls its catkins and leaves at the same time, rather than putting one out after the other as most other plants do.

The seeds of most tundra plants are very small; indeed, most weigh less than 1 milligram. These features not only facilitate dispersal by wind, but are also probably due to the fact that the plants need to conserve energy and cannot afford to manufacture a

The tundra landscape is a treeless one—those tree species that do survive are dwarfs, such as the willow (Salix sp.). Because of the unfavorable conditions, only a few plant species are sufficiently well adapted to this environment, the variety being restricted to mosses and lichens, grasses, sedges, and dwarf shrubs.

Cushion plants, such as Sempervivum, trap air among their low-growing dense cushions of leaves. In this way the plants create an individual microclimate, which may be warmer than the air around them by as much as 40° F. (4.5° C).

heavier seed. Other seeds are carried by water or the animals that visit these regions in summer.

Some seeds lie dormant in the permafrost for long periods: seeds of the Arctic lupine (*Lupinus arcticus*), for example, have been found to germinate after having been apparently frozen for thousands of years. They manage to survive because their sturdy seedcases can resist earth movements and keep the seeds dry and protected from damage, disease, and the elements until the permafrost melts. Most seeds, however, do manage to put down some roots and grow a few leaves before the winter cold stops all growth.

Several plants also reproduce asexually, by means of rhizomes, bulbs, or root stocks, such as some species of cotton grass (*Eriophorum* spp.). This method of propagation has a far higher success rate in the Arctic conditions than seed production. These organs also serve to store nutrients.

Flowering in tundra plants is sporadic; it may be early, draining the nutrient store from the previous summer, or late, using the food manufactured in the same summer. Like the seeds, most flowers are very small and are closely packed together—there can be a hundred flowers in one square yard. In Antarctica, however, three kinds of flowering plants have been seen—an herb and two varieties of grass.

Where the land is flat and boggy, a wet tundra of grass-like sedges (*Carex* spp.) and cotton grass proliferate. Grasses also survive in these areas, growing in tussocks and thus managing to retain warmth and moisture between their leaves. The heath tundra, where permafrost occurs, is dominated by several species of small, compact shrubs, mostly of the berry variety, such as crowberry (*Empetrum nigrum*).

Mosses and lichens

The boggy areas where the frost has lifted the ground at intervals is called "palsa" mire. The hummocks are built up by successions of spongy bog mosses (*Sphagnum* spp.), which survive because they form low mats. Some, such as *Andreaea,* manage to live in exposed areas by growing rhizoids (little roots), which anchor the plant to the surface.

Around the fringes of the icecaps, only lichens and mosses manage to survive—mainly on rock surfaces. Lichens are particularly well adapted to low temperatures and conditions of prolonged drought. They are both fungi and algae combined to form a single structure, living symbiotically. The fungal structure (the outer layer) protects the plant and absorbs water vapor, while the alga (the inner layer) photosynthesizes and creates carbohydrates and other organic nutrients. Some lichens also fix nitrogen from the air. They are slow-growing, only about 1 millimeter per year.

Lichens such as reindeer moss (*Cladonia alpestris*) are rootless and cling to other plants and rocks, especially heat-absorbing rocks in the ice-free zones. They grow when the surface they are attached to warms, and moisture is absorbed directly into the fungal cells. Growth is extremely slow because in severe weather lichens lie dormant and may not reproduce for years. They reproduce vegetatively or by the dispersal of fungal spores, which join with an appropriate alga.

Woody plants in the scrub tundra, for example the dwarf willow (*Salix glauca*), rarely grow more than 3 feet (91 centimeters) high. The small size of the plant helps to reduce its transpirational surface and, therefore, decrease water loss, as well as prevent it from being damaged by high winds. Despite its apparently unlikely relation to willow trees, this plant also has yellow catkins that rely on the wind to disperse their seeds.

Lava flows are fertile sites for plant growth because of their rich mineral content and because the solid rock does not need to be decomposed before plants can colonize it. But in the Icelandic tundra only mosses and lichens can survive, clinging to the exposed surfaces of the rock, being well adapted to endure low temperatures and high winds.

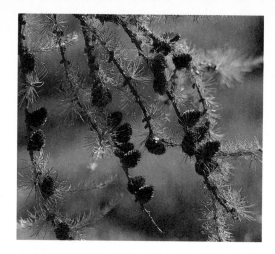

The larch (*Larix* sp.) bears cones but, unlike other coniferous forest trees, is deciduous, losing its leaves every autumn.

Coniferous forests

In the Northern Hemisphere, north of the temperate deciduous forests, the principal plant life is coniferous forest. Because of the commercial value of the timber from these trees (used in building and as a source of wood pulp for papermaking, for example), many of the forests are man-made. The natural coniferous forest, lying mostly between latitudes 45° N. and 70° N., is called the taiga. Farther north it gives way to tundra vegetation, and the trees become sparse and stunted. To the south, it blends into deciduous woodland or grassland (on the North American prairies) and steppes (in central Asia).

There are no large natural forests comparable to those of the taiga in the Southern Hemisphere because land does not extend into the equivalent latitudes, although there are some pockets of coniferous forest south of the equator.

Adaptations of coniferous forests

During the winter, when the ground is frozen, tree roots are unable to obtain water from the soil. Few of the winds bring rain, and although precipitation may reach 10 to 39 inches (25 to 99 centimeters) a year, most of it falls as snow. Trees that grow in these conditions—termed winter drought—must therefore by xerophytic

(drought-resistant), a feature they achieve mainly by their leaf form. The leaves of most conifers are tough, leathery, and evergreen. A waxy cuticle reduces water loss by evaporation, and the toughness prevents the leaves from collapsing or wilting under water stress (otherwise they might be damaged by strong winds, for example). Most leaves of coniferous trees are needle-shaped and highly resistant to frost.

Unlike deciduous trees, evergreens do not need to expend energy putting out new green leaves each spring, and the persistence of their leaves provides a means of conserving nutrients. They can photosynthesize (during daylight) whenever it is warm enough, and in the brief summer months they can concentrate their energy resources on reproduction. The trees themselves tend to be conical in shape, so that they easily shed snow that might otherwise accumulate and, by its sheer weight, break the branches. Any snow that is retained insulates the trees from the cold and reduces transpiration—and hence water loss—from the leaves.

Variety within the forest

Few natural coniferous forests are homogeneous, containing only evergreens. In the Siberian forest, for example, particularly at high altitudes, the dominant species are two kinds of larches, *Larix gmelinii* and *L. dahurica.* The larch is deciduous, but it is extremely hardy and can withstand gales, as well as being rot-resistant. On the lower ground the Siberian pine *(Pinus sibirica)* is common.

Parts of the Siberian forest, like large areas of Canada, occupy boggy ground called muskeg. Those in Canada support the tamarack or American larch *(Larix laricina)*, although the forests in other areas such as Labrador, New Brunswick, and Newfoundland are chiefly spruce (*Picea* sp.) and larch. White spruce *(P. glauca)* grows close to the tundra and black spruce *(P. marina)* around the muskeg. Birch trees (*Betula* spp.) and balsam firs *(Abies balsamea)* are also found in these regions. The cells of the deciduous trees remain undamaged after slow freezing. As a result, the Siberian larches can withstand lower temperatures than evergreens, and in Finland the birches extend farther north than pines and spruces.

The succession of species in a natural forest may take three centuries or more. Birch seedlings quickly grow on ground cleared by a forest fire (A), to form a birch forest (B) that gives way about 60 years later to pines (C). After a further 150 years or so, spruce gradually replaces the pine forest (D).

A   Gap caused by fire

B   Birch forest

C   Pine forest

D   Spruce forest

The eastern side of the North American continent has a more temperate climate than Siberia. Around the Great Lakes precipitation can fluctuate between 20 and 40 inches (50 and 101 centimeters) a year and temperatures between 50° and 104° F. (10° and 40° C). These conditions result in a variety of species. White pines *(Pinus strobus)* and hemlocks *(Tsuga canadensis)* dominate the forests, and red pines *(P. resinosa)* and aspens *(Populus* spp.) are common.

Succession of tree species

There are few virgin forests left in the world. A recent study of the northern regions of Canada and Scandinavia, however, has shown how natural succession of different species—in this case of birch, pine, and spruce—occurs in one place over a period of 300 years, if it is left undisturbed.

The birch is a broad-leaved deciduous tree, which is often found in coniferous forests. When a space is cleared in a forest, by fire or falling trees, the birch (which grows rapidly and needs considerable light) quickly invades it by means of its widely dispersed, windborne seeds. For the next 60 years a birch forest is formed. Under the canopy and in gaps between the birches, pines begin to grow and the woodland changes to a pine association.

The pines, which live for about 150 years, maintain a dense forest in which ground vegetation dies because of the lack of light. Spruce seedlings have difficulty in establishing themselves, but their light requirements are minimal so that, as the pine association dies away, the spruce gradually becomes the dominant (or climax) tree, so forming a spruce association. Because it needs little light and creates great shade, the spruce can maintain its dominance over the pine and birch until fire or felling renews the succession. The cycle then begins again with birch.

Where a space in the forest does admit light, juniper *(Juniperus communis)* and bilberry *(Vaccinium myrtillus)* as well as grasses and herbaceous plants, such as wintergreen *(Pyrola* sp.), are quick to colonize the place until another conifer sapling begins once more to overshadow them.

Other less highly evolved plants also live in the coniferous forest. Fungi and bacteria cover old needles on the forest floor, feeding on the slowly decaying needles, and lichens such as the reindeer moss *(Cladonia rangiferina)* also grow there. Many simple plants live on the trees and are known as epiphytes. They feed on nutrients carried from the air by rain. They include mosses, ferns, and lichens.

The carpet of fallen needles, branches, and cones decays slowly because of the low temperatures. Beneath this layer of infertile material is a leached stratum, which the roots penetrate. It is deficient in nutrients, and so the trees depend largely on the fungi in the litter, which take carbohydrates from the tree and in turn provide it with mineral salts.

Most coniferous forests in the Northern Hemisphere are artificial plantations of fast-growing trees, raised for their timber. Often birches are left standing when the timber trees are felled.

Logs float in a collecting pond at a mill in Canada, waiting to be debarked and ground into pulp for making such materials as paper, hardboard, and insulating board. Wood pulp is also a source of cellulose for the chemical industry.

Temperate forests

Temperate forests cover large areas of the earth, occupying regions that have a high rainfall in spring and summer. Some of these areas experience frosts during four or five months of the year but only one or two months when average temperatures remain below freezing. They have a growing season of at least four months, with a mean daily temperature above 50° F. (10° C). In general, these climatic conditions occur on the margins of continents, and as a result temperate forests are largely absent from the interior of continents, such as Asia and North America, where hot dry summers and very cold winters allow the development of grassland vegetation only.

Temperate forests can be divided into those that contain deciduous trees, and those that comprise evergreens, although the two types of tree are often found in the same forest. The regions where these forests occur can also be separated into cold, cool, and warm temperate climates, which determine the types of trees found there. Very few of the forests remain in an unmodified state—most have been felled and replanted, or selectively harvested for hundreds, if not thousands, of years.

Temperate deciduous forests

These forests usually occur in cold temperate regions, between latitudes 25° N. and 55° N., on the western fringe of Europe reaching eastward, in eastern Asia, and in the northeastern United States. The Southern Hemisphere has few areas that are climatically suitable for these trees.

One of the most striking characteristics of these forests is the loss of leaves in winter and the replenishment by a new set grown in spring. During the long summer days, photosynthesis can be sustained for 16 or more hours because light levels and the availability of water are high. In winter, however, the water supply is low, especially when the ground is frozen, and photosynthesis is reduced because light levels decrease. Deciduous trees have thin leaves that are often fairly large; this kind of leaf maximizes photosynthesis at the expense of low control over water loss. They are, therefore, shed in winter, thus eliminating most of the trees' water loss.

When the soil temperature drops below about 39° F. (4° C), the tree roots cannot draw water from it, which means that no sap can rise to the leaves. The chlorophyll in the leaves breaks down, and they lose their green color, revealing secondary pigments, such as carotenes and xanthocyanins, which give the leaves their red, yellow, orange, and purple colors in autumn. Losses of important nutrient elements in the fallen leaves are minimized by the withdrawal of these nutrients into the branches before leaf fall. A thin layer of cork then grows across the base of the leaf stalk, and the leaf falls off. The fallen leaves decom-

Autumnal leaf fall occurs in response to changes in temperature and day length. A cork layer grows over the base of the leaf stem, cutting it off from the sap, and the leaf eventually drops off the branch.

In a temperate forest the dominant trees occupy the top level with smaller trees forming the shade, or second layer. Shrubs form a story of their own, below which, on the ground level, is an ephemeral, herbaceous layer.

pose to form humus, the nutrients of which are absorbed by the tree roots in the next growing season and recycled.

The wood of deciduous trees is also adapted to support the leaves in their vigorous seasonal growth—it contains vessels and tracheids that allow efficient water conduction that supports the high transpiration rate of the leaves.

A few genera of trees occur throughout these cold temperature forests, but their species vary on the different continents. They include oaks (*Quercus* spp.), beeches (*Fagus* spp.), chestnuts (*Castanea* spp.), birches (*Betula* spp.), and elms (*Ulmus* spp.). Most of the present temperate deciduous forests in Europe are dominated by beech or oak. Other trees generally found growing in association with them include maple and sycamore (*Acer* spp.), ash (*Fraxinus* spp.), and walnut (*Juglans* spp.).

Some conifers also occur in the northern deciduous forests; in the northern forests of the North American continent, for example, white pine *(Pinus strobus)* and hemlock *(Tsuga canadensis)* may be found among deciduous trees.

The cycle of leafing and leaflessness has a strong influence on the association species of deciduous woodlands. In the spring there is a period, before the canopy trees produce their leaves, when the sun can illuminate and warm the soil. At this time many of the perennial woodland herbs conduct most of their yearly photosynthesis, grow, and flower. In western Europe, species such as wood anemone *(Anemone nemorosa),* bluebell *(Endymion non-scriptus),* and oxlip *(Primula elatior)* flower at this time and make most of their vegetative growth. A few then produce thin, large "shade leaves," but most die down to their underground storage organs after midsummer. Many shrubs in these woodlands also flower early before the canopy trees are in leaf, such as hazel *(Corylus avellana).*

Temperate evergreen forests

These forests are found in cool and warm temperate regions and contain both broad-leaved and coniferous types. At the lower latitudes, in the warm temperate regions, deciduous forests are replaced by evergreen, mostly broad-leaved forest. The cool temperate forests, which are coastal, are usually comprised of coniferous trees.

The evergreen broad-leaved trees, such as *Magnolia grandiflora* in the southern United States, do not need to shed their leaves because the temperatures are warm enough to keep soil temperatures above 39° F. (4° C); the roots can therefore constantly absorb water and sap can be supplied continually to the leaves. The leaves of these trees also have waxy surfaces and small stomata, which limit transpiration and avoid excessive water loss. Another example is the genus *Eucalyptus* in southeastern Australia. These trees also hold their leaves vertically so that they are parallel to the sun's rays and, therefore, reduce the effects of its heat.

Other warm temperate regions are also inhabited by various coniferous species, such as pines (*Pinus* spp.), as in southeastern North America, southern China, and parts of Japan. Because the humidity is so high in these areas, there is a rich understory growth of mosses, ferns, and lichens.

Some cool temperate forests grow in coastal mountain slopes where sea winds bring a high annual rainfall. They also contain pines and, in North America, giant redwoods *(Sequoia sempervirens).* Like most conifers their leaves are needlelike and waxy, which reduces transpiration, particularly in the cold winter and under the onslaught of desiccating winds. These trees grow densely and, like the evergreen broad-leaved forests, do not allow much light through, which results in little understory growth.

Bluebells *(Endymion non-scriptus)* carpet a birch forest for the few months that the warm spring sunshine can penetrate the foliage to the ground level. During this time these plants produce most of their vegetative growth. They die down to their bulbs once the leaves of the trees block out the sun, in about midsummer.

Tropical rain forests

Tropical rain forests are the richest biomes on earth in terms of plant species, representing the true apex of diversity in life-forms. A single acre may support 100 different tree species, and the microorganism and animal populations show corresponding richness. The principal forests of this kind occur in the Amazonian Basin, the Congo Basin, and from the Western Ghats of India in a belt across the Malaysian archipelago to New Guinea.

These forests vary slightly in nature depending on their latitude and altitude. In the equatorial regions temperatures range from a high of 93° F. (34° C) to a low of 68° F. (20° C), with as little range between the average temperature of the hottest and coolest months as 2° to 5° F. (1° to 3° C). Rainfall in these areas is more than 80 inches (203 centimeters) a year. Humidity, too, is high, rarely falling below 95 per cent in the lower levels of the forest. Most of these trees are evergreen. Away from the equator the rainfall drops below 78 inches (198 centimeters), and the forests in these latitudes experience a dry season, which alternates with one of copious rainfall. Many of these trees are deciduous in the drier months. The monsoon forests in Southeast Asia are also seasonal with a regular dry season with 5 inches (12 centimeters) or less of rainfall, followed by months in which the rain-bearing monsoon winds restart the seasonal growth cycle. On tropical mountains at altitudes from 2,000 to 10,000 feet (600 to 3,000 meters), a cloud or mossy forest exists, the nature of which reflects the abundant precipitation derived from fog condensing on the vegetation. Despite these differences, all tropical rain forests share a high humidity and density of vegetation, the two main features with which plants have to contend.

The forest of the Guiana Highlands marks the northern edge of the Amazonian rain forest—the biggest tropical rain forest in the world, being 2.4 million square miles (6.2 million square kilometers) in area. The density of the vegetation is clearly visible and is one of the major factors that the plants in these environments have to contend with.

Structure

The structure of tropical rain forests is complex. The tallest trees (emergents) form the so-called emergent layer, thrusting up through the forest canopy at intervals, their crowns spreading above the other trees. These umbrella crowns are usually composed of many smaller dense subcrowns. Most are between 100 and 200 feet (30 and 60 meters) tall, but some, such as the Southeast Asian tualang *(Koompassia excelsa),* may exceed heights of 260 feet (80 meters).

Beneath the emergent trees the canopy extends, usually as much as 150 feet (45 meters) deep. The flattened crowns of the trees interlock to form a virtually unbroken mass. Their trunks may be branchless for 65 feet (20 meters) above the jungle floor, breaking into huge spreading branches as they approach the light.

Below the main canopy are smaller trees, often with vertically elongated crowns. Some are small and slow growing, reaching maturity in the low light levels beneath the main canopy. Others are young, immature specimens of canopy or emergent trees that will mature only when they are given an opportunity to grow into spaces in those upper layers.

The understory layer beneath the enveloping canopy contains shrubs and herbaceous plants, below which—on the forest floor itself—live fungi, bacteria, algae, protozoa, and other microorganisms.

Between the layers and supported by them are other plants, such as lianas, climbers, and epiphytes. Lianas and climbers are rooted in the ground, but use other plants for support as they grow toward the light. The epiphytes—orchids, bromeliads, mosses, ferns, liverworts, and lichens—do not root in the soil but live in an area from the trunk bases to the smallest twigs of the canopy, some of them at heights of 100 feet (30 meters) or more above the ground, on the branches or trunks of trees where they are exposed to the light.

The emergent layer

Towering above the body of the forest the mature emergents are subject to greater fluctuations of climate than are their companions. Winds are stronger, humidity is lower, and temperatures are hotter and more extreme than beneath the shelter of the canopy. To cope with these factors, mature emergent trees develop smaller, tougher leaves than those they bear as young trees. In addition, the leaves of some species of emergents have a waxy outer covering, which helps to reduce water loss. Most of these trees are broad-leaved evergreens.

Taking advantage of the greater air movement above the canopy, many emergent species have winged fruits that are dispersed by the wind to new sites in the forest. For example, the Indo-Malayan dipterocarps (Dipterocarpaceae) have two-winged seeds, and the South American *Cavanillesia platanifolia* has distinctive five-winged seeds.

The canopy

Most canopy trees have oval, smooth, shiny leaves that taper to a point (the drip tip). A possible reason for the success of the smooth pointed leaves is that they shed rain quickly, thus discouraging the growth of tiny lichens and mosses, which flourish on moist surfaces. Even so, some species do have compound leaves, both pinnate and palmate.

In cloud forests the canopy is low and dense, formed by small trees with thick twisted crowns of tiny, leathery leaves (microphylls). Because of the intense radiation at these altitudes, as high as 10,000 feet (3,000 meters) in New Guinea, the leaves have developed a high reflective power.

Some of the canopy trees, particularly those in the drier, more seasonal areas, are deciduous, shedding their leaves at regular intervals. The Indian almond *(Terminalia catappa),* for example, sheds its leaves every six months; other species do so at intervals of slightly more than a year.

The evergreen trees produce their new leaves in flushes rather than continuously. These new leaves tend to be more brightly colored and less rigid than the old ones. One reason for this staggered pattern of replacement may be that the soft leaves are preferred by herbivorous animals, and if these were produced continuously, the animals would destroy the bulk of new growth. By having long intervals in which no new leaves are produced, they are too uncertain a food supply to support a large population of leaf-eaters.

Flowering and fruiting occur in regular seasons. Many species, such as the silk-cotton trees *(Ceiba pentandra),* flower simultaneously through the forest. Individuals may be widely scattered, but even so, simultaneous flowering greatly helps cross-pollination. Fruiting at the same time means that more than sufficient food for seed-eating animals and birds is pro-

Height in feet

Emergents

Canopy

Understory

Forest floor

200

150

100

50

0

Buttresses spread from the trunks of many of the canopy trees, helping to keep the trees upright and spreading their load over a larger supporting area. The roots of these trees are very shallow, their tips growing within a few inches of the soil surface, so they need this extra support.

Tropical rain forests consist of a top layer of emergent trees up to 200 feet (61 meters) tall, a dense canopy of interlocking crowns of shorter trees about 150 feet (45 meters) tall, an understory with young emergents and small, conical trees up to 50 feet (15 meters) tall, and the forest floor. Between the layers are epiphytes and climbers.

duced so that enough seeds remain to germinate. In some species, flowers are produced on the main trunk rather than on twigs or branches, especially on the smaller trees. This may be related to bat pollinators, which cannot reach flowers hidden in a mass of leaves and twigs.

Most seeds in the canopy have some means of dispersal away from the vicinity of the parent tree, where competition for resources is too great. Even though the air beneath the jungle canopy is still, a few large trees have wind-dispersed seeds. The silk-cotton seeds have a light, fluffy coating that carries them on the slightest movement of air, and some of the mahoganies, *Khaya* spp. and *Entandrophragma* spp., have winged seeds.

Animals, however, are the most important means of seed dispersal in the rain forest. Attracted by soft fleshy fruits, such as durian *(Durio zibethinus)*, the animal consumes the pulp, but the hard seeds within are resistant to digestion and pass through the animal unharmed, having gained the advantage of its movement through the forest. A few trees,

such as the sandbox tree *(Hura crepitans)*, have exploding fruits that scatter their seeds.

Once dispersed, the seed then has the problem of germination and establishment in the difficult environment of the forest floor, where there is tremendous competition for light and nutrients. Most plants employ one of two strategies: some trees produce a few large seeds with large food reserves, which fuel the seedling during its slow growth (this growth speeds up if a tree falls nearby, reducing the competition for light and space); other trees produce many tiny seeds, which lie on the forest floor until a gap, made by a fallen tree, allows them sufficient light to germinate.

The understory

Only 2 to 5 per cent of the sunlight available to the canopy reaches the understory, and much of the light that does remain is transmitted through or reflected off leaves, thus losing much of its useful content. When a large tree falls, possibly bringing down with it a number of smaller neighboring trees, it creates a gap where increased light levels that reach the ground layer stimulate a burst of young tree growth and the germination of seeds in the lighted patch.

Fast-growing species first take advantage of the new conditions, with fully grown canopy and emergent trees perhaps taking many decades to reestablish. The plants that do survive in the undergrowth include dwarf palms and soft-stalked species of families, such as Marantaceae (an example of which is the prayer plant, *Maranta* sp.), the ginger family (Zingiberaceae), and the acanthus family (Acanthaceae). These plants usually grow to a height of 10 feet (3 meters) or less. Their leaves are usually broad and pointed, and some species have a reddish tinge to the undersurface. The red is due to the presence of the secondary pigment xanthocyanin.

Understory plants have difficulty with pollination because of the lack of air movement there. They therefore rely on insects. Some flower at night, producing large strong-scented flowers, which attract moths. Others,

The brightly colored bracts of the exotic *Heliconia rostrata* enliven the dark understory of the Amazonian rain forest. The bracts of this tall, perennial, herbaceous plant give rise to numerous flowers, which are pollinated by birds or insects.

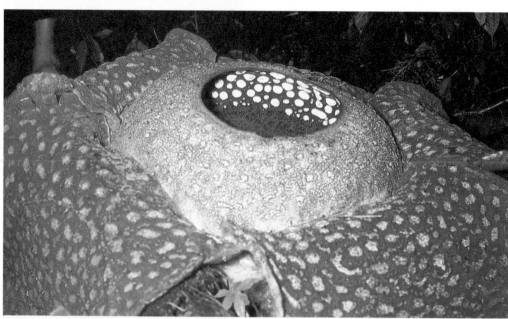

The rafflesia *(Rafflesia arnoldii)*, or monster flower, is one of the most remarkable of the flowering plants on the forest floor. Found in the Malaysian forest, it is a parasite, living inside the stems and roots of vines of the genus *Tetrastigma*. The flower that it produces above the ground is the largest known, measuring approximately 3 feet (91 centimeters) across and weighing about 5 pounds (2.2 kilograms). It smells of rotting meat, which attracts pollinating flies.

such as the cacao tree *(Theobroma cacao)* and the breadfruit plant *(Artocarpus communis),* produce flowers and fruit on their trunks. This phenomenon, known as cauliflory, makes the flowers and large fruits conspicuous, for the purposes of pollination and seed dispersal.

The forest floor

The floor itself is covered with a litter of rapidly decomposing vegetation and organisms that break it down. They are an essential component in the cycle of nutrient flow between generations of plants.

The soil of these forests is poor and intensely leached. A high proportion of the nutrients in the system are locked in the very large biomass, and there is great competition for the nutrients released by decomposition. This is one reason for the shallow-rootedness of many of the trees.

Climbers and epiphytes

Climbers attach themselves to the trunks of trees by clinging roots that may absorb water and nutrients from the surface of their supporters. The lianas, in contrast, start life as a small shrub and gradually grow up to the canopy, using other plants for support. Lianas sometimes twine around other tree trunks, but often hang from the canopy, their crowns interwoven with the crowns of adjacent canopy trees. They have strange, twisted stems composed of wood that is divided into separate strands, which produce a structure of great strength and flexibility.

The epiphytes use other plants for support only. Many, particularly the epiphytic orchids, have specialized, stocky roots with a spongy cortex that takes up water quickly when it is available. Others, such as the tank bromeliads, have cup-shaped leaves or leaf bases which have been known to hold 14.5 gallons (55 liters) in some species.

The strangler fig *(Ficus* sp.) is one (accidental) epiphyte that does eventually kill its supporter. Its seeds are deposited by birds on the branches of canopy trees, where they germinate. Aerial roots grow down and encircle the host tree while the plant grows upward toward the light. Eventually it grows into a tree, shadowing its host, which dies from lack of light as much as from strangulation.

Tropical rain forests are a valuable resource if wisely used. Their luxuriance, however, hides a delicate ecological balance, and their complex communities are easily and irrevocably destroyed by the large-scale land clearance and logging that has taken place in recent years. The loss to humankind would be stupendous if these forests were destroyed before we even fully understand their complexity and learn how to benefit from them.

Epiphytic bromeliads grow on the branches of an emergent tree above the western Amazonian forest, in the foothills of the Andes. These plants store water in enormous "tanks" and survive on the nutrients of decaying bark and leaf litter in the tree hollows.

A liana's woody stem is carried up toward the light by young emergent and canopy trees. Eventually its leaves will develop in the light, intermeshing with those of the canopy trees.

Heath and moorland

The terms "heath" and "moor" apply to extensive areas of land that are uncultivated and virtually treeless, with poor, acid soil—the soil tends to constitute a peat layer overlying sand or gravel. Plants of the heath family (Ericaceae) usually dominate the vegetation. They are found throughout the world usually in arctic, montane, and temperate regions with moderate rainfall and dry summers.

One of the most striking features of this type of environment is the limited species range of plants on such large tracts of ground. There are exceptions, however, such as the species-rich fynbos heath of the Cape in South Africa. In most areas, few species can adapt themselves to such harsh conditions, exposed to strong winds, great fluctuations in temperature, poor soil, and outbreaks of fire.

Adaptations to water stress

The winds and the sun tend to cause rapid evaporation of water from the exposed surfaces of the plants. The roots, therefore, have to absorb water from the soil to replace this loss. But the soil may be too dry to allow the water supply to be restored to its correct level. To counteract this problem, the leaves of these plants have developed various adaptations to reduce the rate of transpiration (these plants are known as xerophytes).

The leaves of heath plants are usually narrow and needlelike, as in bell heather (*Erica cinerea*), or reduced to spines, as in furze (*Ulex europaeus*). This shape reduces the transpiring surface to a minimum. The stomata, through which most water is lost, are usually confined to the lower surface of the leaves; in some species they are protected by hairs, which surround them and trap water vapor, and in others by inwardly rolled leaf margins. This rolling may be permanent, as in the heathers (*Erica* spp.), or temporary, as in many grasses, which flatten out their leaf blades when the water supply improves. These adaptations protect the stomata from drying winds and reduce water loss through transpiration.

Other water-conserving adaptations of plants in these habitats include leaves with thick cuticles, often densely crowded together and thickly covered with hairs underneath. The twigs may also be hairy.

Surprisingly, many xerophytic and xeromorphic heath plants grow in peaty, waterlogged conditions where the need for water conservation is not immediately obvious. But roots cannot survive in permanently waterlogged conditions because the soil contains no oxygen. A plant with a poor root system has restricted water uptake and, therefore, needs to control water loss.

The low-growing form of plants on heaths may be a response to continual high winds that "prune" the crown. In addition, cushion plants and those that form mats on the ground, such as the wild azalea (*Loiseleuria procumbens*), can trap warm air among their leaves, which encourages growth. Their shape also reduces water loss and desiccation.

Nutritive adaptations

Heathland soils are poor in plant mineral nutrients, being characteristically "podsolized" (iron and humus in the upper layers are leached out by rain and carried down to the lower layers). It is thought that the sclerophyllous leaves (toughened by sclerenchyma tissue) of some xerophytic heath plants, particularly those in Mediterranean climates, may develop in nutrient-poor habitats as a response to low nutrient availability. They may also be evergreen, with a high ratio of cellulose to nitrogen. By being evergreen, they maximize the total amount of photosynthesis per unit of nitrogen over the whole life of the leaf.

Many of these plants depend on rain for a large part of their mineral nutrient requirements, but also have mycorrhizal fungi associated with their roots, such as ling (*Calluna vulgaris*) does. In this plant the fungus penetrates the cortical cells of the root and is known as an endotrophic mycorrhiza. Some plants, such as bog myrtle (*Myrica gale*), obtain nitrogen from symbiont bacteria with which they are associated; these bacteria (for example, *Rhizobium*) fix nitrogen from the atmosphere.

Plants such as common dodder (*Cuscuta epithymum*) and greater broomrape (*Orobanche rapum-genistae*) are parasites that obtain

Heather, or ling (*Calluna vulgaris*), frequently dominates heaths together with members of the *Erica* genus. The tough evergreen leaves of these plants have xerophytic qualities, one of which is that the margins roll down to protect the stomata on the underside. These plants have a special relationship with little insects called thrips (order Thysanoptera) that live in the flowers, where they mature. When the winged females fly out to another flower in search of a mate (the males are wingless), they carry pollen on them that is brushed off onto the second flower, and thus cause cross-pollination. In cold climates where bees are rare, these insects are invaluable as pollinators, although heather does also rely on the wind.

their nutrients directly from a host plant. They have no chlorophyll and so cannot manufacture carbohydrates. Instead they take all their requirements from their hosts. Common dodder is often found attached to the stems of heather, furze, and wild thyme (*Thymus* sp.).

Another group of heath plants, which in Europe includes eyebright *(Euphrasia officinalis)* and heath lousewort *(Pedicularis sylvatica),* are partial parasites manufacturing their own carbohydrates, but taking mineral nutrient and water from the roots of grasses.

Fire

Because of the dryness of vegetation in summer and the open nature of the environment, fire is a frequent occurrence, but the plants have adapted to withstand its effects. The species of *Erica* are particularly resilient and grow new shoots soon after fire, from the old stem bases; the seeds, produced in large quantities, germinate freely after a fire. Those plants with underground storage organs, such as ling (with rhizomes), can die back but grow again quickly. For the same reason, bracken, furze, and purple moor grass *(Molina caerulea)* are also fire-tolerant.

The common dodder *(Cuscuta epithymum)* on heaths is frequently found attached to furze *(Ulex europaeus)* from which it feeds as a parasite. Dodder has no chlorophyll—instead, root-like structures (haustoria) penetrate the stem of the host plant and extract mineral nutrients from it. Eventually the host plant dies.

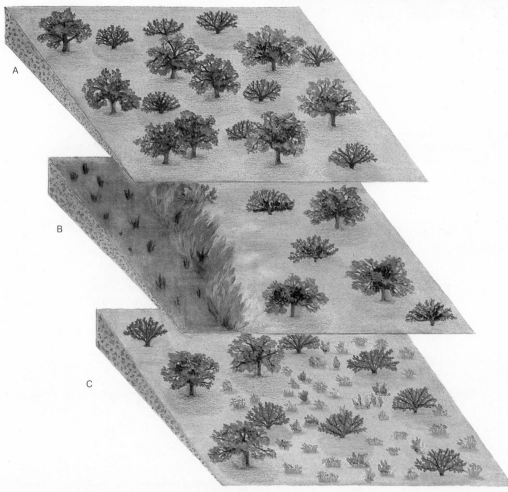

Mediterranean-type scrub, such as chaparral (A), shares with heaths a dependence on fire. Dominant plants, such as chamise *(Adenostoma fasciculatum),* outlive many of the surrounding plants, which, however, have set seeds that lie dormant. Chamise also inhibits the growth of herbaceous plants by producing phenolic toxins, which seep into the ground around it. Fires occur naturally every 15 to 20 years (B), fueled by the dead branches of the chamise and its resinous leaves. They burn off the toxins and cut back the spreading chamise, which survives as underground stems. Fire also induces germination of dormant seeds of other plants. For a few years a herbaceous layer establishes itself (C), until the sprouting chamise starts to accumulate and exude its toxins once more.

Deserts

Few deserts are so absolutely dry that they are completely devoid of plant life. The most extreme deserts occupy a band on about 20° north latitude, from North Africa across the Persian Gulf to the Gobi desert in Mongolia, and a strip about 62 miles (100 kilometer) wide along the coast of western Peru and Chile. These deserts usually receive an annual precipitation of less than 10 inches (25 centimeters), and in some areas, no rain falls for years. Most deserts, however, receive an average annual rainfall of several inches, all falling in one short season, which is sufficient to permit some specially adapted plants to live there.

Not only do these plants have to deal with severe drought conditions, but also the high temperatures that occur during the day—for example, up to 134° F. (57° C) in Death Valley, California—and often very low temperatures at night. Temperatures are also seasonal in some deserts; those that are cold in winter are called "cold" deserts, such as the Gobi, where winter temperatures frequently drop as low as −40° F. (−40° C). Most desert plants are xerophytes (they conserve water); most also share the same means of water storage and heat endurance.

Adapted photosynthesis

Most plants have C_3 photosynthesis, but this method loses a great deal of water through transpiration. Some have adopted strategies such as C_4 photosynthesis in which carbon dioxide is fixed temporarily, released, and then refixed. The second fixing takes place in specialized vascular bundle sheath cells, and the process reduces water loss during photorespiration. These plants, which are mainly grasses, are found in the lower tropical latitudes. Despite their adaptation they still need some water for photosynthesis to take place. The stomata in the leaves have to open, to allow carbon dioxide to enter the plant for use in photosynthesis, which inevitably results in some water being lost. Succulents avoid this problem by keeping their stomata closed during the day, but open at night, admitting the carbon dioxide and losing less water than if they were open during the day. The carbon dioxide is then stored until daylight, when it is metabolized in a process known as crassulacean acid metabolism (CAM).

Alternatively, some plants, such as the creosote bush *(Larrea tridentata),* do not photosynthesize during the hot, dry season, or at the hottest time of the day, but survive in a considerably desiccated state until the air is more humid.

C₄ photosynthesis involves two fixings of carbon. The first, indicated in red, occurs in the middle layers (mesophyll) of the leaf, when carbon dioxide (CO_2) enters them and combines with the 3-carbon substrate phosphoenol pyruvate to form the 4-carbon compound oxaloacetic acid. This acid is converted to 4-carbon malic acid, which is then carried to the specialized vascular bundle sheath cells where it is broken down to produce CO_2. The second fixing, marked in blue, takes place when the CO_2 combines with ribulose bisphosphate. In times of water stress the stomata, through which the CO_2 enters, close to prevent the evaporation of water during transpiration. In arid regions they close at midday when the sun's heat is at its most extreme, and photosynthesis and transpiration are slowed down. They open again when the air is cooler.

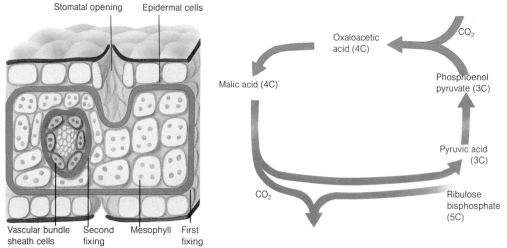

Stomatal opening   Epidermal cells

Vascular bundle sheath cells   Second fixing   Mesophyll   First fixing

Oxaloacetic acid (4C)

CO_2

Malic acid (4C)

Phosphoenol pyruvate (3C)

Pyruvic acid (3C)

CO_2

Ribulose bisphosphate (5C)

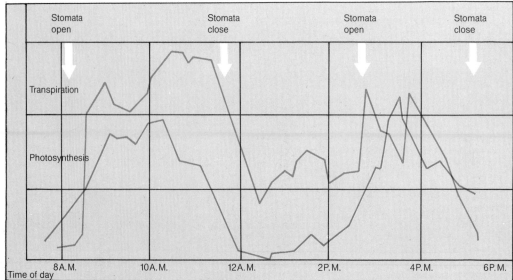

| Stomata open | Stomata close | Stomata open | Stomata close |

Transpiration

Photosynthesis

Time of day   8 A.M.   10 A.M.   12 A.M.   2 P.M.   4 P.M.   6 P.M.

Ephemerals

Desert plants are able to deal with the problems posed by intense heat and an irregular water supply in two ways—they endure them with the aid of morphological and physiological adaptations, or they avoid them, for example by remaining dormant.

The "avoiders" are known as ephemerals. They are mostly annuals, which survive drought in their seed form. Few of them have morphological adaptations to their environmental conditions, and most rely on their dormant seeds for survival. The seeds germinate quickly after rain; the seedlings grow rapidly, and flowering may begin very soon so that the plants can pass through their whole life cycle from seed to seed in a matter of weeks.

The size of some of these plants is also very adaptable—after a single shower they remain very small, but if further rain allows additional growth they may reach a much greater size and produce many more seeds.

Because desert rainfall is erratic, ephemerals would face extinction if all their seeds germinated in response to a single small shower and were then killed by a subsequent drought. The detailed seed germination behavior of only a few desert ephemerals is well known, but virtually all of these have mechanisms that allow germination only after large amounts of rain. These plants also tend to vary the time of germination within a single seed crop: a phenomenon known as seed polymorphism. For example, the dwarf composite *Asteriscus pygmaeus* retains its seeds on the parent plant even after they are ripe. When the plant receives drops of water, the bracts that hold the seeds in place open and allow some of the seeds to fall away. But only a few seeds fall at each wetting, which means that their germination can be staggered, and the chances of success are correspondingly increased. In addition to varied times of germination, the seeds contain a substance called an inhibitor that stops them from germinating. This inhibitor can be washed out by water. The seeds, therefore, need at least two phases of wetting—one to cause their release, and another to remove the inhibitor and allow germination.

The seeds of other ephemerals, such as the bitter melon *(Citrullus colocynthis),* germinate in the dark only, after a series of cycles of wetting and drying that alter the seed coat and allow free passage of oxygen to the embryo. This combination of requirements tends to cause the seeds to germinate only when buried and after several rain showers.

The strict requirements of seeds of different plants for germination cause different spe-

Desert plants bloom during the short rains that temporarily relieve the aridity of deserts. At this time dormant seeds may germinate and flourish, the young plants dispersing seeds that will lie dormant until the next season.

Some euphorbias (*Euphorbia* spp.), like many other succulents, have a leafless, water-conserving stem with longitudinal ridges. These ridges allow the plants to expand and contract with the amount of water they hold. In some succulents, the amount of water stored enables them to photosynthesize for more than a year without replenishment.

cies of ephemerals to appear in response to rains in winter and in summer. In Western Australia, for example, the species that germinate in summer are mainly grasses and sedges, whereas those that develop in response to winter rains are usually dicotyledons, such as the everlasting flower (*Helichrysum* sp.).

Ephemerals, like many other desert plants, depend mainly on insects for pollination. (Although the grasses and sedges are wind-pollinated.) The flowers are often large and showy and are attractive to insects, of which there may be few in these uncertain environments. The rains that stimulate plant growth, however, also encourage the emergence of insects from their dormant stages, so insects may be abundant when the plants are in flower.

Drought-deciduous plants

Another group of desert plants, which lies between the ephemerals and those that tolerate the desert conditions, is the drought-deciduous plants. These plants are perennials, unlike ephemerals, and are woody, but they avoid drought by shedding their small leaves as soon as the water availability is reduced; one example is the ocotillo *(Fouquieria splendens)*. They remain in a state of drought-dormancy until the rain falls again, when they quickly grow a new set of leaves.

Some grasses are also drought-deciduous, but they are not dormant because they rely on water and nutrients stored in rhizomes underground, until the water supply is improved.

Succulents

Succulents are also perennials. They are not woody but have a distinctive fleshy appearance because of their water-storing facility. Water is conserved in large, thin-walled cells (parenchymatous tissue) in the stems or in the leaves. They usually store water in their stems, because most have reduced leaves, or none at all, such as some cacti. The thick, outer cuticle of these plants reduces dehydration, but in addition, the stomata open only at night to allow carbon dioxide entry into the plant.

The most efficient form for water storage is a sphere, which has the smallest possible surface area (reducing water loss through transpiration) for a given volume (to store the maximum amount of water). A number of succulents are spherical, such as *Notocactus, Rebutia,* and some species of *Euphorbia.* The similarity in form of these plants is another example of convergent evolution—they are from completely different families and occur on different continents. The sphere is, however, a form of limited potential in a plant, and very many more desert plants have a cylindrical form, which allows taller growth, such as the Saguaro cactus *(Carnegiea gigantea),* which can reach a height of 65 feet (20 meters).

Neither spherical nor cylindrical cacti are smooth-surfaced; almost all have longitudinal ridges or a large number of conical projections on their surface. In combination with the internal, flexible network of woody strands, the ridged surface of these plants allows expansion and contraction according to the amount of water stored in them.

Moreover, succulents possess other structural features that tend to reduce water loss. Some are pale and shiny, and reflect much of the radiation that falls on them; others are covered with white hairs that perform the same function. Some members of the family Aizoaceae, such as the window leaf plant *Fenestraria,* grow partially buried in the soil or sand with only the tips of the leaves showing on the surface. The leaf tips are transparent and are lined inside with green photosynthetic cells, which are illuminated by the light entering through the "window" in the leaf.

Desert plants are particularly vulnerable to damage by herbivorous animals, because they grow very slowly and do not recover well

Stoneplants (*Lithops* spp.) are heavily camouflaged through their likeness to the surrounding pebbles. These succulents have no stems— the visible fleshy parts are the tips of leaves that are partly buried in the soil. Two leaves grow during each rainy season when a single flower appears between them. The old leaves then wither away.

The shallow root system of most succulents (A) can take up large amounts of water quickly, even during light showers. Xeromorphic shrubs (B) have deep, widely spreading roots, which can get at water over a large area. Deep-rooted plants (C) draw water from the water table far below the soil's surface.

from damage. Many of them survive, therefore, with the help of spines, such as those found on some cacti, or detachable barbs, which discourage feeding animals; others survive by being well-camouflaged, such as the stone plants (*Lithops* spp.), which strongly resemble the pebbles around them. An additional advantage for these plants is the conservation of water when they nestle among the stones.

Xeromorphs

Most xeromorphs are shrubs and trees, which tolerate drought because of the various specializations of their tough leaves. Some have small leaves (or none at all), which may be needlelike, or curled up; their small size means that less surface area is presented to the sun's heat. Some xeromorphs have the stomata on one side of the leaf only (usually the upper side), which are covered when the leaf curls up; this protection has the effect of reducing transpiration, particularly in windy conditions. Others have stomata on both sides and absorb moisture from the atmosphere through them, especially when there is dew or fog around them—an example of such "fog desert" vegetation is the welwitschia (*Welwitschia mirabilis*) which grows in the Namib desert, in southern Africa. In some plants, such as manzanita (*Arctostaphylos* sp.), the leaves are supported vertically to reduce the area exposed to the sun, and others hold their leaves parallel to the sun's rays for the same reason. Those trees that do not have leaves or which lose their leaves in the dry season, such as the paloverde (*Cercidium floridum*), photosynthesize through their stems. The tough structure of the leaves and the internal sclerenchymous tissue prevent the plants from wilting under water stress or from being damaged by strong winds.

Deserts support some trees, particularly around oases or watercourses where brief heavy floods recharge deep soil moisture reservoirs at long intervals. These trees have very deep roots, often reaching a depth of 100 feet (31 meters), that exploit the deep, moist soil layers. Known as phreatophytes, these trees include Joshua trees (*Yucca brevifolia*) and the desert cottonwood (*Populus fremontii*).

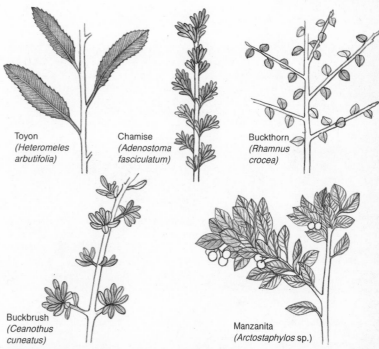

Toyon
(*Heteromeles arbutifolia*)

Chamise
(*Adenostoma fasciculatum*)

Buckthorn
(*Rhamnus crocea*)

Buckbrush
(*Ceanothus cuneatus*)

Manzanita
(*Arctostaphylos* sp.)

Xeromorphic leaves are usually thick and tough, which stops the plants from wilting when water is short, and from being damaged by strong winds. Small leaves reduce the transpirational area and, therefore, evaporation. Buckbrush has sunken stomata, which are thereby protected from desiccation, and manzanita holds its leaves vertically to reduce exposure to the sun.

The strange contorted leaves of the welwitschia (*Welwitschia mirabilis*) function as water channels for the plant. The fog in the Namib desert, where the plant grows, condenses on the leaves and trickles into the center of the plant where a pool of water collects. In addition, water runs down the leaves to their tips and soaks through the ground to the roots. From the base of the plant's partly buried cone-shaped stem, the two broad flat leaves grow to a length of about 6 feet (1.8 meters) and split into ribbons. This plant is a gymnosperm and is the only genus in the order Gnetales.

Grasslands and savanna

Natural grasslands, which occur mainly in temperate regions, and savanna (tropical grassland) represent climax vegetation. The temperate grasslands of the North American prairies, the Eurasian steppes, and the South American pampas differ from those of western Europe, which are artificial. European grasslands were created through the deliberate removal of the original climax forest vegetation. They are maintained today either as meadows, for cut hay, or as pasture, for grazing farm animals. The grasslands of eastern North America are also artificial, the primal mixed and deciduous forests having been cleared to create arable and pastoral land.

Grasslands (except in the pampas) occur naturally in areas where the annual rainfall does not exceed 30 to 40 inches (75 to 100 centimeters) and is no less than 10 inches (25 centimeters). Seasonal differences are marked in such areas. Climate is the most important factor that defines grasslands, although several other features influence the environmental conditions, such as grazing, human activity, fire, soil structure, and topography.

Grass adaptations

One of the most significant features of grasses that enables them to survive in their habitats is their method of growth. They have closely noded underground stems that continuously produce new leaves and large numbers of shoots. Growth occurs through cell division at the bases of the leaves and stems, rather than at the tips as in most other plants. The underground stems are a means of vegetative reproduction, which allows the plant to be closely cropped above ground by grazing animals, burned by fire, die down in cold weather, or lie dormant in times of drought. In addition, the fibrous root systems and rhizomes rarely grow down more than 6.5 feet (2 meters) in tall grasses, and only 2 to 39 inches (5 to 100 centimeters) for short ones, so that they can absorb moisture from the upper layers of soil. They are adapted to take in great amounts of moisture when it is available, to grow during the dry season.

Annual species of grasses overwinter or survive drought by means of seeds. The dense growth of the matted roots, which may also be runners along the surface, traps moisture. In addition the thickness of the cover makes it difficult for other plant species to establish themselves.

Grasses increase their chances of dispersal by having light seeds, which are usually carried by the wind or sometimes by animals.

European grasslands

Many artificial European grasslands have existed since late Neolithic times. They are often classified on the basis of the soil pH (the degree of acidity or alkalinity). Acid grasslands occur on sandy or peaty soils. Well-drained siliceous soils are widespread and form the basis of most rough grazing. They are often dominated by two types of grass: fescue (*Festuca* sp.) and bent (*Agrostis* sp.). Annual herbs are few in this type of grassland. On dry peaty soils, mat grass (*Nardus stricta*) develops, being replaced on wet peat by purple moor grass (*Molinia caerulea*).

Basic grasslands are found on shallow soils overlying such rocks as limestones. They are dominated by fescues, including red fescue (*F. rubra*) and sheep's fescue (*F. ovina*), the same two species found on acid soils. The neutral grasslands, whether pasture or meadow, are usually dominated by perennial rye grass (*Lolium perenne*) and clover (*Trifolium* sp.).

Europe's only natural grasslands are in the arctic-alpine mountain zones. They occur above the timber line, which is as low as 2,000 feet (610 meters) in Britain, but is higher in southern Europe. These alpine grasslands form a climatic climax. Of the numerous plant species found there, the most common grass is sheep's fescue. Other species include sedges (*Carex* spp.) and various herbaceous plants, such as saxifrages (*Saxifraga* spp.). Mountain grasslands are not, however, confined only to Europe, but occur on any moun-

Turf-forming grasses (A) have creeping underground stems (rhizomes) with shallow, matted roots. Grasses that form bunches (B) have independent root systems and generally spread by means of their seeds. Natural meadowland (C) often forms "layers," both above and below ground. Tall herbaceous plants (forbs) bear flowers above the height of the tallest grasses; shorter forbs grow at the level of the short grasses, often blooming in spring before the tall grasses grow; and at soil level mosses and lichens thrive in the leaf litter. The various roots and root systems are similarly stratified.

A

Turf-forming grass

B

Bunch-forming grass

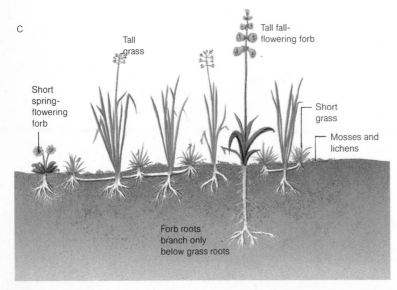

C

Tall grass

Tall fall-flowering forb

Short spring-flowering forb

Short grass

Mosses and lichens

Forb roots branch only below grass roots

Artificial temperate grassland on the fringes of the Black Forest includes pasture set aside for grazing animals, and meadow (foreground). Meadow grass is cut and dried to make hay, for feeding to animals in winter.

tain high enough to extend above the timber line.

Temperate grasslands

The great natural lowland areas of treeless grassland are the prairies, steppes, and pampas (mainly in Argentina). Smaller areas of temperate grassland include the parklands of southern Australia and the downlands of South Island, New Zealand. Large parts of temperate grasslands have been converted into arable land for cereal production of grazing land. For example, the area of natural grassland in North America was halved between 1850 and 1950.

Most temperate grasslands receive an annual rainfall of between 20 and 35 inches (51 and 89 centimeters). Rainfall is a major factor in the occurrence of grasslands, together with extreme temperatures—frozen winters and hot summers—evaporation rates, and local winds. Also important is the fact that grassland regions experience marked seasonal variations characteristic of continental interiors. Rain

often falls in spring or early summer, with droughts in the late summer and autumn.

Drought is a major factor in determining the vegetation of temperate grasslands, because grasses with their small, narrow leaves and extensive, fibrous roots are better adapted to survive droughts than are larger broadleaved plants. Similarly, grasses are better equipped to survive damage by grazing animals and fires that occur at the time of drought. First, the growing points of grasses are near the ground, where they are often protected by debris. Second, the roots of grasses survive even when the leaves are burned, whereas shrubs and trees have much greater difficulty in reestablishing themselves. Grasses also often grow in tussocks. Burning damages the extremities of the tussocks, leaving the moist growing centers unharmed.

Many grasses and legumes, together with hundreds of other species, occur in the temperate grasslands. The prairies of North America are perhaps the most complex botanically. The only trees grow near rivers or on the east-

The wintry steppes of Mongolia *(below left)* are natural grasslands, which support small herds of grazing ponies. Tussock grasses—the example below is tussock sedge *(Carex paniculata)*—often grow in damp ground, as witnessed by the yellow marsh marigolds flowering alongside. If the ground becomes flooded, the tussock humps stick out above the surface of the water.

Resembling a squadron of tanks, combine harvesters cut grain on the vast wheat fields, which have replaced the natural vegetation in the Kazakh region of the Soviet Union.

ern margins where, because of the higher rainfall—about 35 inches (90 centimeters) a year—the grasses reach 4 to 6.5 feet (1.2 to 2 meters) in height. They include such species as bluestems (*Andropogon* spp.), switchgrass (*Panicum virgatum*), and, in wetter areas, sloughgrass (*Spartina* sp.).

The short-grass prairies or steppes are in the west of the continent, where the annual rainfall drops to about 10 inches (25 centimeters) and the prairie grades into desert. The grasses here are 6 to 20 inches (15 to 50 centimeters) tall. They include buffalo grass (*Buchloë dactyloides*) and grama grass (*Bouteloua* spp.).

The mid- or mixed-grass prairies contain grasses between 24 and 47 inches (60 and 120 centimeters) in height. Species include the little bluestem (*A. scoparius*); needlegrass (*Stipa* sp.), a common genus on the steppes; dropseed (*Sporobolus* sp.); wheatgrass (*Agropyron* sp.), another steppe genus; June grass (*Koeleria cristata*); and rice grass (*Oryzopus* sp.). There are also many nongrasslike herbaceous plants, called "forbs," many of which have representatives in the other temperate grasslands of the world.

The Eurasian steppes form a belt from Hungary to China and are, therefore, more fragmented than the prairies. The dominant grasses are spear and feather grasses (*Stipa* spp.) and fescue.

Pampas regions have a higher average annual rainfall than other temperate grasslands, with around 40 to 50 inches (102 to 127 centimeters). Droughts are less common (except on the margins), and the pampas are warmer, with most having frost-free winters.

Plant adaptations in savannas

Drought and fire, caused naturally or by farmers, have reduced the number of plant species in the savannas. The species that do occur show many adaptations to fire, and it is fire

rather than climate or grazing animals that determines the stability of the vegetation.

Many trees have thick, corky, fire-resistant barks that are spongy and saturated with water, as in the baobab (*Adansonia digitata*) and the bottle tree (*Cavanillesia* sp.), an adaptation which is also suited to survival during drought. Trees and shrubs also produce vast numbers of seeds, and many of the herbs have underground food storage organs.

The adaptations of grasses in temperate regions all apply equally to savanna species. One example is pampas grass (*Cortaderia* sp.) of South America, which is grown as a garden plant. In fact, gardeners are advised to burn off old leaves in spring in order to prevent the new shoots from being choked and to provide some fertilizer for the plant. Providing that the burning is rapid, the plant comes to no harm.

The soils of the tropical savanna are generally brown or black and more basic than those of the tropical forest. The dense roots of tussock-forming grasses can, therefore, obtain a firm anchorage and get all the moisture they require.

Types of savanna

Many savannas occupy regions between the equatorial rain forests and the hot deserts. Because of differences in rainfall, there are three main types of savanna. The moist savanna belt that borders the equatorial forests has 42 inches (107 centimeters) or more of rain each year with a dry season lasting 5 or 6 months. Here the grasses may reach 10 feet (3 meters) in height; species of *Hyparrhenia* are typical. In the dry, savanna belt, with 24 to 42 inches (60 to 107 centimeters) of rain a year and a 7- to 8-month dry season, the grasses reach 5 feet (1.5 meters). The thorn savanna belt, with an annual rainfall of less than 24 inches (60 centimeters) and a dry season of more than 8 months, is the driest type. It contains mainly annual grasses with some trees. The ground vegetation grows

In Australia *(left),* the open temperate grasslands also support scattered shrubs and trees—mostly various species of *Eucalyptus.* Sheep crop the grass among the trees.

In South American grasslands, the dominant species is often pampas grass, which produces its characteristic feathery plumes when it blooms *(above).* It is also grown as an ornamental plant.

only to about 20 inches (50 centimeters) or so.

Africa contains the largest single savanna region. It extends across West Africa, between the rain forests and the Sahara Desert, and sweeps through east central Africa, merging in the south into the Namib and Kalahari deserts. The African savanna includes vast tracts of each of the main savanna types.

In South America, the savanna include the llanos of Venezuela, along the Orinoco River, and the campos of Brazil, south of the Amazonian rain forest, two examples of moist savanna. Northeastern Brazil has a very dry thorn savanna with little grass, which is known locally as caatinga.

The Australian savanna stretches across the northern part of the country. It is mostly dry savanna, some of which is difficult to differentiate from desert scrub.

Savanna plants

The Australian wooded savanna is dominated by gum trees—various species of *Eucalyptus.* Like other savanna trees, they are fire-resistant. Even when the crown is severely damaged, shoots and suckers from the base and roots may ensure the tree's survival. One species of *Eucalyptus* even requires fire to allow its seeds to germinate. Fire also ensures that seedlings have a fairly free area in which to grow with a minimum of competition.

Acacias grow in both the Australian and African savannas, although they are of different species. Together with acacias in Africa are the grotesque baobabs. Elsewhere in the African savanna, from Senegal to Uganda, are such fire-resistant genera as *Terminalia* and *Isoberlinia. Commiphora* sp. is found with acacias in the densest savanna types, and the leguminous *Colophospermum mepane* is found in the Zambezi region in the south.

Many grasses found in the savannas are widespread species. Kangaroo grass *(Themeda trianda)* from Australia is known as

red oat grass in Africa. Some tussock grasses *(Poa* spp.) occur in Australia and South America. In these areas, other typical tussock-forming savanna grasses include species of *Sporobolus, Digitaria, Panicum, Setaria, Pennisetum,* and *Sorghum* although they tend to form loose clumps rather than dense raised tussocks. Species of the genus *Hyparrhenia* (and others) have seeds that, when detached from the plant, respond to changes in humidity. Depending on whether it is wet or dry, a bristle (the awn) on the seed twists and untwists. This motion is sufficient to cause it to bury itself in the soil, where it can germinate with the next rains.

The African savanna *(below)* is the home of vast herds of wildebeest, which migrate hundreds of miles in phase with the seasonal growth of the grass. The herds are, in their turn, a source of food for predatory animals and carrion-eaters.

Aquatics

Aquatic plants (hydrophytes) survive in two main habitats—saline and freshwater. Saltwater areas include the shoreline and salt marshes; freshwater plants survive in rivers and streams, and on their banks, in lakes and in ponds. Both types are subjected to permanent immersion or frequent flooding, strong winds and water movement, and unstable soil conditions, which few other plants can tolerate. The major difference between the two kinds is that saltwater plants (halophytes) have to endure high concentrations of salt, whereas freshwater plants do not.

General adaptations

The fact that the density of completely immersed aquatic plants is similar to that of the water around them means that they have little need of support; submerged leaves and stems therefore contain little strengthening tissue.

Leaves and stems underwater also have no cuticle, so that they readily absorb dissolved carbon dioxide, oxygen, and mineral salts from the water.

Freshwater plants have a vascular system but with few woody lignified vessels in the xylem. In these plants the whole vascular system, particularly the xylem, is simplified and in some species is replaced by a cavity, or lacuna. Several aquatic species have many lacunae within their tissues. In floating leaves they are gas-filled and maintain buoyancy, raising the plant to the light so that it may photosynthesize—chloroplasts occur in the epidermal cells of the upper surface, unlike those of land plants. The lacunae also allow oxygen to diffuse rapidly from the surface to the submerged parts.

Marine habitats

Most plants that grow in the deeper areas of the shore are seaweeds. Those that are not tend to live in estuaries or in rock pools.

All seaweeds require light for photosynthesis and cannot grow in water where sunlight does not penetrate. Most species have gas-filled bladders that keep them buoyant when the tide is high so that they remain near the light. All species contain chlorophyll, although red and brown seaweeds also contain other pigments (fucoxanthin and phycoerythrin respectively). Chlorophyll is not particularly efficient in trapping the bluish light that reaches deeper water, whereas the red-brown pigments (which absorb blue) gain additional energy when the plants are submerged. Brown and red seaweeds, therefore, have an advantage over green species and, in fact, only red seaweeds are found in deep water.

Apart from seaweeds, there are a few more advanced plants near the low-water mark, such as eelgrass (*Zostera* sp.) and cord grass (*Spartina* sp.), whose roots may be submerged at high tide. It has vertical roots for anchorage, horizontal roots for obtaining nutrients, and stolons by which it spreads rapidly.

Most seaweeds (apart from the giant kelps) have no vascular system because they need no strengthening tissue, being supported by the water around them. Seaweeds have a thick cuticle that covers a thin photosynthetic layer. The inner layers are formed from densely packed, thick-walled filaments, with a few thin-walled medullary cells between them. These cells may serve to transport water through the plant.

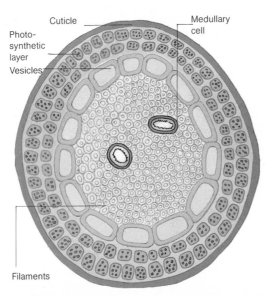

Cuticle
Photosynthetic layer
Vesicles
Medullary cell
Filaments

The elongated ribbonlike leaves of aquatic plants, such as eelgrass (*Zostera* sp.), offer little resistance to moving water and are, therefore, an ideal shape in their periodically turbulent environments. This plant has submerged flowers, which are pollinated under water (one of the few flowering plants in which this occurs).

Shore zonation

Between the high- and low-tide marks on the coast is the intertidal zone. Few plants grow on shifting, sandy intertidal zones, but sea-weeds are often abundant on rocky shores where a clear zonation, or ecological gradient, can be seen. From the low-tide level upwards, the plants increasingly experience desiccation (drying out), high temperatures, and periodic frosts. Many of them have developed rubbery cell walls and produce a coating of mucilage to meet these environmental stresses. The cell walls can contract and expand without damage according to the water content of the plant, and the mucilage reduces desiccation when these plants are exposed to the air.

At the lowest levels are the brown kelps (*Laminaria* spp.), whose long, pliable stipes (stems) make them resilient to violent wave action. Wracks dominate the middle and upper levels of the intertidal zone.

The algae that are characteristic of the lower shore often grow in rock pools at higher elevations, where they remain submerged even at low tide. These pools suffer extreme variations in temperature and salinity. Some red seaweeds, such as the thin-fronded, delicate laver bread (*Porphyra* sp.) that grows high on the shore, survive desiccation and recover when the tide returns.

Salt-marsh, dune, and shingle plants

Salt-marsh plants are subjected particularly to changing salinity levels because the salt content of the soil is increased by incoming tides and by evaporation, and then reduced by rain and dew. Halophytes, such as glasswort (*Salicornia fruticosa*), have a high osmotic pressure maintained by a high cellular concentration of amino acids (proline, for instance), which enables them to absorb water directly from the sea. Some species, such as sea lavender (*Limonium* sp.), have special salt glands to pump out excess salt onto their leaf surfaces.

Plants that grow on sand dunes and shingle are not true aquatics, although they may sometimes be inundated by the sea. They often have a need to conserve water, because the loose soil particles hold little water, and they are frequently buffeted by strong winds. Some have xeromorphic adaptations to reduce their transpiration rate: the prickly saltwort (*Salsola kali*) has tiny leaves reduced to spines; in some species the leaves roll up in unfavorable conditions, as in marram grass (*Ammophila arenaria*); other plants have a thick cuticle, often with a waxy coating or a thick covering of hairs. Low growth, frequently in the form of rosettes or cushions, also avoids the harmful effects of wind and evaporation. Another feature is succulence, in which leaves or stems swell when water is stored in the tissues, as in the leaves of the shrubby seablite (*Suaeda fruticosa*).

Succulence is also seen in the mangrove trees—so typical of the coastal swamps of tropical areas. The succulent leaves retain the water that the plant has absorbed and excrete the salt. The salt is then washed away in the frequent rains. Most mangroves have stilt roots, anchoring the plant in the mud and preventing the waves and tides from moving it.

The lack of oxygen in the mud is overcome by the presence of protruding roots, or pneumatophores, which absorb oxygen from the air and take it down to the roots embedded in the mud. The zones of different mangrove species trap mud and silt, extending the land seaward. Inland from them lies a region of brackish swamps, flooded by the sea only at times of very high tide—a habitat for many tropical aquatic plants.

Freshwater habitats

Freshwater plants have to cope with bodies of water that change rapidly in their chemistry and rate of flow. The chemical composition of the water depends on the rocks over which the water has passed, the water collected from several individual springs, shallow seepage,

Shingle and dunes are extremely unstable habitats, where plants may be buried under sand and stones. Many plants, therefore, have extensive root systems, such as the yellow horned poppy *(Glaucium flayum),* so that they can make new growth despite being deeply covered.

The intertidal zone of coastlines is most frequently inhabited by seaweeds, such as oarweed *(Laminaria digitata)* and thongweed *(Himanthali elongata).* The long, flexible, but resilient, stems of these plants allow them to survive the pounding of the waves.

Freshwater plants in fast-moving river water are usually rooted to the stones at the bottom of the riverbed. Water buttercup *(Ranunculus aquatilis)* is one of the few plants that survives this turbulence and has submerged leaves that are long and narrow and flow with the current without damage.

and surface runoff. In arid regions particularly, there is a great annual fluctuation in the size and chemical properties of river water.

The variation in volume and speed of flow of river and stream water, and strong currents, can damage and uproot plants. Mountain streams are fast-flowing and, therefore, usually contain few plants; those that do survive these conditions include willow moss *(Fontinalis squamosa)*, which is anchored to stones. Sluggish rivers, however, permit plant growth in their shallows and along their margins. Still or slow-moving water in ditches, ponds, and lakes also support far more species.

Freshwater adaptations

As in deep saltwater, light does not reach the

Common duckweed *(Lemna minor)* is a well-adapted, free-floating freshwater plant. Each plant consists of a small green thallus 3-4 millimeters across, which is kept buoyant by air-filled lacunae. It is not differentiated into stems and leaves.

bottom of deep freshwater, and rooted plants cannot grow there. In addition, little light penetrates water that is stained with peat, mud, silt, or microorganisms. The only plants in such habitats, therefore, are free-floating species, notably algae.

Where light does reach the bottom, aquatic plants root in the mud. Some, such as stoneworts *(Chara* spp.) and Canadian pondweed *(Elodea canadensis)*, grow completely submerged. Others, such as waterlilies (Nymphaeaceae) are rooted in the bottom, but their leaves, which are attached to stalks up to 10 feet (3 meters) long, float on the surface.

Emergent aquatics grow on pond and lake edges in water less than 6 feet (1.8 meters) deep. They include reeds *(Phragmites* spp.) and bulrushes *(Scirpus* spp.), which send stems and leaves above the water surface. When these plants are the dominant species, the habitat becomes a swamp.

Freshwater hydrophytes show various adaptations to avoid damage by swamping. Many have a water-repellent cuticle on the upper surface of their floating leaves. (This also reduces water loss by evaporation.) In some species of waterlilies, the leaf margins grow vertically upward to reduce the chance of flooding. The petioles are long and, in some species, are corkscrewlike, which allows the leaves to stretch and contract to accommodate changing water levels. Diaphragms at the internodes of submerged stems prevent internal flooding if the plant is damaged.

Many aquatics have several types of leaves to cope with their watery conditions. Water buttercup *(Ranunculus aquatilis)*, for example, has divided submerged leaves and lobed floating leaves, whereas arrowheads *(Sagittaria sagittifolia)* also have aerial leaves. The floating leaves of aquatics have stomata on the upper surface, whereas the submerged leaves are usually long and narrow, offering minimum resistance to currents. They are often finely divided to provide a large surface for absorption. The aerial leaves are usually like those of terrestrial plants.

During the day, when freshwater hydrophytes photosynthesize, they use up the dissolved carbon dioxide, which may become scarce. Some plants, therefore, such as the quillworts (*Isoetes* spp.), have a special mechanism for absorbing carbon dioxide at night, when the respiration of aquatic animals and plants causes a carbon dioxide build-up.

The roots of freshwater plants do not take in water, but function mainly in extra nutrient absorption. They also serve as means of anchorage in bottom-rooting species and balance in free-floating species.

Most hydrophytes have flowering stems that project above the surface. The stems are usually supported by floating leaves, but such plants as waterlilies have floating flowers. Aerial flowers are pollinated by the wind or insects. A few species, however, have flowers that are adapted for pollination by water. The free-floating hornworts (*Ceratophyllum demersum*), for example, bear tiny flowers, which open underwater. Their stamens become detached, float, and burst, releasing pollen grains that sink slowly, reaching the submerged stigmas. During floods, when aquatic plants cannot easily produce aerial flowers, submerged, cleistogamous (non-opening) and self-pollinating flowers may be produced. The seeds of hydrophytes are usually dispersed by water. Some emergent aquatics, such as the bur reed (*Sparganium* sp.), often have inflated seeds that float to the edges of lakes where they germinate.

Vegetative reproduction is also common. New fronds bud from the side of duckweed (*Lemna* sp.) and break off to form separate plants, and detached pieces of Canadian pondweed will root and grow independently. The aquatic fern, *Salvinia*, reproduces by the breaking up of old stems.

The carnivorous bladderwort (*Utricularia* sp.) augments its nutrient supply by sucking insects into bladderlike traps in its submerged leaves and absorbing nitrogen from their bodies. This underwater plant sends up shoots above the surface when it blooms, so that the flowers can be pollinated by insects or the wind.

Frost damage is a winter hazard to freshwater plants. Water starworts (*Callitriche* spp.) and water soldiers (*Stratiotes aloides*) avoid it by sinking to the bottom in winter and rising again in spring. Waterlilies survive by deciduousness and by storing food in their stout rhizomes, buried in the mud. In the spring new leaves grow, and food is manufactured once more. Frogbit (*Hydrocharis morsus-ranae*) produces special winter buds (turions) on stolons that sink to the bottom when the plant dies in autumn. After remaining dormant in winter, they rise to the surface and form new plants.

In the freshwater tape grass (*Vallisneria spiralis*), the male plants flower underwater; the buds float up to the surface where they open. The flowers on the female plants rise above the water where they are pollinated by the floating male flowers. Once fertilized, the female flower is drawn underwater where the ovule develops. The mother plant dies away and the new seed develops into a new plant.

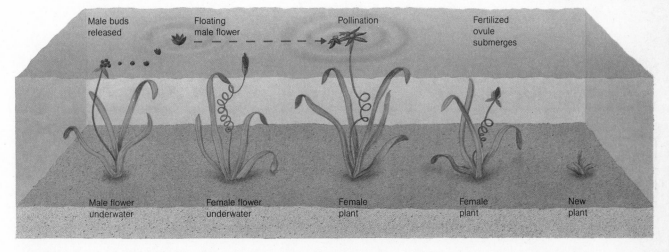

Male buds released   Floating male flower   Pollination   Fertilized ovule submerges

Male flower underwater   Female flower underwater   Female plant   Female plant   New plant

---

Fact entries

The high specific heat of water (4.179 joules per gram) means that it can lose or gain a great amount of heat before its temperature changes. The microclimatic variability of aquatic environments is thus less extreme than terrestrial ones.

The chemical composition of freshwater varies daily or within the space of a few months and depends on several environmental factors, including fertilizers and pollutants. But the composition most often encountered in parts per million is: bicarbonate 58.4, calcium 15.0, silicon dioxide 13.1, sulfate 11.2, chloride 7.8, sodium 6.3, magnesium 4.1, potassium 2.3, and iron 0.67.

The chemical composition of seawater is largely a mixture of chloride (19,000 parts per million) and sodium (10,550). The other elements and compounds include sulfate (2,460), magnesium (1,290), calcium (400), potassium (380), bicarbonate (140), bromide (65), and boric acid (25).

Saprophytes and symbionts

One of the most remarkable adaptations of plants to their environment is their method of obtaining food. Apart from the many autotrophic plants that manufacture food by photosynthesis there are some heterotrophic organisms that live off other organisms (as parasites), or off their decaying matter (as saprophytes) or in a mutually beneficial relationship (as symbionts). They are frequently found in inhospitable environments such as dark, dense forests, glacial polar and tundra regions, and even underground, but they also occur in our everyday environments.

Saprophytes are organisms that secure their food directly from the dead and decaying tissues of other organisms. They do so because they lack chlorophyll and cannot photosynthesize or because they contain few green parts, which allow the manufacture of only a small amount of the nutrients that they need. They include bacteria, some algae, fungi, and some flowering plants.

Symbiosis means, literally, living together. Some biological definitions restrict the meaning to a permanent association of two different organisms with a movement of metabolites between the two in which each derives an advantage from the other. Many symbioses involve an alternation between parasitism and symbiosis. Symbioses may involve an association between plants and animals, such as the algal cells in the coelenterate *Hydra,* in sea squirts and mollusks, or between different plant types, to form lichens, root-nodules, and mycorrhizas.

Saprophytes

True saprophytes secrete enzymes to break down the complex carbohydrates and proteins of food sources and then absorb the soluble foodstuffs into their cells. The most familiar saprophytes are fungi, particularly the basidiomycete mushrooms, and slime molds. Their hyphae form a meshed network called a mycelium, which spreads over the substrate and penetrates it. The hyphae secrete digestive enzymes that dissolve the solid components of the surrounding material; the solution is then absorbed through the membranes of the fungal body.

Most flowering saprophytes are orchids and are found in tropical Asia and Australia. They start their life as achlorophyllous, saprophytic tissue underground, nourished also by mycorrhiza; they later develop green stems and leaves. In some orchids, however, these parts may take several years to appear, and other species remain completely saprophytic throughout their life. In most of these orchids the plant lies underground except when flowering, for example Indian pipe *(Monotropa uniflora)*, but several species even flower underground, like the Australian orchids *Cryptanthemis slateri* and *Rhizanthella gardneri.*

Lichens

A lichen is a permanent association between a fungus and an alga in which the two symbionts form a single thallus. The fungus parasitizes the algal cells, extracting the carbohydrates that are formed by algal photosynthesis. It also lives saprophytically on algal cells that die. In turn, the fungus protects the alga from high light intensity and provides it with a structure that is more resistant to desiccation than the algal cell walls are.

The algal symbiont is usually a blue-green or green alga; the fungal symbiont is in most cases an ascomycete, although a few lichenized basidiomycetes are known. Each species of lichen is an association of a particular algal and fungal species. Most display one of three morphologies: leafy (foliose), encrusting (crustose), and erect and tufted (fruticose).

Lichens occur worldwide and can tolerate nutrient-poor, hostile environments. They grow on exposed rock in deserts and polar regions, on solidified lava, on the bark of trees

The saprophytic orchid
Indian pipe *(Monotropa uniflora)* has no chlorophyll and lives underground. It sends up shoots above ground only when it is about to flower, each shoot bearing a single bloom. The plant lives off the decaying leaf litter on the forest floor.

and on leaf surfaces (especially in tropical rain forests), on gravestones, and on the asbestos roofs of buildings. The main deterrent to lichen growth is atmospheric pollution—many species are sensitive to such pollutants as sulfur dioxide.

Root-nodules

The symbiosis between certain soil bacteria and leguminous plants to form nitrogen-fixing root-nodules is of vital importance to modern agriculture. The root hairs of legumes are invaded by the aerobic bacterium *Rhizobium,* which penetrates the cortical tissue and multiplies there at the expense of the host cell nutrients and enzymes. The host cells divide and enlarge to form a nodule, the cells of which become densely filled with millions of bacteria. The bacteria cells fix atmospheric nitrogen and the legume digests the bacteria, thus obtaining the nitrogen compounds for food. The nodule finally dies, and large populations of undigested bacteria return to the soil. The root-nodules of alder (*Alnus* sp.) and other trees contain symbiotic actinomycetes, which are also capable of fixing nitrogen.

Mycorrhiza

A mycorrhiza is a symbiotic association between the hyphae of certain fungi and the roots of higher plants. The mycorrhizal fungus increases the solubility of soil minerals and improves the uptake of nitrogen, potassium, and phosphorus by the host plant, protects the host roots against pathogens, and produces plant growth hormones. In return, the fungus receives a carbohydrate food supply from the photosynthetic activity of the host.

Two main types of mycorrhiza occur. In endomycorrhiza the fungal hyphae live inside the host root between and inside the cells; the fungi are usually zygomycetes, although those found in the aerial roots of tropical orchids are basidiomycetes. In ectomycorrhizas a mantle of fungal hyphae covers the root externally with some hyphae growing among the cells of the cortex; these fungi are mainly gilled or pore basidiomycetes and include *Boletus* and some puffballs, although some are ascomycetes, such as truffles (Tuberales).

Fungal sheath

Fungal hyphae

Epidermis

Endodermis

Xylem cells

A   B

The roots of a plant without fungi (A) absorb water and what mineral nutrients they can from the surrounding soil. Many plants, however, have mycorrhizal fungi surrounding their roots (B). These fungi extract minerals more easily from the soil, which they pass to the roots through their hyphae that penetrate the root epidermis. In turn, they absorb some of the carbon compounds manufactured by the plant through photosynthesis.

The encrusting lichen *Xanthoria palietina* is a common feature on gravestones.

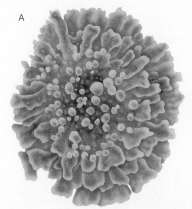

A

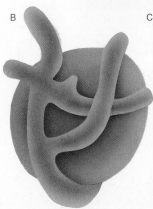

B

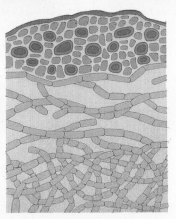

C

A lichen (A) forms when fungal hyphae surround an algal cell (B). Gradually the hyphae and algal cells multiply. The photosynthetic algal cells become trapped in the upper layers of the thickly intermeshed hyphae. Loosely interwoven hyphae form the middle layer of a mature lichen (C).

Plant products

Civilization makes extensive use of raw materials and chemicals derived from plants. Products such as rubber, oils, textile fibers, dyes, and pigments are present in many aspects of our daily lives. Apart from food crops, by far the most important plant resource we use is wood. It provides us with lumber and is manufactured into other products, the most significant of which is paper.

Of the 10 billion acres of land covered by forest, only about 40 per cent is exploited. Central Africa, southeastern Asia, the Soviet Union, and the Amazon region are among the most heavily forested areas in the world. However, Finland, Sweden, Norway, and Canada collectively produce two-thirds of the world's wood-based products. They are highly industrialized countries with the capacity to process lumber into boards, panels, or pulp. The timber industry of these countries is based on their extensive conifer forests. Conifers are softwood and make the best pulp for paper because of the long fibers of the wood. Nearly all the trees in the forest can be utilized, and conifer forests are, thus, extremely valuable, producing more timber per acre than any other kind including tropical forests.

Lumber

Despite the increasing use made of steel and concrete, lumber is still often employed for heavy constructions, such as bridges, harbors, and mine shafts. Some treated softwoods and some temperate and tropical hardwoods have the necessary strength, durability, and rot resistance for such building work, for example greenheart *(Nectandra rodiei)* and some members of the genus *Shorea.* Plywood, which is manufactured mainly from softwood pines, is used extensively in the housing industry, which accounts for more than half the world's consumption of this material.

The combined physical properties of solid wood often give it an advantage over other materials. It is, for example, an excellent heat insulator. The specific heat capacity of wood is similar to metals but it is a poorer conductor of heat because it contains air in its cells. For this reason, wood is, for example, used for saucepan handles. The lightest woods, such as balsa *(Ochroma lagopus),* are good insulators because of their large, air-filled cells and are used for containers for chemicals and liquefied gases because they keep them cool and stable.

Different types of timber may have specific qualities that can be used. One variety of willow, *Salix alba,* for example, is the only lightweight wood with the right degree of resilience to be suitable for cricket bats. Mallets and the sheaves and blocks of pulleys are made from Lignum Vitae *(Guaiacum officinale),* a wood so dense that it sinks in water. Many musical instruments are also made from wood, but only a few high-density timbers are suitable for xylophones. Rosewood *(Dalbergia* sp.), for example, is one of the few woods to produce a musical note when struck, the length and thickness of each strip determining its pitch. Conversely, low-density materials, such as cork bark, absorb sound and are used in concert halls to reduce echoes.

Worldwide demand for pulpwood-based products, such as chipboard, fiberboard, and paper, is growing faster than the market for

Wood is one of the oldest building materials and is still used extensively today. In this concert hall, the wooden paneling has two functions: it looks attractive and also reduces echoes. Many musical instruments are made of wood. For example, spruce (*Picea* sp.) is often used for the front of violins, and bows are usually made from Brazilwood (*Caesalpinia* sp.).

solid wood products. For example, in the early 1980's the demand for paper increased by 4 per cent. About 88 million tons of pulp are produced annually, of which more than 50 per cent is used for paper.

Recent developments have created a process whereby the advantages of wood can be combined with plastic. Low-quality wood is impregnated with such chemicals as vinyl acetate and exposed to gamma rays. The radiation polymerizes the vinyl compound to a hard plastic, producing a rock-hard material known as Novawood. Wood alone lacks such strength because, although the tensile strength of each cellulose fiber is stronger than steel, there are no linkages between them. It is for this reason that natural vegetable fibers, such as cotton, need to be spun and woven in order to make strong textiles.

Other plant products

The wide use of wood and other vegetable materials is dependent as much on their chemical composition as on their physical properties. Cellulose is the world's most abundant natural organic compound; it constitutes 42 per cent of wood and 95 per cent of cotton. It is a complex carbohydrate made up of about 3,000 glucose units. When chemically processed, it can be manufactured into materials, such as cellulose acetate, triacetate, and nitrate, that have a wide range of applications from plastic films to propellant explosives. Cellulose is also a beginning ingredient for making methanol and other alcohols in the chemical industry, some used as fuels.

The textile industry makes use of both raw materials and chemicals derived from plants. For example, cotton is woven in a relatively unaltered state and is used extensively for clothing and furnishing fabrics, whereas synthetic textiles, such as viscose, are chemically derived from cellulose.

The pharmaceutical industry also draws on the natural chemicals found in many plants.

Aspirin was originally made from chemicals extracted from the bark of several kinds of willow (*Salix* spp.) although now the drug is artificially made.

Other plant extracts, such as oils, dyes, resins, and gums are valuable raw materials for the cosmetic, food, and printing industries. Yet another important plant extract is rubber, which is obtained by tapping the latex produced by some species of tropical and subtropical plants. More than 85 per cent of the world's natural rubber is grown in Malaysia and the Far East, the greater part of it destined for the production of tires for motor vehicles. Other uses for natural rubber are footwear, carpet backing, and conveyor belts.

In Morocco, outdoor vats are used for dying leather. Natural dyes that are extracted from plants include red from the madder plant *(Rubia tinctorum),* saffron from the yellow stigmas of the crocus *(Crocus sativus),* and blue from the indigo plant *(Indigofera tinctoria).* Tannin is used in the processing of hides and is found in most plant tissue but is commonly extracted from tree bark.

Rape *(Brassica napus)* is an important oil-producing plant. It is increasingly cultivated in northern Europe, the Soviet Union, and Canada because it is a rapid grower and is resistant to cold climates. The oil is used in the preparation of margarine and in certain industrial processes.

Wood

Wood is the hard substance of trees and shrubs that makes up the trunk and the branches. It is one of the most important plant products that is used both in its natural state and in a variety of processed forms.

Two-thirds of the world's wood requirements are supplied from the boreal conifer forests, which form a zone at high northern latitudes spanning the Soviet Union, Canada, and Scandinavia. Softwoods, such as fir (*Abies* sp.), pine (*Pinus* sp.), and spruce (*Picea* sp.), grow mainly in this region whereas hardwoods come from many parts of the world. Teak *(Tectona grandis)* and mahogany *(Swietenia mahagoni),* for example, grow in the tropical rain forests while the temperate forests are populated with oak (*Quercus* sp.) and beech (*Fagus* sp.).

Wood preparation

Before wood can be used industrially it must go through a number of processes. Felled trees have their branches removed and enter the sawmill as "green" round logs. After they have had their bark removed the logs are sawn into planks, sorted, and trimmed. The lumber must then be seasoned to match the moisture levels of its destined environment.

Wood acts like a sponge; it absorbs moisture and swells in damp air, but shrinks in dry atmospheres when the water evaporates. The wood of the balsa tree *(Ochroma lagopus),* for example, contains enough air space in its cells to absorb hundreds of times its weight in water. Seasoning not only minimizes shrinkage, but also increases resistance to fungal decay, insect attacks, and metal corrosion. In addition, seasoning makes the wood more receptive to paints, varnishes, and preservatives.

The traditional method of treating wood is air seasoning. Lumber is stacked outside under cover, each length separated by "stickers" that allow the free flow of air. The moisture must, however, evaporate from the surface of the wood at about the same speed as it moves out from the center, or the drier surface will split and shrink. Metal cleats may be driven into dense hardwoods to prevent splitting, and sheets may be draped over very green lumber to slow surface evaporation.

Today, the faster kiln drying method of seasoning is more popular. The lumber is fed into a chamber where the temperature and humidity levels are initially low. As the moisture content of the wood falls, the humidity is reduced further, and the temperature increased until the wood reaches the desired moisture level. A fan circulates the air and dehumidifiers remove the moisture.

Fully automated kilns are costly because each type of lumber requires different treatment. Kiln drying allows for faster turnover of stock, although large planks of wood, such as oak, may still take several weeks to dry. This method of seasoning also achieves the lower moisture levels in woods that are required for precision work such as high-class joinery and flooring in modern centrally-heated houses and offices where the humidity is low.

Logs are transported by water in countries with good river systems. During the cold months of the year, the logs are piled onto the frozen rivers. When the ice melts they are floated downstream, often held together to form large rafts that are pulled to the sawmills by powerful tugboats. This is the most economical means of transportation, although large quantities of logs are also moved by rail and road.

Logs can be cut in several ways. Method A produces wide planks but these tend to warp. Methods B and C produce planks that are more stable but less economical. Waste wood can be burned to power the sawmill or processed into pulp.

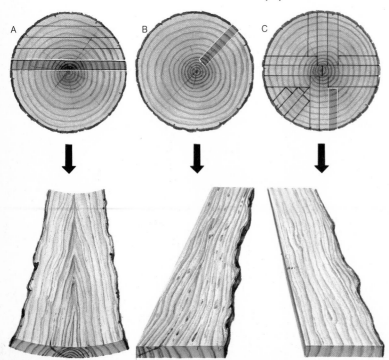

Veneer and composite woods

Many good-quality logs are sliced or peeled into thin sheets known as veneers. The logs are usually softened first to reduce the risk of splitting, and then cut to the requisite length and clamped into a lathe which turns the log against a peeling knife. The sheets are dried to a moisture content of 6 to 8 per cent and graded as face, back, or core, depending on the quality. Highly patterned veneers such as walnut (*Juglans* sp.) are used for decorative furniture. Woods that are too valuable to use in a solid form—for example, teak—are also used as veneers over a cheaper core material, such as blockboard.

Plywood was the first composite wood material to be manufactured on a large scale. It is still the most widely used today. Traditional plywood timbers include birch (*Betula* sp.) in Europe, Douglas fir (*Pseudotsuga menziesii)* in North America, and spruce in Scandinavia. Plywood is made by gluing several sheets of veneer together. The quality of each sheet in the plywood "sandwich" usually varies and the back and inner plies are generally of poorer-quality grades.

In the plywood sandwich, the grain of each veneer lies at right angles to the grain of the neighboring layer. The number of layers is usually odd, so that the grain on the two outer layers runs in the same direction. This grain-crossing structure gives the wood greater tensile strength and resistance to humidity and temperature changes because it minimizes "movement."

Because of its strength and resistance to variations in heat, plywood is used extensively for furniture and partitions. It also is used instead of solid wood when a thin but rigid material is needed. Curved plywood products, such as boats and chairs, can be made from molded plywood. The glued veneers are put between two halves of a shaped mold before being pressed. Alternatively, the plywood is molded into shape by fluid pressure inside a flexible bag.

Laminated lumber and blockboard

Laminated lumber is made from boards of seasoned lumber that are glued together with the grain running parallel in each layer but with the outer veneers at right angles to the core. For curved products, thin, malleable boards are simultaneously glued and bent to shape. Large columns, arches, boat keels, and decks are often made from this material because large planks can be made of uniformly seasoned wood and the thickness of planks can be increased at points of maximum stress. Laminated maple (*Acer* sp.), for example, is used for high-stress sports equipment, such as golf clubs, tennis rackets, and hockey sticks.

Blockboard is another form of sandwich construction consisting of a core of wooden blocks held together by surface veneers. The solid core prevents the timber from bending, and its grain runs at right angles to the veneers for strength and stability. Light woods, such as pine, may be used for the core blocks because the strength of the board lies in its construction rather than the strength of the wood.

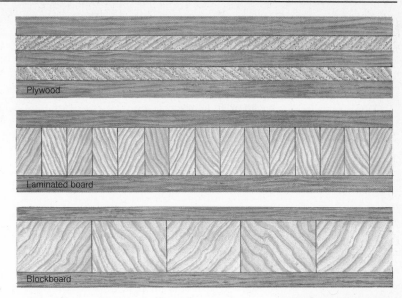

Plywood

Laminated board

Blockboard

"Sandwich" construction timbers are increasingly used in the building industry as an alternative to solid wood. The development of effective adhesives has made composite wood stronger and more adaptable.

Wood-frame construction is a traditional form of housebuilding. This method is widely employed in the United States, Canada, Scandinavia, and Australia.

Woodchip

Woodchip, made by grinding up logs or waste wood, is the raw material for making wood pulp for paper and rayon manufacture (dealt with in other articles) and the basis of what is termed reconstituted wood. The market for reconstituted wood products, such as chipboard, particle board, and fiberboard, has expanded greatly since their introduction in 1940. World demand for them is currently growing faster than that for solid wood, and it is expected to increase by 3 per cent per annum up to the year 2000.

The industry began as a way of recycling waste and poor quality wood, but the versatility, consistent quality, and manufacturing precision achieved by modern production processes qualify these wood-based boards for a wide range of uses, including panels for walls, ceilings, floors, doors, furniture, automobiles, and toys.

Chipboard and particle board

The production of chipboard begins when cutting blades shred shavings, splinters, and flakes of wood into tiny particles resembling coarse sawdust. These are cleaned, dried in heated tumble drums to remove moisture, and then graded. The chips are passed over a weighing belt that feeds information back to a thermal-setting resin dispenser. The correct amount of resin is dropped onto the chips in a fine spray and is mixed in by huge rotators.

The sticky chips then shower down onto a table, where they build up into mats of coarse sawdust. Thick "mattresses" form, which are first squashed in a cold press, then dampened to counteract condensation before they are clamped in a second, heated press for 10 minutes. They emerge as hard, flat chipboard. After pressing, the sheets are stacked to cool for several days to allow the chips to settle. They are then trimmed and sanded, or coated with varnish, plastic, or resin.

Extrusion is an alternative method of producing chipboard in which the chips are forced horizontally between heated metal plates that determine the thickness of the board. The resulting material has higher tensile strength, but lower bending strength.

The thickness of chipboard ranges from .25 to 1 inch (6 to 25 millimeters), with coarse chips in the middle and finer chips on the surface. A stronger, lighter board is made up of fine chips throughout. High-density board 40 to 50 pounds per cubic foot (640-800kg/m³) is used for such products as flooring, which rely on strength and stability. Labor costs are also less for laying high-density chipboard than for laying floorboards. Medium-density board 30 to 40 pounds per cubic foot (480-640kg/m³) is used for paneling, furniture, and shelves, whereas low-density board is best for

Woodchip is a versatile raw material that, with the addition of a thermal setting resin, can be made directly into chipboard. Alternatively it can be further broken down into wood pulp, which in turn can be made into hardboard or softboard. Wood pulp is also a source of crude cellulose for making paper, rayon, and explosives.

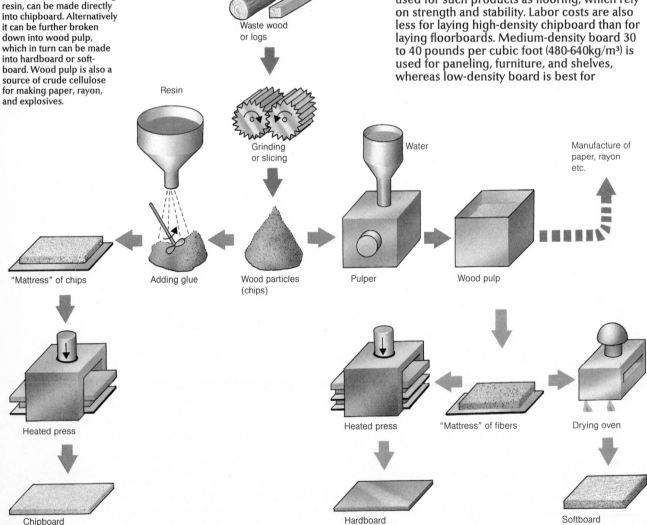

Waste wood or logs

Resin

Grinding or slicing

Water

Manufacture of paper, rayon etc.

"Mattress" of chips

Adding glue

Wood particles (chips)

Pulper

Wood pulp

Heated press

Heated press

"Mattress" of fibers

Drying oven

Chipboard

Hardboard

Softboard

A mountain of wood-chips grows beneath the conveyor at a mill *(left)* which has further broken down the coarse pieces in the foreground (produced by slicing logs).

A "mattress" of glue-treated woodchips *(above)* enters a heated press on an endless belt in a continuous process for manufacturing high-density chipboard.

insulation, ceilings, and roof deckings. All un-treated chipboards are not weather-resistant.

Waferboard, a stronger version of chip-board, is made of parallel layers of long, waferlike strands of wood, which give them a resilience that matches plywood, but at one-third of the price. Other variations include hy-bridboard, which consists of a particle core with veneers on each surface so that it resem-bles plywood.

Wood-cement particle board is a new product manufactured in Germany, Hungary, and Switzerland that employs cement powder instead of synthetic resins as a binding agent. As a result, the board has excellent dimen-sional stability and is fire-resistant. Its main po-tential lies in low-cost housing in tropical re-gions, and as wall paneling in public buildings.

Hardboard

Like chipboard, hardboard is made from forest thinnings and sawmill waste, but the chips are further reduced to fibers by steam, mincing machinery, or explosion. In the explosion process hot, high-pressure steam bombards the chips until they disintegrate. The fibers are cleaned, screened, sized, and mixed with addi-tives, such as rosin, wax, paraffin, and chemi-cals, to increase their resistance to decay, fire, insects, and water.

The most popular method of producing sheets is air-felting. Resin adhesive is added to the fibers, and the mixture is fed onto a mov-ing wire mesh to dry. In wet-felting, glue usu-ally is not added because the softened lignin from the wood is sufficient to bind the fibers together.

The mats are cut into lengths and squeezed between rollers in a hot oven or press. The temperature and pressure determine the type and density of board.

To produce wet-felted hardboard, wet

sheets are pressed in a machine with metal plates. After pressing, they may be treated with heat and humidity to improve their strength and water-resistance. Higher density boards may be tempered with oil before they are trimmed and packed to make them resist-ant to abrasion and weathering.

Hardboard has one smooth side and a gauze-marked reverse side. Without the gauze, which allows water and steam to es-cape during the pressing and heating proc-esses, the boards would explode.

Hardboards are usually high-density, so they are suitable for flooring, shopfitting, flush doors, and furniture. For such products as kitchen cabinets, some hardboards are given a decorative overlay or a coating of enamel or plastic.

Softboard and cork

Unlike hardboard, softboard is not com-pressed. Instead, the wet sheets are dried in a hot-air tunnel oven to ensure that a low den-sity of 22 pounds per cubic foot (350kg/m³) or less is maintained. Softboard is ideal for heat and sound insulation in walls, ceilings, and roofs, where a little sagging is acceptable. Bitumen-impregnated board is used where thermal insulation combined with water-resist-ance is required, as in roofing.

Most cork comes from the thick outer bark of the Mediterranean cork oak *(Quercus suber)*. In summer the bark is stripped away from the living trees, seasoned, and then sub-jected to a steaming process to soften the cells. The hard outer bark is peeled off, and the soft inner cork is pressed into sheets. Nat-ural cork waste now supplies the raw materi-als for cork compositions, which are used for flooring and decorative wall tiles.

Wood pulp and paper

One-third of the world's timber is processed into wood pulp, and most of it is used to make paper and board. Pulping is necessary because woody tissue is not pure fiber, but is a rigid compound of cellulose (49 per cent), lignin (21 per cent), hemicellulose (15 per cent), and small amounts of minerals, proteins, and nitrogen. The cellulose fibers must be extracted from the binding lignin substances before they are soft enough for processing into paper and board.

In addition to forests planted specifically for pulp, one of the main sources of raw material is forest thinnings, which are trees that have been felled to allow others to grow to their full height. Wood residue from sawmills is an important alternative source of wood for pulping and has the advantage of arriving at the mill already chipped.

Waste paper is increasingly used as a raw material for both economic and ecological reasons, to the extent that the United States uses 12 million short tons (10.9 metric tons) of recycled paper annually.

Mechanical pulping

The mechanical or groundwood method of pulping is a traditional process that involves breaking down the timber between rotating grindstones under a constant flow of water. This method produces low-grade pulp, most of which is used for newsprint. For higher quality pulp, the water pressure is increased, breaking the fibers down further. The mixture is screened, and any large lumps are removed.

The main advantages of groundwood pulping are a high yield and, therefore, a low price. This process, however, weakens the fibers so some chemical pulp is normally added to lend adequate strength. Newsprint, for example, requires 20 per cent of chemical pulp to every 80 per cent of mechanical pulp. In addition, the residual lignin in mechanical pulp tends to go yellow with age, and so it is largely used for making "throw-away" products, such as tissues and napkins. Softwoods, such as conifers (which have long fibers and a low density), are favored for this method.

The refiner-groundwood process has developed as a result of the increased availability of wood chips from sawmills. Chips are fed into mills that reduce them to fiber fragments, and the resulting pulp, although less opaque than groundwood pulp, is much stronger; some hardwoods can be included in the mix for bulk. Nearly 50 per cent of Canada's mechanical pulp is now made by a second-generation refiner process known as "thermomechanical pulping," where the chips are preheated by steam, allowing the fibers to soften without discoloration.

Chemical pulping

Higher quality pulp can be produced by "cooking" wood chips in chemicals to remove impurities, including the lignin "glue" that binds the fibers together and causes paper to yellow. There are three main methods of chemical pulping: the sulfite or acid liquor process, the soda process, and the more pop-

Before logs are processed into pulp, their bark is removed. In some factories the bark is removed by powerful jets of water. Alternatively, logs are fed into stripping drums where they jostle together until their bark peels off.

Stripped logs are cut into wood chips about one-half inch long before being pulped. In mechanical pulping, chips are mashed between grindstones under a constant flow of water, whereas chemical pulping involves "cooking" the chips in chemicals. After cleaning, the pulp is often bleached, and mixers may be added. Pulp is piped into a head box that distributes the liquid over a fast-moving mesh. Water drains out of the pulp leaving a "sheet" of fibers that are then pressed between rollers into paper.

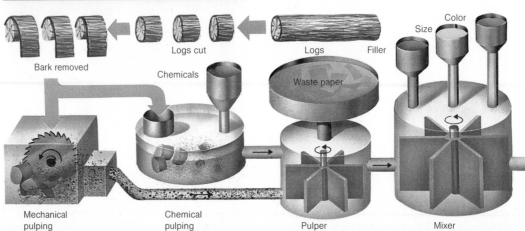

Bark removed

Logs cut

Chemicals

Logs

Filler

Size

Color

Waste paper

Mechanical pulping

Chemical pulping

Pulper

Mixer

ular sulfate or alkaline liquor process. Sulfite liquor cooking is used mainly for spruce and some hardwoods. Inside a steam "digester," wood is pressure-cooked in a bisulfite solution mixed with sulfur dioxide gas for up to 12 hours. The pulp is then cleaned of lumps, bark remnants, and chemicals before refining. The remaining sulfite liquor, however, causes serious pollution problems if it is not disposed of carefully.

Alkaline liquor processes are used primarily for hardwoods and nonwoody fibers, such as grasses and rags. In addition they are used particularly for conifers because the alkali helps to dissolve their high resinous content. The soda process involves cooking wood chips in a caustic soda (sodium hydroxide) solution, but this method produces relatively low-grade pulp. The "kraft" or sulfate process is a more popular method where chips are cooked in a solution of caustic soda and sodium sulfide at high temperatures and under pressure. Some mills still use batch digesters in which chips are cooked in separate loads. The more efficient continuous digester allows a constant flow, which not only avoids delay but also guarantees greater uniformity in the quality of pulp.

In the digester, chips are mixed with cooking liquor, heated under pressure, and washed to remove the separated lignin and remaining liquor. The liquor-lignin mixture is burned as fuel to generate steam for the process, and the chemicals are recovered for reuse. The kraft method produces a strong, dark-brown pulp suitable for wrapping-paper.

A combination of chemical and mechanical processes is semimechanical pulp. The chips are softened in a solution of sodium sulfite and sodium carbonate or bicarbonate before they are de-fibered in a refiner.

Preparing pulp

After thorough cleansing, pulp is often bleached to transform its dirty brown color into white. Bleaching entails four stages of chemical treatment, all of which must be carefully controlled to avoid damage to the fibers. The pulp is chlorinated and then treated with caustic soda, sodium hypochlorite, and finally chlorine oxide.

To make fine printing paper, pulp must be refined. The fibers, which are stiff and hollow at this stage, are passed through a series of

metal disks that cause them to collapse, break, and fray. This process is essential if the fibers are to spread and interlock to form a strong sheet of paper. The length of time spent in the refiner determines many of the properties of the final sheet; the longer the refining process, the higher the quality of paper.

The final stage of preparation before the pulp is ready to pass to the papermaking machine is mixing, which determines the color, texture, strength, water-resistance, and opacity of the paper. China clay and calcium carbonate may be added to fill the gaps between fibers for a smoother paper and to give exceptional whiteness. Sizing agents, such as resin, are added for water-resistance, and dyes and pigments are added for color; fungicides may also be added.

Papermaking

When pulp is piped into the papermaking machine, it consists of 99 per cent water and 1 per cent fibers and additives. By the time the pulp has been processed into paper or board, it contains only 5 to 6 per cent water. Today, most papermaking machines are controlled

The pulp-making and papermaking processes are often carried out at different factories. If pulp is to be transported long distances, excess water is evaporated to produce "air dry" pulp. When this pulp arrives at the paper factory, water is added before it is fed into the papermaking machine.

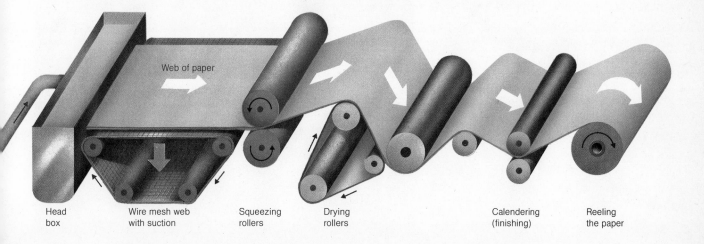

| Head box | Wire mesh web with suction | Squeezing rollers | Drying rollers | Calendering (finishing) | Reeling the paper |

The United States is the world's leading manufacturer of paper. In 1984 the U.S. produced more than three times as much as Japan and four times as much as neighboring Canada. Unlike the North American countries, Japan had to import nearly all of the timber and pulp used to make paper.

Annual Paper Production

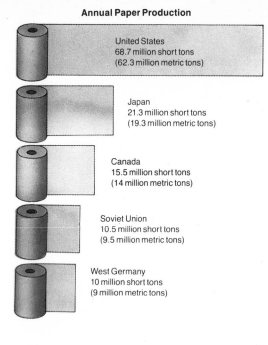

United States
68.7 million short tons
(62.3 million metric tons)

Japan
21.3 million short tons
(19.3 million metric tons)

Canada
15.5 million short tons
(14 million metric tons)

Soviet Union
10.5 million short tons
(9.5 million metric tons)

West Germany
10 million short tons
(9 million metric tons)

by computers that monitor the amount of pulp flowing in, the moisture content, weight, and coating, and ensure that the finished reel of paper is consistent.

A paper machine can measure up to 300 feet (91 meters) in length and is able to produce a continuous sheet of paper more than 18 miles (29 kilometers) long in a single hour. Current trends, however, favor smaller machines that are more efficient and cost less to run, the traditional Four-drinier machine being the most widely used today.

Forming sheets

Pulp is pumped from the refiners to a pressurized head box, which ejects a continuous flow of the liquid material onto a fast-moving wire or plastic mesh. Fibers in the pulp form in the direction of the flow, and as the mesh vibrates from side to side, the fibers interlock to form a web. Much of the water in the pulp drains out, assisted by suction boxes beneath the mesh. The thickness of paper is determined by the speed of the mesh in relation to the amount of pulp released from the head box. The eventual width of the roll of the paper is dictated by the width of the mesh and can vary from 6 to 30 feet (1.8 to 9.1 meters).

Toward the end of the mesh, a cylinder covered in fine wires (a dandy roll) presses the sheet flat and an emblem may be engraved on this roll to imprint a watermark in quality bond papers. If the roll is engraved with cross-hatching, the paper will look "woven," and if parallel lines are produced, the paper is said to be "laid." The sheet is further pressed and drained of water by a suction "couch roll."

From the mesh, the sheet is transferred onto a felt blanket and a series of felted presses extract more water from it by compression. At this stage, the web of fibers has a water content of about 65 per cent before it is squeezed between the felt blanket and about 50 heated drying drums.

Some water is absorbed by the felt and some evaporates in a cloud of steam. For every ton of paper produced, about 2 tons of water evaporate. Finally, only about 5 per cent moisture remains in the paper, and this level is necessary to prevent the paper sheet from cracking.

Cardboard is made on the same principle as paper but generally by using a different technique. A cylindrical wire roll rotates in a bath of liquid pulp, and as water is drawn through the roll, a layer of fibers is deposited on the surface. The layer is transferred to a felt blanket, where other layers of fiber are added to build up a thick cardboard, and then put between presses.

Coating and calendering

Coatings provide paper with a smoother, more uniform surface on which to print. They consist of such pigments as titanium dioxide

Handmade paper *(below left)* and machine-made paper *(right)* are produced using the same basic technique. A watery suspension of wood pulp is floated across a wire mesh, which traps the cellulose fibers when excess water is drawn through it. The mesh is then shaken to make the fibers interlock and form a "sheet." The final size of the sheet of paper or width of the roll depends on the dimensions of the mesh.

or clay, mixed with adhesives and water, and are applied either by equipment in the drying process or on a separate machine. Coating may be applied to a sheet in several layers and on one or both sides of the paper until the required finish is reached.

At the end of the machine, the paper passes through a calender: a series of polished iron rollers or stacks that give the paper a glossy finish. The more rollers it passes through, the smoother the finish and the thinner the paper. A high-gloss finish is achieved by super-calendering, which involves a series of alternately stacked metal and fiber rolls, separate from the papermaking machine.

After calendering, the paper is wound into a roll around a metal core. It may be supplied as a roll or cut into sheets. High-speed sheeting machines can cut as many as eight rolls at the same time.

Other sources of pulp

Because cellulose fiber is the essential component in pulp for paper, a vast number of plants represent potential raw material for papermaking. Annual plants, for example, contain more nonfibrous cells than fibrous and produce a pulp similar to hardwood, although they demand a milder refining process. Straw is pulped in a mixture of lime and water and is still made into paper or board on a small scale in parts of Europe and Asia.

Esparto *(Stipa tenacissima),* a Mediterranean desert grass, has good papermaking properties. Its leaves have a higher cellulose content than most nonwood plants, and its fibers are more uniform in size and shape. The thick-walled fibers retain their springy, sinuous form after drying and make a bulky, opaque, stable, and resilient paper.

Bagasse, the pulp obtained from sugar cane, is a useful source of paper material because it contains 65 per cent fiber, 25 per cent pith cells, and 10 per cent water-soluble substances. Provided the pith is removed during pulping, bagasse produces a relatively smooth paper and is used in Latin America and the Middle East. Bamboo has also been found to produce a satisfactory pulp and, in good conditions, yields more fiber per acre than any other plant because, although it is classified botanically as grass, its stems are unusually dense and hard like those of woody plants.

The highest quality alternative source of paper pulp is cotton rag. Rag bonds, which are usually a combination of cotton and wood fiber, are strong, fine, and smooth and suitable

Papermaking machines are capable of producing rolls of paper more than 5 feet (1.5 meters) in diameter and more than 30 feet (9.1 meters) wide. Sometimes the rolls of paper are cut on the machine, or they may be transported whole.

The printing industry uses a large quantity of paper. Newspapers are usually made mostly from mechanical pulp, whereas high-quality magazines and books are generally made from chemical pulp.

for bank notes, legal documents, and business letterheads. Rag papers are watermarked to specify their cotton content and are priced accordingly.

Fact entries

Fiber characteristics determine the properties of manufactured paper. The most important wood pulps are chemical wood pulp and mechanical wood pulp.

Chemical wood pulp is made by chemical digestion processes from both coniferous and nonconiferous woods. Coniferous fibers are flat and relatively long (3-4 millimeters) due to the growth characteristic of the conifer, giving high strength. Nonconiferous fibers are broader and shorter, rarely longer than 1.5 millimeters, and produce lower-strength papers but with good opacity and better bulk than coniferous fiber. Mixing the two types of fiber to take advantage of these different characteristics is common.

Mechanical wood pulp is usually formed from spruce that has been ground into pulp. Fibers are 3-4 millimeters long, but are often broken in the reduction process. The pulp contains a large proportion of materials other than cellulose. Because of this, the mechanical papers are weak, requiring the addition of a proportion of chemical pulp to strengthen them; thus they deteriorate quickly. They are cheap to produce, however, and so are suitable for newsprint.

Rayon and cellulose

Rayon is the oldest of the artificial fibers, although it is not totally synthetic (but is made by chemically modifying natural cellulose). World production averages 3 million short tons (2.7 million metric tons) a year, a quantity surpassed in the textile industry only by cotton. This success is partly due to the low cost and abundance of its raw material, cellulose, which constitutes 42 per cent of wood and 95 per cent of cotton. About three-quarters of rayon output is produced from highly refined wood pulp.

Viscose rayon

Most of the world's rayon is now made by the viscose process. Sheets of wood pulp are first dissolved to form an alkali-cellulose slurry by steeping them in 18 per cent aqueous sodium hydroxide solution. After steeping, the cellulose is pressed under high pressure and as much caustic soda as possible is removed. It is then shredded into crumbs, which helps to distribute the caustic more evenly, and heated in a process called aging.

In an automatic aging room the crumbs are treated with oxygen to lower the degree of polymerization, which prevents premature hardening. Next follows the critical xanthation process, in which the mercerized alkali-cellulose is cooled and mixed with carbon disulfide to form cellulose xanthate. This yellow substance is dissolved in dilute caustic soda to form a clear syrup, known as viscose, which is filtered to remove any impurities.

Once the xanthate groups attached to the cellulose molecule have redistributed (in a "ripening" process), closer molecular chains can be formed, and the viscose is ready for spinning. First it is extruded through the holes of a spinnerette into a bath of a salt and an acid. This solution usually contains 15 per cent sodium sulfate, which removes water from the cellulose xanthate, and 10 per cent sulfuric acid, which helps to regenerate cellulose from the viscose. The extruded material forms a continuous filament containing 85-90 per cent cellulose. The size of the spinnerette determines the destiny of the yarn. A very narrow nozzle, for example, is used for making artificial hair, whereas a wide nozzle produces rayon for artificial leather fabrics. Extrusion through a narrow slit produces sheets of transparent viscose film, known as cellophane.

The fibers are spun continuously, reeled, then washed in water and bleached in sodium hypochlorite solution. After the fibers are cut to size, an appropriate finish may be applied to counteract any natural slipperiness or stickiness during weaving, before they are wound on to bobbins for shipping.

Viscose rayon fabrics—once marketed as "artificial silk"—are comfortable to wear, are cool, like cotton, but more absorbent, and can be brushed to make them warmer. Although viscose rayon creases and burns easily, it can be treated with a crease-resistant finish.

Cuprammonium rayon

Today, fibers made by the cuprammonium process, an expensive technique, are manufactured only for highly specialized purposes. Almost all artificial kidney machines, for example, use membranes prepared from cuprammonium rayon films and fibers. They are more supple, cause less bloodclotting, and have better dewatering properties than viscose rayon membranes.

In the cuprammonium process, wood pulp is mixed with aqueous ammonia, copper sulfate, and caustic soda until it produces a 10 per cent cellulose blue solution. Although it is wet spun, unlike viscose, coagulation is slow. The filaments are extruded into water, which also passes through the spinnerette, causing the fibers to elongate. As a result of this "stretch spinning," the filament size is smaller than viscose, even though the spinnerette holes are larger. The threads are hardened as they pass through a dilute sulfuric acid solution, which also removes the ammonia and copper for recycling.

Acetate rayon

The first important application of cellulose acetate was as a nonflammable varnish for fabric-covered aircraft in World War I. The first acetate yarn (known as Celanese) was developed from the redundant stocks of acetate after the war. The cellulose is steeped in acetic acid, then treated with acetate anhydride and

Viscose *(right)* is a sticky substance made by treating cellulose with various chemicals *(see illustration on opposite page)*. To make rayon, the viscose is forced through tiny holes into a bath of acid, and the filaments combined and pulled from the bath as a yarn *(below)*.

sulfuric acid. Each glucose unit in cellulose combines with three molecules of acetic acid and forms cellulose triacetate; but because it does not readily accept dyes in this form, one acetate molecule is removed (by adding water) to produce cellulose diacetate. The fibers are washed, dried, dissolved in acetone, and then extruded through a spinnerette sited 20 feet (6 meters) above the ground. As the solution descends, it is warmed by a current of hot air, which evaporates the acetone. The acetate fibers are then lubricated before twisting and winding.

The resulting cloth is more like natural silk than any other fiber. It is crease-resistant, mothproof, and water-repellent. Triacetate, sold as Tricel and now often combined with cotton, is popular for its drip-dry qualities.

The early commercial uses of cellulose acetate as photographic film, in shatterproof glass, and for contact lenses and varnishes are now threatened by acrylics, nylons, and other totally synthetic materials made from petroleum-based products. However, some experts speculate that a petroleum shortage and rising oil prices may lead to greater use of cellulose.

Nitrocellulose

The explosive properties of cellulose nitrate (often known as nitrocellulose or guncotton) are largely derived from the polymeric and fibrous structure of cellulose. It is used as a propellant explosive for rockets and guns and in cartridges for small arms. Its properties depend, however, on the extent of nitration, a ni-

trogen content of more than 13 per cent being necessary to make an explosive. When the nitrogen content is limited to 11 or 12 per cent, it may be used for lacquers and films, and at 10 per cent nitrogen, plastics may be manufactured from it. Low-viscosity nitrocellulose lacquers may also be produced by heating cellulose and nitrogen with water under pressure but, like other forms of cellulose nitrate, they suffer from the disadvantage of extremely high flammability.

Cellophane is a transparent material mainly employed for wrapping, especially for foodstuffs such as candy. It is chemically identical to rayon, but is produced by extruding viscose through a narrow slit so that it takes the form of a thin film or sheet.

In making rayon (below), sheets of wood pulp are steeped in alkali (sodium hydroxide, NaOH), pressed damp dry and crumbled, and, after an aging process, dissolved in carbon disulfide (CS$_2$) to form cellulose xanthate. This substance is reacted with more alkali to make viscose, which is filtered before being extruded into a bath containing acid. The resulting rayon yarn is washed, bleached, and dried before being wound on reels.

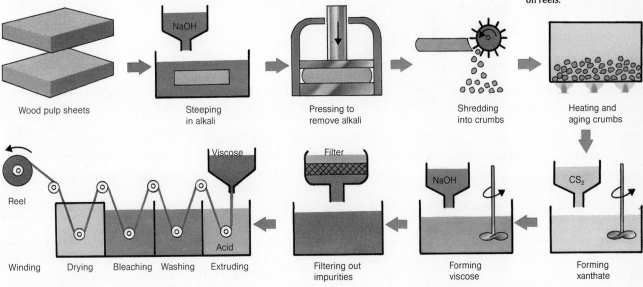

Wood pulp sheets — Steeping in alkali — Pressing to remove alkali — Shredding into crumbs — Heating and aging crumbs

Winding — Drying — Bleaching — Washing — Extruding — Filtering out impurities — Forming viscose — Forming xanthate

Fact entries

Chardonnet, Hilaire de (1839-1924), a French chemist and industrialist who, in 1878, first developed a type of rayon by means of a process he devised based on cellulose nitrate. He began manufacturing it in 1889.

Cross, Charles Frederick (1855-1935), a British chemist who, with his partners Bevan and Beadle, patented the viscose rayon process in 1892, thus establishing the artificial silk industry. He also pioneered the development of cellulose acetate.

Schönbein, Christian Friedrich (1799-1868), a Swiss-born German chemist who in 1846 made guncotton (nitrocellulose) through a process that had been discovered seven years earlier by T. J. Pelouze in France.

Swan, Joseph Wilson (1828-1914), a British inventor who first made nitrocellulose safely into fibers in 1883. He used carbonized forms of the nitrocellulose fibers as filaments in his early vacuum light bulbs.

Vegetable fibers

The most important plant products after foodstuffs and timber are fiber crops. They exert economic, social, and political influence both at the local level and on an international scale. Throughout the world millions of people are employed in growing them, and major industries are based on processing the fibers into yarns and textile fabrics.

Synthetic fibers have made significant inroads into the textile market in recent years but—particularly since the increase in the price of petroleum, the base material for many synthetic fibers—the natural products remain competitive. Genetic modifications to the fiber plants have improved yields. And compared with their chief "natural" competitors—fibers made from wood pulp derived from timber—most vegetable fiber crops mature in months rather than the decades required by trees.

There are three main types of vegetable fibers, classified as soft, hard, or short. The soft (or bast) fibers are extracted from the stems of plants and include jute, flax (linen), hemp, ramie, and kenaf. Hard fibers, such as manila hemp, sisal, henequen, and New Zealand flax, are gathered from the leaves for providing hard cordage or brush and have suffered more from the impact of synthetic fibers (which can be made stronger). Cotton, the world's most important vegetable fiber, belongs to the third group, the short fibers, produced from the "hair" on the seeds; they also include kapok and coir (from coconut).

Fiber structure and characteristics

The bast and hard fiber strands are bundles of numerous overlapping, parallel-fiber cells. The cell walls consist of minute microfibrils (the smallest units visible under a microscope), which are composed of cellulose chains linked by hydrogen bonds. The orientation of the microfibrils determines each fiber's elasticity.

Cotton is unique among the natural fibers. Each fiber is a single tubelike cell made up of 20-30 layers of cellulose. When the cotton boll (fruit capsule) opens, the fibers dry into twisted ribbons with spiraling microfibrils.

A fiber must be at least 100 times longer than it is wide to be suitable for spinning into thread for weaving. Although its length measures up to 3,000 times greater than its width, cotton is relatively short—only one-third of the length of flax—and can pose problems for the spinner and weaver. Fibers of the finest Sea Island cotton (Gossypium barbadense) are up to 1.5 inches (38 millimeters) longer than those of coarse Indian blanket cotton (G. herbaceum). Natural twist in the fibers also contributes to quality. Flax (Linum usitatissimum) has nodes that help the fibers lock together during spinning, but cotton has up to 2,000 natural twists (in alternate directions) to every inch.

Tensile strength, flexibility, and elasticity

Cotton can easily be spun by hand, as here in Ecuador. Similar simple spinning techniques are still employed elsewhere in South America, as well as in Africa and India. The resulting yarn is generally woven into cloth on hand looms.

Mechanized cotton spinning, first introduced in Britain at the beginning of the Industrial Revolution, is now employed throughout the industrialized nations of the world. The factory illustrated *(right)* is in China, which has overtaken traditional producers like India as a manufacturer of cotton textiles and clothing. Neighboring Hong Kong, Taiwan, and Thailand also produce many cotton goods.

Sisal, seen here *(left)* being cultivated in Nigeria, is a type of agave *(Agave sisalana)* that is grown for the tough fibers in its long, sword-shaped leaves. Originally from Yucatan, Mexico, the plant is now cultivated in all tropical parts of the world. The fiber, known as sisal hemp, is removed by machine *(right)*, draped over poles, and then left in the sun to dry. It is stronger and more rot-resistant than jute and is used mainly to make ropes, cordage, and twine.

are important if a fiber is to withstand processing stress. Good colorfastness and resistance to decay are needed if it is to be marketable. The newly harvested fiber also has to be quick to clean if it is to be economically produced. Ramie *(Boehmeria nivea)*, for example, has never competed with cotton or linen because it is difficult to clean. The selling price, however, may be largely determined by the amount of moisture the final fabric will absorb. Cotton's tubular structure allows it to take up and release water rapidly, which makes it useful for toweling, comfortable to wear, and receptive to dyes and bleaches.

Cotton—from fiber to fabric

When a cotton boll bursts, four or five tufts of fiber emerge, each containing several seeds; it is then harvested. The fiber, or lint, is sent to a cotton gin to be separated from the seeds and is packed into 480-pound (218-kilogram) bales. When it is ready for processing, the bale is opened, beaten to loosen the fibers, then formed into a sheet, known as a lap, on a scutching machine. Different qualities of cotton are often blended at this stage to ensure a uniform yarn. The roll of fiber is straightened on a high-speed carding machine (a revolving spiked cylinder), which disentangles and cleans the fibers until they form a thin web. The length of time the cotton remains in the carding machine determines the cleanness and quality of the fiber.

Only the longer fibers produce good-quality cotton, so the short fibers (known as noils) are extracted by combing and spun into cheaper yarns. The long fibers emerge as a sliver of strong, smooth material. This sliver passes through a series of rollers, which draw it out into a finer strand and twist it into roving.

Spinning involves elongating and twisting the cotton to the required thickness and length, then transferring it onto bobbins for weaving. The ring frame, invented by John Thorp in the United States in 1828, drafts and twists simultaneously and is used for large quantities. Spinning speeds have recently been significantly increased by the open-ended technique, often referred to as O-E spinning, which uses high-speed rotor disks for twisting the yarn. More delicate qualities are manufactured on a spinning mule, which drafts, spins, and twists in three separate operations. Doubled yarns, for thread and hosiery, are produced by twisting several yarns together. Moistened roving produces a cleaner, more compact thread, but the correct moisture level is crucial.

Three types of yarn are produced: warp, or longitudinal threads; weft, or filling yarn for crosswise lacing, with less twist; and knitting yarns. The warp and weft are woven together on high-speed looms in modern factories. The Sulzer loom allows a wider fabric to be produced and at higher speeds, and it has introduced a more efficient method of weft insertion.

After weaving, further processing is sometimes needed. To increase the luster, strength, and absorbency, some fabric is mercerized.

Cotton fibers take the form of hollow tubes of cellulose, as can readily be seen at the cut ends of the cotton in this electron micrograph of cotton velvet (a fabric with a furry pile made by cutting through small loops formed during the weaving). The fibers are shown enlarged about 400 times.

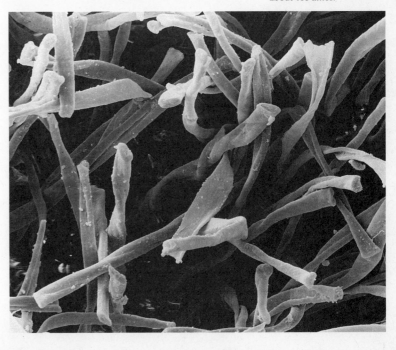

In the plants illustrated *(right)*, the leaves or stems are the source of fibers, which are comparatively long. Many are removed from the plants by retting, a process in which the leaves or stems are soaked in water until the fibers can be separated and removed. The softer, short fibers of cotton and kapok are easier to collect because they come from the woolly "hair" on the seeds.

Jute
Corchorus capsularis

Manila hemp *Musa textilis*

Indian hemp *Cannabis sativa*

Sisal *Agave sisalana*

Ramie *Boehmeria nivea*

Raffia palm *Raphia ruffia*

Flax *Linum usitatissimum*

This technique, devised in 1850 by John Mercer, a self-taught chemist, involves dipping the tensioned cloth into a cold concentrate of caustic soda or liquid ammonia for two to three minutes, then washing it off. Finally, the cloth may be scoured to remove dirt or oil, bleached with sodium hypochlorite or hydrogen peroxide, and colored with synthetic dyes.

The immediate future promises interesting new developments, such as the shuttleless loom, cotton grafted with polymers to produce a cloth with new properties, and greater automation in the finishing stages.

Soft or bast fibers

Bast fibers come from the soft stem or phloem of dicotyledonous plants. They are made up of cell bundles cemented together by nonfibrous gummy substances composed of lignin, pectin, and cellulose. Before the fibers can be extracted from the stem, the gums must be softened, dissolved, then washed away. This process, known as retting, involves immersing the plant stalks in water or exposing them to dew. Bacteria ferments the woody tissues, and enzymes dissolve the binding pectic substances until the fibers can easily be separated.

Known also as linen after its plant of origin, *Linum usitatissimum*, flax is the strongest of the vegetable fibers. Linen garments estimated to be at least 3,500 years old have been recovered from Egyptian tombs. Such resistance to decay and strength made flax the main source of cloth until the arrival of cotton in about 1800. Compared with cotton, however, flax's lack of elasticity caused its popularity to suffer, particularly because it cannot withstand the stresses of high-speed power looms; today it is reserved for high quality, durable, but expensive, household cloth.

The Soviet Union produces more than half of the world's total supply of fiber flax. But the best qualities of linen come from Ireland and Belgium, where the river water in which the flax is retted is thought to impart a particularly desirable, rich, creamy color and texture to the linen.

Extracting the fiber

Flax stems are pulled, rather than cut, from the soil by machines that bundle the stems for retting. The better grades of Belgian flax may be retted twice—first for two and one-half days then, after rinsing and drying, for a further day at 90° F. (32° C).

After retting, the stems are split by mechanical breaking rollers and then passed to a turbine scutcher. There the stems are beaten by blades to separate the fibers and crush the pith. The long fibers are combed and all the short fibers removed for coarse-fiber production. Following this so-called hackling process, the long fibers are drawn out through rollers to form a sliver, and then wound on to bobbins for spinning.

Wet spinning is employed for fine linen and warp yarns. The roving is passed through hot water to soften the fibers and to allow them to slip easily over each other. New spinning methods have been devised for flax, including a twistless process that uses the plant's natural pectins to bind the fibers. How-

Jute is grown mainly in the Indian subcontinent. Its uses include the making of carpets *(below)*, which takes advantage of the ease with which it can be dyed a large range of bright colors. Jute is also widely employed for making sacking and burlap.

ever, ring spinning on a flyer machine remains the most economical method.

The flax is then bleached and woven into a range of fabrics, from heavy canvas to fine linen for handkerchiefs. Flax also lends itself to blends with other fibers, such as cotton, Terylene (Dacron), wool, and acrylics, so that the durability of linen can be combined with the lower cost and greater elasticity of other materials.

Hemp

Hemp is extracted from the stem of the well-known drug-producing plant, *Cannabis sativa*. Coarser than flax and very resistant to rotting, it is manufactured into marine cordage, heavy-duty tarpaulins, and, until recently, sailcloth. The higher-quality, water-retted fiber, which turns a creamy white, can be used for finer textiles (one-third of the population of South Korea wears hemp clothing). Unlike flax, hemp is cut in the field after the flowering season. Summer hemp contains better fiber than winter hemp and is normally water-retted to form finer cloth. Hemp is processed in the same way rather than being machine hackled.

Ramie

Also known as China grass and rhea, ramie is the longest, broadest, and one of the strongest textile fibers, but it is very costly to process. Unlike flax, hemp, and jute, it is not retted and the fiber is taken from the stalk by hand. The bark is scraped off in ribbons, which are cleaned in a strong soda solution. They are left to ferment in hydrochloric acid, then returned to the soda to soften and remove the gum. Once the fibers have been extracted, combed, and sorted, ramie is processed in the same way as flax.

Jute

Most jute is white and comes from the Indian herbaceous annual *Corchorus capsularis*. (*Corchorus olitorius* yields the rarer russet-colored tossa jute.) Although jute is the cheapest natural textile fiber and is easy to dye and spin, it is weak, deteriorates quickly as a result of its low cellulose content, and does not bleach well.

The finer qualities are spun into yarn and processed like flax, but 75 per cent of jute is made into burlap, sacking, twine, and carpet backings. As a packaging material, it has difficulty competing with kenaf, roselle, and synthetics such as polypropylene, largely because there has been little mechanical progress in India, the center of the jute industry.

Kenaf

Kenaf, which derives from the Asian plant *Hibiscus cannabis*, is now used increasingly as a substitute for wood pulp. It is stronger, lighter, more water-resistant, and—because the stems are less woody—is better suited to mechanized fiber separation than is jute.

Flowering flax creates a field of blue in the Belgian countryside. Linen, the fabric made from it, was once the only alternative to wool for the people of Europe before cotton was imported from the East and, later, from America.

Fact entries

Arkwright, Richard (1732-1792), a British inventor, devised the water spinning frame in 1768. It produced a cotton yarn strong enough to be used on power-operated looms, which led to the establishment of the huge cotton mills of the Industrial Revolution. At first water power was used; later stationary steam engines were installed to drive the textile machinery.

Hargreaves, James (1722?-1778), a British engineer, invented the spinning jenny in about 1764, which doubled the speed of production, because the frame allowed 8-10 threads to be spun concurrently.

Cartright, Edmund (1743-1823), a British inventor and clergyman, developed and perfected the power loom.

Crompton, Samuel (1753-1827), combined the advantages of Arkright's frame and Hargreaves' jenny in the mule spinning frame in 1779. This was developed into the modern self-acting mule, still used today for delicate yarns.

Whitney, Eli (1765-1825), an American inventor, developed in 1793 the cotton gin, a machine for separating cotton fibers from the seeds. This led to the huge expansion in cotton cultivation in the southern United States—and the importation of slave labor.

Alcohol and other chemicals

Ripe grapes *(right)* contain glucose, a simple sugar that can be fermented in the wine-making process to produce ethyl alcohol.

Living plants are biochemical factories. In addition to cellulose (a plant's main structural material used for making paper and rayon), there is a wide range of chemicals produced by various plants, from sugars and fats to complex compounds employed as drugs, dyes, and pigments. Some chemical substances, such as tannins, may be extracted directly from plants. Others, such as alcohols, are made by processing plant materials.

Sugars and starch

The most common sugar in plants is glucose, a product of photosynthesis and the building block, or monomer, from which the natural polymer cellulose is made. Glucose is the principal sugar in grapes. Other simple sugars, known chemically as monosaccharides, that are derived from plants include fructose (in various fruits and in honey) and ribose (in the polymeric backbone of the nucleic acid DNA).

Disaccharides, formed of two monosaccharide units joined together, are more complex sugars. They include maltose (from malt, or sprouted barley) and sucrose (from sugar beet or sugar cane), the sugar used in cooking and for sweetening beverages. This sugar has been used for nearly 8,000 years. It was extracted from sugar cane first in India and much later (after about 300 B.C.) in the Middle East; it was introduced to the Americas by Europeans in 1493. Sugar was not obtained from beets until the eighteenth century. Maple syrup is a sugary sap extracted from various North American species of maple trees (*Acer* spp.).

The chief polysaccharides—polymers made of thousands of monosaccharide (glucose) units—are cellulose and starch. Cellulose and its uses are described in other articles in this section. Starch is a storage material in cereal grains, roots, and tubers such as potatoes. Apart from being the principal ingredient in various kinds of flours, it is also used to make adhesive paste and sizing for textile fabrics.

Vegetable oils and fats

Various plants are grown for the oils contained in their seeds, from palms and olives to flax (the source of linseed oil), sunflower, and specially developed strains of safflower. Vegetable oils are used to make soap and in foodstuffs. One of the more recent additions to the list of oil-bearing plants is soybean (*Glycine* sp.). Since its potential was first realized in the 1930's, annual output has increased more than 200 times, and soy now occupies 68 million acres (27.5 million hectares) of arable land in the United States. The food industry uses most of the oils extracted from soybeans in such

Tannins have long been used for curing animal hides to make leather, either in a traditional way as in Morocco *(below)* or in modern tanneries. A much more recently introduced plant product is soy oil, which is extracted from the seeds of the soybean plant *(below right)* and used in various foodstuffs.

Grape-pickers in France work along rows of Pinot vines, the variety employed for making Champagne. Carbon dioxide gas, a by-product of the fermentation process, is retained to give the wine its sparkling, effervescent quality.

products as candy, ice cream, margarine, mayonnaise, and sausages. Other soy oils are used to make glycerin, paints, and soaps.

Numerous other plants yield industrial oils. Citrus seeds, tung (*Aleurites* sp.), and linseed (from flax, *Linum* sp.) provide the bases for enamels, paints, and lacquers; rice bran produces a hard wax and an oil employed in rust-proofing. Linseed and soy oils can be chemically processed to make vinyl ethers, which in turn are polymerized to make tough plastic film.

Safflower *(Carthamus tinctorius)*, originally from India, has been genetically modified so that its seeds yield 40 per cent oil with a linoleic acid content of nearly 80 per cent, hence its popularity as a low-calorie, low-cholesterol ingredient in cooking and salad oils. Recently, new strains have been introduced with a high oleic acid content, making them competitive with olive oil.

Castor *(Ricinus communis)*, originally an ornamental plant from Africa, is now widely grown for its oil-rich "beans." Castor oil is a good lubricant and an ingredient in polyurethane foam plastics, printing inks, and adhesives. Genetic modification has succeeded in creating a uniformly short plant with tripled yields of oil.

Another new and successful product of plant breeding is a member of the Scandinavian mustard family, known as crambe (*Crambe* sp.). Its seeds contain large quantities of erucic acid, which also constitutes up to 50 per cent of rapeseed oil. The substance has found profitable application as a lubricant in the continuous casting method of making steel. It is also used in the processing of rubber and some plastics.

The seeds of a Mexican desert plant called jojoba *(Simmondsia californica)* yield a liquid wax which is used as a "tough" industrial lubricant in place of spermaceti oil from whales. It is also an ingredient of some cosmetics and shampoos.

The flowers of many plants contain oils—ex-tracted by squeezing in presses, using solvents, or by careful steam-distillation—which are the chief aromatic ingredients of perfumes. Also called essential oils, they are the basis of flower-growing industries in several Mediterranean countries. Yields are predictably low—for example, 1.25 tons of rose petals are needed to produce 1 pound of rose oil—and the value of the oils is correspondingly high.

Alcohols

Traditionally, alcohol (specifically ethyl alcohol, or ethanol) is made by fermenting sugars or starch, one of the earliest chemical processes to be discovered. In wine making, yeast is employed to ferment the sugars in fruit; in beer making, the source of the alcohol is the starch in cereals, such as barley. (Any sugary or starchy plant material, however, can be fermented to make alcohol). The fermentation process is accompanied by the evolution of carbon dioxide gas, which is what gives the effervescent quality to beer and some wines.

Most ordinary wines (as opposed to fortified wines such as port and sherry) contain 8 to 15 per cent alcohol, whereas beers seldom have more than 2 to 6 per cent. To extract concentrated alcohol from such sources they have to be distilled (giving 95 per cent ethyl alcohol).

Ethyl alcohol manufactured for commercial purposes is usually "denatured" (to prevent misuse) by adding the highly poisonous substance methyl alcohol (methanol). Also called wood alcohol, it can be made by the destructive distillation of wood—that is, by heating pieces of wood strongly in the absence of air. Methyl alcohol can be added to gasoline to produce "gasohol," an experimental liquid fuel for motor vehicles. Like ethyl alcohol, methyl alcohol is also used as a solvent and as an important starting material in synthetic chemistry, particularly for making monomers for the production of plastics.

An unusual liquid wax, incorporated into some cosmetic preparations, is obtained from the crushed "beans" of the Mexican jojoba plant. Jojoba oil is also used as a lubricant for machinery.

Tannins

Since the first animal skins were made into leather, tannins have been used to soften and cure hides. They are complex chemicals called polyphenols, found mainly in the bark and heartwood of hardwoods, such as oaks (*Quercus* spp.) and sweet chestnuts (*Castanea* spp.), as well as in the Australian acacia (*Acacia* sp.) and South American quebracho trees (*Aspidosperma* spp.). Mangrove bark, coniferous trees, the nuts of the betel palm, and the leaves of the tea plant are also rich sources of tannins, whose natural function in the plants is probably to prevent decay. They are usually extracted by boiling the vegetable material in water.

In addition to their use in leather making, tannins have many other applications; they are used, for example, in the manufacture of dyes and inks and as coagulants in the early stages of rubber processing.

Drugs from plants

Many drugs occur in the leaves, fruits, seeds, and roots of various plants, and although most can be made synthetically in the laboratory, such is their complexity that it is often more economical to use the natural sources.

Most plant drugs are alkaloids—nitrogen-containing compounds that have an alkaline reaction. Those derived from leaves include atropine, from belladonna (*Atropa belladonna*); digitalis, from foxgloves (*Digitalis* spp.); cocaine, from the South American coca shrub (*Erythroxylon coca*); and strychnine, from the evergreen *Strychnos nux-vomica*. People in southeastern Asia have traditionally chewed the leaves of betel-pepper (*Piper betle*), now the source of a counterirritant drug, and the addictive nature of cigarette smoking has been attributed—at least in part—to the presence of the alkaloid nicotine in the leaves of tobacco (*Nicotiana tabacum*).

In the case of certain trees it is the bark that is the source of drugs; for instance, the antimalarial drug quinine comes from the cinchona tree (*Cinchona officinalis*), originally from South America but now also cultivated in Java, and pseudopelletierine, an antihelminthic drug, comes from the pomegranate tree (*Punica granatum*). In other cases it is the plant's roots that provide the drug; reserpine, for example, which is used for treating high blood pressure, occurs in the roots of the tropical rauwolfia (*Rauwolfia serpentina*), and ginseng is extracted from the roots of the Chinese panax (*Panax ginseng*).

The best-known plant whose seeds yield drugs is the poppy (*Papaver somniferum*), source of opium and its morphine derivatives. Like all alkaloids, the opium compounds are highly poisonous, although the most toxic is probably ricin, extracted from the seeds of a castor plant (*Ricinus sanguineus*), which has been considered as a possible agent for chemical warfare.

Dyes and pigments

Before the development of the synthetic dyestuffs industry, plants were a major source of colorants for dyes, inks, and paints. Dye plants were grown as farm and plantation crops, and included woad (*Isatis tinctoria*) and indigo (*Indigofera* sp.), whose leaves yield blue dyes,

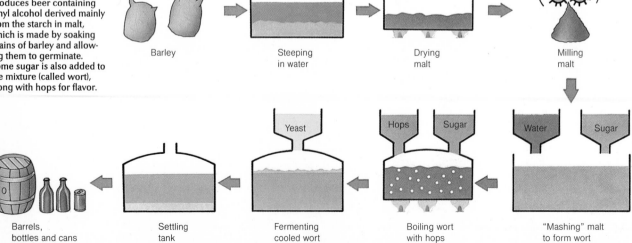

Brewing is a fermentation process (using yeast) that produces beer containing ethyl alcohol derived mainly from the starch in malt, which is made by soaking grains of barley and allowing them to germinate. Some sugar is also added to the mixture (called wort), along with hops for flavor.

Barley → Steeping in water → Drying malt → Milling malt → "Mashing" malt to form wort (Water, Sugar) → Boiling wort with hops (Hops, Sugar) → Fermenting cooled wort (Yeast) → Settling tank → Barrels, bottles and cans

Sugar cane, resembling bundles of dried sticks, is a difficult crop to handle and requires special machines, although much of the actual cutting is still done by hand. It is now grown in most tropical countries as a source of table sugar and molasses; part of this crop, from Barbados, will be fermented to make rum.

and madder *(Rubia tinctorum),* which contains alizarin and various other red dyes in its roots.

The leaves of henna *(Lawsonia inermis)* are still used for dyeing hair and by many Asian peoples for coloring their nails reddish-brown and for decorating the skin. Another red pigment with cosmetic uses (it is employed as rouge) is made from safflower petals. The similarly named saffron, or autumn crocus *(Colchicum autumnale),* yields a yellow pigment employed for dyeing textiles and coloring food.

The chemical indicator litmus—which has a blue color in alkaline solutions and a red color in acid ones—is prepared from various species of lichens, particularly those belonging to the genus *Variolaria.*

Chemicals from wood pulp

The liquors that remain after the various processes for preparing wood pulp in papermaking—once discarded as waste—are a rich source of chemicals. In the United States, for example, more than 80 per cent of the annual production of turpentine and rosin is obtained from so-called "black liquor," a by-product of the sulfate process for papermaking. Turpentine is condensed from the vapors and purified by distillation, and the concentrated liquor used as a lubricant and source of rosin, for sizing paper, and as a drying agent in paints and varnishes.

Another product of pulp manufacturing is lignin, which may be burned as a fuel (usually for making steam at the paper mill) or added to clay slurries in the ceramics industry (to reduce their viscosity) or to mud slurries employed as lubricants when drilling oil wells. Lignin can also be hydrogenated—that is, it can be reacted with hydrogen at high temperature and pressure in the presence of a catalyst—to give high-molecular-weight cyclic alcohols used as plasticizers (softeners) for plastics. Vanillin, a flavoring agent that tastes of vanilla, can also be manufactured synthetically from lignin.

The castor oil plant *(left)* has creamy-yellow flowers that give way to prickly capsules containing a large seed or "bean." The seeds are the source of castor oil, used as a lubricant and starting material for making plastics; they also contain the poisonous substance ricin.

An Indian woman's hands display intricate patterns drawn on using the vegetable dye henna, made from the dried leaves of a plant widely grown in India and northern Africa. Sometimes the color is made purple by adding the blue dye indigo.

Rubber

Rubber latex drips into collecting cups from cuts in the bark of rubber trees *(Hevea brasiliensis, far right)*. Almost two-thirds of the world's production of natural rubber comes from trees grown on smallholdings in Malaysia, Indonesia, and Thailand.

Rubber has been one of the most important materials derived from plants since the middle of the nineteenth century. In 1839, the American, Charles Goodyear, invented vulcanization, a process in which raw rubber is blended with sulfur to make it both strong and pliable over a range of temperatures. It is only in the last 40 years that synthetic rubbers—products of the petrochemical industry—have seriously challenged the natural material.

Today more than 40 per cent of the world's natural rubber comes from Malaysia (most of the rest is grown in Indonesia and Thailand), from smallholdings and plantations growing the South American rubber tree *Hevea brasiliensis*. This plant grows well only within a "rubber belt" that extends about 700 miles (1,100 kilometers) on each side of the equator, and then only at altitudes below 1,000 feet (305 meters). The raw rubber takes the form of a milky latex, which is "tapped" from the trees by making a spiral cut in the bark of the trunk.

The production of natural rubber has increased nearly 95 times since the beginning of the century, largely to meet the demand created for motor vehicle tires; the motor industry uses almost 70 per cent of the 4.75 million short tons (4.3 million metric tons) produced each year. But synthetic rubbers take a larger share of the market—60 per cent of the 10 million short tons (9.1 million metric tons) produced annually goes into making tires—although the soaring oil prices of the 1970's helped to reduce the threat to natural rubber.

Composition and properties of rubber

Rubber is a natural polymer, consisting of small molecules of the hydrocarbon isoprene linked together to form long coiled chains. When rubber is stretched and then released, the long-chain molecules bounce back to their original length, giving rubber its elastic properties.

Natural rubber is resistant to alkalis and weak acids but swells in many organic liquids, such as gasoline and lubricating oils. It dissolves in various volatile organic solvents, producing a rubber solution that finds application as an adhesive. It is a good electrical insulator, although for this purpose rubber has been almost entirely superseded by synthetic plastics. The individual properties of processed rubbers are largely influenced by chemicals added during the manufacturing process.

Processing rubber

Liquid latex, from rubber trees, has to be solidified before it can be sold or further processed. Some solidifies naturally on the tree, but most is coagulated artificially. Any dirt is filtered out and formic (methanoic) acid is added, which causes the liquid latex to "curdle" and coagulate. The coagulum is granulated, dried, and shaped into bales.

About 10 per cent of natural rubber is used in the latex form, where its elasticity and pliability are important for such products as rubber gloves and catheters. The other 90 per cent must first undergo special processes according to what end-product is required.

Before further processing, rubber is masticated by rollers or rotors that break down the polymer molecules. The heat evolved softens the rubber and it becomes plastic. Strength and elasticity are restored by vulcanization

The main steps in the processing of natural rubber into an industrially useful material are chemical: the addition of formic acid to coagulate the liquid latex and, at a later stage, heating with sulfur to bring about vulcanization.

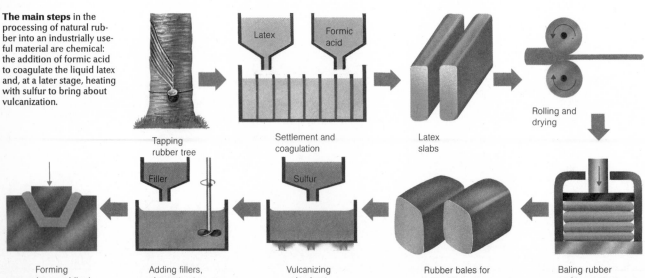

Tapping rubber tree

Latex   Formic acid

Settlement and coagulation

Latex slabs

Rolling and drying

Forming (e.g. molding)

Filler

Adding fillers, pigments etc.

Sulfur

Vulcanizing using heat

Rubber bales for transshipment

Baling rubber under pressure

with sulfur at 284°-356° F. (140°-180° C). This causes the material to become thermosetting and thus resistant to wide temperature changes. Vulcanized rubber can be stretched up to eight times its original length and yet remain perfectly elastic—that is, it returns to its original length when released.

During vulcanization, the sulfur atoms form cross-linkages between the chains of rubber molecules to produce a more rigid three-dimensional structure. But too much sulfur and, therefore, too many cross-linkages results in a rigid, nonelastic material. Various other substances are also included. Antioxidants are added to prevent the rubber from perishing; oils to soften it and assist processing; insoluble wax to reduce cracking; pigments to supply color; and fillers that, at a slight cost to strength, increase wear resistance. Rubber that is used for car tires, for example, contains 30 per cent of carbon black as a filler. Other products—erasers and floor tiles, for instance—may have white powder fillers such as chalk, silica or zinc oxide.

Shaping rubber

The usual method of making dry rubber goods is by molding. A simple eraser, for example, is heated under pressure in a mold so that it emerges both vulcanized and shaped. For more precision and higher production rates, injection molding is used. In this process a softened rubber mixture is injected at high speed through small holes into a mold or set of molds. Heat and pressure are again applied to vulcanize it. Surgical rubber goods, such as thin latex gloves, are produced by dipping shaped formers into precompounded liquid latex, and then drying and vulcanizing the products.

Rubber hoses, tubes, and hollow casings

are formed by extrusion. The rubber mixture is forced through a die, rather like squeezing toothpaste from a tube, and vulcanized using hot air. Rubber sheeting (used for weather balloons), fabric-reinforced sheeting (used, for example, on hovercraft skirts), and proofed fabric (used for raincoats) are all formed on a calendar. This is a machine with three rollers, two of which squeeze the rubber into a sheet. To produce a waterproof material, fabric is fed through the lower rollers so that the rubber sheet is pressed into it.

An inflatable rubber boat carrying 11 men *(above)* shoots the rapids on a fast-flowing river, testifying to the strength and resilience of rubber. The scientist *(below)* uses polarized light to study the stress patterns in a motor vehicle tire. More than two-thirds of the natural rubber produced goes into making tires for the automotive industry.

Fact entries

Condamine, Charles Marie de la (1701-1775), was a French botanist who in 1735 discovered the wild rubber tree in South America. Impressed by the waterproofing and elastic properties of latex, he used it for casing his own equipment. In 1876, the Englishman Henry Wickham was commissioned to collect seeds of the wild rubber plant and took them to London for propagation. Plants from these seeds were taken to Ceylon (Sri Lanka) and Malaysia, where they formed the nucleus of the rubber-growing industry.

Dunlop, John Boyd (1840-1921), was a Scottish lawyer who founded the tire industry when he patented the pneumatic tire for bicycles in 1888. By the turn of the century rubber tires were being manufactured for the automobile industry.

Macintosh, Charles (1766-1843), was a Scottish chemist who invented a method of waterproofing fabric in 1823. He used a solution of rubber in coal tar naphtha pressed between two sheets of cloth to produce a lightweight, rainproof fabric. Raincoats that used the fabric were popularly named for him.

The French cotton plant
(Calotropis procera) is a flowering herbaceous plant that produces latex. When a leaf is snapped, the latex flows freely from the plant tissue.

Latex and other plant gums

Latex is a milky-white liquid that occurs in the cells of some flowering plants. It is a complex mixture of substances that may include fats, waxes, and various gum resins. It circulates the plant tissue like sap in branched tubes, conducting other substances and acting as an excretory reservoir. Latex is produced especially by plants of the family Asclepiadaceae, but also by those in the Sapotaceae, Euphorbiaceae, and several others.

Gums, unlike latexes, are clear, yellow, or amber liquids that harden into translucent solids when exposed to the air. The families Leguminosae, Rosaceae, and Sterculiaceae contain most of the gum-producing trees, which convert cell tissue into gum, probably by enzymic action. In some species, the gum collects in ducts to heal damaged tissue and, in others, such as gum arabic *(Acacia senegal)*, oozes from the bark in response to injury.

Resins are obtained from the sap of various plants; like latex and gums, they consist mainly of hydrocarbons based on isoprene, and their main chemical compound is abietic acid. They may be tapped straight from the tree or collected from the ground, sometimes as fossilized lumps (amber). Shellac is produced from the resinous excretion of a scale insect *(Laccifer lacca)* that feeds on various resin-containing trees, such as the soapberry *(Sapindus* sp.) and acacia *(Acacia* sp.) trees of India and Burma. Most resin, however, is tapped from pines, particularly the pitch pine *(Pinus palustris)*, which grows in North America.

Natural latex

Most of the commercially used latex is extracted from the Pará rubber tree *(Hevea brasiliensis)* and is processed into rubber, the subject of the previous article. Other important products derived from natural latex include gutta-percha, balata, and chicle.

Gutta-percha is a yellow or brown leathery material from the latex that is produced primarily by the *Palaquium oblongifolia* tree. This tree grows wild and is cultivated on plantations in Malaysia, the South Pacific, and South America. To extract the latex, trees may be felled or rings cut in the bark. On plantations, fresh leaves are chopped, crushed, and boiled in water to remove the latex.

Gutta-percha becomes plastic and water resistant when it is heated. It can, thus, be used as an insulating material. It is employed for underwater electrical equipment as well as for golfballs and chewing gum. Development in synthetic materials, however, has meant that the use of gutta-percha has largely been replaced by products such as polyethylene, nylon, and vinyl resins.

Balata is a hard, rubberlike material made from the milky juice produced by some tropical plants, notably the bully tree *(Manilkara bidentata)*. The trees are grown particularly in Guyana and the West Indies. Balata is often used as a substitute for gutta-percha to make golfballs and belting.

The llareta *(Azorella glabra)* is a ground-hugging cushion plant that grows high up in the Bolivian Andes. It exudes drops of resin that harden when exposed to the air. Bolivians use the resin as fuel because it produces intense heat when burned.

Chicle is said to contain both rubber and gutta-percha and is a pink or brown material consisting of partly evaporated milky sap. The sap is obtained mainly from the *Achras zapota* tree, which grows in the West Indies, Mexico, and Central America. Chicle was originally developed as a base material for chewing gum, but has been largely replaced by synthetic products.

Some herbaceous plants produce latex, such as the rubber dandelion *(Taraxacum koksaghyz).* The roots of this plant, which is widely cultivated in the Soviet Union, are composed of 8 to 10 per cent rubber.

Plant gums

Gums are soluble in organic solvents, such as alcohol and ether, but they form a gelatinous paste when steeped in water—qualities that have found applications in many industries. The most widely used gum is arabica, which is extracted from the *Acacia senegal.* It consists mainly of calcium, potassium, and magnesium salts of arabin (a complex polysaccharide, which, on hydrolysis, yields glucovonic acid and various simple sugars).

Gum arabic has many applications, the most familiar of which are as an adhesive and as the main glue used for postage stamps. It is employed in surgery to bind severed nerves and will maintain blood pressure because it matches the osmotic pressure of blood. The printing industry is a major beneficiary of gum arabic, particularly in lithographic processes where it acts as a demulcent in the preparation of chemical emulsions. This property also makes it useful for thickening inks.

Large quantities of gum are consumed in food and are used in pharmaceutical products. Its sticky texture makes it an excellent binding and thickening agent for lozenges, pills, and candy, and its pleasant smell and consistency also render it a popular additive in a variety of foods and cosmetics. Gum benzoin, which is obtained mainly from the snowbell tree *(Styrax benzoin),* is used in these products, as is gum tragacanth, which is the dried exudation of the milk vetch *(Astralagus* sp.).

Resins are used to make a diverse range of products, from paints and varnishes to turpentine and perfume. The pine essence of some resins adds fragrance to numerous household products and the distinctive taste to Greek retsina wine. Turpentine, or oil of turpentine, is an aromatic liquid made by distilling resin. It is employed as a solvent and as a vehicle or thinner for oil paints. Some resins have antiseptic properties and are added to cough syrups and mouthwashes.

Amber—a yellowish, usually translucent, fossilized resin from the extinct pine tree *Pinites succinifera,* which once grew along the Baltic coast of Europe—softens when heated and can be fashioned into ornaments and jewelry. It also generates static electricity when rubbed, a property that (from the Greek *elektron,* meaning amber) gave rise to the word electricity.

Rosin is the residue from the distillation of the volatile oils of resin. As well as being used for paints and varnishes, it is also applied to violin bows and, in a powdered form, is used by ballet dancers and gymnasts to prevent themselves from slipping.

Camphor is a resinous material that is extracted from the camphor tree *(Cinnamomum camphora),* which grows in Indonesia, China, and Japan. It is steam-distilled from the chopped-up wood of trees, which must be at least 50 years old. Like other resinous products, camphor is used in lacquers and varnishes, but it is also an ingredient in the manufacture of some moth-repellents and explosives.

In Portugal, the maritime pine *(Pinus pinaster)* is tapped for resin. Oil of turpentine is made from distilled resin and is used as a thinner for oil paints and as a solvent.

Amber is fossilized resin and occurs naturally as irregular nodules. It is usually orange or brown in color and may be opaque. This piece of amber *(above)* was found in the Baltic region of Poland. The insect inside was trapped before the resin hardened.

Conservation and reclamation

The number of vascular plant species considered to be in danger of extinction is roughly estimated to be about one-tenth of the total number of plant species in the world. It is not just the extinctions that are a cause of concern, but the time scale within which they are occurring. Plants cannot evolve fast enough to withstand habitat destruction by, for example, bulldozing, overgrazing, or damage by pollutants. Indeed, the problem is growing ever more critical as the human population on earth increases.

The plant world is essential to all animal life, including humans, as a vital stage in the food chain. All our food, from cereal crops to grazing livestock, is directly or indirectly a plant product. In addition, plants protect soil from erosion and, frequently, nourish it; they also play a major role in the world's climate.

The three major arguments for conservation are economic, climatic, and esthetic. Of them all, the economic one has the greatest immediate impact. This argument is also the strongest in justifying land reclamation. If species are to be conserved in their original habitats, then more land must be developed to cope with human population expansion and the consequent agricultural needs.

Economics of conservation

In the United States it has been estimated that nearly one-quarter of all drugs obtained on prescription in any year are obtained from plants. They include tincture of arnica (from mountain arnica, *Arnica montana*), atropine (from belladonna, *Atropa belladonna*), codeine and morphine (from the opium poppy, *Papaver somniferum*), and quinine (from the bark of the *Cinchona* tree). About 80 per cent of major drugs probably can be derived from plants more cheaply than they can be made in the laboratory.

But many plant species that are potential sources of drugs are in danger of becoming extinct before we learn to exploit their special properties. One example is a member of the periwinkle family Apocynaceae, *Catharanthus coriaceus,* which is found in Madagascar in very small numbers and is threatened by grazing and burning. This plant could be of great use although its medical value has not yet been thoroughly investigated—its genus is known to contain 70 alkaloids, some with clinical value in the treatment of cancer.

Plants provide many products other than drugs, including rubber and gums (*see* previous articles), tanning agents, dyes, fibers, insecticides, perfumes, waxes, cosmetics, preservatives, turpentine, and oils. This last product has seen an interesting development: sperm whale oil was used from the 1930's for several years as a high-pressure lubricant and had no equal. By the late 1960's these whales

The winter garden in the Champs Élysées in Paris was, like many nineteenth-century public conservatories, a repository for exotic and rare plants as well as a place for recreation. These gardens were like nature reserves on a small scale and were a means of conserving endangered species while exploiting them for their decorative value.

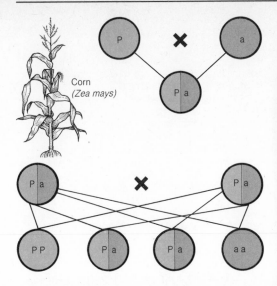

Corn
(Zea mays)

were greatly reduced in number and approaching extinction. Fortunately, it had been discovered that oil from the jojoba nut *(Simmondsia californica)* can replace the sperm whale oil as a lubricant and so reduce the need to hunt these animals, which are now protected.

Forests, being the richest sources of timber, are being exploited everywhere. For example, the equivalent of several square miles of forest is cut down in Malaysia every day for export. In 1950, 35 per cent of the earth's land surface was covered in forest; today it is about 30 per cent. Apart from supplying the timber industry, wood is still a major source of fuel—it provides 31 per cent of the world's fuel needs and plays a large role as a source of energy, mainly in developing countries. But in many forests, once the plant cover is removed, the soil is easily washed away, and the ground is left infertile.

Unlike fossil fuels, wood is renewable; it can also be converted to various other fuels and, thus, be competitive in a world economy. Controlled and artificial regeneration of trees is, therefore, desperately needed to ensure that stocks of timber will be replenished for future generations and that, with care, forests will always provide what is required.

Yet another economic need is that of soil conservation. The removal of plant cover almost inevitably results in soil erosion to some degree; for example, heavy rains can gradually turn a deforested hillside into a bare rocky slope, washing away all the soil and depositing it in rivers or lakes. In river watersheds this erosion can cause rivers to silt up; similarly, reservoirs and lakes may silt up, preventing their use for either water supply or hydroelectricity. But it is not only in watersheds that the removal of the native vegetation brings problems of erosion. The removal of plant cover on plains may lead to wind erosion of the soil and the creation of dust bowls, similar to what happened in the United States during the 1930's, when much of the farmland of the Middle West was destroyed. Conversely, however, it is often possible to reduce erosion by introducing plants to protect the soil from the effects of wind and rain.

Pets and domestic animals have also caused a great deal of destruction. Grazing may pre-

vent seed formation, and overgrazing can kill off plants or at least keep them at subsistence level so that they die without seeding or even managing to reproduce vegetatively. The presence of grazing animals, such as goats, on small islands with endemic plant species has had a drastic effect on the plant life there. Proper grazing rotation could conserve some grasslands as pasture and is now practiced in certain areas. Controlled burning is encouraged in these areas because it causes the leaf litter to release its nutrients and thus help to increase nitrogen levels in the soil, as well as to stimulate new plant growth. The addition of artificial fertilizers also helps to maintain the vegetation.

Conservation for food

Food must also take its place in any economic consideration of conservation. There are about 3,000 plant species that have been recorded as providing humans with food, but the greater part of present-day agriculture is based on fewer than 30 species. Of these, three plants are of particular importance: rice *(Oryza sativa)*, wheat *(Triticum* sp.), and corn *(Zea mays)*; about half of all arable land in the world is taken up with their cultivation. The dependence on such a small number of crops is potentially disastrous, because monocultures are more susceptible to disease than are mixed crops.

Hybridization often uses the gene pool in wild crop plants to improve cultivated varieties. Research has been done into the possibility of breeding a perennial variety of corn *(Zea mays, above left)*. The dominant gene (P) in the wild perennial variety is bred with the recessive gene (a) in the cultivated annual variety. When the hybrids (Pa) cross-fertilize, three out of four will be perennial. Similarly, rice *(Oryza* sp.), which occurs naturally in tropical and subtropical regions, can now be grown in Portugal *(above)*, where it provides a staple crop, having been bred to withstand temperate conditions. The need to conserve wild plants for their genetic importance is slowly being acknowledged.

Land reclaimed from the sea has for centuries been turned over to pasture, arable farming, or horticulture. One of the largest such reclamation projects—the Zuider Zee scheme—has been undertaken in the Netherlands. Over the decades, this country, which covers 15,892 square miles (41,160 square kilometers), has reclaimed about 3 per cent of that area.

Some potential crop plants, however, are threatened species, such as the Yeheb bush *(Cordeauxia edulis)*, which grows on the Somali-Ethiopian border and is being killed off by overgrazing. It produces nuts that have a very high protein content and are, therefore, a valuable food source. It can grow in the most arid parts where other legumes cannot survive, and, once planted, it needs no tending. It is, therefore, very suitable as a crop for the nomadic populations of the area.

These and other wild crop plants bear the characteristics that make it possible to develop new and better varieties of crops by breeding in disease-resistance or greater yield. This is done genetically using a repository of genes (a gene pool). These gene pools survive in places such as uncultivated grasslands and rain forests that are of inestimable value as a gene bank—a value which disappears as these areas are destroyed.

Climatic conservation

The presence of vegetation and its removal is thought to affect the climate. A forest, for example, is continually giving off water vapor

Algae farming is an alternative means of producing feed and fertilizers and indirectly may protect plants from exploitation. Bacteria in ponds feed on waste, producing carbon dioxide that is used by algae in the water, together with sunlight, in photosynthesis. The algae are skimmed off the water, filtered, dried, and then used.

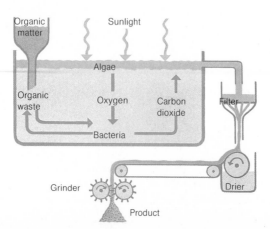

into the air that may affect the amount of rainfall over the forest. Its destruction may have more than just a local effect on rainfall. There may be, for this reason, a desperate need to conserve the world's rain forests, which are being irrevocably destroyed.

Plants also remove carbon dioxide from the atmosphere and store it. After deforestation, and the loss of humus by erosion, carbon dioxide is released into the atmosphere and accumulates there, leading to a "greenhouse effect." It is thought that if the carbon dioxide content of the atmosphere is raised by even a small amount it will cause the average annual temperature to rise by a few degrees. This increase in temperature could melt the polar icecaps, which would raise the sea levels and cause climatic conditions to alter.

At present, 22,000 million tons of carbon dioxide are added to the atmosphere every year. Afforestation and the conservation of forests is needed to remove and store it. It has, therefore, been suggested that large-scale afforestation of fast-growing trees be undertaken and, indeed, there are 250 million acres (101 million hectares) of newly created forest today—a figure that could be doubled by the end of this century.

Another alarming fact that impresses on us the need for plant conservation is that 30 per cent of the oxygen on this planet is produced by terrestrial and freshwater plants (the balance comes from marine algae). Were this source to be depleted, it would have serious consequences for living organisms.

Esthetic conservation

There is no doubt that plants are visually appealing to many people and, while satisfying horticultural needs, can often be combined with recreational areas. Forests and gardens, for example, have been places of leisure activity for centuries. The commercial value of forests need not be reduced by conservation or recreational needs. Botanic gardens and nature reserves also serve as reservoirs for endangered species, in which they can maintain genetic variability and act as a gene pool for future hybrids. Wildlife is closely associated with vegetation and in conserving large tracts of plant growth, we threaten animal life less.

Reclamation

The conservation of plants is the first step in preserving our plant world, but there is also a pressing need for more space for expanding human populations, their food, and that of their livestock. This space can be retrieved from coastal dunes and marshes, deserts, and disused quarries and mine dumps.

Land has been reclaimed from the sea for centuries. These days, the Dutch method of empoldering is most often employed in western Europe. Sediments formed from alluvial gravel, sand, silt, and decaying vegetation are carried in by the tide, accumulate behind artificial dikes, and the enclosed land is drained. Gradually rain leaches most of the salt out of the highly fertile soil, which can then be used for agriculture. In West Germany in this century alone, about 30,000 acres (12,000 hectares) of marine alluvium have been reclaimed in this way.

In tropical and equatorial regions, however, many marshes are high in sulfides, which when exposed to the air become sulfates, making the soil too acid for crop production. In southeastern Asia and India, rice is grown economically on such soils by not totally draining the land and avoiding the use of heavy machinery on it, which would break up the soil.

Coastal and desert dunes can be stabilized in several ways—for example, by planting grasses or succulents on them, by spraying resins onto the sand surface, or by covering it with polyethylene sheeting. Once stabilized they can be planted with crops, with trees for timber, or even forage plants. In the Wellington province of New Zealand, for example, pampas grass *(Cortaderia selloanna)* has been grown on stabilized sand as a food reserve for cattle. Desert reclamation has combined stabi-

lization of the sand with various methods of irrigation and the addition of fertilizers and chemicals.

Apart from shores and deserts, some areas of land devastated by industrial machinery and strip mining have also been reclaimed. In parts of the Australian desert, for example, the sand has been heavily nined for mineral salts, and the soil structure has consequently been destroyed. The toxic mining wastes reduced the possibility of natural reclamation of the area, but with the application of at least 4 inches (10 centimeters) of topsoil vegetation cover could be established. Banksia seedlings were planted together with sorghum to hold the topsoil. Nitrogen and phosphate fertilizers were applied, and wattles *(Acacia* spp.) and gums *(Eucalyptus* spp.) were then planted.

The reclamation of land for recreational purposes is an increasing trend. Here, for example, disused gravel pits have been filled with water to provide facilities for sailing and other water sports. This is a suitable reuse of land that has been disturbed by quarrying and that is not easily converted to agricultural use. In a small way it meets the demands of expanding populations.

Fact entries

Of the thousands of endangered plant species some are particularly important in evolutionary terms or for their commercial or genetic potential.

The tarout cypress *(Cupressus dupreziana)* of southeastern Algeria is of great ecological value in the desert, being one of the most drought-resistant,

frost-tolerant species, and is suitable for timber. But it is threatened by grazing and only 153 specimens exist.

Artemisia granatensis, which grows in the Sierra Nevada in Spain, has been so popular as a tea and an ingredient for alcoholic drinks that it is now virtually extinct.

The bois de fer *(Vateria seychellarum)*, which is endemic to Mahé Island in the Seychelles, numbers about 50 trees, which are threatened by uncontrolled felling. The timber is of a very high quality and could be a valuable gene pool for hybridization. Its sweet-smelling resin could also be useful to the perfume industry.

The Hawaiian hau kuahiwi *(Hibiscadelphus giffardianus)* is of scientific interest in that it exemplifies the coevolution of an endemic plant and animal species. Its tubelike corolla is adapted for pollination by honey creepers whose bills fit the curve of the corolla. Only 10 such trees and a few seedlings survive.

The caoba *(Persea theobromifolia)* is a fast-growing tree with great commercial value. The 13 surviving trees, which are protected in Ecuador, are genetically compatible with the cultivated avocado and could be useful in hybridization.

Forest management

Given good management, trees are a renewable natural resource that provide many products including fuel, lumber, wood pulp, fiber, and food for human and animal consumption in the form of fruits, bark, and leaves. Forests are also ecologically valuable because they recycle nutrients, fix energy and water, and keep the soil fertile. They may also influence rainfall and climate generally.

The problem is that pressure from the need for space for cash crops and felling for lumber has led to large-scale destruction, particularly of tropical rain forests, which are a major source of hardwood timber for the world. In 1981, tropical forests were being destroyed at the rate of 125 acres (50 hectares) a minute.

Forests are delicate systems which, if disturbed, can be permanently destroyed, as has been the case with many tropical forests. It is, therefore, in our own interests to extend, conserve, and manage the forests of the world rather than simply exploit them for short-term gain. Proper scientific management of forests (silviculture) includes the establishment, development, and reproduction of trees to provide salable lumber in the shortest possible time, to control erosion, protect watersheds, provide recreation and enhance the landscape, to protect animals, and to make provision for agriculture.

Forest establishment

Afforestation is the primary establishment of forests in previously unforested areas or those that have long been deforested. To begin, the ground needs to be broken up and drained and, if sloping, may also be terraced to prevent runoff of water. Soil and fertilizers, such as phosphate, are then applied in the planting holes. The soil, climate, quality, and type of timber expected are considered, but the trees chosen are not always indigenous; more importantly they need to be fast-growing and hardy: for example, Sitka spruce *(Picea sitchenis)*, which is used in Britain; Monterey pine *(Pinus radiata)*, which is widely grown in warm temperate climates, most extensively in New Zealand; and Caribbean pine *(Pinus caribaea)*, which is planted throughout the seasonal tropics and subtropics. The fast-growing pines are used for pulp. Other fast-growing trees make veneer logs, such as *Gmelina arborea,* which is grown in Brazil. With good management, trees take up to 50 years to mature; to attain saw log size, a mature forest ecosystem may take twice as long to reestablish.

Seedlings are first raised in a nursery where they may have been bred for hardiness, fast growth, or dense or soft wood. They are usually planted out when one to four years old, during their dormant period. They can be planted at other times provided they are guaranteed water to prevent them from drying out before the roots establish themselves—during a tropical rainy season, for example. After planting, the trees are weeded for the first few years until they are tall enough to overtop and suppress any weeds.

The number of trees planted in a given area depends on the species. In temperate areas hardwoods such as ash (*Fraxinus* sp.), beech (*Fagus* sp.), and oak (*Quercus* sp.) are planted 5 feet (1.5 meters) apart. Conifers such as larch (*Larix* sp.) and pines (*Pinus* spp.) are planted 5 to 6.5 feet (1.5 to 2 meters) apart, whereas poplars (*Populus* spp.) are planted 16.5 to 19 feet (5 to 5.8 meters) apart.

When the developing trees are about 8 to 10 years old the forest floor is generally cleared of bushes and woody climbers. The low branches of the trees are removed in a process called brashing, which helps to reduce the number of knots in the mature timber. The trees are thinned out about 12 to 15 years after planting, the thinnings providing the first lumber crop. Their removal allows the final crop to achieve its maximum potential.

Spruce saplings, in the foreground, are grown for 10 years, when they are cut for pulpwood. Spruce wood is thought to make some of the best paper pulp. These trees grow faster and on poorer soils than do broad-leaved species.

Brashing, the removal of the lower branches of trees when they are about 10 years old, serves to reduce the number of knots in the mature timber. The removed young wood is then used for pulp.

Diseased and unsatisfactory trees are also removed at the same time.

In caring for forests, such factors as frost, snow, lightning, sunlight, water, and wind need to be considered. Measures taken to reduce the damage done by these elements include proper drainage, adequate provision of water, and shading seedlings. Fires are often the major hazard, causing damage that varies from slight bark scorching to complete destruction. They can occur in the soil (especially when it is peaty), among the surface litter, or on whole trees. Surface fires, if not too intense, may be beneficial. Such fires are deliberately started in mature eucalyptus (*Eucalyptus* sp.) forests in Australia, for example, where they prevent the build-up of a deep flammable litter layer so that the intensity of fires is kept small. Many species of gum need fires to trigger germination. To prevent fires from spreading, fire lines 33 feet (10 meters) or more across are created and kept clear of vegetation.

Monocultures versus mixed forests

Forests containing only a single species are easier to manage than are mixed forests because planting takes less time, thinning requires less skill, and the timber is uniform. The advantages of mixed forests may, however, be much greater than those of monocultures. For example, the risk of fire is reduced in a mixed deciduous-conifer forest. Mixed planting also allows advantage to be taken of species preferences for growing conditions. In addition, the timber of some species is more valuable when mature, and a mixed system allows such species to be grown with others in which the younger wood is commercially valuable.

Mixed forests are sometimes created by underplanting. In a forest of about 30 to 50 years old, shade-tolerant trees are planted in the understory, the overstory casting only a light shade over it. Suitable understory trees are hemlock (*Tsuga* sp.), beech, and silver fir (*Abies alba*). Underplanting helps to improve the quality of the main crop, produces more wood per given area, and encourages animals.

Pests and diseases are a problem, especially with monocultures, among which they spread quicker than in mixed forests. Aphids and sawflies, for example, create galls, and mites, moth larvae, scale insects, and some fungi can cause defoliation. Other fungi damage the wood, fruits, and roots, and eventually kill the trees. The application of insecticides, such as nicotine and malathion, fungicides, tar-oil washes, copper compounds, and burning are effective in reducing disease. However, these measures can at the same time damage the trees and kill off other animal life. Natural control of these pests is, therefore, preferred—insect-eating birds and other animals can provide some measure of control. Animal life is, however, more abundant in natural mixed forests than in monospecific plantations.

Lumber extraction

In the planted forest everything is organized to extract lumber as economically as possible, which is usually by removing all the trees and then replanting the whole area. This method is known as clear-felling or clear-cutting. The area to be felled is calculated by dividing the total area of forest by its rotation time (the time a species needs to grow before it can be cut). If, for instance, a total forest is 500 acres (200 hectares) with a rotation of 100 years, then the area cut and replanted each year is 5 acres (2 hectares). The rotation times vary depending on the species; oak requires 100 to 150 years, and poplar, 40 to 45 years. For a fast-growing tropical tree grown for pulp, less than 40 years may suffice.

The advantages of clear-felling are that it is the simplest system to manage, no seedling trees are damaged during felling, and replanting is more dependable than natural regeneration (even if it is more expensive). If, however, planting is not started soon after felling, the soil may gradually begin to deteriorate

The growth rates of forest trees vary depending on the species. Of the softwoods, Monterey pine is one of the fastest growers, sometimes shooting up as much as 18 feet (5.5 meters) in one year. Wellingtonia grows more steadily, slowing down as it reaches 100 years old. Among the hardwoods, ash grows fast, often reaching 100 feet (30 meters) well before it is 100 years old. It achieves a mature height of about 150 feet (45 meters). In contrast, beech grows very slowly to begin with but later spurts up to reach about 85 feet (26 meters).

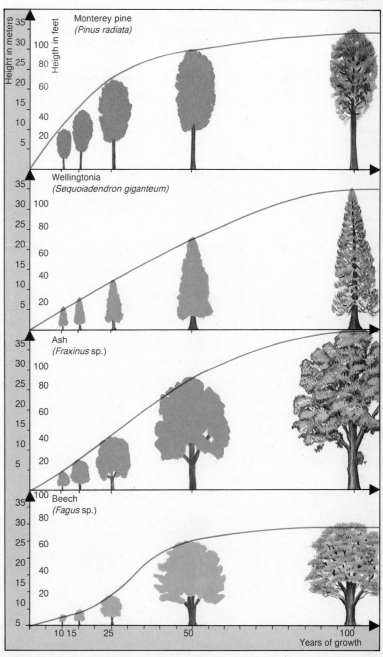

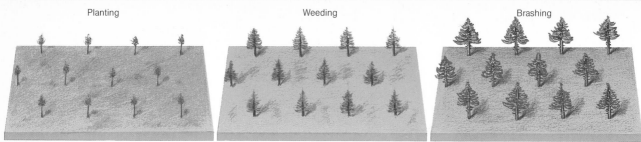

Planting   Weeding   Brashing

The management of a larch forest grown for timber starts when the saplings, of between two and four years old, are planted. From four to seven years old they are weeded and then, at about eight to ten years, the lower branches are cut off for pulp. Two years later they are thinned, the wood also being used for pulp. They are felled all at once when mature, and soon after the ground is replanted.

Fires are often deliberately caused in Australian eucalyptus forests to limit the undergrowth and initiate seed germination. If the understory were allowed to become too dense and were set alight, the fires would be less controllable.

through erosion or oxidation. In addition, the absence of mature trees to provide cover for young seedlings may slow down their establishment.

A mature natural forest presents a slightly different problem in lumber extraction. A selective system may be operated, in which trees are felled singly, in twos and threes, or in small areas of up to one-third of an acre (in a temperate forest). The trees are felled when mature or when commercially valuable.

The advantages of this system over clear-felling are numerous: natural regeneration is the norm after selective felling and is supplemented by planting only where necessary; the soil is not exposed, so there are no problems of erosion or landslip; and seedlings are protected by the surrounding trees. Moreover, the financial returns are immediate because the trees are already mature. The disadvantages of selective felling are the difficulties and extra cost of extraction and the damage that may be done to the young regenerating trees.

Forests can be felled in strips instead of a block, which simplifies the problems of extraction. Cut at right angles to the prevailing wind in the lee of the wood, the strip is sheltered

and can be seeded from the standing trees. When regeneration is underway the next strip can be cut. This is repeated until the whole mature forest is cleared.

Another variant of selective felling is the polycyclic system in which selected mature trees are felled to open up the canopy, which allows previously shaded seedlings to grow and develop. A second felling thins out the canopy further to allow the regeneration process to continue. The final felling removes all the mature trees. The advantages and disadvantages are similar to those of single group and strip-felling.

Coppicing techniques

Coppicing systems have been used in Europe for hundreds of years and provide a mixture of large and small hardwood timber. Because it relies on regrowth from a cut stump, however, this method cannot be used for conifers, which do not normally regenerate from a stump.

A coppice wood is composed of a number of stumps in various stages of regeneration that are managed on a short rotation, dependent on the species. For ash the rotation time

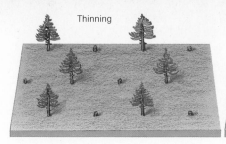
Thinning

Felling

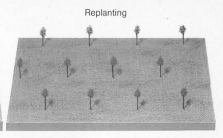
Replanting

can be as little as 5 years, for alder (*Alnus* sp.) it can be 25 years. Initially a mature tree is felled to leave a stump, or stool, 1.5 feet (46 centimeters) high. This is allowed to regenerate, and the new shoots grow until they reach the correct cutting size. The shoots grow quickly, nourished by the mature root system. The coppice is generally cut in strips or blocks, the area to be cut being calculated by dividing the size of the coppice by its rotation time.

A number of species are suitable for this treatment and include hazel (*Corylus* sp.), sweet chestnut (*Castanea* sp.), hornbeam (*Carpinus* sp.), and birch (*Betula* sp.). The life of the stools varies depending on the species—for oak it is more than 100 years.

If the coppice is combined with tall trees, the system is known as coppice-with-standard. The stools are mixed with "standard" trees which are typically oak. The standards are normally felled on a rotation that is, for convenience, a multiple of the stools' rotation; they may themselves be regenerated by selecting and retaining one shoot from a coppice stool, rather than grown as "maidens" from seedlings.

Other factors of management

Considerations of erosion and watershed management are important in forestry. Large-scale clear-felling can cause erosion, waterway and reservoir silting, damage to fisheries, and loss of drinkable or usable water. Good forest management by the regular opening up of the forest canopy increases the diversity of forest structure and consequently that of the flora and fauna.

Population pressures and increasing demands for space for crop cultivation has led in some places to a need to devise management programs that allow the production of food and wood from the same land. Mixed cropping and grazing has also been implemented in forestry plantations.

The potential of forestry as a source of rural development, rehabilitation of degraded land, water catchment, and provision of shelter and recreation is now being appreciated. So too is the need to safeguard the diversity of the species-rich natural forest ecosystems—not simply for the sake of diversity, but for the sake of life on earth.

Abundant, vertical slim branches are the distinctive mark of coppiced trees. The low thick stump, or stool, in the foreground regenerates new shoots every time the old ones are cut for timber. Once a widespread practice in Europe, coppicing is decreasing.

The effects of acid rain—caused by sulfurous pollution in the atmosphere—are evident in the dying foliage of these conifers growing in the Black Forest of Germany. Gradually the trees will die, destroying the habitats of birds and other animals that live in the forest.

Shore and desert reclamation

Most coastal plains are rich in plant nutrients and are, therefore, suitable for agriculture. But a combination of human activities, overgrazing, and erosion can reduce this potential. With enough water for irrigation, shores and even deserts can also be used for cultivation, although the loose composition of sandy soil (and its large grain size) causes rain water to soak through it rapidly, leaching out the nutrients. Such terrain is also particularly vulnerable to wind erosion, which tends to strip away the topsoil. For thousands of years people have tried to reclaim coastal and desert land, to stabilize the areas, and eventually cultivate them.

Shores and dunes

Estuaries and shorelines are reclaimed initially to protect the land from tidal flooding and the seepage of salt water.

Coastal dune systems are also formed to protect the hinterland. They usually comprise a frontal dune, which forms a buffer zone, and a hind dune, which protects the sheltered areas from salt spray or sand-drift damage. Dune formation can be encouraged by placing an obstacle in the path of the prevailing wind, which causes it to slow down and deposit some of the sand that it is carrying. The obstacles may be fences but most often consist of plants. Marram grass (Ammophila arenaria), for example, has a rapid rate of upward growth, is perennial, and can reproduce vegetatively. It therefore increases the rate of sand accumulation while keeping above the rising levels. Dunes produced in this way typically reach a width of 100 feet (30 meters) or more

and a height of 33 feet (10 meters) in about 10 years. Other dune-forming methods include the spreading of a film of rubber compound on the mobile sand, which stabilizes it enough to allow the germination and growth of such grasses as couch grass (Agropyron juncei-forme).

Once the initial stabilization of the dune has been achieved, tree lupines (Lupinus arboreus) are frequently planted to further stability, together with the spiny sea buckthorn (Hippophae rhamnoides), which discourages animals and people from trampling on the dune surface, causing it to erode.

Dunes are made usable in several ways after stabilization. Nitrogen fertilizer is usually added, and shrubs such as Scotch broom (Cystisus scoparius) are planted as an intermediate step before trees are established. Crops of lucerne or alfalfa (Medicago sativa) are planted in temperate areas to introduce nitrogen into the soil. Two to four years after planting marram grass, the dunes are sufficiently stabilized to introduce tree species that can tolerate salty winds, such as Monterey pines (Pinus radiata), gum trees (Eucalyptus spp.), and acacias (Acacia spp.). These plants are deep-rooted and can resist drought. They also grow rapidly and can soon form a stand of mature trees. Acacias help to increase the nitrogen content of the soil by means of bacteria contained in their root-nodules.

In Argentina, crops of rye and sorghum, with the addition of millet, have successfully stabilized dunes covering 15 acres (6 hectares) in as little as 18 months. This has then facilitated the spread of natural vegetation.

Succulent plants survive on coastal dunes because their thick cuticle allows them to withstand the abrasive wind and the salt spray that reaches them from the sea. The plants form an obstacle to the wind and cause it to deposit sand grains and so increase the size of the dune. The plants' roots stabilize the dune surface and reduce its erosion by wind and water.

Deserts

The main cause of desertification is inappropriate methods of land use on the fragile semi-arid marginal lands.

Desertification can be reduced by the rational use of land resources from the individual level upward, by the introduction and improvement of proper irrigation methods, increased soil moisture storage, the restoration of degraded pastures, and the improvement of strategies of pasture rotation.

Many desert areas have large deposits of artesian water which may be raised to the surface by simply boring a hole and allowing the water to surface naturally. Once water is available, the difficulty of irrigating plants is obviously reduced.

One of the problems of irrigation is that, depending on the mineral composition of the water, if it is allowed to dry on the soil it can lead to the salinization or alkalinization of the soil, and vegetation cannot be established. To counteract salinization, flushing irrigation is used to keep the soil constantly moist; the careful application of chemicals to the soil, such as gypsum, prevents alkalinization.

Pastures that have been overgrazed have been improved in some desert areas, as in Kazakhstan, by the introduction of forage plants. These include prostrate summer cypress *(Kochia prostrata)*, oriental saltwort *(Salsola orientalis)*, and Mexican mesquite *(Prosopis* sp.). The value of these shrubs is that when grown in stands they reduce wind speed and protect the soil from drying out and contracting. In addition, they survive the parching summer heat (whereas many other plants die down) and so provide a food source in summer. They also have a richer protein content than many grasses do.

The use of sand covers, such as oil resins or polyethylene sheeting, helps to prevent some evaporation from the sand surface and stabilizes it so that plants may be established. Fuel-oil mulches have also been used to stabilize dunes but preclude the establishment of natural vegetation. On many stabilized areas, vegetables have been cultivated on experimental production plots, such as the Negev Desert in Israel. These experiments have been successful particularly with the application of nitrogen, phosphorus, potassium, and, occasionally, manure. Increasing effort is being put into land reclamation with these methods, particularly because of the land and food shortages resulting from overpopulation.

Irrigation systems that draw on water from oases have been constructed in some desert areas. The water is distributed by sprinklers and furrows to newly planted vegetation.

Polyethylene tunnels permit enclosed cultivation in desert areas with no specific preparation of the sand. The environment within the tunnel is controlled and stabilized and normal greenhouse cultivation techniques of temperature and humidity control apply.

Plant taxonomy

The Plant Kingdom

Kingdom	(Superphylum) or Phylum	Common name	Subphylum	Class
Procaryota	Schizophyta	blue-green algae and bacteria		Schizophyceae Schizomycetes Mollicutes
Eucaryota	(Phycophyta)	algae		
	Chlorophyta	green algae		Chlorophyceae Charophyceae
	Xanthophyta	yellow-green algae		Xanthophyceae
	Chrysophyta	golden algae		Chrysophyceae Haptophyceae
	Bacillariophyta	diatoms		Bacillariophyceae
	Pyrrophyta	dinoflagellates		Desmophyceae Dinophyceae
	Cryptophyta			Cryptophyceae
	Euglenophyta	euglenoids		Euglenophyceae
	Phaeophyta	brown algae		Phaeophyceae
	Rhodophyta	red algae		Rhodophyceae
	Mycota	fungi	Myxomycotina Eumycotina	Myxomycetes Chytridiomycetes Hyphochytridiomycetes Plasmodiophoromycetes Oomycetes Zygomycetes Trichomycetes Ascomycetes Basidiomycetes Deuteromycetes
	Lichenes	lichens		Ascolichenes Basidiolichenes
	Bryophyta	mosses and liverworts		Bryopsida Hepaticopsida Anthocerotopsida
	Pteridophyta	club mosses, horsetails, and ferns		Psilopsida Lycopsida Sphenopsida Filicopsida
	*Spermatophyta	seed-bearing plants	Gymnospermae Magnoliophytina	Cycadopsida Gnetopsida Coniferopsida Magnoliopsida Liliopsida

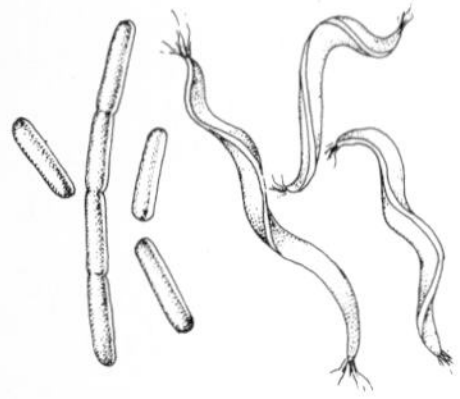

Bacteria

Algae

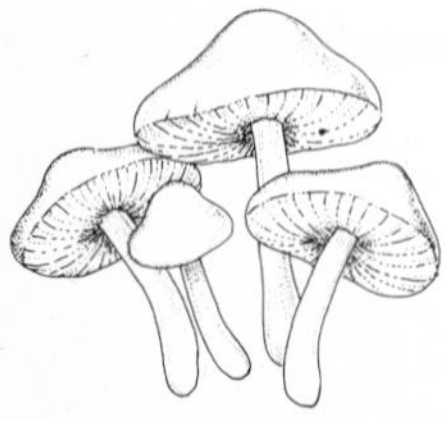

Fungi

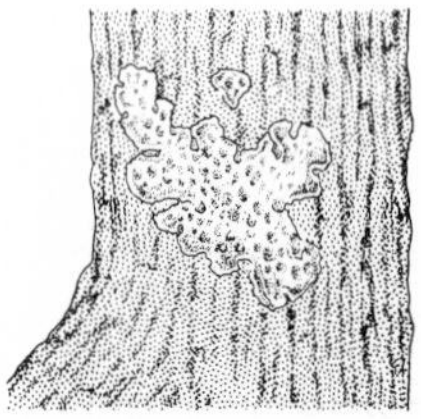

Lichens

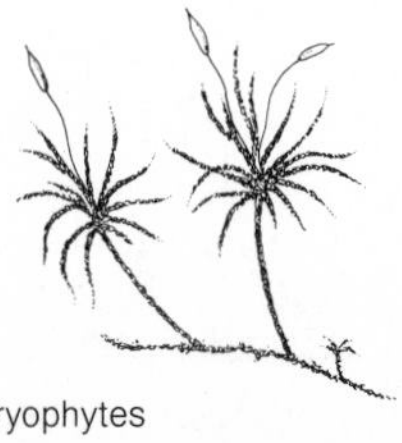

Bryophytes

Pteridophytes

Spermatophytes

*Spermatophyta (seed-bearing plants)

(Subphylum) or Class	Subclass	Order		
(Gymnospermae) Cycadopsida		Cycadales	Nilssoniales	
Gnetopsida		Welwitschiales	Ephedrales	Gnetales
Coniferopsida		Ginkgoales	Coniferales	Taxales
(Magnoliophytina) Magnoliopsida	Magnoliidae	Magnoliales Piperales	Laurales Aristolochiales	Nymphaeales
	Ranunculidae	Illiciales Ranunculales	Nelumbonales Papaverales	Sarraceniales
	Hamamelidae	Trochodendrales Eupteleales Hamamelidales Urticales Casuarinales	Betulales Myricales Juglandales Cercidiphyllales Didymelales	Eucommiales Barbeyales Fagales Balanopales Leitneriales
	Caryophyllidae	Caryophyllales Polygonales	Cactales Plumbaginales	Theligonales
	Dilleniidae	Dilleniales Theales Passiflorales Begoniales Tamaricales Ericales	Ebenales Malvales Thymeleales Paeoniales Violales Cucurbitales	Capparales Salicales Diapensiales Primulales Euphorbiales
	Rosidae	Saxifragales Fabales Nepenthales Myrtales Rutales Geraniales Cornales	Rhamnales Santalales Proteales Rosales Connarales Podostemales Hippuridales	Sapindales Polygalales Celastrales Oleales Elaeagnales
	Asteridae	Dipsacales Polemoniales Lamiales Calycerales	Gentianales Scrophulariales Campanulales Asterales	
Liliopsida	Alismatidae	Alismatales	Hydrocharitales	Najadales
	Liliidae	Triuridales Iridales	Liliales Zingiberales	Orchidales
	Commelinidae	Juncales Bromeliales Eriocaulales	Cyperales Commelinales Restionales	Poales
	Arecidae	Arecales Arales	Cyclanthales Pandanales	Typhales

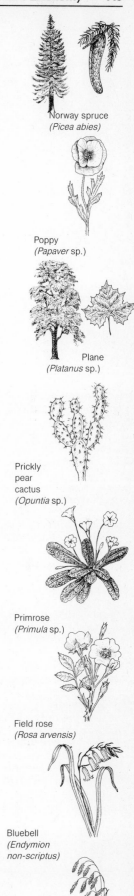

Norway spruce (*Picea abies*)

Poppy (*Papaver* sp.)

Plane (*Platanus* sp.)

Prickly pear cactus (*Opuntia* sp.)

Primrose (*Primula* sp.)

Field rose (*Rosa arvensis*)

Bluebell (*Endymion non-scriptus*)

Hairy brome (*Bromus ramosus*)

Glossary

In the following glossary, small capital letters (that is, STAMEN) indicate terms that have their own entries in the glossary.

A

abscission layer A layer of thin-walled cells that forms at the base of a leaf. It breaks at leaf-fall. Similar layers may also occur in bark or at a branch base.

achene A type of fruit consisting of a single dry seed.

actinomorphic Having a radial or star-shaped symmetry, as has the flower of a buttercup.

aerenchyma A type of tissue found particularly in water plants. Generally loose and spongy, it has air spaces between the cells.

akinete A resting cell in some green algae. It is provided with food reserves and serves as a means of VEGETATIVE reproduction.

alburnum The soft sapwood of a tree.

alkaloids Natural substances found in plants which affect the physiology of animals. Some of these organic bases, such as quinine and strychnine, are used in pharmacology.

alternation of generations The occurrence in the life cycle of a plant of two forms, differing in appearance and number of chromosomes, in regular alternation. One form reproduces sexually, the other asexually.

ameboid Shaped or moving like an ameba, a single cell with a flowing form.

amino acids Fatty acids which contain an amino (NH_2) group; these are the building blocks of which PROTEINS are made.

anaerobic respiration A form of respiration in which free oxygen plays no part. Many plants have the ability to break down sugars to alcohols under these conditions. The same process is involved in fermentation of wine and beer.

androecium The collective name for the male parts of a plant, particularly the STAMENS in a flower.

anemochory The distribution of seeds by the wind.

annual A plant that germinates, lives, reproduces, and dies within a single growing season.

annual ring An annual ring in a cross section of tree trunk is the product of a single year's growth.

annulus Any structure having the form of a ring. The annulus of a fern SPORANGIUM is a ring of thick-walled cells which form a mechanism for tossing out the ripe spores. The ring of cells that ruptures to release spores from a moss capsule is also termed an annulus.

anther The part of the STAMEN of a flower in which the pollen is produced.

antheridium In flowerless plants, the part in which the male GAMETES are produced.

apical meristem An area of cells at a growing tip which can divide and differentiate into mature tissues.

apocarpous Describes a flower in which the CARPELS are separate from one another.

archegonium The part of a plant that contains the female sex cell. In liverworts, mosses, and ferns the archegonia are small flask-shaped organs with the sex cell in the body of the "flask" and a canal in the neck down which the male cell swims for FERTILIZATION.

ascospore One of the SPORES formed within an ASCUS.

ascus A thin-walled cell in which SPORES form, found in a group of fungi which includes the yeasts and the penicillin mold.

association A group of plant species growing together that are characteristic of a particular habitat. The group is often labeled by naming it after the species that is perceived to be the dominant one in the habitat.

autotrophic Describes a plant that manufactures its own food from simple inorganic materials and is not reliant on other organisms for nourishment.

auxin Sometimes called a growth substance, an auxin is any one of a group of substances that act as chemical messengers, being produced in one part of a plant and having an effect at another.

awn A stiff, bristlelike projection, like those which make up the "beard" on the flower spike of barley, or that on the fruit of the storkbill.

B

balsams Aromatic compounds produced by plants.

basidiospore The name for the characteristic SPORES formed by the group of fungi known as Basidiomycetes. This group includes the typical mushrooms and toadstools which bear the SPORES on "GILLS" beneath the cap.

basidium The cell or group of cells from which the SPORES form in Basidiomycete fungi.

biennial A plant that germinates and grows one year, reproducing and dying in the next.

biflagellate Bearing two FLAGELLA, as do some algae.

binary fission A simple cell division in which the NUCLEUS divides into two, followed by a similar division of the cell body.

biosphere That part of the earth and its atmosphere that is capable of supporting living things.

bract A leaf below a flower or flower head. The flower develops in the axil of the bract.

bulb A large underground bud made up of leaf bases

which are swollen with food reserves.

bulbil A fleshy bud with food reserves produced above ground and capable of giving rise to a new plant.

C

Calvin cycle Another term for the "DARK REACTION" of photosynthesis, it is named after M. Calvin who received the Nobel Prize in 1961 for his analysis of the process.

calyx The SEPALS, the outer WHORL of flower parts that protects the petals in the bud.

cambium A layer of tissue in a root or shoot that actively divides and gives rise to new permanent tissues. Cambium gives rise to secondary thickening.

canal cell One of the cells in the central part of the "neck" of an ARCHEGONIUM.

capsule A closed boxlike structure, such as the seed case of the poppy flower, or the spore case of a moss.

carbohydrates A group of compounds that includes sugar, starch, and CELLULOSE, consisting of carbon, hydrogen, and oxygen. Oxidation of carbohydrates provides energy for cells. Large-molecule carbohydrates such as CELLULOSE and PECTIN are also important to the structure of plants.

carotene A fat-soluble organic compound that acts as a yellow or orange pigment in plants such as the carrot. Carotin is a spelling variation.

carpel One of the divisions of the female part of a flower, consisting of OVARY, style, and STIGMA. A flower may have a single carpel or several.

cell totipotency The ability of dividing cells to produce differentiated cells, the type depending on the stimuli which affect their growth.

cellulose A large-molecule carbohydrate that forms the cell wall in plants.

chemosynthetic Describes organisms, such as some bacteria, that can synthesize organic material from simple chemicals without the process of PHOTOSYNTHESIS.

chitin A CARBOHYDRATE derivative that forms an important part of the skeleton in invertebrate animals, and is also found in the cell walls of fungi.

chlorophyll The green pigment of plants. It has several types but is chemically always based on a tetrapyrrole ring containing magnesium. Chlorophyll is the substance that traps light energy to begin the process of PHOTOSYNTHESIS.

chloroplast A cell ORGANELLE found in the cells of green plants. It contains the CHLOROPHYLL and forms a unit for PHOTOSYNTHESIS.

chromosome One of many cell bodies present in the NUCLEUS that becomes visible by staining at cell divisions. Chromosomes carry the genes that determine the characteristics of a species.

circumnutation The spiral movement shown by the growing tip of a plant.

citric acid cycle A process occurring during respiration in the cell. During the cyclic process, which involves the oxidation of pyruvic acid, the compound citric acid is one of the first formed, so giving the name. During this process excess energy from various compounds is converted into high-energy phosphate bonds that store chemical energy for the cell.

cladogram A diagram that attempts to express the relationships of organisms by putting onto the same branch of the diagram only those organisms that share a character that is unique to their group.

climax A stable COMMUNITY of plants that is fully adapted to a particular set of conditions. The climax vegetation may be reached only after a series of stages in which other types of vegetation colonize an area and are subsequently ousted.

coenocytic Describes a plant or tissue that possesses a number of nuclei but has no dividing cell walls.

coleoptile The sheath covering the first pair of true leaves of a grass.

coleorrhiza The sheath covering the young root of a grass.

collenchyma A support tissue found in leaf stalks, midribs, and young stems. It consists of PARENCHYMA cells which may have CHLOROPLASTS but are strengthened by CELLULOSE thickening in the walls.

commensal An organism living with another and sharing its nourishment, but with no ill effect on either.

community A group of plants consistently growing together under a certain set of conditions and forming a recognizable whole, such as the plants characteristic of heathland.

companion cell A type of cell found in flowering plants. Companion cells, which retain their nuclei, are associated with the sieve cells of PHLOEM tissue.

compound leaves Leaves made up of several distinct parts or leaflets that are separate down to the midrib, such as the leaves of ash or chestnut.

conidiophore The part of a fungus that bears a CONIDIUM.

conidium A SPORE which forms from a fungal body without any sexual process.

conjugation The joining together of two cells whose nuclei fuse and give rise to new individuals. It occurs particularly in algae, such as Spirogyra.

connective The piece of tissue that separates the pollen-bearing lobes of an ANTHER in a flower.

convergent evolution The development of similar structures or characteristics in two organisms that are not closely related, and believed to be caused by evolution in response to similar conditions in their environments.

cordate Describes a leaf shaped somewhat like the ace of spades in a card deck.

cork A protective layer of dead cells on the outside of a stem or root. Cork cell walls are impregnated with waxy substances that make them relatively impermeable.

corm An underground storage organ consisting of a swollen stem. It may resemble a bulb but has no overlapping fleshy leaves.

corolla The collective name for the petals of a flower.

cotyledon A leaf which is present in the seed of a plant. It may remain there or may be raised and become green during GERMINATION, although it is usually a different shape from subsequent leaves.

cross-pollination POLLINATION which involves pollen from one flower traveling to the STIGMA of any other flower of the same species.

cultivar A variety of plant which has been produced in cultivation.

cuticle A layer that covers the outside of epidermal cells.

cutin The mixture of fatty substances that forms the CUTICLE.

cytoplasm The living contents of the cell excluding the NUCLEUS.

D

dark reaction That part of the process of PHOTOSYNTHESIS that can take place in the dark following the capture of light. In the dark reaction, carbon dioxide is fixed and incorporated into compounds in the cell.

daughter cells Cells that are the first generation product of a division of cells.

deciduous Describes trees and shrubs in which the leaves are all shed at a particular season.

decomposers Organisms that help to break down the organic remains of animal and plant bodies into simpler materials.

decurrent Running downwards. This term may be applied to the GILLS of fungi which run down onto the stalk, or to leaves with a continuing wing onto a stem.

dendrochronology The science of analyzing tree rings. It may be used in calculating the age of trees or lumber, in correlating past events, and in tracing former fluctuations in climate.

dendrogram A diagram which displays data in the form of a branching, treelike pattern, as, for example, some evolutionary trees.

diaspore Any part of a plant that is capable of being dispersed and giving rise to a new plant.

dichogamous Describes a flower in which pollen and OVULES are not mature at the same time, so the flower is unable to fertilize itself.

dichotomous Branching into two equal parts, each branch dividing into two again, and so on. This pattern of growth is characteristic of many "primitive" plants.

dicotyledon A flowering plant in which two seed leaves are present in the seed.

digitate Describes a compound leaf in which the individual leaflets spread like the fingers of a hand.

dimorphic With two distinct forms. Used particularly of flowers such as primrose and bogbean where two different forms of flower ensure CROSS-POLLINATION.

dioecious Describes plants in which male and female organs are on different individuals.

diploid The condition of having two basic sets of CHROMOSOMES, one set from each parent, unlike GAMETES, which have a single set.

disaccharides Sugars such as sucrose that are composed of two simple sugars, or MONOSACCHARIDES.

disk florets The small flowers that make up the central part, or disk, of a composite flower such as a daisy. Disk florets are usually trumpet-shaped and symmetrical.

disruptive selection A type of selection in which a species adapts to the surroundings in two or more different ways, which gives an advantage under certain circumstances. In so doing it may abandon the former middle ground of average characteristics for the species, leading to splitting of the species.

dominant A plant species that by its size or number of individuals determines the characteristics of the vegetation in a particular area.

dormant Describes a seed, bulb, or other plant structure that is in an apparently resting condition with no growth and a minimum of metabolism.

drupe A fruit in which the seed is surrounded by a stone and then by a fleshy layer. Plums and sloes are drupes.

duramen The hard central region of a tree trunk; the heartwood.

E

ectotrophic Finding nourishment from outside, as in some fungi that surround roots and extract nourishment from them.

elaisome An oily particle on the outside of a seed that acts as an attractant to insects such as ants which aid the seed's dispersal.

elater A spirally thickened cell in the spore capsule of liverworts. Its movements assist spore dispersal.

embryo-sac The part of a flowering plant that represents the gametophyte generation. It contains eight nuclei including the female GAMETE.

emergent A forest tree that grows so tall that its crown emerges above the rest of the trees.

endoplasmic reticulum The network of folded membranes within a cell that is concerned in making PROTEINS.

endosperm Starchy food tissue that surrounds the embryo in a seed.

endotrophic Feeding from within, as in fungi, which penetrate the root tissues of their host.

endozoochory Transport of a plant seed within an animal.

enzyme A PROTEIN produced by a cell that acts as a catalyst in a living organism, speeding up chemical reactions.

ephemeral A plant that is able to germinate, grow, and fruit in a very short period. Many weeds and desert plants have life spans of only a few weeks.

epidermis The layer, usually one cell thick, over the surface of a plant.

epiphyte A plant that grows attached to another plant, but without being a PARASITE.

F

fertilization The union of a male sex cell with a female sex cell to form a new individual.

fibril A tiny threadlike structure. A root hair.

fix To incorporate into an organism an element from the inorganic surroundings, such as carbon or nitrogen.

flagella Tiny whiplike processes, attached to some single-celled organisms and GAMETES, which by their lashing, move the cells.

floret One of the small flowers in a flower head.

follicle A type of fruit formed from a single CARPEL which splits along one side to release its seeds.

forb Any low plant in grassland that is not a grass.

fruiting body A well-defined, spore-bearing structure, such as a toadstool.

funicle The stalk of an OVULE.

G

gametangia Organs that produce sex cells.

gamete A sex cell, capable of taking part in FERTILIZATION.

gemmae Buds or other vegetative outgrowths that are capable of forming new individuals.

generative cell The smaller of two cells into which a POLLEN GRAIN divides. The generative cell divides to produce two male GAMETES.

geotropism A plant growth response that is initiated by gravity.

germination The starting into growth of a seed or SPORE.

gibberellin A plant hormone that stimulates growth in shoots.

gills The vertical divisions under the cap of a toadstool.

glycolysis The process of breaking down glucose in living tissue to pyruvic acid. This is a stage of respiration that can take place in the absence of oxygen.

granae Minute particles within the CHLOROPLAST of a plant cell in which the CHLOROPHYLL is concentrated.

guard cells The two cells that surround a pore, or stoma, on a plant. As they change shape the pore opens or closes.

gynoecium The female part of a flower. Also spelled gynaecium or gynaeceum.

H

halophyte A plant capable of living in very salty conditions, such as on a seashore.

haploid Describes a cell that has only one basic set of CHROMOSOMES. GAMETES are haploid, and some whole plants, such as the gametophyte generation of liverworts, may be.

haptotropism The response by stems or TENDRILS to the stimulus of touching an object.

haustoria The roots of parasitic plants, or outgrowths from a fungus, that take nourishment from a host's tissues.

heartwood The central core of the hardest wood in a tree.

heath A type of vegetation, found mainly on acid sandy soils, which is dominated by heathers.

helophyte A marsh plant.

hemicellulose A sugar polymer found in some plant walls.

herbaceous Describes a plant without a woody stem.

hermaphroditic With both male and female sexual parts.

heterokont With FLAGELLA of unequal length.

heterosporous Producing two sizes of SPORE, as do some ferns.

heterostyly Having styles of different lengths, as do primrose flowers, thus ensuring CROSS-POLLINATION.

heterotrophic Describes organisms that feed on others because they are unable to manufacture their own food.

homosporous Producing SPORES all of about the same size.

hydrolysis The splitting of organic compounds through reaction with water.

hydroseral succession A succession of plant types that begins with the colonization of a wet environment.

hydrostatic skeleton Support that is obtained from the water content of a body.

hydrotropism Plant movements in response to the stimulus of water.

hygromorphic Adapted to a wet habitat.

hyphae The threadlike structures making up the main body of many fungi.

I

indusium A protective cover, particularly the scale or flap that protects the spore-producing bodies in ferns.

inflorescence A whole flower head including all the individual flowers on it.

inhibitor A substance that prevents a process from taking place.

innate Originating from within.

integument A covering layer, particularly the outer layer of an OVULE or a seed.

isogamy Sexual reproduction in which the two GAMETES that unite are of similar size, as in some algae.

K

kinin A substance that stimulates growth or division of plant cells.

Krebs cycle A cyclic process in cell respiration. In it pyruvic acid is broken down in the presence of oxygen with the release of energy for cell metabolism.

L

lanceolate Spear-shaped, describing a leaf that is long and tapers to a point at the tip.

lateral bud A bud which forms in the angle between a leaf and a stem, often giving rise to a side-shoot.

latex The milky juice that oozes from some plants when they are damaged. It may contain a complex mixture of compounds. The latex of some plants, such as the rubber tree, is of economic importance.

leached Describes soils in which mineral salts and plant nutrients have been washed out by water percolating down.

leaf-node The point on a stem from which a leaf grows.

legume A plant of the family Leguminosae, which includes the peas, beans, lupines, and acacias. They all have seed pods of the same type.

lenticels Pores through the CORK layer on the outside of a plant. Lenticels permit diffusion of gases in and out.

leptosporangiate A fern in which the SPORANGIUM arises from a single cell.

light reaction The first part of the process of PHOTOSYNTHESIS in which light energy is captured by CHLOROPHYLL and passed to other compounds in the cell.

lignified With cell walls thickened with LIGNIN.

lignin A complex compound that becomes mixed with the CELLULOSE layers of a cell wall and gives it strength and rigidity. It gives a plant its "woody" characteristics.

ligule A small flap or scale on the upper surface of a leaf near its base.

loculi Small compartments, such as the cavities in ANTHERS or OVARIES.

M

manoxylic Describes wood with a soft, loose texture.

medullary Belonging to the pith in the middle of a stem.

megaphylls Fern fronds.

megasporangium A structure containing MEGASPORES.

megaspore A large SPORE that gives rise to a PROTHALLUS with female sexual organs.

megasporophyll A leaflike structure bearing MEGASPORANGIA. The scale of a female cone in conifers.

megastrobili The female cones on a conifer tree.

meiosis The process of "reduction division" in which a cell with two basic sets of CHROMOSOMES (the DIPLOID state) divides to produce new cells that contain only one basic set of chromosomes (the HAPLOID state). In animals and flowering plants this reduction takes place when the sex cells form. In lower plants it typically takes place during spore formation when the SPOROPHYTE generation gives rise to the gametophyte generation.

meristem Any region of a plant where the cells are actively dividing, as for example at growing tips.

mesomorphic Describes a plant adapted to live under conditions where extremes, whether of temperature or rainfall, are not generally experienced.

mesophyll The PARENCHYMA of a leaf, the tissue between the upper and lower EPIDERMIS concerned in PHOTOSYNTHESIS.

microclimate The climate on a small scale as it affects a living organism. It may differ, for example, on two sides of a hill or, on a very small scale, there may be specialized microclimates under a stone or at a tree base.

micropyle A small pore, particularly that in the OVULE of a flower that allows the entry of the tube from a POLLEN GRAIN. This pore persists in the seed and is readily visible in some plants, such as the broad bean.

microsome A small particle within a cell visible by electron microscopy. Microsomes are associated with the ENDOPLASMIC RETICULUM.

microsporangium A structure containing MICROSPORES.

microspore A small spore that gives rise to a PROTHALLUS that bears male sex organs.

microsporophyll The scales of a male cone in conifers. Any leaflike structure bearing MICROSPORANGIA.

microstrobili Male cones of conifers and other gymnosperms.

mitochondria Microscopic bodies within cells that may appear as grains or filaments. They are the "powerhouses" of the cell where energy is released for the cell's work.

mitosis A type of cell division in which both the original cell and those derived from it have two basic sets of CHROMOSOMES (the DIPLOID number), giving a straight-forward replication. This is the normal type of cell division in the nonsexual parts of an organism.

monocotyledon A flowering plant in which there is a single SEED LEAF or COTYLEDON, within the seed, as in grasses or lilies.

monoecious Describes a plant in which both male and female organs are carried on the same individual.

monopodial Describes a stem in which growth is continued from the same growing point at the tip, rather than through the development of strong side branches.

monosaccharides Simple sugars such as glucose and fructose.

moor A vegetation type found on wet peaty soils. According to the degree of saturation of the soil the DOMINANT plant may be sphagnum, cotton grass, or heather.

morphogenetic Describes internal secretions that affect the growth and form of a plant.

morphology The structure and form of an organism.

motile Capable of independent movement as a whole organism.

mycelium The web of threads that make up the body of many fungi.

mycorrhiza An association between a fungus and a higher plant with apparent benefits for both. The MYCELIUM of the fungus forms an intimate association with the plant roots.

N

nectar-guides Markings on flower petals that guide insects to the nectar and help to ensure POLLINATION. The marks may sometimes only be visible to insects with vision extending into the ultraviolet range.

nucellus The body of the OVULE of a plant; the thin-walled cells between the embryo and its INTEGUMENT.

nuclear membrane The thin membrane surrounding the NUCLEUS of a cell.

nucleic acids Complex organic acids present in the NUCLEUS of cells and, to a lesser extent, in surrounding CYTOPLASM. Nucleic acids provide a coded pattern for PROTEIN synthesis in the cell and, in the CHROMOSOMES, carry genetic information from one generation to another.

nucleolus A dense round mass visible in the NUCLEUS of many cells that enlarges when the cell is synthesizing.

nucleus The major ORGANELLE of the cell, usually shaped as a sphere or spheroid. It controls the synthetic reactions in the cell and contains the CHROMOSOMES that are responsible for heredity.

nyctinasty Movements, sometimes called sleep movements, shown by plants in response to the alternation of day and night.

O

oogamy A type of sexual reproduction in which there is a union of a large nonmotile female egg-cell with a smaller MOTILE male GAMETE, as in algae such as Volvox.

oogonia Organs that bear female reproductive cells in algae.

oospheres Unfertilized female egg cells of algae or higher plants.

organelles A general term for the distinct units that are visible within cells by microscopy, such as the NUCLEUS or the CHLOROPLASTS. Each type of organelle is believed to have its own function.

osmosis The process by which water diffuses through a cell membrane permeable to water from a weaker solution to a stronger solution.

osmotic pressure A measure of the concentration of a solution. It is the pressure which would need to be applied to prevent the entry of water into the solution by osmosis.

ova Female egg cells.

ovary The part of the flower that contains OVULES, at the base of the CARPEL.

ovate Egg-shaped, describing leaves wider near the base.

ovule In a flowering plant the structure which contains and surrounds the female egg-cell. After fertilization it develops into the seed.

P

palmate Describes leaves in which several leaflets arise from the same point and spread like fingers on a hand.

pappus A ring of hairs, such as that on a dandelion fruit, that may aid dispersal.

parasite An organism that lives by taking nourishment from another living organism, giving no benefit in return. Many fungi and some higher plants such as dodder are parasites.

parenchyma A plant tissue consisting usually of thin-walled undifferentiated cells with some intercellular spaces.

pathogens Disease-producing microorganisms.

pectin A CARBOHYDRATE polymer that cements together plant cell walls.

pedate Describes a compound leaf divided to the base into three main lobes, the two outer lobes each divided into two.

peltate Describes a leaf or any other plant organ that is more or less circular with a stalk in the middle of the underside.

perennation Survival from one growing season to another.

perennials Plants that survive for several years or more.

perianth The petals and SEPALS that surround the sexual parts of a flower.

pericarp The outer wall of a fruit. Derived from the outer wall of the OVARY, it may be dry or fleshy.

periderm The outer layer of bark, made up of PHELLODERM, PHELLOGEN, and CORK.

perisperm Food tissue in some seeds, such as cardamom, derived from the NUCELLUS of the OVULE.

petaloid Describes a SEPAL or a leaf that is colorful and resembles a petal.

petiole A leaf stalk.

phellem See CORK.

phelloderm The cells formed to the inner side of the cork cambium, usually of the PARENCHYMA type.

phellogen The cork cambium, the layer of dividing cells running round a stem that produces CORK cells to the outside and PHELLODERM to the inside.

phenotypic Characteristics produced by the organism in response to stimuli in the environment.

phloem The plant tissue concerned with the transport of food material in higher plants. Typically the cells of the phloem are long and tubular, the nuclei have gone, and the cells are connected by porous "sieve-plates."

photolysis The breakdown of a molecule through the action of light.

photoperiodism The response of a plant to changes in the relative length of day and night.

photosynthesis The process of building up CARBOHYDRATES from carbon dioxide and water that is carried out by green plants. For this they use energy derived from light captured by the CHLOROPHYLL that they contain.

phototactic Describes a movement made in response to the stimulus of light.

phototropism Directional growth of a plant in response to the stimulus of light.

phreatophytes Plants with long roots penetrating deep down into the soil for water.

physiological Relating to life processes.

phytoplankton Plants, especially microscopic ones, that drift in the water that surrounds them.

pinnate Describes a compound leaf consisting of two

rows of leaflets, one on each side of the central stalk.

pioneer species The first species of plant to colonize a newly available patch of ground.

pistil The female parts of a flower; the GYNOECIUM.

plantlet A small young plant. Refers particularly to plants that reproduce vegetatively.

plasma membrane The outer membrane of a cell surrounding the living cell contents.

plasmodium A type of organization shown by slime molds in which an AMEBOID mass with many NUCLEI moves and feeds.

plastids Microscopic ORGANELLES found in the CYTOPLASM of plant cells. Many plastids contain pigment, for example the green CHLOROPLASTS.

plumule The growing point of the first shoot of a plant, present in the embryo within the seed.

pneumatophores Specialized roots that grow up from water in some plants, such as swamp cypress. Sometimes used to describe air bladders in water plants.

podsolized Turned into a podsol, a layered soil in which plant nutrients have been washed from the upper layers.

pollen grains The male sex cells or MICROSPORES of a flowering plant or conifer. Pollen grains contain NUCLEI with one basic set of CHROMOSOMES (the HAPLOID number).

pollen mother cells The cells within the ANTHERS that each divide to give four POLLEN GRAINS.

pollen sacs Cavities in the ANTHER in which pollen forms.

pollination Any process by which ripe pollen is transferred from the ANTHER to the STIGMA of a flower.

pollinators Animals that assist in POLLINATION.

polygamous In botany, describes a species, such as the ash, that bears male, female, and HERMAPHRODITIC flowers.

pome A type of fruit in which the outer flesh is formed from the RECEPTACLE. Apples and pears are pomes.

primary root The first root that develops in a plant, derived from the RADICLE present in the embryo.

procaryotes Organisms such as bacteria and blue-green algae that lack a distinct NUCLEUS within their cells.

propagation The increase of plant numbers by vegetative means. In cultivation this increase is achieved by such devices as taking cuttings.

proteins Essential constituents of living cells, proteins are compounds with large molecules built up of AMINO ACIDS.

prothallus The small plant formed when a SPORE germinates and contains the organs that produce the sex cells, as in the life cycles of ferns. Sometimes refers to the initial growth stages of lichens.

protonema The threadlike plant that first develops from the asexual SPORE of a moss, giving rise later to the typical moss plant, or plants.

pulvinus A thick, fleshy base to a leaf stalk.

pycnoxylic A compact type of wood found especially in pine trees.

R

radially symmetrical Describes an organism in which like parts are arranged around a vertical axis. Flowers such as buttercups and wild roses are radially symmetrical.

radicle The embryo root contained within a seed.

receptacle The upper end of a stalk bearing the parts of a flower. In some algae it is the end of a branch bearing reproductive organs. In some other plants it is a cuplike structure bearing reproductive organs.

reduction division See MEIOSIS.

reticulate With a netlike appearance.

rhizoids Small rootlike projections that anchor a plant to a surface. They may be present in mosses, liverworts, algae, and ferns.

rhizomes Underground stems, usually horizontal, persisting for more than one growing season. They may be rootlike, but have buds and leaves. Irises and couch grass are examples of plants with rhizomes.

rhizophores Special root-bearing branches in club mosses.

root-hairs Hairlike outgrowths from plant roots that increase the absorptive area.

S

samara A single-seeded type of fruit in which there is a membrane that forms a wing which assists in dispersal.

saprophyte A plant that gets its food from dead and decaying organic matter rather than making its own.

scalariform Ladderlike in appearance, as are some types of cell thickening, or some forms of conjugation in algae.

sclereid A cell with tough lignified walls, usually with no living contents. "Stone cells" of this type give the gritty texture found in pears, but are found in many other plants in which toughness is required.

sclerenchyma Tissue made up of SCLEREIDS, the supporting tissue of a plant.

sclerophyllous Describes plants with hard, tough leaves that are often small and have a thick CUTICLE. Such plants are characteristic of dry places.

secondary meristem A region of cell division in a plant that produces an increase in thickness rather than elongation of the stem or root. The CAMBIUM and CORK cambium are secondary meristems.

seed leaf A COTYLEDON, a thick, fleshy storage leaf found in the plant embryo inside the seed.

self-pollination Pollination of a STIGMA by pollen from the ANTHERS of the same flower.

self-sterile Describes the condition in which a flower is unable to be fertilized by its own pollen.

semipermeable membrane A membrane that allows the solvent of a solution to pass through, but does not allow the passage of the dissolved substance. In living systems the solvent is usually water.

sepals The outer ring of flower parts, usually green and leaflike, but sometimes colored like petals.

septate Divided by walls into compartments.

sessile With no stalk, as in some leaves or flowers. Fixed in position, rather than mobile.

seta Any bristlelike structure. The stalk that bears the spore capsule in mosses and liverworts.

sexual reproduction Reproduction in which a male and female sex cell fuse to produce a new individual.

sieve tube A cell in the PHLOEM that transports food materials.

sorus An associated group of spore-bearing organs (SPORANGIA) in ferns. Also refers to groups of sporangia in other lower plants.

spermatophyte A seed-bearing plant, gymnosperm or angiosperm.

spermatozoids Male sex cells which can move by means of FLAGELLA, as in ferns and liverworts.

sporangia Walled structures in which SPORES are produced in ferns, or equivalent parts in other plant groups.

sporangiophores Stalked structures bearing SPORANGIA.

spore A specialized reproductive cell that can give rise to a new plant.

sporophylls Leaflike structures that bear SPORANGIA.

sporophyte In the ALTERNATION OF GENERATIONS found in plants, the generation with two basic sets of CHROMOSOMES (the DIPLOID number) that reproduces asexually by means of SPORES.

stabilizing selection A type of natural selection in

which the same characteristics prove successful over many generations, minimizing the changes in the organism.

stamen The male reproductive organ of a flower, consisting of a stalk bearing an ANTHER within which the male sex cells (pollen) are produced.

stigma Part of the female reproductive organ of a flower, the stigma is the swollen tip of the stalk (style) leading up from the OVARY, on which pollen sticks.

stolons Creeping horizontal stems of a plant, from which new plants may arise, radiating from a central rosette. The term is sometimes confined to the description of such stems that grow underground to distinguish them from above-ground runners.

stomata The pores in leaves and young stems through which gas exchange can take place. Each stoma is surrounded by a pair of GUARD CELLS.

stomium The part of the spore case of a fern that breaks open to release SPORES.

T

tendril A modified leaf or stem, threadlike and used for climbing.

transduction A process by which genetic material is transferred from one bacterium to another by means of a phage.

translocated Describes materials that are moved from one part of a plant to another.

transpiration The process in which leaves give off large quantities of water vapor into the air. The water passes through the plant from roots to leaves in what is called the transpiration stream.

tropism A growth movement in response to an external stimulus.

tropophytic Adapted to growing under alternately wet and dry conditions.

tube nucleus One of two NUCLEI in the pollen cell or MICROSPORE, it plays a part in regulating the growth of the pollen tube and disintegrates before FERTILIZATION.

tubers Swollen underground stems containing food stores.

turgor pressure Rigidity of plant tissue due to pressure of water within the cells stretching the cell walls.

tyloses Intrusions from other cells that may eventually block XYLEM vessels.

U

unicellular Consisting of a single cell.

unilocular With a single compartment, as have some OVARIES.

V

vacuoles Cavities in the substance of a cell, generally fluid-filled.

vascular bundle One unit of the fluid-conducting tissue of a plant, consisting of groups of XYLEM and PHLOEM cells.

vascular plant Those plants that have a specialized fluid conducting system, the vascular system.

vegetative Describes functions that are carried out without sexual reproduction being involved.

vessels Water-conducting tubes in the XYLEM made up of cells joined end to end.

volva A ring of tissue on the stalk of a ripe toadstool.

W

whorl A single ring of leaves, petals, or other organs.

X

xanthophyll One of a group of yellow or orange hydrocarbons that act as pigments in plants.

xeromorphic With a structure adapted to dry conditions. This term is usually used to describe leaves.

xerophyte A plant that is able to survive in very dry conditions.

xylem The water-conducting tissue of plants, made up of two types of cell, VESSELS and tracheids. It forms the wood tissue and so also provides mechanical support.

Z

zoochory The dispersal by animals of seeds or SPORES.

zoophytes Plantlike animals.

zygomorphic With only one plane of symmetry. Bilaterally symmetrical, as the flower of a sweet pea.

zygospore A thick-walled SPORE. Such spores form a resting stage in some algae and fungi.

Index

Credits

The following have provided photographs for Part 5: Science Photo Library 24; Aquila Photographics 53; Heather Angel 10, 29, 31, 33, 34, 35, 36, 37, 39, 41, 42, 45, 54, 56, 60, 67, 69, 70, 73, 76, 79, 80, 82, 84, 85, 86, 88, 93, 95, 97, 101, 103, 104, 105, 106, 108, 109, 123, 126, 128, 129, 132, 133, 135, 141; H. Axell/Natural Science Photos 46, 61, 69; C. Banks/Natural Science Photos 65; Biophoto Associates 26, 94, 99; Biophoto Associates/ Science Photo Library 25; Frank V. Blackburn/Nature Photographers 141; Peter Bloomfield 110; Dr Tony Brain/Science Photo Library 14; Paul Brierley 15; Building Research Establishment 17; Brinsley Burbidge/ Nature Photographers 23, 65; Dr Jeremy Burgess/ Science Photo Library 31, 49, 79; Camerapix/Alan Hutchinson Library 101, 111, 116, 118, 122, 123, 124, 126, 127, 136, 143; W. Cane/Natural Science Photos 62; Kevin Carlson/Nature Photographers 125; Brian Carter 11, 51, 73, 75; M. Chinery/Natural Science Photos 98; Ron Croucher/Nature Photographers 138; A. Eddy/Natural Science Photos 83; Mary Evans Picture Library 15, 134; M. Freeman/Natural Science Photos 90; Geoscience Features 28, 32, 84, 111; Eric Gravé/Science Photo Library 19, 71; C. Grey-Wilson/Nature Photographers 42, 62;

James Hancock/Nature Photographers 140; Robert Harding Picture Library 118, 121; J. Hobday/Natural Science Photos 91; Holt Studios Ltd 21, 58; Indian Tourist Office 129; Institute of Geological Sciences 133; Nicholas Law 60; John Lythgoe/Seaphot Ltd: Planet Earth Pictures 137, 138; G. A. Matthews/Natural Science Photos 88; G. Montalverns/Natural Science Photos 40; Marion Morrison 78, 93; Tony Morrison 16, 63, 81, 82, 92, 103, 132, 142; Dr Gopal Murti/Science Photo Library 20; Natural Science Photos 76, 85; Nature Photographers 53, 72; G. Newlands/Natural Science Photos 38; Novosti Press Agency 102; The Photosource 47, 74, 112, 143; Reed International 117; R. Revels/Natural Science Photos 21, 107; M. Rose/Natural Science Photos 105; Science Photo Library 123; Stammers/Greenwood/Science Photo Library 18; L. S. Stepanowicz 27; Tony Stone Worldwide 8, 9, 17, 43, 44, 45, 47, 51, 53, 57, 59, 64, 77, 87, 101, 103, 113, 115, 136; M. W. F. Tweedie/NHPA 92; C. A. Walker/ Natural Science Photos 66; P.H. & S.L. Ward/Natural Science Photos 22, 68; Weyroe Ltd 115

The Indian leopard *(Panthera pardus fusca)*—one of the largest, most endangered cats.

**Part
6**

The
Animal World

Acknowledgments

Consultant Editors
Mike Janson and Joyce Pope

Consultants and Contributors
Ray Aldridge   Ginny Johnson
Nicole Bechirian   Nick Law
Robert Burton   Jane Mainwaring
Jonathan Elphick   Joyce Pope
Thom Henvey   Nora Spears
Casey Horton   John Stidworthy
Dorothy Jackson   Jude Welton
Mike Janson   Peter White

Artists and Designers
Eric Drewery   David Parker
Mick Gillah   Mick Saunders
Nicki Kemball   Charlotte Styles
Aziz Khan   Alan Suttie

Bull Publishing Consultants Ltd
Wendy Allen   Nicola Okell
Harold Bull   Martyn Page
John Clark   Polly Powell
Eric Drewery   Hal Robinson
Kate Duffy   Sandy Shepherd
Ursula Fifield

Part 6 Contents

Preface

The quest to explore the known world and to describe its creation and subsequent development is nearly as old as mankind. In the Western world, the best known creation story comes from the book of Genesis. It tells how God created the Earth and all living things. Modern religious thinkers interpret the Biblical story of creation in various ways. Some believe that creation occurred exactly as Genesis describes it. Others think that God's method of creation is revealed through scientific investigation. *The Animal World* presents an exciting picture of what scientists have learned about the enormous variety of Earth's animal life.

The editorial approach

The object of this publication is to explain for an average family readership the many aspects of science that are fascinating and vitally important for an understanding of the world today. The content has therefore been made straightforward, concise, and accurate, and is clearly and attractively presented. It is also a readily accessible source of scientific information.

The often forbidding appearance of traditional science publications has been avoided. Approximately equal proportions of illustrations and text make the most unfamiliar subjects interesting and attractive. Even more important, all the drawings have been created specially to complement the text, each explaining a topic that can be difficult to understand through the printed word alone.

The thorough application of these principles has created a publication that encapsulates its subject in a stimulating way, and that will prove to be an invaluable work of reference and education for many years to come.

The advance of science

One of the most exciting and challenging aspects of science is that its frontiers are constantly being revised and extended, and new developments are occurring all the time. Its advance depends largely on observation, experimentation, and debate, which generate theories that have to be tested and even then stand only until they are replaced by better concepts. For this reason it is difficult for any science publication to be completely comprehensive. It is possible, however, to provide a thorough foundation that ensures any such advances can be comprehended. It is the purpose of each part in this series to create such a foundation, by providing all the basic knowledge in the particular area of science it describes.

How to use this material

This material can be used in two ways.

The first, and more conventional, way is to start at the beginning and to read through to the end, which gives a coherent and thorough picture of the subject and opens a resource of basic information that can be returned to for re-reading and reference.

The second allows this set to be used as a library of information presented subject by subject, which the reader can consult piece by piece, as required.

All articles are presented so that the subject is equally accessible by either method. Topics are arranged in a logical sequence, outlined in the contents list. The indexes allow access to more specific points.

Within an article scientific terms are explained in the main text, where an understanding of them is central to the understanding of the subject as a whole. Fact entries giving technical, mathematical, or biographical details are included, where appropriate, at the end of the article to which they relate. There is also an alphabetical glossary of terms at the end of each part, so that the reader's memory can be refreshed, and so that the material can be used for quick reference whenever necessary.

All articles are relatively short, but none has been condensed artificially. Most articles occupy two pages, but some are four, or occasionally six to twelve, pages long.

The sample two-page article opposite shows the important elements of this editorial plan and illustrates the way in which this organization permits maximum flexibility of use.

(A) **Article title** gives the reader an immediate reference point.

(B) **Section title** shows the section in which a particular article falls.

(C) **Main text** consists of approximately 850 words of narrative information set out in a logical manner, avoiding biographical and technical details that might interrupt the story line and hamper the reader's progress.

(D) **Illustrations** include specially commissioned drawings and diagrams and carefully selected photographs that expand and clarify the main text.

(E) **Captions** explain the illustrations and connect the textual and visual elements of the article.

(F) **Annotation** of the drawings allows the reader to identify the various elements referred to in the captions.

(G) **Theme images,** where appropriate, are included in the top left-hand corner of the left-hand page, to emphasize a central element of information or to create a visual link between different but related articles. In place of a theme image, certain articles have a list of terms, units, and abbreviations relevant to the article concerned.

(H) **Fact entries** are added at the foot of the last page of certain articles to give biographical details, physical laws and equations, or additional information relating to the article but not essential to an understanding of the main text itself.

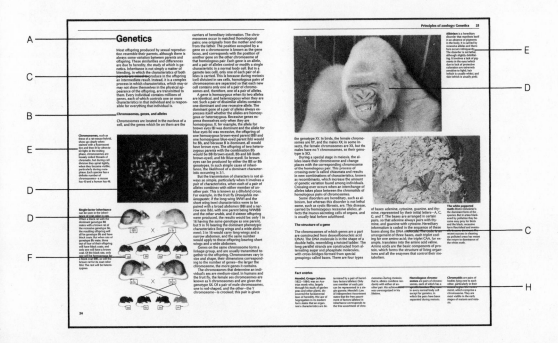

Introduction

Flight is one of the most distinctive features of birds, which separates them into their own group within the animal kingdom. There are, however, birds that no longer fly; but most still retain the feathers that aid flight in birds that do.

The twentieth century may be seen by future historians as a period in which people throughout the world learned to see the study of animals in a fresh light. The change in attitude had already begun following the publication of Charles Darwin's theory of evolution, which burst on the world in 1859. Its result was revolutionary.

Among the ancient Greeks, Aristotle had pointed the way for modern zoology, in his studies of the animal kingdom. Yet centuries later, in the Middle Ages, animals were still regarded as things that had been created simply for the use and entertainment of humankind.

The human being was regarded as the lord of creation. Even the word "zoology" was unknown until the middle of the sixteenth century. From then until the beginning of the present century, the study of animals was no more than the province of learned men with time on their hands.

Until the second decade of this century, the word "zoology" had little place in the vocabulary of the average person. University students who elected to spend their time studying zoology were regarded as "a little odd" and were told that there was no future in the study. But to those with foresight the first rumblings of a tremendous upheaval could be heard. How and when it happened is difficult to trace. Looking at the books and university courses available around 1920 we can compare what was happening then with the state of things today.

In 1920, if you went into a bookshop and asked for books on zoology, the assistant would take you to a dim corner and point to a shelf on which were a few somberly-bound textbooks. This would happen in the best of bookshops. In the others, to ask for books on animals was to risk having the assistant, most likely, stare at you as if you had taken leave of your senses. Today, most larger bookshops have rows of shelves laden with such books, or even a section of the shop devoted exclusively to books on zoology.

The difference between the books themselves these days is no less spectacular. The old textbooks were illustrated with artists' sketches. Those that were illustrated with photographs contained black-and-white images, mainly of stuffed animals or zoo specimens. Today, good books on zoology are filled with color photographs of live animals in the wild, and colorful, informative diagrams.

Formerly, in the more enlightened schools, Nature Study was taught in the lower grades, and this consisted mainly of botany. It was not until the 1950's that the Association of British Zoologists was formed, its main purpose being to press for the teaching of zoology in schools. Universities offered courses in zoology, but the zoology department was usually in some odd corner of the building, appearing to have been an afterthought.

It was, however, the courses that were taught that gave the firm clues as to the standing of the subject in academic circles. The classification of animals was a first consideration. Just as the grocer had his goods arranged on neat shelves, the better to be able to find them easily, so the animal kingdom was divided into phyla, classes, and families, the better to pigeonhole knowledge and find one's way among the million or more known species. But the main emphasis was on comparative anatomy, which involved lectures on internal organs, especially the skeletons, together with the cutting-up of dead animals, known as dissection. So strong was this slant in the total teaching of zoology that students were talking about it as necrology (the study of dead things) as contrasted with biology (the study of living animals).

Also, about the middle of the century, several important events took place. Scientists began to pay more attention to the way animals behaved rather than how they were

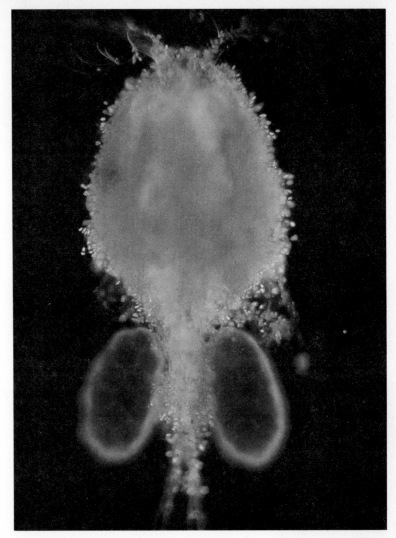

made. They began to experiment with them in the sense that they watched what they did and experimented with the causes that influenced their behavior. At first, these experiments were done in the laboratory. Soon the studies were taken into the field. With the knowledge gained in laboratory studies, wild animals were watched or, as we now prefer to say, they were observed, in their natural habitat, with the observer in hiding. This new science was called ethology. The name dated back to the seventeenth century and was used first to mean the study of ethics or morals, and later for the study of character.

At the same time, more attention was given to the relationship between the animal and its environment, which had been known simply as natural history but later became known as ecology. These words *ethology* and *ecology* are two examples of how the language used in zoology was changing, and it indicates how scientific language has changed in the last half century or so. Nowhere is this more evident than in that word, so commonplace today—"gene." The word was coined in 1913. By the early 1920's university lecturers, who glibly used the word "chromosome," were telling students that there were parts of the chromosome that determined the course of heredity. They did not know what these parts were but knew that they were microscopic and, for

Animals and plants often live together in symbiosis—each feeding from the other. Green algae can be seen here living in such a relationship under the skin of a cyclops, a tiny crustacean. Despite its size, this animal and many others like it play an important role in marine food chains. They feed on phytoplankton and themselves form a large part of the diet of marine animals.

African elephants wade across a lake in Zambia. They are the largest living land animals, and so need to eat vast amounts of vegetation. This appetite is often the source of acute problems if their range is restricted—by human settlements, for example—and the vegetation around them is quickly consumed. They are a great worry to conservationists, who see the need for restricting elephants to game reserves to protect them, but also acknowledge that these animals need far more space than is left for them.

want of a better name, called these microscopic particles "ids."

Before long the word "gene" had crept into zoological language, replacing "id." Such was the speed at which zoology and other biological sciences were advancing, that a whole new science (genetics) was beginning to predominate. In the short space of time from 1913, genetics has developed an importance and weight which, with genetic engineering, may in the near future be fundamental to the welfare of the whole of creation—plant, animal, and human.

Another important development was the invention of the electron microscope toward the end of the 1920's. The first microscopes enabled scientists to study animal structures magnified to ten times their actual size. But soon this was improved to a hundred times. By the time zoologists were talking about "ids," microscopes were available that allowed the investigator to see things magnified one thousand times. The electron microscope now magnifies one hundred thousand times. The zoologist fortunate enough to have access to this fabulous new invention was able to see face-to-face the tiny particles of living matter, the genes that meant so much to our understanding of life itself.

At the other end of the scale from microscopic studies a new activity in macroscopic studies burst forth in zoology, represented by phenomena such as butterfly collecting and bird watching. They were to become important social activities, as well as constituting a significant trend in zoology.

Toward the end of the nineteenth century butterfly collecting was very popular. During that period a naturalist was always portrayed in cartoons as a bearded gentleman in a tweed suit with knickerbockers brandishing a net on a long handle, chasing a butterfly. Butterflies were collected because of their bright colors. They were mercifully killed, so as not to damage them, and stuck with pins in drawers in glass-fronted cabinets, making a fine display

that pleased the eye. These collections led, of necessity, to studying the habits of these insects, to know where and when to find them. Their classification became essential, and eventually this seemingly harmless pursuit led to a vast expansion of entomology (as the study of insects was called), itself an offshoot of zoology.

People have always been interested in birds, partly because of their songs, but especially for their colors. But in the late 1920's and early 1930's, with the advent of the automobile as a popular means of transport, and a universal impulse to get out into the country, bird watching gained popularity in a most surprising manner. The growth of the hobby was truly phenomenal, as were its side effects. The class Aves (birds) soon became the best-documented group of animals, with the most stable classification. Not the least of the subsidiary fields of study was that of behavior. Bird-watching and its side effects could be justifiably described as a natural history mass movement with the general public. By their enthusiasm, encouragement, and insistent thirst for knowledge, the public pressed the professional ornithologists to greater efforts in their researches.

The large numbers of people studying wildlife for themselves brought about an awareness of the need for conservation. From time to time during past centuries far-sighted people have realized that the human race was in danger of destroying its own environment. Theirs were, however, voices crying in the wilderness. Then, in 1872, the first national park, Yellowstone, was founded in the United States (more for the preservation of natural scenic landscapes than for the benefit of the animals living therein). Thirty years later, the Sable Game Reserve, later called the Kruger National Park, was established in South Africa. Since 1925, when the Albert National Park was founded in the Congo (now Zaire), the movement has spread until now the land surfaces of the world are plentifully dotted with parks and nature reserves. The movement toward conservation led to the formation of the International Union for the Conservation of Nature (IUCN).

Even the most ardent champions of the IUCN realized that they needed the support of the average person if its objectives were to be fully achieved. As the science of zoology came into its own, this support was forthcoming. It was aided by the increasing popularity of bird-watching, which itself was due in no small part to modern technical achievements such as color photography, color printing, and the perfection of television.

Once again, there was something resembling a mass surge. Ordinary people everywhere were becoming aware that all life is interdependent, that pollution is a destructive force to be guarded against, and that wild animals in particular are in danger of disappearing from the face of the earth. It was no surprise to find that the World Wildlife Fund became an instant success. The world was ready for it.

A few years before the outbreak of World War II, there appeared on railway stations in London posters proclaiming that our attitude to animals conditioned the way we treated our fellow humans. It was left to those reading these posters to put their own interpretation on this message.

Knowledge brings understanding and sympathy. An increasing knowledge of zoology could bring greater understanding of and sympathy for animals and humans. Perhaps we are seeing, in the many protest movements together with the increasing interest in conservation, the beginning of a resurgence in tune with the spirit of that poster message.

Insects are the most successful animals on earth—there are nearly a million species. The reason for their success is their tremendous adaptability, which has allowed them to survive for over 400 million years through major climate changes that have caused the extinction of other animals. This adaptability will probably ensure their survival through future cataclysmic changes.

Principles of zoology

There are almost 1 million different species of animals living in the world today, and new ones are constantly being discovered. They range in size and complexity from microscopic single-celled creatures to the giant blue whale, weighing up to 180 tons. Faced with the task of bringing some sort of order to the living world, zoologists consider two key factors: definition (is it an animal?) and classification (what place does it occupy in the animal kingdom?).

What is an animal?

Apart from inanimate objects, we also share our world with living organisms, including plants and animals. The difference between inanimate objects and living things is not always apparent—crystals grow, for example—but only animate organisms have the fundamental characteristic of energy change known as metabolism.

Almost all the world's energy is provided initially by the sun. Plants trap a proportion of this energy and use it, through photosynthesis, to build up the sugars and starches that form a major part of their tissues. During this process they take minerals and water from the soil and carbon dioxide from the atmosphere. They release oxygen into the air, which is a waste product of their metabolism.

Animals, however, cannot use such simple chemicals to build up the complex substances from which they are made. Instead, they must eat and digest food, and reorganize the products of digestion to form their own tissues. But in order to release the potential energy of their food, animals require oxygen, and during these metabolic processes they emit carbon dioxide as a waste product.

Thus, plants and animals are complementary, each depending on and using the other's wastes, which are constantly recycled. This great continuous energy flow is aided by a host of decomposers, especially bacteria and fungi. They break down dead material and waste into a form that may be used again by plants.

The distinction between a plant and an animal is often difficult to make among the simplest organisms, because some contain chlorophyll and can build their own food, but also hunt and feed. Of the more developed organisms, however, animals may generally be distinguished more easily by their quick responses to stimuli and their considerable powers of locomotion. In addition, only plants possess cellulose in their cell walls and contain the pigment chlorophyll.

Animal species

Plants and animals are generally classified according to a hierarchical system devised by the eighteenth-century botanist, Carolus Linnaeus. In this system, each unit is grouped with related forms into a larger taxon, which then constitutes part of the next larger group, and so on. The term "species" is used as the basic unit of classification.

Scientists agree that a species can be an arbitrary category only, within which there is room for genetic diversity. They also agree that species change gradually, adapting themselves to environmental variations as successful genetic strains outbreed the less successful ones. A species is generally thought to be a population of organisms that are similar in structure and function, and capable of interbreeding freely in the wild. The words "freely" and "in the wild" are important qualifications because it is not uncommon for two different kinds of animal to be capable of producing offspring. A cross between a horse and a donkey, for example, produces a mule. In these kinds of crosses, however, the resulting hybrid is usually completely sterile or lacks the necessary vigor to compete with other parental types. Consequently, such crosses do not contribute to the gene pool—that is, to the variety of genetic forms available.

Classification

The need for an internationally accepted classification is twofold: first, to be able to identify a particular species throughout the world, and second, to group related kinds into larger groups that reflect evolutionary relationships. Common, or vernacular, names are usually too

Rotifers are named after their wheellike corona, which beats in a circular motion to achieve movement. These aquatic animals occur in abundance—about 1,500 species are known to exist—and are among the smallest multi-cellular organisms.

imprecise for scientific use.

The lion, for example, is designated by the scientific name *Panthera leo,* which indicates that it is the species *leo* belonging to the genus *Panthera.* This genus also includes the jaguar *(P. onca)* and the tiger *(P. tigris).* These animals all belong to the family Felidae (the catlike animals) which, in turn, belongs to the order of flesh-eating animals called the Carnivora. This order also includes other animals with similar features, such as tooth arrangement and skull form.

As a member of the order Carnivora, the lion does not much resemble the anteater, for instance, which belongs to the different order Edentata ("toothless"). But both have mammalian features and so are designated members of the class Mammalia. All mammals have a vertebral column and are therefore placed in the subphylum Vertebrata, along with fishes, amphibians, reptiles, and birds. The vertebrates share with their apparently dissimilar relatives the lancelets and sea squirts an axial stiffening rod (a notochord), and all are placed in the phylum Chordata.

Using this phylogenetic system of classification—species, genus, family, order, class, subphylum, and phylum—it is possible at each level to see the relationship between animals of different species. But only the genus and species names are required to uniquely identify an animal. Thus the binomial classification of the lion is *Panthera leo.*

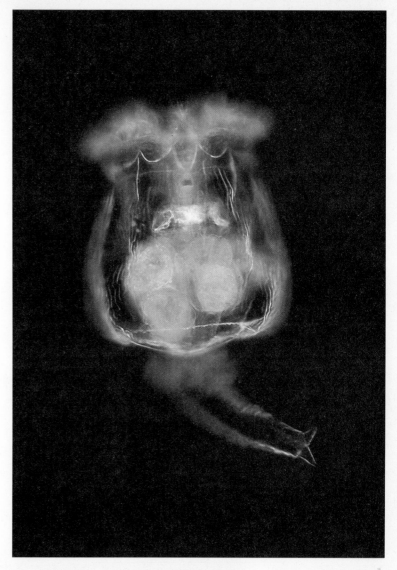

Aquatic environments are rich in microscopic organisms that provide a good food source for higher animals. Lakes such as this, in tropical Africa, are frequently inhabited by the Greater and Lesser Flamingo, which cohabit harmoniously because of the variety of food available. The Greater Flamingo sifts worms, mollusks, and small arthropods from the mud, whereas the Lesser Flamingo filters blue-green algae only from the lake bottom. These birds thrive in this environment because their long legs and necks facilitate wading and feeding in deep water.

The animal cell

The term "cell" was first used by the English naturalist Robert Hooke in 1665 to describe the "great many little boxes" he saw when viewing a thin slice of cork through a microscope. The word was derived from the Latin word for a small room *(cella)*. Today, with the aid of electron microscopes, we have a more detailed view of living plant and animal cells, but Hooke's observation was the first time that living matter was recognized to be built of basic units rather than of continuous material.

Some of the cells of which plants and animals are composed have a particular function and are therefore not all exactly the same; even so, they have some features in common. An aggregation of like cells forms a tissue—for example, nerve cells make up nerve tissue—and combinations of tissues in turn form an organ, such as the brain.

The structure of cells

A cell consists of a nucleus, which is surrounded by a jellylike substance called the cytoplasm, enclosed in a cell membrane. This cell membrane (also called the plasma membrane) controls the passage of substances into and out of the cell. The membrane is only 0.00001 millimeter thick and is made up of layers of lipid (fat) molecules sandwiched between layers of protein. The cell membrane is said to be semipermeable, because it allows only certain chemicals to move in and out of the cell but prevents the passage of others.

The cytoplasm contains several kinds of structures, among which are many tiny structures called organelles. Many of the cell's life activities take place in the cytoplasm, and each organelle has a vital role in maintaining the continuing life of the cell.

Organelles

Most of the cytoplasm of a mature cell is filled with elaborate folded membrane systems called endoplasmic reticulum. One type is rough and is involved with the synthesis of proteins; the other is smooth and is concerned with the manufacture of fat molecules. On one side of the membranes lie the ground substance of the cytoplasm and the soluble proteins of the cell; on the other there are many enclosed pockets called cisternae. It seems likely that the endoplasmic structures play an important role in the transport of substances throughout the cell. They also provide a large surface area where essential chemical reactions take place; many enzymes that are important for the cell's metabolism are found on the cytoplasmic side, whereas their products are found in the cisternae.

The granular structures that are attached to the walls of the rough endoplasmic membranes are called ribosomes. But not all of the cell's ribosomes are attached—some swim freely in the cytoplasm. Those that are attached to the endoplasmic reticulum are concerned with the building of proteins to be transmitted to other parts of the body; those that float freely, however, aid the synthesis of the proteins that remain in the cell.

Structures similar to the smooth endoplasmic reticulum are found near the cell nucleus and are called Golgi bodies. In fact, the smooth reticulum seems to be continuous with these bodies. The smooth membranes of these structures enclose large, flattened cisternae. The role of Golgi bodies appears to be the collection and storage of the protein substances that are produced from the cisternae of the rough endoplasmic reticulum. Once they are collected, the individual packages

An animal cell *(below)* is characterized by the various structures within it, chief of which are the nucleus (with its nucleolus), mitochondria, and folded layers of endoplasmic reticulum.

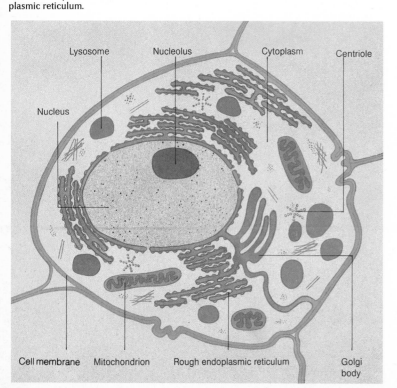

Lysosome   Nucleolus   Cytoplasm   Centriole

Nucleus

Cell membrane   Mitochondrion   Rough endoplasmic reticulum   Golgi body

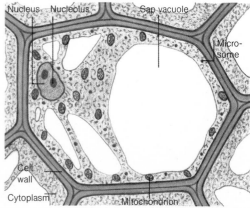

Nucleus   Nucleolus   Sap vacuole

Microsome

Cell wall

Cytoplasm   Mitochondrion

A typical plant cell *(above)* differs from an animal cell in that it has rigid cell walls (the spaces within which are filled with cellulose); a large permanent vacuole in the center of the cytoplasm; and chlorophyll, located in the chloroplasts.

of protein, which are surrounded by a membrane, are transported to the cell for secretion.

The rough endoplasmic reticulum also produces packages of enzymes called lysosomes. Under acid conditions, these bodies rupture and release their enzymes, which break down the major components of the cell. If the cell is damaged in any way, the lysosomes release their enzymes, which destroy the cell itself. Their use lies in the destruction of damaged cells or of those that are no longer needed and in the digestion of "foreign" cells, such as bacteria.

Mitochondria are another group of organelles found in the cytoplasm. They are elongated and have a double membrane that encloses a fluid-filled interior. The inner membrane comprises a series of deep folds called cristae. The mitochondria are the powerhouses of the cell, because they generate the energy that is needed to keep the cell's essential processes going. The enzymes needed to extract energy are located on the inner membrane of the mitochondria and appear to be arranged in such a way as to derive maximum efficiency from the process. They oxidize nutrients and release energy in the form of ATP (adenosine triphosphate), which is used in the syntheses of cell materials. This oxidative process is called internal or cellular respiration.

The nucleus

The nucleus controls all the cell's activities. It is spherical or elliptical and is bounded by two membranes that together form the nuclear membrane. The outer membrane seems to be an extension of the rough endoplasmic reticulum, and has several small pores through which nuclear material and large molecules pass.

Inside the nuclear membrane is a substance called the nucleoplasm that contains the chromosomes and nucleolus. The nucleolus is a spherical body that is dense in ribonucleic acid (RNA) and is the active center of protein and RNA manufacture. The chromosomes are composed of deoxyribonucleic acid (DNA) and are the blueprints for the cell's structure in the form of a genetic code. Chromosomes can be seen as thickened rods when a cell is actively dividing, but in the resting phase, the DNA is distributed throughout the nucleoplasm, when only fine threads of chromatin can be seen. These threads form the basis of the chromosomes as they thicken up again prior to cell division.

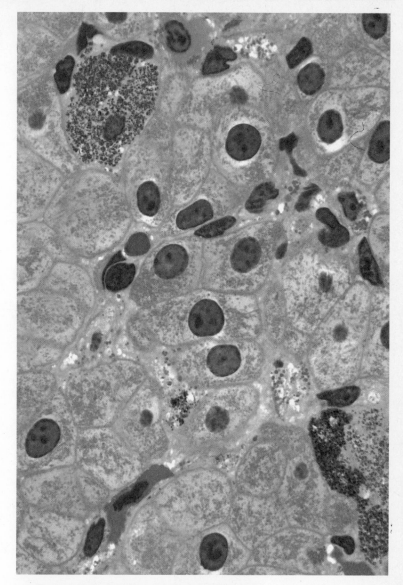

Cells are stained *(above)* so that they can more readily be studied. These liver cells from a salamander would otherwise be impossible to see.

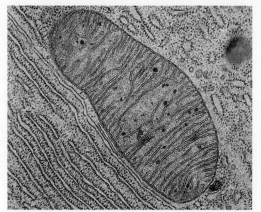

All animal cells have at least one mitochondrion *(left)* and usually many more. These powerhouses are the sources of the energy-forming processes of the cell.

Fact entries

Energy generation in the cell starts when the products of the breakdown of carbohydrates, fats, and proteins by enzymes in the process of digestion are further broken down in the cell into simpler compounds. Hydrogen atoms from them are combined with oxygen atoms in the cell to form water. The reaction between water and adenosine triphosphate (ATP) causes it to lose its third phosphate group and it becomes adenosine diphosphate (ADP), which is stored in the mitochondria. The hydrolysis— the chemical reaction of any compound with water—of the third phosphate group results in the liberation of energy which is used, for example, in muscular contraction.

Protein synthesis is the building-up of proteins which takes place in the ribosomes (particles of the cell to which proteins attach themselves). A protein is composed of amino acids, which are brought to the ribosome by transfer ribonucleic acid (RNA). The code for the arrangement of these amino acids is brought from the deoxyribonucleic acid (DNA) (which stores the genetic code for the cell) in the nucleus to the ribosome by a molecule of messenger RNA.

Anatomy and physiology

All organisms, whether plant or animal, must reproduce, grow, breathe, eat, excrete, and be able to respond to their environments; special areas of animals' bodies are often organized to accomplish each of these tasks. These specialized cells may vary from animal to animal, but the chemical processes involved in the activity are usually the same. Differences in anatomy have arisen because, among other reasons, of the emergence of life from the water onto land, which has meant that various features have had to be modified to accommodate the exigencies of terrestrial life. But one of the most important developments in the pattern of anatomical organization is the occurrence of segmentation, first seen in the earthworm. It occurs in all higher groups, even if only in the embryo stage.

Structural variations

Three basic support systems exist in the animal kingdom: a water-based, or hydrostatic skeleton; a hard outer case, or exoskeleton; and a hard internal support system, or endoskeleton.

The hydrostatic skeleton is a simple, fluid-filled cell and is found in animals such as amebas. In higher invertebrates such as coelenterates, nematodes, annelids, and echinoderms, water held inside the body is shifted by muscles to bring about a change in shape or position of the animal. But most invertebrates have an exoskeleton that is segmented and bears jointed legs. Muscles, which enable these animals to move, are attached to the inside of the skeleton.

The Greater Gliding Possum, *Schoinobates volans,* planes from one treetop to another on a membrane, which stretches from its neck to its feet. This structural adaptation to its environment—heavily forested areas—avoids it having to run down one tree to get up another.

The supporting structures of animals consist of the hydrostatic skeleton or fluid-filled cell (A) of some protozoa and coelenterates, the exoskeleton or hard, outer covering (B), found in other invertebrates, and the endoskeleton, which exists in all vertebrates, such as fishes (C) and cats (D).

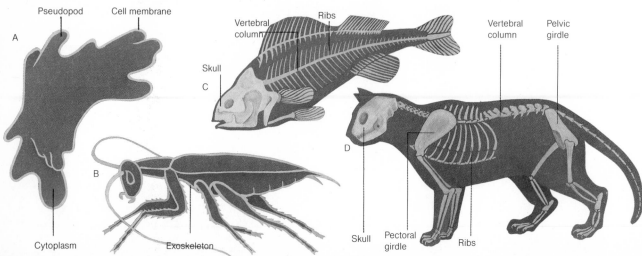

Pseudopod   Cell membrane

A

Skull

C

Vertebral column   Ribs

Vertebral column   Pelvic girdle

D

B

Cytoplasm   Exoskeleton

Skull   Pectoral girdle   Ribs

The main problem with this structural arrangement is that the exoskeleton is heavy and eventually becomes too heavy for the internal muscles to lift. This may be the reason for the small size of most invertebrates with such a structure.

In contrast, vertebrates have an endoskeleton, which is an internal set of bony supporting structures. The backbone is strengthened by girdles to which limbs are attached. Each bone of the skeleton has muscles fixed to its surface toward the end of the bones. These muscles work in antagonistic pairs, one contracting while the other relaxes. The joints of the vertebrate body are enclosed in a synovial capsule and are lubricated by synovial fluid.

The basic structure of an animal also determines how it will grow, and the growth patterns of animals differ greatly. Considering two extremes, amebas and mammals, the first increases in size until it divides into two smaller individuals; mammals, too, grow to an adult size at which time they mature and become reproductively active, but they have special growth centers near the tips of their long bones where the cell division that enables growth takes place; in addition, their skull bones are separated by cartilage which allows the skull to grow—it stops when the bones meet.

Respiration

Most animals need the chemical processes that result from gas exchange to survive. The development of respiratory organs within the animal kingdom has resulted in a variety of forms. But from the simplest to the most complex arrangement they are mainly concerned with two processes: external respiration, which involves the intake of oxygen and its transport to each cell in the body; and internal respiration, which is concerned with the chemical processes that use the oxygen.

External respiration finishes when the oxygen crosses the respiratory surface and enters the cells. This surface, where the exchange of gases takes place, varies from animal to animal, but has certain features in common: it is moist and thin (normally one cell thick); it is permeable, allowing substances in solution to pass through it; and in some multicellular animals, it is supplied with means of transporting

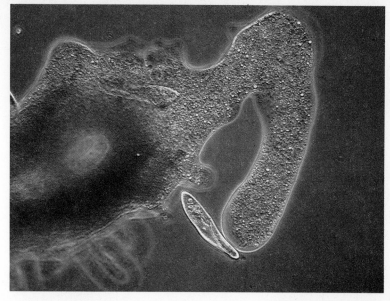

oxygen to the cells, such as blood vessels. Oxygen enters single-celled animals and coelenterates through the cell wall, so the whole surface of the animal is its respiratory surface.

In the earthworm, the moist skin of the animal also acts as the respiratory surface but its body is too thick for the oxygen to simply diffuse from the outer layer to the inner cells, so a blood circulation system has developed, which is able to carry dissolved oxygen to all parts of the body.

In terrestrial arthropods, a series of air tubes (tracheae) runs from the outer surface into the body and ends in special areas of gas exchange, the alveoli. Each alveolus is kept moist so that oxygen can dissolve into the water film and thus leave the alveolus to diffuse into the body cells. Aquatic invertebrates with an exoskeleton and aquatic vertebrates have a gill system that acts as a respiratory surface, extracting oxygen from the incoming water.

Land vertebrates have lungs that contain the air tubes, alveoli (the respiratory surface), and a supply of blood vessels to carry the oxygen to other parts of the body. In mammals, the lungs are protected by a ribcage and

Single-celled protozoa, such as amebas, move by extruding their cytoplasm, which flows forward to form pseudopodia (false feet). This method of locomotion is also used to trap food. The foot flows around and envelops a food particle, which is broken down by digestive enzymes.

Digestion in lower animals is simple: amebas (A) engulf food and digest it only with enzymes; insects (B) have a mouth and a simple digestive tract. But vertebrates (C and D) have a higher metabolic rate and so need to consume more; they therefore have digestive glands and long intestines.

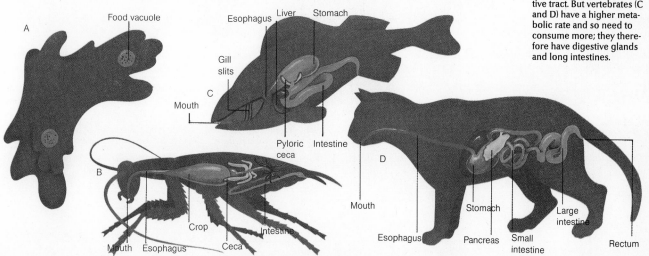

Fledgling songbirds are nestbound and unable to see at birth, and for several weeks are dependent on their parents for food. This is in contrast to many less sophisticated animals, such as larvae and young insects, which after birth are able to fend for themselves. The vulnerability of young birds makes them easy prey for predators and means that they need constantly to be guarded by their parents, from whom they learn to fly and sing.

body. Smaller nerves branch from it to other parts of the body, and so a basic information-collecting service is formed.

The environmental demands on vertebrates are greater than those on invertebrates. They have, therefore, developed a specialized complex nervous system composed of a brain and a dorsal nerve cord, which is protected by the spinal column. The brain is connected to the eyes, nose, ears, and other parts of the head by a series of cranial nerves. The rest of the body is served by the spinal nerves that join the spinal cord. Mammals and birds have larger brains than other vertebrates because their warm blood provides the stable internal environment necessary for the development of the brain.

The evolution of sensory organs can be seen particularly in the eyes; in some crustaceans and some worms, sight is only sensitive to light—these animals have simple clusters of photoreceptors, called ocelli, which guide them toward and away from light. In higher animals, the sensory cells are so organized that an image forms inside the eye. Most vertebrates have lateral vision in which a separate two-dimensional image is formed by the eye on each side of the head. But in mammals and birds of prey the eyes have turned forward so that a single image of the same object is formed; this is stereoscopic vision and is three-dimensional.

separated from the rest of the internal organs by a muscular sheet, the diaphragm. The ribs and diaphragm act together to pump a continuous stream of fresh air into the lungs. Air entering the lung dissolves in the film of water in the alveolus chamber and so diffuses through the chamber wall into the blood vessels. The hemoglobin in the blood transports the oxygen to the cells.

The nervous system

Every animal has sensory apparatus, the increasing complexity of which can be followed from aquatic to terrestrial animals. Simple organisms like amebas are sensitive over the whole surface of their bodies to general stimuli because no particular area is responsible for collecting specific information. Jellyfish and sea anemones have identifiable nerve cells that form a nerve net across the surface of their bodies, but they have little specialization and respond generally to stimuli such as light and dark, acid and alkali, hot and cold.

In worms and arthropods, some nervous tissue is concentrated at the front of the body. In these animals, a primitive brain joins a thick ventral nerve cord that runs the length of the

Digestion and dentition

In all animals, whether simple or complex, food is digested by enzymes that convert it to its simplest form. Amebas simply engulf food particles and package them into a food vacuole into which digestive enzymes are secreted. These enzymes break the food down into its chemical parts. In coelenterates, food is taken in through the single opening—the mouth. The lining of the internal cavity then secretes enzymes that digest the food material, and ameboid cells inside the cavity engulf the digested food. Unused food is rejected from the body via the mouth.

Most other animals have a tube that runs from the mouth to the anus. The food enters the tract via the mouth, which opens into the buccal cavity, where the digestive process be-

Circulation in amebas (A) consists only of water flowing in and out of the cell through a semipermeable membrane. Insects (B) have a dorsal blood vessel which contains a 13-chambered heart. Cold, colorless blood is pumped forward by muscular contractions in the vessel and returns backward through the blood spaces to reenter the heart. Fishes (C) have a ventral blood vessel from which segmented vessels branch and run through the gills to join the dorsal vessel, which distributes blood to the body. Fishes and mammals (D) have a four-chambered heart, but oxygenated blood in mammals is distributed by arteries; veins return deoxygenated blood to the heart.

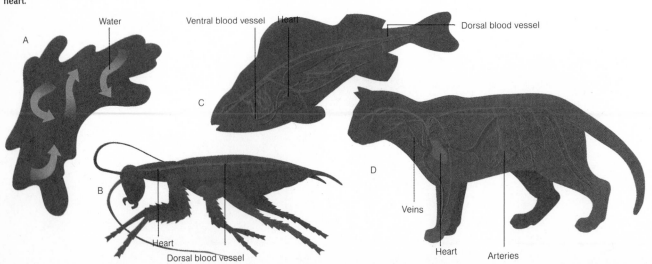

Water

A

Ventral blood vessel   Heart   Dorsal blood vessel

C

B

Heart
Dorsal blood vessel

D

Veins

Heart   Arteries

gins. The food then passes along a muscular section of the tube, pushed by waves of contraction (peristaltic waves) until it reaches the stomach. Most of the digestive process occurs in the stomach or an area close to it. Once digestion is completed, the useful materials are assimilated, whereas the residue is passed out of the body via the anus.

In addition, specialized glands are often present (particularly in vertebrates) that produce secretions that aid the digestive process. In mammals, for example, the liver produces bile, and the pancreas releases digestive enzymes into the small intestine. Food broken down by enzymes is assimilated into the blood supply and taken to the liver. The liver begins the elimination process of any unnecessary chemicals.

Most animals also contain microorganisms that live in their digestive systems; theirs is a commensal relationship in which they share a food supply but do no harm to each other. There are also some cases of symbiotic relationships, such as some termites, which rely on protozoa in their gut to break down the wood that they eat.

Most animals merely swallow their food, making no attempt to break it up. In some groups, such as birds and some insectivores, tiny stones are present in the stomach that help to degrade the food and facilitate enzyme action. Most vertebrates use their teeth to hold food only before swallowing it. Mammals, however, chew their food. They have a lower jaw, which is made of a single pair of bones with differentiated teeth. This change from other animals must be a result of the warm-bloodedness of mammals—they use their jaws much more than any other group because they need food to satisfy their high metabolic rate; to get all the nutritional value they can from food they must start processing it in the mouth. They have developed different types of teeth for this purpose. Generally, herbivorous animals have very long jaws with a battery of flat-topped, grinding cheek teeth, which break up plant material that would otherwise be impossible to digest. Meat-eating animals have sharp teeth, or canines, which are used to kill their prey. But they also have slicing cheekteeth, or carnassials, which are used to cut the meat into swallowable pieces.

Omnivorous mammals have a combination of flat-topped cheekteeth with sharp, cutting edges and spatulate incisors for biting.

Excretion

Excretion is the process that eliminates waste from the body. In many simple organisms waste diffuses out via the body wall. In larger animals, however, special organs have developed to deal with this process.

The circulatory and respiratory systems in vertebrates remove carbon dioxide and water from the body, whereas the kidneys filter out excess chemical substances brought to them by the blood. These substances, which include nitrogen from the breakdown of proteins, excess salts and sugars, hormones, and water, pass out of the blood into the kidney tubule. Harmful substances then collect in the bladder and are passed out of the body in the form of urine. In some animals, such as insects and terrestrial gastropods, for whom water retention is essential, dry uric acid crystals are excreted. In others, such as fishes, for whom water loss is not as great a problem, waste is excreted as ammonia, the formation of which requires water.

The newborn young of grazing animals are fully active soon after birth—this young wildebeest could get on its feet within seven minutes of being born. They feed on mother's milk for several months but, unlike nestbound fledglings, can move around independently.

Respiration in amebas (A) involves oxygen diffusing into the cytoplasm and carbon dioxide diffusing out. In insects (B), air is conducted through tracheae to the blood, into which oxygen diffuses. Fishes (C) extract oxygen from water, which passes into the mouth and out through the gills. Mammals (D) breathe with lungs, where oxygen diffuses into blood vessels.

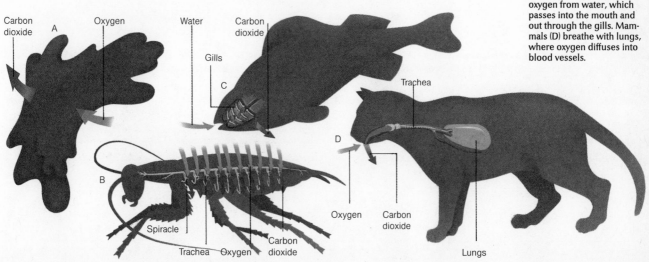

Carbon dioxide

Oxygen

A

Water

Carbon dioxide

Gills

C

Trachea

B

D

Spiracle

Trachea Oxygen

Carbon dioxide

Oxygen Carbon dioxide

Lungs

Reproduction

Death from old age, predation, disease, injury, or sudden environmental change is an ever-present threat to animals. A species can survive and adapt, however, because its members reproduce themselves. When animals reach adult size they become sexually mature and able to reproduce. They do so in one of two basic ways—by asexual or sexual reproduction. Asexual reproduction involves only one parent, whereas sexual reproduction involves two adult individuals.

In many animals the development of reproductive cells is induced by hormones and pheromones. These chemical substances may, in certain climates, be activated by environmental factors, such as the longer days and additional light in spring and early summer. The production of hormones also influences courtship and mating behavior. The young are usually born some time later at a time of plentiful food supply. This coincidence of birth with abundant food increases the individual's chances of survival.

Asexual reproduction

Only the more primitive animals reproduce asexually. It is a less complicated means of reproduction but has the disadvantage of producing offspring that are identical to their parents. There is no shuffling of genetic material between generations, and therefore less variation within the population.

The simplest method of asexual reproduction—binary fission—is found in unicellular organisms such as amebas. These animals simply split their nucleus in two by mitosis (cell division) and the cytoplasm separates to surround each new nucleus. The parent no longer exists as a single unit but has become two "daughter cells."

Two other methods of asexual reproduction—fragmentation (or regeneration) and budding—are also found in animals that are capable of sexual reproduction. Regeneration is the process by which animals, such as hydras and sponges, break off parts of their bodies; each part then grows into a new adult individual. Budding involves the development

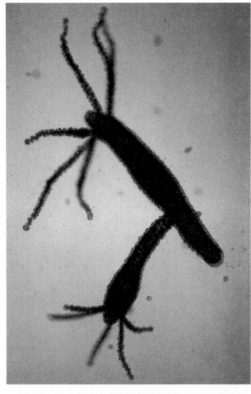

Budding is a method of asexual reproduction and is characteristic of coelenterates such as *Hydra*. It differs from regeneration in that specialized cells are involved. These cells on the body surface grow rapidly to form an outgrowth, or bud, and develop into a smaller copy of the parent.

During amplexus (intercourse), the male Surinam toad *(Pipa pipa)* clings to the female and fertilizes the eggs by covering them with sperm. The young pass the tadpole stage in the mother's back, coming out of the skin when they are about $2\frac{1}{2}$ months old.

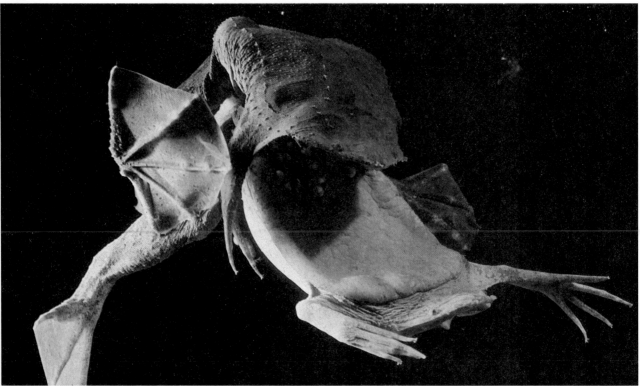

on the body surface of an outgrowth, or bud, which grows into a smaller copy of the parent and eventually detaches itself. In certain corals, for example, buds appear on the body of an adult polyp, or on the connecting sheet. These buds grow larger, separate from the parent, and begin to deposit their own limestone in the colony. In this way, thousands of individual animals, all derived from a single parent, may form great colonies of coral. In some animal groups such as coelenterates, there is an alternation of sexually and asexually produced individuals, one stage being the dominant, usual state for that species, the other being a temporary phase.

Sexual reproduction

The two parent organisms involved in sexual reproduction each produce special sex cells, or gametes. Female gametes (eggs) are formed in an ovary; they are usually much larger than the male gametes (in fact they are the largest single cells) and contain nutrients that feed the embryo. They are also virtually immobile. The male gametes (sperm) are formed in the testicles, are usually very small, and move extremely fast by means of a flagellum, a whip-like tail.

Gametes contain half the number of chromosomes that every other adult cell in the body possesses, and so are called haploid, whereas the body cells contain two corresponding sets of chromosomes (homologous chromosomes), and are diploid. This reduction in the number of chromosomes is affected by meiosis.

When the nuclei of two gametes fuse together during fertilization, the resulting cell, or zygote, contains the full number of chromosomes and two sets of hereditary information, one from each parent. Not all this information is used in the new organism, but is selected according to the rules of genetics—the offspring exhibit features of both their parents but are not exact copies of either. It is this variation that confers an advantage on animals that reproduce sexually.

Sexuality and fertilization

Some animals, such as hydras, flatworms, earthworms, and snails, have both ovaries and testes in each individual, and are called hermaphrodites. Tapeworms fertilize themselves, but most hermaphrodites cross-fertilize with other members of their species. In most animals, however, the male and female sex organs are found in different individuals.

Those animals that live in water reproduce there; their reproductive cells do not need to be protected because they are surrounded by an aquatic medium. But terrestrial animals do not have a watery environment in which fertilization can take place, and so have developed special reproductive fluids to carry the reproductive cells. They also have special organs to effect the transfer.

For fertilization to occur it is important that the sperm and eggs are deposited close to each other. The mobile sperm swim to an egg, attracted by chemicals in the surrounding fluid; but because sperm consist mostly of genetic material, they have a very small energy

Mitosis (A) is the process by which all body cells are produced. Meiosis (B) occurs only in sex cells. They both involve several phases during which a diploid cell is split. During prophase the centrioles separate and form a spindle around the nucleolus, which disappears. The chromosomes collect at the spindle's equator with the centromeres on the spindle threads. In mitosis, the centromeres divide and migrate to opposite poles, but in meiosis whole chromosomes polarize. The cell then splits. In mitosis the chromosomes unwind and revert to chromatin threads. Each daughter cell contains one half of each original pair of chromosomes and replicates the other half. In meiosis, the two new cells split again so that the four resulting cells are haploid, containing only one half of each original pair of chromosomes.

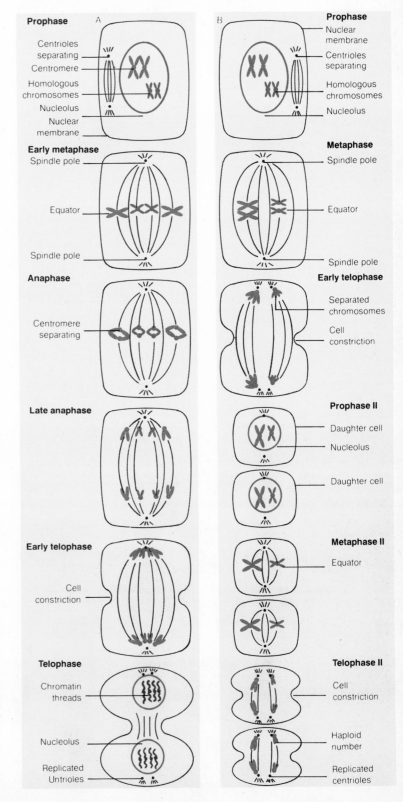

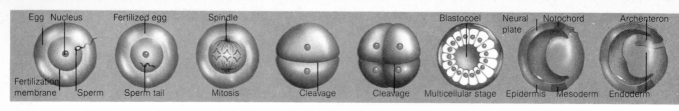

Egg Nucleus | Fertilized egg | Spindle | | | Blastocoel | Neural plate | Notochord | Archenteron

Fertilization membrane Sperm | Sperm tail | Mitosis | Cleavage | Cleavage | Multicellular stage | Epidermis | Mesoderm | Endoderm

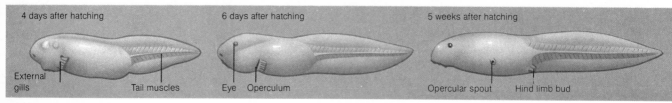

4 days after hatching | 6 days after hatching | 5 weeks after hatching

External gills | Tail muscles | Eye Operculum | Opercular spout Hind limb bud

The fertilization of a frog egg is followed by mitotic division of the egg, called cleavage. The egg cleaves into a two-, four-, and then eight-celled organism. A cavity (blastocoel) forms as cleavage continues and the cells start to differentiate (gastrulation). The skin and body cells then start to develop.

store and usually cannot survive for more than 24 hours under normal conditions. For this reason most animals, especially land-dwellers, set several mechanisms in motion to ensure the meeting of sperm and egg.

The simplest form of fertilization exhibited by higher animals is spawning, found in creatures that breed in water, such as fishes and frogs. This method requires exact timing of the release of gametes from both sexes, or the egg will not be fertilized. The female usually releases her eggs first, and the male then fertilizes them by covering them with sperm.

Fertilization in aquatic animals is usually external, but land animals such as reptiles, birds, and mammals rely mostly on internal fertilization. During intercourse the male deposits his sperm inside the female, and the sperm swim to the egg.

Oviparity and viviparity

Most reptiles and birds, though they have internal fertilization, lay their fertilized eggs in shells outside their bodies; the eggs develop outside the mother. This egg-laying process is known as oviparity. The most advantageous form of reproduction, however, is viviparity, which is exhibited by placental mammals and

ensures that the fertilized egg implants inside the mother. It is nourished by the mother's bloodstream until birth, when it has reached an advanced stage of development and looks like a smaller version of the adult. Some fish, amphibians, and reptiles produce eggs that remain inside the female until the young hatch, but are not nourished directly by her. This process is called ovoviviparity.

Insects

Most insects reproduce sexually and produce yolk-filled eggs, which follow three different patterns of growth before the insect becomes an adult or imago.

The most highly evolved insects, such as butterflies and bees, develop by complete metamorphosis. They hatch from their eggs as larvae and do not resemble their parents. The larvae spend their lives eating and growing. This growth is normally achieved by molting. When the insect is full-grown, eating stops, and the bloated larva becomes a pupa—such as the chrysalis of a butterfly. Inside the pupal case the adult insect body develops and eventually emerges.

Another pattern of development, incomplete metamorphosis, is exhibited by the group of insects that includes dragonflies and cockroaches. The insects hatch from their eggs as nymphs, or naiads, which resemble the parents, but are wingless, smaller, and sexually immature. Like larvae, nymphs eat all the time. They do not enter a pupal stage, however, but grow and shed their hard outer skin until they reach adult size, when they become sexually mature.

The most primitive kinds of insects, such as the wingless bristletails (order Thysanura), hatch as miniature replicas of their parents and no metamorphosis is apparent.

Fishes and amphibians

The reproductive behavior of fishes varies considerably between species. A herring, for example, may shed tens of thousands of eggs and rely on external fertilization, whereas a dogfish reproduces by internal fertilization and produces very few eggs, which are enclosed in an egg purse to protect them while they develop.

Amphibians are considered to be more advanced than fishes, but they are not fully adapted to life on land and always return to

Young mammals depend on their mother for food which, during the first few weeks or months of life, takes the form of milk. Parental care also includes keeping the infants clean and protecting them from predators.

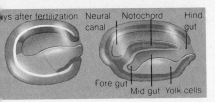
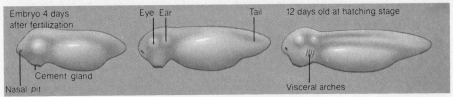

ys after fertilization | Neural canal | Notochord | Hind gut | Fore gut | Mid gut | Yolk cells

Embryo 4 days after fertilization | Eye | Ear | Tail | 12 days old at hatching stage | Cement gland | Nasal pit | Visceral arches

12 weeks after hatching | uth elops | Fore limb | 13 weeks after hatching | Develop limbs | Tail reabsorbed | Frog

water for breeding. Most amphibians fertilize externally. Frogs and toads, for example, mate after they have exchanged specific courtship signals. The mating process (amplexus) involves the male seizing the female and sitting on her, which induces both of them to release gametes into the water simultaneously. The fertilized eggs first go through a larval stage, when they hatch as tadpoles, and gradually metamorphose later into adult amphibians. In some salamanders, however, the young are born live and do not go through a larval (tadpole) stage.

Birds

Birds all reproduce by internal fertilization. Unlike amphibians, they do not rely directly on water for breeding, but the hard-shelled eggs they lay each contain a "private pond" in which the embryo floats and develops. Because birds are warm-blooded the embryos must be kept at body temperature to develop. The temperature is maintained by incubation, a process which is usually carried out by the female, but which in some species is performed by the male while the female goes off in search of food. Incubation can take two to three weeks or more, before the young chicks hatch. In the

case of some birds, the female continues to brood for long periods after they have hatched because the chicks are born blind, helpless, unable to feed themselves, and without feathers to keep them warm.

Mammals

Mammals fertilize and develop internally. Monotremes, among mammals, are egg-layers, and have a uterus structure similar to that of reptiles. In other mammals, the uterus structure varies greatly—female rabbits and kangaroos, for example, have a double uterus and vagina, cows have a two-horned (bicornuate) uterus, and human females have a single, triangular uterus. While the embryo grows inside the mother's uterus, it is supplied with oxygen and nourishment from the mother's bloodstream via the placenta and is kept at a constant warm temperature. The mother can continue with a normal life up until a few hours before birth, after which the young mammal is entirely dependent on her for milk until it can eat solid foods.

A developing frog embryo elongates as it nears hatching and various sense plates become visible, as does a cement gland in the mouth area, and visceral arches. About four days after the tadpole emerges, tail muscles develop and external gills appear around the visceral arches. It attaches itself to plant matter with its oral sucker. About a week after hatching, an operculum grows across the gills, which wither. The eyes develop and the cement gland disappears. About six weeks after hatching, a hind leg buds, followed by forelegs. The mouth then widens and the tail shortens. The metamorphosis is complete at about 13 weeks.

A two-headed Pacific Gopher snake *(Pituophis catenifer)* is the result of the same reproductive process that creates Siamese twins. It occurs when a fertilized egg splits partially into two during an early stage of the egg's development. Mutations such as these rarely survive because their internal organs are often greatly deformed; they are therefore weaker and more vulnerable.

Genetics

Most offspring produced by sexual reproduction resemble their parents, although there is always some variation between parents and offspring. These similarities and differences are due to heredity, the study of which is genetics. Inheritance is not simply a matter of blending, in which the characteristics of both parents are mixed to produce in the offspring an intermediate result. Instead, it is a complex process in which characteristics, which may or may not show themselves in the physical appearance of the offspring, are transmitted to them. Every individual contains millions of genes, each of which controls one or more characteristics in that individual and is responsible for everything that individual is.

Chromosomes, genes, and alleles

Chromosomes are located in the nucleus of a cell, and the genes which lie on them are the carriers of hereditary information. The chromosomes occur in matched (homologous) pairs; one originally from the mother and one from the father. The position occupied by a gene on a chromosome is known as the gene locus, and corresponds with the position of another gene on the other chromosome of that homologous pair. Each gene is an allele, and a pair of alleles control or modify a single characteristic in a normal body cell. But in a gamete (sex cell), only one of each pair of alleles is carried. This is because during meiosis (cell division) in sex cells, homologous pairs of chromosomes are separated so that each new cell contains only one of a pair of chromosomes and, therefore, one of a pair of alleles.

A gene is homozygous when its two alleles are identical, and heterozygous when they are not. Such a pair of dissimilar alleles contains one dominant and one recessive allele. The dominant gene of a pair of alleles always expresses itself whether the alleles are homozygous or heterozygous. Recessive genes express themselves only when they are homozygous. If, for example, the allele for brown eyes (B) was dominant and the allele for blue eyes (b) was recessive, the offspring of one homozygous brown-eyed parent (BB) and one homozygous blue-eyed parent (bb) would be Bb, and because B is dominant, all would have brown eyes. The offspring of two heterozygous parents with the combination Bb would be BB (brown-eyed), Bb and bB (both brown-eyed), and bb (blue-eyed). So brown eyes can be produced by either the BB or Bb genotypes. In such simple cases of inheritance, the likelihood of a dominant characteristic occurring is 3:1.

But the transmission of characters is not always so simple, particularly when it involves a pair of characteristics, when each of a pair of alleles combines with either member of another pair. This is known as a dihybrid cross. For example, in the fruit fly *Drosophila melanogaster*, if the long wing (WW) and the short wing (ww) characteristics were to be paired with a broad abdomen (BB) and a narrow one (bb), with one parent being WWBB and the other wwbb, and if sixteen offspring were produced, the results would be: only 1 in 16 having the same genotype as one parent, but 9 in 16 bearing the dominant phenotypic characteristics (long wings and a wide abdomen); 3 in 16 would carry long wings and a narrow abdomen, and the same number would apply to those offspring bearing short wings and a wide abdomen.

Genes on the same chromosome form a linkage group, and are usually transmitted together to the offspring. Chromosomes vary in size and shape, their dimensions corresponding to the number of genes—the larger the chromosome, the more genes it contains.

The chromosomes that determine an individual's sex are medium-sized. In humans and the fruit fly, the female sex chromosomes are known as X chromosomes and are given the genotype XX. Of a pair of male chromosomes, one is rod-shaped, and the other—the Y chromosome—is crooked; this pair is given

Chromosomes, such as these of a rat-mouse hybrid, show up clearly when stained with a fluorescent dye and then lit by ultraviolet light. In the resting phase, chromosomes are loosely coiled threads of chromatin, but during cell division they spiral tightly, when they become visible, particularly during metaphase. Each species has a definite number of chromosomes—a mouse has 40 and a human has 46.

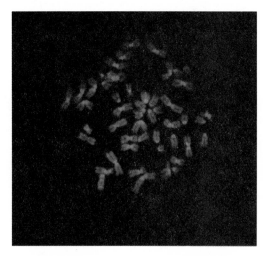

Single-factor inheritance can be seen in the inheritance of coat color in rats. When a black rat with the dominant genotype BB mates with a brown rat of the recessive genotype bb, the resulting offspring will all be genotype Bb and have black coats. But when rats of genotype Bb mate, three out of four of their offspring will have black coats, and only one will have a brown coat. Of the black rats, only one will be homozygous for a black coat (BB), as will the brown rat for its coat color (bb). The rest will be heterozygous.

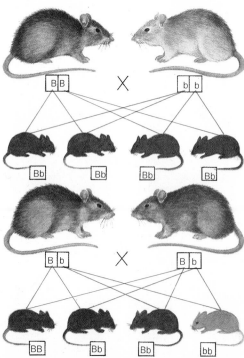

Albinism is a hereditary disorder that manifests itself in an absence of pigments in the body. It is carried by recessive alleles and therefore occurs infrequently. The disorder is not lethal, although slightly debilitating. It involves a lack of pigments in the eyes (which due to lack of protective coloration are extremely sensitive to light), hair (which is usually white), and skin (which is usually pink).

the genotype XY. In birds, the female chromosomes are XY, and the males XX; in some insects, the female chromosomes are XX, but the males have no Y chromosomes, so their genotype is XO.

During a special stage in meiosis, the alleles leave their chromosome and change places with the corresponding chromosome of the homologous pair. This process of crossing-over is called chiasmata and results in new combinations of characteristics, known as recombinants, which increase the amount of genetic variation found among individuals. Crossing-over occurs when an interchange of alleles takes place between the chromatids of homologous pairs of chromosomes.

Some disorders are hereditary, such as albinism, but whereas this disorder is not lethal some, such as cystic fibrosis, are. This disease, carried by homozygous recessive alleles, affects the mucus-secreting cells of organs, and is usually fatal before adulthood.

The structure of a gene

The chromosomes of which genes are a part are constructed from deoxyribonucleic acid (DNA). The DNA molecule is in the shape of a double helix, resembling a twisted ladder. The long parallel strands are constructed from alternating sugar and phosphate molecules, with cross-bridges formed from special groupings called bases. There are four types

of bases: adenine, cytosine, guanine, and thymine, represented by their initial letters—A, C, G, and T. The bases are arranged in certain pairs, so that adenine always pairs with thymine, and guanine with cytosine. Hereditary information is coded in the sequence of these bases along the DNA molecule. The code is an arrangement of three bases, each triplet coding for one amino acid; the triplet CAA, for example, translates into the amino acid valine. Amino acids are the basic components of protein, which forms the structure of living organisms and all the enzymes that control their metabolism.

The white peppered moth *(Biston betularia)* is the dominant form of the species. But in areas blackened by pollution they became easy prey for birds and the black, recessive form flourished and eventually became dominant. The recent success in cleaning up polluted areas has meant the return to dominance of the white moth.

Fact entries

Mendel, Gregor Johann (1822—1884), was an Austrian monk who, largely through his study of garden peas and other plants, discovered the fundamental laws of heredity. His Law of Segregation in its modern form states that an organism's characteristics are determined by a pair of hereditary factors (alleles). Only one member of each pair can be represented in a single gamete. Mendel's Law of Independent Assortment states that the free assortment of factors (alleles) in inheritance corresponds to the free assortment of chromosomes during meiosis; that is, alleles combine randomly with either of another pair. His achievement was unrecognized in his lifetime.

Homologous chromosomes are pairs of chromosomes, each of which has a specific function. They exist in every normal body cell except for gametes, in which the pairs have been separated during meiosis.

Chromatids are pairs of bodies lying next to each other, particularly in their central region (the centromere), which comprise a chromosome. They are most visible in the early stages of meiosis and mitosis.

Behavior

In order to survive, an animal must be able to adapt itself to changing factors in its environment: in other words, it must respond. Its responses include simple reflexes based on instinct and learning, as well as more complex patterned behavior, such as the division of labor among some communities. Mating and feeding are the most important activities and are often the motive for rituals of behavior.

A rat placed in a Skinner box (A) will quickly learn how its surroundings work. It sits and waits (B) for the stimulus—the flashing light—when, it has learned, if it presses the lever (C) food can be obtained (D).

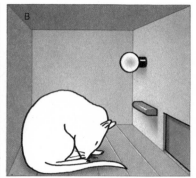

Instinct and learning

All animals are born with a range of innate behavior patterns. The knowledge to do certain things is controlled genetically and is called instinct. This form of inherited behavior helps an animal survive in its environment.

In addition to instinct, animals are able to learn ways of coping with their environment and can thus modify their behavior to deal with problems that they have encountered before. The ability to learn is taken by some behaviorists to be a measure of an animal's intelligence.

But most animals use a combination of instinct and learning to adapt to their environment; the longer an animal's life span and the more complex its life style, the more learning has a role to play. A large predatory mammal, for example, has a built-in hunting ability that is improved by learning from the other members of its group. A fly, by comparison, which lives for only a short time, has as its sole purpose to feed and breed successfully before it dies. It does not have the time to learn how to find a mate, or where it would be best to lay its eggs. Instinct provides the fly with a fixed set of adaptive responses so that it can cope even though it has no previous knowledge of a situation. Instinct is also important when there is no parental care, when the animal is not able to learn by example.

Instinctive reaction is characterized by two features: it is the same for all members of a species, and it can be initiated by a simple stimulus. But the division between instinct and learning is not immediately obvious. All animals of a particular species show the same reaction to a particular stimulus, even if they have been isolated from birth, although

The courtship ritual of gannets *(Sula serrator)*, which breed in large communities, is essential to the male in the first breeding year to enable him to establish the sex of any apparently unmated bird, because there are few superficial distinguishing sexual characteristics. In the ceremony two birds elongate and twist their necks. In subsequent breeding seasons the partners will recognize each other and come together again.

Ticks are drawn toward sunlight (A), by the smell of butyric acid, given off by warm-blooded animals (B), and the warmth of flesh into which they sink their proboscis and suck up blood (C). But experiments with a warm, water-filled balloon onto which butyric acid is smeared show that a tick is just as likely to drop onto the balloon and suck up the water.

animals also often carry out learned activities in a similar stereotyped fashion, which may appear to be instinctive. Responses learned in isolation vary, however, among individuals of a species, depending on how they were taught.

An animal's ability to learn and remember is, to a certain extent, dependent upon the life it leads. A worker bee, for example, must be able to learn the position of its hive and of flowers that are good for foraging, but a fly does not need this ability. It is not surprising then that experiments have proved that whereas bees can easily remember the position of plates of food, flies are less able to do so.

Insight is probably the highest form of learning—when the answer to a problem arrives in a sudden flash. The term is used to describe the rapid solution of a problem, too fast for a trial and error process. An example of this is the immediate construction by some chimpanzees of a "ladder" from objects in order to retrieve fruit that is too high to get at by stretching.

Another type of learning is imprinting, which is thought to occur only over a short, critical period when the animal is very young, or at crucial times of an animal's life, such as at the production of offspring. Imprinting occurs in both mammals and birds. Young songbirds, for example, are not able to sing an adult version of the species song if they have never heard it. They will sing, instead, a simple version of the song, without any characteristic trills. But a young bird that has heard the adult song only once will be able to sing it perfectly at a later stage because it has imprinted the song.

Small animals and birds also imprint any object that is near them soon after birth. This "maternal" imprinting ensures that the young follow the mother, as waterfowl do. But young birds can be persuaded to imprint balloons, cardboard boxes, and even human beings.

Apart from maternal imprinting, there is also sexual imprinting. An animal which has, for some reason, managed to imprint the wrong species, or an inanimate object, will not mate with its own kind. This imprinting was illustrated in an experiment where a male Zebra finch *(Taeniopygia guttata)* was raised by a pair of Bengalese finches *(Lonchura striata)*. When it reached maturity, it was placed in a cage with a female Zebra finch and a female Bengalese finch; the male ignored the female of his own species and courted the Bengalese female, despite her lack of interest.

Imprinting is also thought to be olfactory and may account for a mother's recognition of her offspring, as in ungulates, such as cows or wildebeest. When a mother gives birth, she imprints the smell of her offspring and is then able to identify it in a herd.

The role of sense organs

In addition to instinct, learning is closely associated with responses caused by stimulated sense organs. Most animals are aware of and respond to changes in light, gravity, temperature, and noise but do so in different ways.

Many animals forage for food that they bring back to their home, but they need to orient themselves in the environment and recognize signs to find their way back. Digger wasps (family Scoliidae), for example, recognize landmarks around their burrows, but only the pattern of them. If the pattern were changed, for example, they would not immediately recognize the position of their burrows.

Stimuli such as those used in courtship displays are often spread over a few hours or days and have a cumulative effect on an animal. The effect breaks down defensive barriers between the male and female so that copulation can take place, and also brings the female into a sexually receptive state. This is necessary—indeed it can be vital—particularly in scorpions and spiders, which at the ap-

A feeding animal will generally allow competitors to approach only within a certain distance—the boundary of its "feeding territory." Here a lioness has even temporarily abandoned her kill to rush at scavenging hyenas and frighten the intruders away. Only when she has eaten her fill will they be allowed to pick over the remains.

Combat among the males of a herd is often the means of asserting rights over territory, females, and the dominant position in the herd. Among animals such as Thomson's gazelle *(Gazella thomsoni)*, males and females form separate herds. A few dominant bucks lead the bachelor herds, and during the breeding season try to attract females into their territory to mate with them.

proach of an animate object, even if it is a member of its own species, assume an aggressive position. In such cases, if a male intending to mate does not approach the female cautiously, he may be attacked or killed.

Animals respond to stimuli that are quite different from those discernible by human beings. For instance, it was a puzzle for many years to zoologists why some flowers that depended on bees for pollination were completely white and apparently had no guiding pattern (nectar-guides). It was later found that bees can see ultraviolet light, and that some flowers have very distinctive ultraviolet patterns. Insects can, in addition, be sensitive to the plane of polarized light.

Color also plays a part in stimulating sexual behavior—for example in stickleback fish *(Gasterosteus aculeatus).* The male changes color at the mating season—his belly becomes red and his back turns a blue-white. This coloration attracts females, who, by now, are plump with eggs. The male guides a female to a nest that he has constructed. She enters it, and he nudges her from behind, causing her to release the eggs. She then swims away, and the male enters the nest and fertilizes the eggs.

Many visual stimuli to which animals respond are crude. For example, a robin will attack a clump of red feathers on its territory during the breeding season, and some cuckoos automatically feed a gaping mouth whether it is that of a fish or a fledgling. But some stimuli are supernormal; these are releasers that evoke a greater response than the natural releaser—such as egg size and color. Oyster catchers (family Haematopodidae) and other birds, for example, will try to brood an egg considerably larger than their own in preference to their natural egg.

Animals often respond preferentially to different stimuli. Herring-gull chicks *(Larus argentatus),* for instance, prefer a high level of contrast on a bill at which they peck to elicit food from the parent. When hungry, they peck at a red patch on the lower mandible of the parent's yellow bill, which causes it to regurgitate food. But it has been found that a red and white striped pencil is a better releaser than a real gull bill. This is a case of misfiring, when the animal's behavior is elicited under inap-

propriate circumstances and does not attain its goal.

Scent organs are essential for most animals in the recognition of scent trails to food sources, but scent is also important in communicating fertility. At the time of estrus, many female mammals secrete odiferous pheromones which are detected by the males.

Parental behavior

Different animals rear young in very different ways. In some ducks, the male deserts the female to mate with others in that season. In sticklebacks, however, the female leaves the male to brood the eggs and care for the young fish until they become independent. But among birds and mammals both parents often care for the young, which may be unable to feed themselves or maintain an adequate body temperature for several weeks after birth.

Ties between parents and their offspring are not necessarily exclusive. Among prairie dogs *(Cynomys ludovicianus),* for example, which live in communities for most of the year, the young are suckled indiscriminately by any lactating female and are groomed by any male.

Feeding

The life styles of all animals are organized around their methods of obtaining food. Some parasites, for example, modify the behavior of an intermediate host for the next stage of their life cycle. Many parasitized fish swim close to the surface of the water, unlike those free from parasites, making it more likely that they will be caught by fish-eating birds, and thus pass the parasites on to another host.

Many animals feed in groups, which has the advantage of security. It is more likely that a predator will be detected by one member of the group sooner than if the animals are feeding separately. In addition, animals grazing in a group look up less than when they are on their own, which means that each individual can spend more time eating.

Social behavior

Some animals are solitary all the time, and others are solitary most of the time but come together for certain activities, for example to migrate. A species of locust *(Locusta migratoria)* has a solitary phase, when its coloring is green. But when environmental conditions are favorable, the insects change color to black and russet and become part of a migratory swarm. Some birds, such as the Eurasian robin *(Erithacus rubecula)*, will attack any member of their own species that comes near their territory, but will join a flock that migrates as winter approaches.

Other animals collect together and coordinate their activities. Termites, ants, and bees, for example, live in tightly regimented societies or colonies. The division of labor between the different animals in the colony is strict, and the number of different kinds of individuals depends on what the colony requires for its survival. The colonies are controlled by chemicals called pheromones, which are produced by the queen. These chemicals and the high degree of physical contact between members of a hive ensure cohesion.

Most primates live in groups. These are less regimented than those of social insects, but order is maintained by a social hierarchy, which is ruled over by a single dominant male, usually the oldest and largest. This male has the first choice of the best food and most receptive females. Aggressive confrontations are usually avoided by the use of a large number of facial expressions and dominant or submissive gestures.

Animals that live in close communities often hunt together. Lions, for example, hunt by stalking and then ambushing their prey. But hunting dogs run down their prey in packs, the average size of which is six males and two females. There is usually no dominant dog, male or female, although a dog will determine the direction of movement of the group. The dogs return to the lair after the kill, where the pups wait, and the whole pack is fed on regurgitated meat.

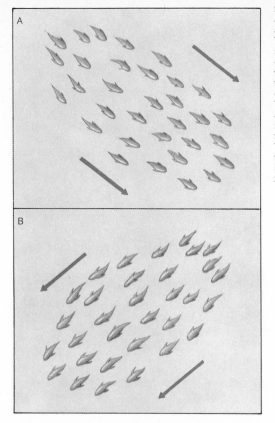

Animals such as hunting dogs, which have a high-protein diet, can afford to spend a lot of time in activities such as play because the energy value of the food they consume is high. Play involves romping and mock fighting and is important to young animals because through play they learn skills that they will need as adults.

Schooling fish are remarkable in the way they travel and communicate in shoals. The shoals are elliptical in shape (A), and contain fish of roughly the same size, which travel at equal distances away from one another, at the same speed. There does not seem to be a leader, and a change of direction is made by all the fish at the same time (B). This indicates a communication between the fish, but it is not fully understood by zoologists.

Grooming is practiced by most mammals, but among primates, particularly Old World monkeys, it reflects rank order and serves to maintain the hierarchy of the group. Subordinate individuals spend more time grooming dominant clan members than being groomed themselves. Male baboons *(Chaeropithecus sp.)*, for example, lie in front of females, which are expected to groom them. The males groom back, but for not as long. Grooming is also an indication of reassurance and friendliness.

Invertebrates

Of the million or so existing animal species, more than 95 per cent have no backbone and are classed as invertebrates. They have a wide variety of shapes and sizes, from microscopic single-celled (acellular) animals only a fraction of a millimeter in length, to the giant squid (*Architeuthis* sp.), which may measure up to 55 feet (17 meters) long and is strong enough to fight with whales that prey upon it. Invertebrates have an extraordinary range of different life styles, and occur at every level of—and play a vital part in—the complex food web that links all forms of life.

The range of invertebrates

There are about 33 invertebrate phyla, but because new groups are continually being discovered and the classification of invertebrates is constantly under revision, the exact number and distribution of phyla is debatable.

Nine groups are particularly important because they represent about 90 per cent of all living invertebrates. From the simplest form to the most complex these nine phyla are: acellular animals (Protozoa); sponges (Porifera); jellyfish and their allies (Cnidaria); flatworms (Platyhelminthes); roundworms (Nematoda); snails, squids, and clams (Mollusca); earthworms,

ragworms, and leeches (Annelida); insects, spiders, and decapods (Arthropoda); and starfish and sea urchins (Echinodermata).

The protozoa are all very small, ranging from 3 millimeters in length to a microscopic size consisting of a single cell, within which all the functions of life are carried out. For this reason, many scientists classify protozoa in their own subkingdom to distinguish them from the multicellular animals, which are classed as Metazoa. The simplest multicellular group is the sponges, with some 10,000 species.

The cnidarians include the jellyfish, sea anemones, corals, and hydroids. They are one of the most simply organized of the multicellular animal groups, having two layers of cells that surround a tubular body cavity, with an opening at one end forming a mouth, and no specialized tissues for respiration or excretion. Most cnidarians are marine animals, although there are a few freshwater species. The platyhelminths fall into three classes—the free-living turbellerians, the parasitic flukes (Trematoda), and the parasitic tapeworms (Cestoda). They have developed a little further than the cnidarians, having three layers of body cells, but most of them lack a body cavity, a circulatory system, and an excretory system; these functions are carried out by cells on the sur-

The zebra spider *(Salticus scenicus)* is a jumping spider and a member of the phylum Arthropoda—the largest group of animals, containing about 900,000 species. Jumping spiders can leap a short distance; they hunt primarily by sight and have the best vision of all spiders. Their eight eyes are arranged in two rows of four; they consist of a large number of receptors and can perceive a sharp image of considerable size. In addition to their keen eyesight, the spiders have chemosensitive hairs at the tips of their appendages.

face of the body. The turbellarians and flukes have a digestive tract that opens from the mouth. The Cestoda, however, absorb food directly from their hosts and have evolved with no digestive tract at all.

The roundworms, or Nematoda, are unsegmented and usually have a digestive tube with a mouth at one end and an anus at the other. The gut is surrounded by a fluid-filled cavity—the pseudocoel—which acts as a hydrostatic skeleton. They are an extremely successful group and are found free-living in all environments, although most of the 10,000 known species are parasitic. Nearly all vertebrate animals and many invertebrates can be hosts to parasitic roundworms.

The annelids, or segmented worms, are the most highly developed worms. They are divided into three major groups: bristle worms (Polychaeta), most of which are marine; earthworms (Oligochaeta), which are mainly freshwater and terrestrial; and leeches (Hirudinea), which are found in the sea, freshwater, and on land.

The phylum Echinodermata includes starfish, sea urchins, sea lilies, sea cucumbers, and brittle stars. These five distinct groups are based on the same radial structure, usually consisting of five or ten arms radiating from a single mouth. They are exclusively marine and are all slow-moving or fixed to one spot and unable to move around.

The phylum Mollusca is the largest after the arthropods, containing more than 100,000 species, and probably the most sophisticated of all invertebrates. Most mollusks have a hard shell enclosing a soft body, and although they

Sea slugs (order Nudibranchia) are gastropod members of the phylum Mollusca, which also includes snails, limpets, abalones, and slugs. Among the most brilliantly colored of all marine invertebrates, they have no shell (unlike most other mollusks). Some have colored tentacles called cerata along their dorsal surface.

conform to a general anatomical pattern, their external body forms are extremely varied. The mollusks contain seven main classes—univalves, or Gastropoda (such as snails); bivalves, or Bivalvia (which contains oysters, mussels and clams); octopuses and Cephalopoda squids; tooth shells, or Scaphopoda; chitons, or Polyplacophora; Monoplacophora; and Aplacophora.

The arthropods are the most successful invertebrates in terms of numbers of species: the arthropod phylum contains more than three-fourths of all the different kinds of animals. All have jointed limbs and segmented bodies, covered by a hard exoskeleton. This body covering acts as a protective armor and as a frame onto which muscles can attach. The largest class of arthropods are the insects (Insecta), which are primarily land-dwelling. Crustaceans, which are found mainly in salt and freshwater, are the second largest class of arthropods and show a greater diversity of structure and physiology than the insects. They range from the relatively advanced lobsters, crayfish, and crabs, to the tiny copepods that graze on the phytoplankton in the oceans. The third group comprises the arachnids—the spiders, ticks, scorpions, and their allies—which are mostly terrestrial and usually have four pairs of legs, no wings or antennae, and pincers rather than simple mouths. Of the six remaining classes of invertebrates, only the centipedes and the millipedes are represented in great numbers.

The minor phyla

The remaining phyla include the smallest phylum Placozoa—with only a single species—and Priapuloidea, which contains only nine known species of tiny, cucumber-shaped, seabed-dwelling worms. Most of the small phyla comprise marine species that are sand or seabed dwellers.

Some invertebrates seem to form a transition between the invertebrates and the vertebrates. These are the hemichordates (such as acorn worms), the tunicates (including sea squirts), and the cephalochordates (lancelets), which are members of the phylum Chordata and have a simple skeletal rod (or notochord) at some stage of their development.

Protozoa and sponges

Stentor sp. is a large ciliate, about one inch (2.5 centimeters). The cilia around the rim of its trumpet-shaped body are joined to form membranelles, or plates, which beat to create feeding currents. It is a selective suspension feeder, rejecting those food particles that are of no nutritive value to it.

The Protozoa are divided into four subphyla: the Sarcomastigophora (amebae and flagellates), the Ciliophora (ciliates), the Sporozoa, and Cnidospora. They are acellular organisms and constitute the simplest animal group. Most of them are microscopic. They comprise about 20,000 species and are found in almost every habitat where moisture is present—in marine, freshwater, and terrestrial

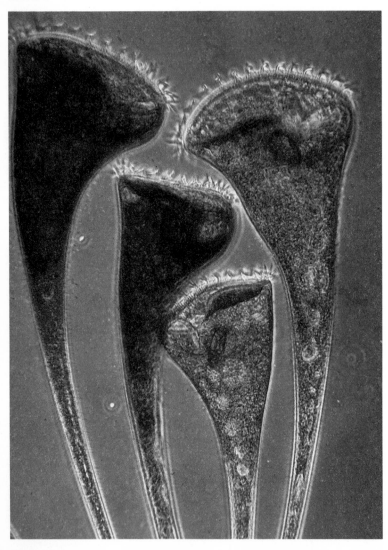

environments—and also as parasites in most animals. Because of their resistant spores, some protozoa can withstand extremes of temperature and humidity. It is not surprising, then, that they are among the most numerous animals in the world. Some protozoa share similar features with certain sponges, which suggests that these two groups may be related.

Amebas and flagellates

Amebas have a constantly changing body shape and move by producing pseudopodia (false feet). The cytoplasm of the ameboid cell is extruded at one point to form the pseudopodium as the animal moves forward. The common *Amoeba* has a naked cell surface, but a variety of shelled forms exists; the genus *Difflugia,* for example, constructs a case from minute grains of sand, whereas other amebas secrete intricate shells of calcium carbonate and silica. These shells contain holes through which the pseudopodium can be extruded to collect food particles.

Some amebas are parasitic, such as *Entamoeba coli,* which lives in the human large intestine. Found in up to 30 per cent of the world population, it does not transmit disease, but scavenges bacteria and food detritus. Such a nonharmful association is termed commensalism. But the related *Entamoeba histolytica* is harmful and causes amebic dysentery.

In contrast to amebas, flagellates move using a long, hairlike structure called a flagellum, which beats like a whip to provide propulsion. Most flagellates have a fixed body shape (usually oval), and almost all reproduce asexually by binary fission; but there is considerable diversity between species. Choanoflagellates, for example, have a delicate collarlike structure that surrounds the base of the flagellum and helps to collect food particles. Similar collar cells (choanocytes) are found in sponges, which suggests a possible link between these two groups. In some collared flagellates, the individuals do not separate after cell division, but give rise to a colony.

Most flagellates feed on small particles and organic materials dissolved in the surrounding water. But some, such as the green *Euglena* commonly found in ponds, are able to pro-

Macronucleus

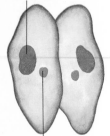 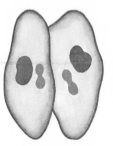 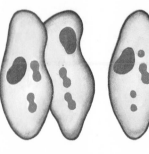 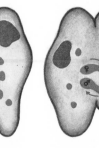 

Micronucleus

Synkaryon

The ciliate *Paramecium* reproduces by conjugation. When two adults with compatible micronuclei come together, the micronucleus of each divides twice. Three of the four new cells disintegrate but the fourth continues to divide. The cell walls joining the two ciliates dissolve, and the male nuclei of the two conjugants are exchanged. The adults then separate, and development of the synkaryon continues in each one. At about this stage the macronucleus starts to disintegrate and is resorbed. The synkaryon divides three times, produc-

duce their own food by photosynthesis. The presence of the photosynthetic pigment, chlorophyll, has led many biologists to classify such flagellates as algae (simple plants). In all other respects, however, they are identical to flagellate protozoa.

Many flagellates live in association with other animals. *Trichonympha,* for example, lives in the intestine of termites. The termite relies on the protozoan to digest the wood that it eats—a mutually beneficial relationship known as symbiosis. But some flagellates are blood parasites, such as *Trypanosoma,* and cause disease (in this case African sleeping sickness).

Ciliates

The most complex and diverse species of protozoa owe their name to the cilia (short hairlike fibers similar in structure to flagella), which grow in orderly rows on the body and beat rhythmically to propel the animal. In many ciliates, the cilia occur only on parts of the body, whereas in others they form plates or "membranelles." Still others have cilia that are fused into stiff cirri and used as legs for crawling. Ciliates reproduce asexually by binary fission, or sexually by conjugation. They differ from other protozoa in that they have two nuclei—a macro- and micronucleus (other protozoa have only one).

Sporoza and Cnidospora

These organisms, the spore-formers, have no distinct locomotory adaptations because they are all parasitic. They live in all animals and are often transmitted by insect vectors. Their name comes from the production of spores, or cysts, during the infective stages of their life. The life cycle of this group is complicated—reproduction alternates from asexual to sexual. Asexual reproduction involves the binary fission of spores, usually in the host. The offspring develop into gametes, which mature and fertilize other gametes that eventually produce spores.

Sponges

Sponges comprise the phylum Porifera (pore-bearers) and represent the simplest level of multicellular animals. Most of the 5,000 species are found in shallow waters, although some live in deep water. They range in length from one-quarter of an inch to more than 4 feet (0.5 centimeter to 1.2 meters).

In contrast to the colonial protozoa, sponges consist of several cell types, each of which performs a specific function and is independent. This feature means that regeneration is easy—if a sponge is fragmented, the cells simply organize themselves into a new sponge.

The simplest sponges are tubular with an external layer of epithelial, or lining, cells. The internal surface is covered with flagellated collar cells (choanocytes), which maintain a water current through the sponge. Food particles are extracted from this current, which is also used for gas exchange and waste removal. Water is drawn in through small pore sells in the walls of the sponge, and ejected from the large mouth (osculum). More advanced sponges have complex systems of canals and chambers, through which water is channeled.

Sponges reproduce sexually and asexually. Most are hemaphroditic and produce eggs and sperm at different times, but some are dioecious. Asexual reproduction occurs by budding. In addition, some sponges produce gemmules that survive when the parent body disintegrates in winter. In spring the gemmule develops into an adult sponge. Sexual reproduction occurs when sperm is released and enters another sponge in the water currents.

Glass sponges, or hexactinellids, comprise the class Hexactinellida, and are mainly deepwater sponges. Like other sponges they have special cells that secrete the skeleton, which is made up of spicules, or tiny needlelike structures. In bath sponges, these spicules are composed of a horny protein called spongin, but in glass sponges they are made of silica. These siliceous spicules are fused to form a six-pointed shape, from which the class name of the glass sponges is derived.

ing eight new cells. Three of these dissolve, four start to attain macronucleus status, and one continues to divide as a micronucleus. The cili-

ate itself then starts to divide. The four macronuclei polarize, two at each end, and when the cell finally divides it also contains one

micronucleus. The micronucleus in both new ciliates continues to split and the macronuclei again polarize, so that when the two ciliates

divide, the resultant four cells each contain one micro- and one macronucleus.

Coelenterates

The coelenterates are among the simplest of the metazoans (multicellular organisms with cells organized into tissues), and include those animals in the phylum Cnidaria, such as corals, jellyfish, hydras, and sea anemones, and the comb jellies of the phylum Ctenophora. The largest species is the arctic jellyfish *(Cyanea artica)*—7 feet (2.1 meters) across with tentacles 100 feet (30 meters) long—and the smallest are the individual polyps of some coral colonies, most of which are less than one inch (2.5 centimeters) in diameter. Coelenterates comprise about 9,000 species and are probably the most common macroscopic marine animals, especially in tropical and subtropical coastal waters. Furthermore, the corals create reefs and atolls, which are some of the world's most diverse and productive habitats.

General structure

Cnidarians have two basic forms—polyps and medusas—which are radially symmetrical, with no definite front or rear ends. The flowerlike polyps are attached at their base to their mother organism, and have a mouth on the upper side, surrounded by tentacles. Medusas, commonly known as jellyfish, are free-swimming, bell-shaped organisms, with a mouth on the underside. In the typical life cycle of a cnidarian, the two basic forms alternate—polyps bud off medusas, which then produce a larval polyp, and so on. One form is usually dominant, however, and in some species the other is omitted altogether.

The coelenterate body comprises two layers of cells—an outer epidermis and an inner gastrodermis—separated by a layer of jellylike matter: the mesogloea. The two layers of cells surround a central cavity (coelenteron)—or digestive cavity—and contain muscle cells that contract to bend the body or retract the tentacles. In cnidarians the epidermis contains stinging cells (nematocysts) to immobilize prey. The food is then pushed by the tentacles through the mouth into the coelenteron, where it is digested by enzymes and absorbed by the gastrodermis.

Many coelenterates often form colonies of thousands of individuals. In the simplest colonies all individuals are identical, but feed and reproduce separately. In more advanced colonies, however, such as those of some corals and hydrozoans, several different forms are present (polymorphism), and each type undertakes a different function. But in many there are nervous connections between individuals—if one polyp is touched, the whole colony contracts.

Hydrozoans

Some members of the class Hydrozoa, such as the common freshwater *Hydra*, have no medusa stage, although many other members of the class develop both polyps and medusas, and some display the medusoid form only. In the reproductive cycle of most hydrozoans, sexually reproductive medusoids bud off the parent asexually and either drift free or remain attached to the parent organism (when they are known as gonophores). In the *Hydra*, however, reproduction is more commonly asexual, by budding from the parent.

Most hydrozoans are colonial and, although normally attached, move by a creeping action at the base. Most of them are green, because of the presence of symbiotic algae

The sea nettle *(Chrysaora hyoscella),* common in the coastal waters of the Atlantic Ocean and Mediterranean Sea, has a diameter of 12 inches (30 centimeters). Its fringing tentacles are covered with nematocysts—or stinging cells—as are its four trailing arms, which presents a danger, although not a fatal one, to swimmers.

In the reproductive cycle of most jellyfish the egg released by the adult medusa becomes a ciliated planula larva, which develops into an attached polyp. When medusoid layers bud off the polyp it is called a scyphistoma, and when the young medusas (ephyrae) are mature enough to detach themselves, it is known as a strobila.

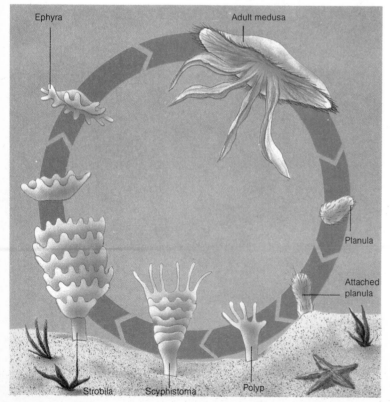

Ephyra

Adult medusa

Planula

Attached planula

Strobila   Scyphistoma   Polyp

(zoochlorellae) in the gastrodermal cells (body wall).

The best-known hydrozoan, the Portuguese man-of-war (*Physalia* sp.) has a common hydrozoan feature—an air-filled cushion that acts as a float. Its tentacles comprise a colony of polymorphic polyps.

Jellyfish

Jellyfish (class Scyphozoa) consist of a swimming bell fringed by tentacles, with a four-cornered mouth on the underside. Around the mouth are four trailing arms which, like the tentacles, are well supplied with nematocysts (stinging cells). Jellyfish swim by contracting and releasing a ring of muscle cells; balancing organs (statocysts) and simple light receptors around the bell margin help them to remain upright. As their name suggests, they contain large amounts of the jellylike mesogloea, which helps to control buoyancy, and also acts as an elastic support for the body.

Sea anemones, corals, and ctenophores

The sea anemones and corals of class Anthozoa (flower animals) have a polyp stage only. These are often large and complex, with the coelenteron divided by partitions, or septa. Many sea anemones have large attachment disks and thick, leathery bodies, which allow them to survive on rocks that are exposed at low tide.

Corals are essentially polymorphic colonial sea anemones, although solitary forms do exist. The polyps secrete skeletons, the exact form of which defines the species, such as the delicate sea fan (*Gorgonia* sp.). Reef-building corals flourish only in tropical and subtropical coastal waters where temperatures are above 65° F. (18° C), and the water is less than 100 feet (30 meters) deep. The necessity for shallow water seems to reflect the light requirements of the photosynthetic algae (zooxanthellae), which live in the gastrodermal cells. The coral skeleton is built up faster in species with zooxanthellae than in those without them, possibly because algal photosynthesis increases the production of calcium carbonate (which creates the skeleton) by removing carbon dioxide.

Ctenophores, or comb jellies, are grouped with cnidarians because they are also radially symmetrical, jellylike, and composed of two layers of cells. But the gastrovascular cavity of the cnidarians has become a canal system in the ctenophores, and the medusoid shape only has been adopted and modified into a sphere or oval. There are two classes: those with tentacles, such as the most common form, the sea gooseberry *(Pleurobrachia pileus),* and those without. These animals are marine and are usually found swimming among plankton; many are luminescent. They move using ciliated bands called comb plates. The cilia fuse into plates during the development of the animal; by beating these plates consecutively from the head to the tail, they swim through the water. Ctenophores catch their prey using lasso cells (colloblasts), which have a similar function to that of nematocysts in cnidarians, but they are adhesive rather than paralyzing.

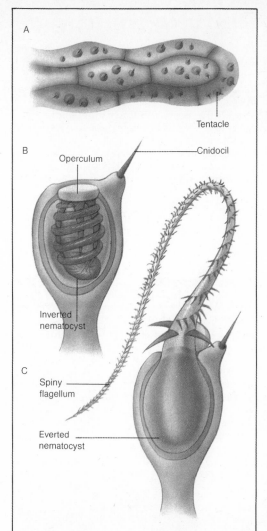

A

Tentacle

B

Operculum

Cnidocil

Inverted nematocyst

C

Spiny flagellum

Everted nematocyst

Nematocysts (stinging cells) are abundant on the tentacles of coelenterates (A). These oval cells contain an inverted tube at one end of which is a flagellum, often covered with spines, coiled tightly around the bulb of the tube (B). On the activation of a protruding hairlike trigger (cnidocil), the cell lid (operculum) snaps open, the nematocyst whips out, everting itself (C), and the toxins contained in it are ejected through the spines.

Sea anemones, like most coelenterates, are carnivorous, the larger ones feeding on small crustaceans. The nematocysts in their tentacles do not have a cnidocil, nor an operculum; they often simply break through the capsule wall. The tentacles surround an oral disk that contains a mouth. Prey is carried to the mouth, which is widened by muscles, and the prey is swallowed whole.

Platyhelminthes

The phylum Platyhelminthes (flatworms) is divided into four classes: the turbellarians (Turbellaria), the monogeneans (Monogenea), the flukes (Trematoda), and the tapeworms (Cestoda). Most turbellarians are free-living; the other three are exclusively parasitic. As their common name suggests, flatworms are flattened, soft-bodied organisms. Most flukes are microscopic, but intestinal tapeworms may grow up to 100 feet (30 meters).

General features

Compared with the simpler coelenterates, flatworms show several advanced characteristics: for example, the body is bilaterally symmetrical and has a definite head end. Free-living flatworms are active animals, and in many species the head carries pairs of eyes, as well as chemoreceptors. There is also a concentration of nerve cells at the front end of the body that forms a primitive brain, in addition to the diffuse nerve net similar to that of the cnidarians.

The flatworm body is composed of three layers of cells, whereas in coelenterates there are only two. Between the epidermis and the gastrodermis (which lines the digestive cavity), there is a layer of mesodermal cells. Oxygen reaches this middle cellular layer by diffusion because these animals are so highly flattened

that a specialized breathing system is not required. The mesoderm contains the complicated reproductive organs, which are made up of different types of cells. This differentiation represents a higher level of organization than that found in the coelenterates, which possess tissues, but not organs.

As in *Hydra,* the digestive cavity in flatworms (apart from tapeworms) has one entrance only and no separate exit, with the result that undigested food is ejected through the mouth. In turbellarians, this digestive cavity is often highly branched, so that food can be distributed to all parts of the body.

Turbellarians

The turbellarians include all free-living flatworms. Some species grow up to 25 inches (60 centimeters), but most are about one-half inch (13 millimeters) long. Most freshwater species are drab and inconspicuous, whereas tropical marine species may be very colorful.

Turbellarians do not swim freely, although they live in water, but creep along the bottom. The epidermis is equipped with minute, hairlike cilia and glandular cells, which secrete mucus in which the cilia beat, enabling the flatworm to glide along. They also have bands of muscles that allow complex bending movements of the body.

Most turbellarians are carnivorous, feeding on small animals, or necrophagous (feeding on dead animals). Many secrete mucus and an adhesive to entangle their prey, before using the protrusible pharynx to break it up into small particles. In some cases, the prey is ingested whole.

Compared with parasitic flatworms, turbellarians have a simple life cycle. Most species are hermaphroditic, with male and female sex organs in the same individual. Self-fertilization does not usually occur, however, and a partner is needed for fertilization to take place. Sperm is exchanged between the two individuals, and both lay fertilized eggs in egg capsules or gelatinous masses. After two or three

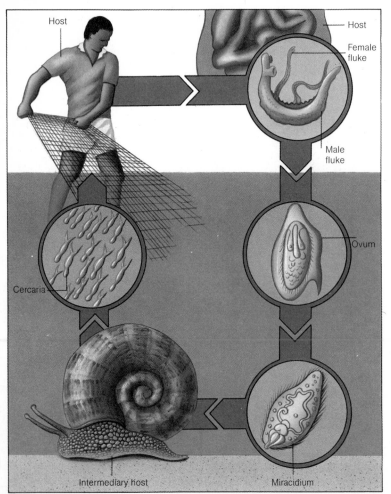

The blood fluke *Schistosoma mansoni* breeds in the host's intestine or bladder. Fertilized eggs pass out in the feces, develop into larvae (miracidia), and are released in water. In an intermediary host they breed cercariae, which burrow into a third host.

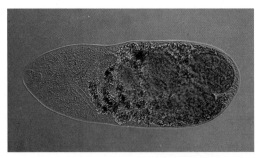

The small intestinal fluke *Metagonimus yokogawei (above)* is one of many that are found particularly in Asia. This species has only one intermediary host, usually snails or fishes. It is transmitted to vertebrate hosts that eat raw fish and mollusks.

weeks, young flatworms resembling their parents hatch from the eggs.

Some turbellarians also reproduce asexually; the body constricts in the middle and the hind portion breaks off to form a complete new individual. Using the same principle, if an individual is cut in two, the front half will form a new tail and the rear half a new head.

Flukes

These flatworms occur as internal parasites (order Digenea) and external parasites (class Monogenea). They generally have leaf-shaped bodies with suckers or, rarely, hooks to attach to their hosts. As a result of their parasitic habits, adult flukes lack the sense organs and layer of cilia that are found in turbellarians.

Another feature found in flukes and typical of most parasites is a high reproductive ability, which ensures that at least some offspring reach suitable hosts. Not only do the adult flukes of internal parasites produce large numbers of eggs, but the larvae of these flukes also reproduce within their hosts.

External parasites are often found in the gill cavities of fish, where they have to withstand strong water currents. They feed on blood and gill tissue. Internally parasitic flukes may be found in many vertebrates as well as in other invertebrates. The liver fluke *(Fasciola hepatica)* is a well-known parasite found in the bile passage of the liver of sheep and cattle, where it inflicts fatal damage. This fluke has a complex life cycle which involves several hosts. The eggs leave the vertebrate host in the feces and hatch in water into free-swimming larvae (miracidia). These larvae swim until they encounter a snail—the intermediate host—into which they burrow. Inside this host the larvae multiply and eventually leave the snail as another larval form—cercaria. Up to 600 cercariae may be produced from a single miracidium. These then encyst on grass, where they are eaten by the vertebrate host, in which they develop into sexually mature flukes.

Tapeworms

The adults of this parasitic group are found as internal parasites in the alimentary canal of vertebrates. Like the flukes, tapeworms have no obvious sense organs, and their complex life cycle usually involves two more hosts. The beef tapeworm *(Taenia saginata)*, for example, has two hosts—cattle and man.

Tapeworms have no digestive system—indeed, they do not need one, because they are surrounded by digested food in the gut of their host, and they simply absorb nutrients through their cuticle. These worms consist of a head, or scolex; segments or proglottids bud off from the neck. The head usually bears hooks and suckers for attachment to the gut lining of the host. The proglottids remain attached in a long chain as they mature, finally breaking off and leaving the host in the feces. The eggs hatch from the proglottids once they have been eaten by the intermediate host.

The candy-striped flatworm *(Prostheceraeus vitatus)* is a member of the order Polycladida. The order name refers to the many-branched intestinal system with which the organism digests its food. It is marine and reaches 2 inches (5 centimeters) in length. Gland cells below the epidermis secrete an adhesive substance that allows the flatworm to stick to a substrate or to prey. The combination of this substance with beating cilia and muscular contractions enables the flatworm to move over any surface.

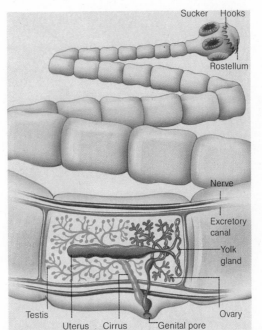

The reproductive segment (proglottid) of a tapeworm contains male and female reproductive organs. During copulation, the cirrus of the male is inserted into the genital pore of another proglottid, and the fertilized eggs are stored in the uterus. Cross-fertilization usually occurs with a proglottid from another worm in the same host or with another proglottid on the same worm if the worm has twisted around itself. The proglottid breaks off the parent organism, and when the eggs are mature the proglottid wall ruptures, releasing them.

Nematodes and annelids

In the evolution of metazoans the stage of development after that of the three-layered structure of the flatworms seems to be the appearance of a fluid-filled cavity, or coelom. This body cavity occurs in two forms: the pseudocoelomates—such as the aschelminths, which include the gastrotrichs, rotifers, kinorhynchs, nematodes, and nematomorphs—and the eucoelomates, or true coelem. Another feature which appears at this stage is metamerism, or segmentation, displayed particularly in the annelids. All of these animals share some features but are too different to be placed under one phylum, so each has its own.

Ribbon worms

This group, known as nemerteans, are not pseudocoelate because a solid tissue (paren-

chyma) fills the cavity between the gut and the body wall. In this respect they resemble the flatworms but are more highly specialized because they have more complex nervous and circulatory systems, and an alimentary canal with a mouth and anus.

Most of the 600 or so species are marine burrowers and feed on invertebrates. They have a remarkable food-catching apparatus—an eversible tube (the proboscis), which is shot out by hydrostatic pressure through a pore in the head. In many species the proboscis simply coils around the prey but in some it has teeth and stabs prey.

Roundworms

This group, the nematodes, is the largest of the aschelminths, containing about 10,000 species. They are found in most environments, and millions may occur in only a couple of acres of soil.

Nematodes have cylindrical bodies, which taper at each end and are covered in a thick protein layer called the cuticle, which is shed periodically as the animal grows. The cuticle and body wall are permeable to water, which flows in and out continuously. The intestine of these organisms runs from the mouth to the anus and is enclosed by longitudinal muscles along the length of the body. Roundworms move like snakes by contracting these muscles, helped by the elasticity of the cuticle and the pressure of the fluid in the pseudocoel. They have a simple nervous system, as do most aschelminths; the brain is situated anteriorly and comprises a ring of ganglia, from which nerves run down the length of the body.

Nematodes have separate sexes and give birth to larvae that resemble the adult. Many are parasitic—some only in the larval stage, others only when they are adult, and still others are parasitic throughout their life. Parasitic nematodes, such as *Dorylaimida* sp., damage crops by sucking the contents from punctured plant cells or by feeding on the tissues inside the plant.

Nematodes also parasitize animals, including humans. The hookworm *(Necator americanus)* does great harm by feeding on the blood and cells of the intestinal lining; female hookworms produce many eggs, which leave the host's body in the feces. In unsanitary living conditions, the eggs hatch, and the young hookworms enter the human body by boring through the skin of the feet.

Annelids

Annelids are worms in which the body is divided into many segments, and as such are a little more developed than the pseudocoelomates, which are unsegmented. The phylum Annelida has three classes: Polychaeta, Oligochaeta, and Hirudinea. In the polychaete ragworm *(Nephthys caeca)* each segment of the body—apart from the head and the last segment—is identical, and the external and internal organs are repeated in each segment. In the oligochaetes, such as the earthworms, and

The nematode *Ascaris* sp. parasitizes the intestine of humans, cattle, and pigs, as well as other invertebrates. The adult worms breed in the intestine, and the eggs develop in cysts in the feces. When this excrement is taken in by another host, the eggs hatch in and break through its small intestine. Once in the bloodstream, they are carried to the lungs, make their way to the mouth, and are swallowed. The young worms then burrow into skeletal muscle, remaining there until the flesh containing them is eaten by another host.

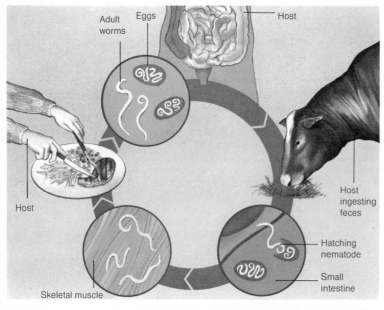

Adult worms · Eggs · Host · Host ingesting feces · Hatching nematode · Small intestine · Skeletal muscle · Host

Rotifers are so called because the head region of these organisms has a crown of cilia that beat very fast to propel it, and in some species looks like a spinning wheel. This species, *Philodina gregaria*, retracts its corona as it creeps along the substrate, and uses the two spurs at its foot as a means of attachment. The white oval shape in the head region is the mastax, or pharynx, which is used to catch and break up food. The orange area is the stomach. This species reproduces by parthenogenesis only and has no males.

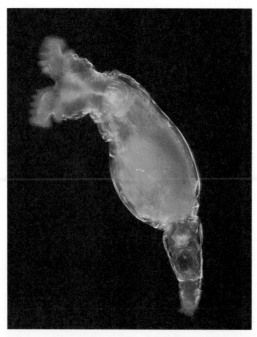

the leeches (class Hirudinea), some segments are specialized for particular functions and are not all identical. Like nematodes, annelids have a space in the body surrounding the gut but, because it is formed in a different way during the development of the embryo, it is called a coelom.

Polychaete annelids are marine. Some, such as the ragworm, are fast-moving predators, with a well-developed head region that has eyes, sensory tentacles, and powerful jaws. They move by using the fleshy leglike extensions of the body (parapodia) on each segment. Other polychaetes, such as lobworms, (*Arenicola* sp.), burrow in mud; still others are sessile and live in tubes, as do the fan worms *(Sabella pavonina)*.

Most of the 3,000 or more species of oligochaetes are burrowers and live in freshwater and terrestrial habitats. Instead of parapodia, each body segment has a few stout bristles (setae). These worms travel by peristaltic contractions, as do burrowing polychaetes, using the bristles as a temporary anchor.

As in polychaetes, the reproduction of oligochaetes is usually sexual, but they contrast with the polychaetes in that they are hermaphroditic, each worm having both male and female sex organs. These are situated toward the front end of the animal in different segments. During copulation earthworms come together in opposite directions with their undersides pressed together. They are held together by a mucous tube which is secreted by the glands in the clitellum (an enlarged segment girdling the body). The clitellum of each worm attaches itself to the segments containing the spermathecae of the other worm. Sperm is moved to the clitellum by muscular contractions and passes through a groove in the clitellum into the spermathecal opening of the opposite worm. After a few days, the clitellum secretes a hard ring of material, which slips forward and collects eggs and sperm as it moves over the genital openings. When it comes off the worm, the ends seal up; this cocoon can carry 20 eggs, which hatch after about 12 weeks.

The tubeworm *Spirographis spallanzani* is an annelid that inhabits the Mediterranean Sea. It lives in a tube that is made of sand cemented by an organic material that it secretes from special glands, and is constructed on the sea bed. The movement of small cilia on the tentacles of the worm creates water currents, which carry food toward its mouth.

Leeches are found in fresh water, the sea, and on land. They share several features with oligochaetes, including hermaphroditism, fertilization in a cocoon secreted by a clitellum, and the lack of parapodia, but the coelom has been lost during secondary adaptation, except in one species.

Leeches have flattened, muscular bodies with a sucker at each end, which is used as an anchor while they move by extending and contracting the body. Most leeches are ectoparasitic, feeding on the surface of their host. The front sucker is clamped onto the victim's skin, and the teeth in the leech's mouth then make a small cut, which is unnoticed by the host due to an anesthetic that is secreted by the leech. While the leech sucks blood out of the wound, it secretes a chemical (hirudin), which prevents the victim's blood from clotting. Bloodsucking leeches feed infrequently, but when they do feed they can draw out several times their own weight in blood in one meal.

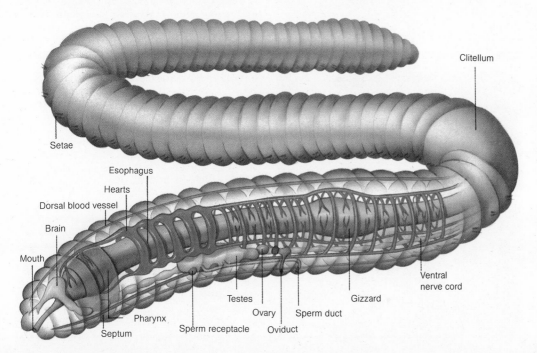

Setae
Esophagus
Hearts
Dorsal blood vessel
Brain
Mouth
Clitellum
Pharynx
Septum
Testes
Ovary
Sperm receptacle
Oviduct
Sperm duct
Gizzard
Ventral nerve cord

Earthworms diffuse gases and water through the cuticle (skin), although oxygen is also distributed by hemoglobin in the blood. These animals have five hearts from which branched vessels carry blood along the length of the body. The nervous system of earthworms is well developed compared with that of the flatworms: clusters of cerebral ganglia form a brain from which two nerve cords run, and although the worm has no eyes, it has photoreceptors in the epidermis, particularly at its front and back ends.

Echinoderms

The phylum Echinodermata (spiny-skins) consists of about 5,000 species of exclusively marine organisms, which include such well-known animals as starfish and sea urchins. The description "spiny-skins" is derived from the calcareous (limy) plates that form the endo-skeleton of these animals, which in some species is covered with spines. These spines are particularly prominent in sea urchins.

The most obvious feature of these animals, however, is their five-rayed, or pentamerous, symmetry. It is surprising, then, that the rich fossil record of echinoderms (made possible by the presence of the skeletal plates) shows that some of the earliest species were actually bilaterally symmetrical. This evidence, plus the fact that modern forms pass through a bilaterally symmetrical larval stage, suggests that radial symmetry is a secondary adaptation.

The relationship between the echinoderms and other invertebrate phyla is somewhat obscure. It was initially thought that echinoderms and hemichordates (primitive chordates) were closely related because of the similarity between the larvae of the two groups. It is now believed, however, that the resemblance is due not to homologous (genetically similar) characteristics but to the adaptation of different organs to perform the same function (a process that is known as convergent evolution).

Starfish

Starfish, or sea stars (class Asteroidea), are the most familiar echinoderms. They consist of a central disk, from which five arms arise (although some species have more than five arms). These animals move using tube feet (podia), which are found in a groove (the ambulacral groove) under each arm. Each tube foot ends in a suction disk, which allows the starfish to stick to rocky surfaces; when moving over sand, however, the tube feet are used as stiff legs.

Tube feet are also used to deal with prey, which usually consists of bivalves, such as clams and oysters. The tube feet exert enough pressure to open them slightly so that the starfish can push its now inside out stomach into the gap (the stomach can squeeze through a space as small as 0.1 millimeters). The stomach then secretes enzymes that slowly digest and absorb the victim before it is eaten. The starfish intestine has five branches, one in each arm. Indigestible fragments are usually ejected via the mouth (there is an anus on the upper surface but it is seldom used).

Within each arm there is also a pair of gonads (sex organs). Reproduction in most echinoderms is a simple process. The sexes are separate, and sperm and eggs are released into the water, where fertilization occurs. The larvae that hatch are called bipinnariae and metamorphose gradually into the adult form. A few species copulate, and the eggs develop in a brood chamber without going through a larval stage. Starfish are also able to reproduce by fragmentation—or regeneration, as this process is sometimes called—but this is only an occasional occurrence.

In large numbers, starfish can have a devastating ecological effect. The population of the crown-of-thorns starfish (Acanthaster planci), for example, has increased in the Pacific Ocean in recent years, and, because it feeds on the live corals, has destroyed whole areas of coral reef.

Brittle stars

The 2,000 species of brittle stars (class Ophiuroidea), which occur at all depths of the ocean, are easily distinguished from starfish by the sharp demarcation of their central disk, and by their very long arms. They also differ from starfish in several other ways. Locomotion is achieved not by tube feet but by muscular movements of the arms. Most brittle stars feed on small living or dead organisms, but do not have an intestine or anus, and indigestible fragments are ejected through the mouth. Starfish (and sea urchins) breathe by means of skin gills, which are located all over the body surface, whereas brittle stars use respiratory

The water vascular system of echinoderms is an arrangement of fluid-filled canals. A porous structure (madreporite) links the aboral surface with a ring canal near the oral surface. Radial canals run from this water ring along the underside of each arm and give rise to lateral canals, which end in a bulbous ampulla; this itself ends in one or more tube feet (podia). When the ampulla contracts, fluid is pushed into the podia and elongates them. As it touches a surface, the center of the tip of the podium contracts to form a vacuum and sticks to the surface.

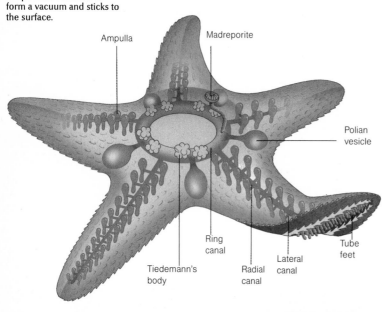

Ampulla

Madreporite

Polian vesicle

Ring canal

Tiedemann's body

Radial canal

Lateral canal

Tube feet

The brittle star *Ophiothrix fragilis* lives in dense communities on muddy, gravel substrates. It is a small animal, its disk being only about one-half inch to just over one inch across. Brittle stars are the most mobile echinoderms. They move by lifting the disk off the substrate, extending one or two arms forward, and trailing two behind, while the lateral arms push against the bottom with the aid of spines. This species has hooked spines on the oral surface, which provide additional traction during locomotion.

pouches (bursae), which occur near the arm bases.

Sea urchins

Most sea urchins (class Echinoidea) have a globular body, with the skeletal plates fused together to form a hard shell (the test). In most species, the body is further protected by sharp spines, which may be poisonous. Some of the spines are movable, articulating in sockets in the skeletal plates, and are used for locomotion. The spines of some species of urchin are also used for boring holes in coral or rock, into which the animals wedge themselves to prevent removal. In addition to spines, the skin surface of urchins and asteroids carries tiny pincerlike structures on stalks, called pedicellariae, which are used for defense, catching small prey, and cleaning the body surface.

The tube feet of echinoids protrude through holes in the skeletal plates in 10 longitudinal rows. In heart urchins and sand dollars (*Clypeaster* sp.) the podia are modified for respiration, and locomotion is achieved by means of the spines only. These urchins also burrow in sand, which has resulted in the spines being modified: the heart urchin has reduced spines to assist burrowing, giving it a furry appearance, and the sand dollar's body is covered with tiny movable spines used for crawling and digging.

Sea urchins are omnivorous and often scavenge on organic debris. The mouth is on the underside (oral surface), and the anus on the upper side (aboral surface).

Sea cucumbers, sea lilies, and feather stars

As their name suggests, sea cucumbers (class Holothuroidea) are cucumber-shaped echinoderms, elongated along the oral-aboral axis. They have soft bodies, covered with a glandular skin, and the skeletal plates have been reduced to microscopic ossicles.

Sea cucumbers burrow in sand. To breathe, they have tubes known as "respiratory trees" which carry seawater into the body from the anus, so that gaseous exchange can occur in-

ternally. The podia and skin surface are also used for respiration.

Sea lilies and feather stars (class Crinoidea) are among the most primitive of echinoderms. They resemble a starfish that has been inverted, and (in the case of the sea lily) attached to the sea bed by a stalk. Most fossil echinoderms are of this form. The sea lily skeleton, which stands on the stalk, is cup-shaped with arms. Tube feet are present in a groove on the upper surface of the arms, but they are used solely for respiration. Food (usually plankton) is collected by the arms and directed to the mouth on the upper surface by cilia.

The feather stars resemble sea lilies and, like them, develop from the larval stage into an attached form. They differ from sea lilies, however, in that they are free-living as adults, either creeping along the seabed or swimming.

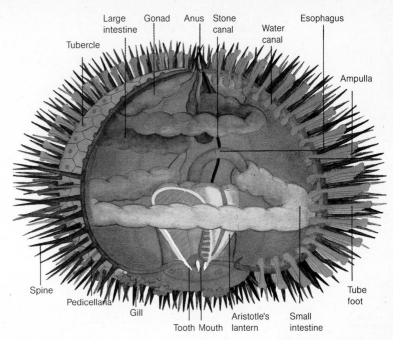

Large intestine · Gonad · Anus · Stone canal · Water canal · Esophagus · Tubercle · Ampulla · Spine · Pedicellaria · Gill · Tooth · Mouth · Aristotle's lantern · Small intestine · Tube foot

Sea urchins display the characteristic five-rayed symmetry most interestingly in the mouth. This consists of five pyramidal plates worked together by muscular action to scrape up food, and is called an Aristotle's lantern because it resembles an old-fashioned lamp. From the mouth, the esophagus ascends and joins the small intestine, which does a complete circuit inside the urchin; but when it joins the large intestine it does another circuit in the opposite direction before it joins the rectum.

The sea cucumber (*Cucumaria saxicola*) ranges from 4 inches (10 centimeters) to 3 feet (91 centimeters) in length. Its tube feet are arranged more or less along the pentamerous divisions. In the region of the mouth the tube feet have been modified to form tentacles, which are used for food-gathering. This species feeds on plankton, which it sifts through the feathery tentacles.

Mollusks

More than 100,000 species of the phylum Mollusca are known to exist, and scientists find about 1,000 new species every year. The three largest of these are the Gastropoda, which consist of snails, slugs, and limpets; Bivalvia, which include oysters, mussels, and clams; and Cephalopoda, containing squids, cuttlefish, and octopuses. In addition to the more than 100,000 known species, the fossils of about 100,000 other species have been found. Mollusk fossils have been found in rocks about 550 million years old and are often well-preserved because of their hard shells. But despite their age and the intact fossils, the origin of mollusks and their relationship to other invertebrates is still obscure.

Mollusk anatomy

The three main mollusk classes look very different, but all follow the same basic plan. The main bulk of the body contains the internal organs and is called the visceral mass. All mollusks have a skinlike organ called a mantle—a fleshy extension of the body wall—which hangs down on each side of the visceral mass. The space between the mantle and the visceral mass is called the mantle cavity. The mantle secretes the shell, which is present in most mollusks. In mollusks with no outside shell, the mantle forms a tough cover around the body organs.

Almost all aquatic mollusks breathe with the aid of ctenidia (comblike gills in the mantle cavity), which are covered with many small, hairlike structures called cilia, whose rhythmic movement draws water over the gill surface. Oxygen is taken up from the water current by blood that flows through the gill filaments, and carbon dioxide diffuses out of the gill filaments into the exhalant current.

The kidneys and anus open into the mantle cavity, and waste is also carried away by the exhalant current. In some species, the edges of the mantle may be joined to form tubes called siphons, which create a one-way flow of water through the mantle cavity. Many mollusks also

have sensory cells on the edge of the membrane of each afferent gill. These organs (called osphradia) are thought to be chemoreceptors, which detect the juices of prey or other food sources. They also determine the level of sediment in the incoming water, too much of which would block the delicate gill filaments.

Gastropods

The ancestral gastropod had a mouth and anus at opposite ends of the body, as do the larvae of present-day gastropods. But early in the development of larval gastropods a remarkable change takes place—the visceral mass twists through 180°. This process, known as torsion, is important because it brings the mantle cavity from a lower posterior to an upper frontal position. The shell then only needs one opening, and the mantle cavity provides a space into which the young gastropod can withdraw for protection.

The problem of fouling by waste released over the head is avoided by having holes in the shell that direct excrement away from the head (as is found in keyhole limpets and the abalone), or by shifting the anus to the side. A one-way water flow through the mantle cavity also avoids this problem.

The left and right sides of the gastropod body grow at different rates because of the spiral shape of the shell—the organs on one side do not develop, and the visceral mass, mantle, and shell become spirally coiled; this development also makes the long digestive system more compact.

Most aquatic gastropods breathe by means of gills, but the land-dwelling snails and slugs (subclass Pulmonata) lack gills, and have modified the mantle cavity into a lung. Air is moved in and out of the mantle cavity by raising and lowering the mantle, which is moist and has a rich blood supply—essential features for gaseous exchange to take place.

Pulmonates show another adaptation for a terrestrial existence in that nitrogenous waste is excreted as uric acid crystals. This is in contrast to aquatic gastropods; they excrete nitrogenous waste as ammonia, which is toxic in concentrated form and therefore requires

The common garden snail, *Helix* sp., is typical of terrestrial pulmonates and shows clearly how the gills that lie in the mantle cavity of aquatic gastropods have evolved into a lung in terrestrial gastropods. The visceral mass becomes twisted during torsion, but in addition, the anal and pulmonary openings come to lie next to each other at a single opening in the shell, the pneumostome. The position of the pneumostome at the side of and behind the head helps to prevent fouling.

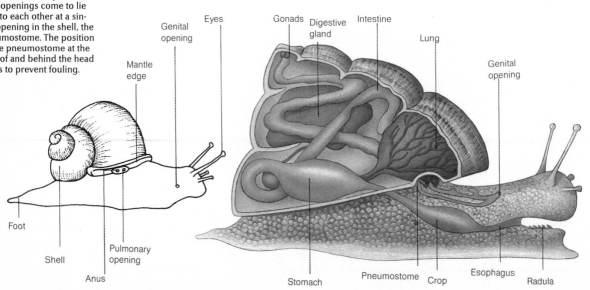

a large amount of water to dilute it.

Gastropods are generally considered to be inhabitants of damp places, but the terrestrial adaptations and, more importantly, the possession of a shell, into which the animal can withdraw and seal itself off from the environment, have enabled them to invade such unlikely regions as deserts. Some pulmonates have secondarily returned to an aquatic existence, but they still breathe by means of a lung.

Most gastropods move on a flat sole, which in many species has a large pedal gland. This gland secretes mucus onto the surface over which the sole moves. Locomotion is achieved by waves of muscular contractions that pass down the foot. In the sea hare (*Aplysia* sp.) the foot is formed into folds, or parapodia, which may be used for swimming; in the sea butterflies (Pteropoda) the parapodia are drawn out into membranous wings.

Most gastropods feed using a radula—a serrated band of teeth—to rasp off fine particles from their food. Many species, such as land snails and limpets, feed on vegetation; others, such as whelks, are carnivorous. They detect their prey by means of the osphradium. The mouth of carnivorous gastropods often lies on an extension of the head, called the proboscis. The radula of these species has fewer, larger teeth than the plant-feeding gastropods; in the cone shells (*Conus* spp.) it has become a stalklike stinger with which they stab and inject a poison into their prey. Carnivorous gastropods damage oysters by drilling through part of the shell using the radula. This is achieved by secreting a chemical that softens the oyster shell, which is then worn away by the radula. By alternately softening and rasping the shell the carnivore makes a hole in the shell, through which it can insert the proboscis to eat the oyster.

Aquatic gastropods have separate sexes, but land snails and slugs are hermaphroditic. The sperm of dioecious gastropods are either shed into the water, where they fertilize eggs from the females, or are introduced into the female with a penis. Eggs are deposited singly, in strings, or in a thin shell. Some are carried in the female until they hatch.

In some gastropods, the young pass through two stages: the first is the "trochophore" stage, in which the larva is roughly spherical with a band of cilia for movement. It later develops a shell to become the veliger larva. In other gastropods, the trochophore stage remains in the egg, which hatches to produce the veliger, and in some species, both the trochophore and veliger stages remain in the egg.

Some aquatic snails transmit human platyhelminth parasites, such as the liver fluke and the blood fluke (*Schistosoma* sp.), the cause of bilharzia.

Sea slugs are gastropods which, in secondary adaptation, have become untwisted so that the mouth and anus are at opposite ends of the body. The cluster of appendages on this species are secondary gills arranged around the anus. Some sea slugs are protected by the stinging cells of their jellyfish prey, which settle in the extensions of the sea slug's body.

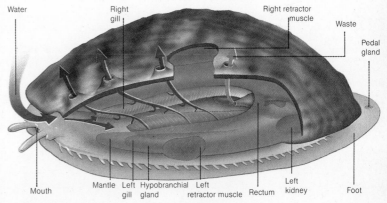

Water | Right gill | Right retractor muscle | Waste | Pedal gland

Mouth | Mantle | Left gill | Hypobranchial gland | Left retractor muscle | Rectum | Left kidney | Foot

The abalone, or ormer (*Haliotis tuberculata*), is a primitive gastropod that lives in shallow water. Its broad shell is asymmetrical with a single spiral only and, in this species, has five holes. The incoming water bathes the gills and gas is exchanged. The exhalant current removes carbon dioxide and waste and flows out through the holes.

The Queen scallop *(Chlamys opercularis)* is a bivalve mollusk that is mainly sessile. It swims by jet propulsion, clapping its valves together, but usually only when disturbed. During the evolution of mollusks, these animals lost their head, with the result that all their sense organs are found on the edge of the mantle. These organs consist of eyes and tentacles that carry tactile and chemoreceptor cells. Scallops filter-feed, and breathe through W-shaped ciliated gills, which direct a complex pattern of water currents through the body.

Bivalves

The class Bivalvia includes clams, oysters, and mussels, and is characterized by the possession of a shell that is divided into two halves joined by an elastic ligament.

Bivalves are mainly marine, although some have invaded fresh water. The foot is adapted for burrowing mainly in mud and sand, but some species can bore into hard material; the shipworm *(Teredo navalis)*, for example, drills into wood using the roughened edges of its shell, and other species even bore into rocks.

The body is long and laterally flattened, surrounded on each side by two lobes of the mantle. Each lobe secretes a shell called a valve. The gills hang from the roof of the mantle cavity and lie on each side of the body. They are used for collecting food as well as for breathing. Bivalves have no head—it would be impossible to perceive stimuli while buried in the sand—so the sense organs occur on the edges of the mantle, and these detect light and test inhalant water currents.

Most bivalves are filter-feeders, filtering very small food particles from the water. The gills are highly modified for this purpose and secrete mucus, in which food particles are trapped. A complex arrangement of cilia draws water into the mantle cavity, sorts the particles, and carries food to the mouth. Fleshy folds near the mouth (palps) sort the trapped particles, and nonfood material is passed out with the exhalant current while food particles pass into the stomach. There a gelatinous rod called the crystalline style is rotated by cilia and rubs against the stomach wall and style sac, releasing enzymes that partly digest the food particles. Further digestion occurs within the cells of the digestive glands that surround the stomach.

Most bivalves use the foot as a burrowing organ. The two valves close and water is pushed out of the mantle cavity, which loosens the mud and makes the movement of the foot easier. (Some species have serrated shell edges that also break up the mud and facilitate burrowing.) Blood is then pumped into irregular channels, called blood sinuses, in the tissue of the foot. This action makes the top of the foot swell and anchors the animal. Contractions of the foot muscles then pull the animal down.

Most bivalves are sluggish, but some, such as the razor clam, have a thin, streamlined shell and large foot and can burrow very rapidly. Scallops use jet propulsion to swim, by clapping the two valves of the shell together. Other species, such as oysters (which cement themselves to rocks), and mussels (which attach themselves to surfaces by strong threads of organic material to prevent being dislodged by waves), are unable to move.

In most bivalves, males and females shed sperm and eggs into the water, where fertilization produces a trochophore larva, which develops two valves to form the veliger larva. The veliger swims around in the open sea for approximately two weeks before settling on the bottom to become an adult. In the freshwa-

The squid *(Loligo* sp.) is carnivorous, feeding mainly on fish and crustaceans. It locates its prey with its highly evolved eyes, darts toward it by rapidly ejecting water from the mantle cavity, and seizes the prey with its two tentacles. The prey is pulled to the mouth and held by the squid's arms while its head is bitten off by the predator's powerful horny jaws. Large chunks are torn off the prey, pulled back by the radula and swallowed. Only the gut and tail are rejected.

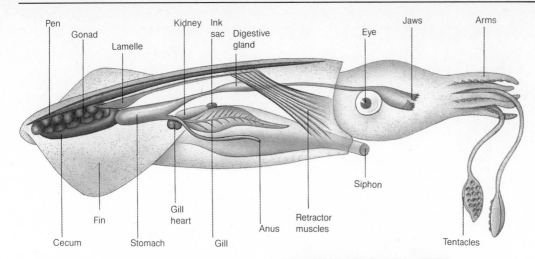

Pen · Gonad · Lamelle · Kidney · Ink sac · Digestive gland · Eye · Jaws · Arms · Siphon · Fin · Gill heart · Anus · Retractor muscles · Tentacles · Cecum · Stomach · Gill

Squids, like all cephalopods, are highly adapted to a deep-sea, carnivorous existence. The water that flows through them is used for locomotion and as the animals' oxygen source. They can cruise or hover as well as dart, using the fins as stabilizers. They have eight arms and two tentacles to catch prey with. Food is absorbed not in the digestive gland, as in other mollusks, but in the cecum.

ter mussel, however, the female carries eggs on her gills. Sperm enter the mantle cavity with the water currents and fertilize the eggs there. The larvae then leave the mantle cavity and live parasitically on the gills of fish, until they develop into adults.

Cephalopods

The cephalopods represent the highest stage of molluskan evolution. The three main groups belong to the subclass Coleoidea and are the squids (order Teuthoidea), the cuttlefish (order Sepioidea), and the octopus (order Octopoda).

All cephalopods are adapted to a free-swimming life in the sea, but only one living species has an outer shell—the nautilus. Most other cephalopods have an inner chambered shell, which varies from species to species. In the cuttlefish, it is called a cuttlebone, and in the squid, a pen. It lies along the dorsal parts of the animal's body and is mostly filled with gas. Toward the tail end, however, it is filled with liquid, which adds weight to that part, whereas the rest of the air-filled structure provides lift in water.

In the cuttlefish and the squid the shell has been reduced to a small plate, and their bodies are elongated and streamlined. The octopus, however, is less streamlined and lacks a shell. The edges of its mantle are fused together forming a bag around the body, from which the head protrudes, surrounded by tentacles. The octopus usually crawls around the seabed using the suckers on its tentacles, but is capable of jet propulsion when fast movement is necessary. The propelling movement is achieved by pumping water into the mantle cavity and forcing it out through a funnel below the head.

All cephalopods are carnivorous. Cuttlefish and squid catch their prey with two long tentacles, with suckers at the tips, and with arms (8 in the cuttlefish, 10 in the squid), which are equipped with suckers all along their length. The octopus, however, has eight tentacles of equal length, any one of which is used to grab the prey. The prey is bitten with the two horny jaws, and the octopus's poisonous saliva then enters the wound and paralyzes the prey. Large pieces of flesh are torn off, pulled into the mouth by the radula, and swallowed.

The octopus has the most highly developed brain of all invertebrates. The brain is large

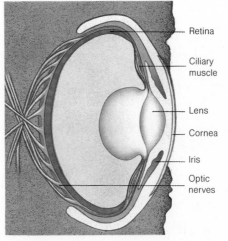

Retina · Ciliary muscle · Lens · Cornea · Iris · Optic nerves

The cephalopod eye is highly developed and resembles the vertebrate eye in structure. The retina contains photoreceptors, which are pointed toward the light source, whereas in vertebrates the cones point away from it. An image is formed, but how clear it is is not known. Color vision is also present.

and, at least in the squid and octopus, can learn and remember information. Most cephalopods rely on their good eyesight to detect food and enemies. In addition, sensory cells on the octopus's tentacles detect minute concentrations of chemicals, which also alert it to the presence of prey or to possible danger.

Many cephalopods can camouflage themselves in seconds, changing color by the expansion or contraction of small bags of pigment in the skin. Some species also have an ink sac—a pouch off the intestine—which releases a cloud of black liquid through the anus when the animal is alarmed, behind which it can make its escape. It is the color of this ink that gives some of these animals their Latin name—Sepia.

Male cephalopods produce sperm enclosed in a case called the spermatophore. One of the male's arms is modified to transfer the spermatophore into the mantle cavity of the female, where the eggs are fertilized. The female may stick them onto rocks, where they develop into adults without passing through a trochophore or veliger stage.

Introduction to arthropods

The phylum Arthropoda contains more than three-fourths of all the different kinds of animals. It includes crustaceans, spiders, and insects, as well as many smaller groups. Insects make up the largest class of arthropods in terms of the number of species. Among the most important groups of arthropods are insects, crustaceans, arachnids, centipedes, and millipedes.

An arthropod's exoskeleton, which is jointed to allow movement, is hardened and does not grow with the animal. As a result, it must be periodically shed—a process known as ecdysis—in order to allow growth. The arthropod body is usually divided into head, thorax, and abdomen, although in some groups there may be no clear distinction between the three regions. The head and thorax may be fused, forming a cephalothorax, or the abdomen may be reduced in size. The head typically carries feeding and sensory appendages. Each segment of the body usually has a pair of jointed appendages, which are modified for specific functions in different species.

Arthropods have a body cavity (coelom), but it is small and contains only the gonads and excretory organs. The other internal cavities form a hemocoele (blood cavity). The circulatory system is open, with a dorsally situated heart. The digestive system consists of a tubular gut which runs from the mouth to the anus. The foregut and hindgut are lined with chitin and are shed at ecdysis. Excretion is through specialized Malpighian tubes and the anus is terminal.

The nervous system has a dorsally positioned brain and a ventral nerve cord, which has branches called ganglia in each segment. Tactile bristles are also a common feature. Eyes, which may be simple or compound, are usually present—compound eyes are unique to arthropods and allow the formation of a highly defined image.

Trilobites

The trilobites are a fossil group of marine arthropods (class Trilobita) which were once extremely numerous but became extinct toward the end of the Paleozoic era, about 230 million years ago.

Most trilobites were less than 4 inches (10 centimeters) long, and the body was divided into a head (cephalon), thorax, and tail (pygidium). The cephalon was composed of four or five fused segments and carried a pair of antennae, a mouth, a pair of eyes, and four pairs of biramous (forked) appendages, which functioned as both gills and legs. The segments of the trunk were articulated, whereas those of the pygidium were fused to form a solid shield. Each segment of the thorax possessed a pair of walking legs.

Horseshoe crabs

Despite their name, horseshoe crabs (order Xiphosura) are not crabs at all, but primitive marine arthropods. They are the only surviving members of a large group of animals that lived millions of years ago.

The body is divided into two parts: the *prosoma,* which is covered by the shell and includes the head; and the abdomen. On the ventral surface of the *prosoma* is a mouth, with a pair of pincerlike feeding appendages called chelicerae, and five pairs of walking legs. There are five pairs of abdominal appendages which are modified as gill-books, which are similar to the book lungs of spiders; they keep a constant current of water circulating over the gills, and also act as paddles, providing propulsive power for the animal. The nervous system is well developed, but the eyes are not; they can detect movement, al-

The dorsal exoskeleton of trilobites was much thicker than the ventral one, which is why most fossils display the dorsal view. The name Trilobita derives from the triple-segmented transverse divisions that run down their length. They were bottom dwellers and scavenged for food.

This species of horseshoe crab *(Limulus polyphemus)* is found in the shallow coastal waters of Asia, the Gulf of Mexico, and the northern Atlantic. Its telson (tail), which it uses to push with and to dig with, is also used to make threatening gestures, as in this position.

though they cannot form an image.

During mating, the female horseshoe crab carries the male on her back to shore, where she lays from 200 to 1,000 eggs in each of several holes that she digs. The male then fertilizes the eggs. Newly hatched horseshoe crabs are called trilobite larvae because of their similarity to the larvae of that class.

Pycnogonids

The class Pycnogonida contains about 600 species of carnivorous marine animals known as sea spiders. They feed on corals and sponges and are found in all marine waters. The head bears chelicerae, a mouth which is a cylindrical proboscis, and four eyes. The similarity of pycnogonids to true spiders is only superficial. Pycnogonids have a segmented abdomen and legs that end in claws, whereas spiders do not have these characteristics.

Chilopods and diplopods

The animals in the class Chilopoda are commonly known as centipedes, and those in class Diplopoda, as millipedes.

Centipedes have one pair of antennae on the head, and two pairs of jaws, in contrast to millipedes, which have at least the front pair of maxillae modified to form a lower lip (gnathochilarium). Centipedes have eyes that may be simple ocelli (a cluster of photoreceptors) or modified compound eyes, whereas if eyes are present at all in millipedes, they are only simple ocelli. Centipedes are flattened and divided into a large number of segments, each of which, apart from the first, carries a pair of long, slender, walking legs.

Millipedes are vegetarian scavengers. Their body is also segmented, but is usually cylindrical. The first four trunk segments differ from the others in that the first is legless, and the following three bear only one pair of walking legs. These four segments together are sometimes called the thorax. The abdomen has many segments, which are fused together in pairs (diplosegments). Each diplosegment bears two pairs of short legs, and as a result, a millipede may have as many as 115 pairs of legs. Nevertheless, they are not good runners and, when attacked, they protect themselves by coiling up; many species emit a foul-smelling secretion from special stink glands on the sides of the body.

Millipedes and centipedes are found mainly in damp conditions, such as rotting logs or in leaf litter, because they do not possess a waxy cuticle with which to reduce water loss.

Both groups have separate sexes, and the female lays eggs that are fertilized by the male. Some species lay the eggs in a "nest," where they are guarded by the female, but others, such as the centipede *Lithobius*, lay one egg at a time and then leave it. The young resemble the adult, and, in some species of centipedes, have the same number of segments; but other young centipedes and all millipedes have fewer body segments than do the adults.

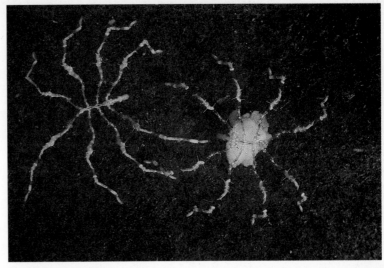

Pycnogonids, or sea spiders *(above)*, such as this species *Endeis pauciporosa*, are notable for their ovigerous legs. In the male they are well developed and are used to carry around masses of fertilized eggs until they hatch.

Centipedes are carnivorous and kill their prey with a large pair of poison claws (maxillipeds) found in the first body segment. Each claw has a pointed fang that is fed by a poison gland. This cave centipede (*Scolopendra* sp.) is eating a cricket.

Crustaceans

The crustaceans became the major group of marine arthropods when the trilobites and giant sea scorpions (Eurypterida) became extinct. The size of the group has tempted some zoologists to make it a subphylum—it contains about 30,000 species and includes such animals as water fleas, barnacles, crabs, lobsters, shrimps, and wood lice (pill bugs). It also includes tiny zooplankton, which live near the surface of the sea and occupy an important position in aquatic foodchains.

Characteristic features

The exoskeleton, which is composed of chitin and, in some species (such as crabs), is hardened with calcium salts, is molted periodically to enable the animal to grow. This is an important process in the life of crustaceans (and other arthropods), and occurs in a strict sequence of events. First, useful materials, such as calcium salts, are reabsorbed into the body; the new cuticle is then laid down underneath the old one; the animal swells up, causing the old cuticle to split, and finally, the new cuticle is hardened. Before the new cuticle hardens, the animal is easy prey for predators and usually seeks shelter during this period.

In many crustaceans an outer shell, or carapace, covers the exoskeleton of the thorax or anterior trunk segments. Typically, the body consists of a head, thorax, and an abdomen, but often the head and a number of thoracic segments are fused to form a cephalothorax. The head region has two pairs of antennae, which is characteristic of crustaceans. It also has one pair of mandibles, which in most species are heavy and have grinding and biting surfaces, and two pairs of maxillae.

The trunk region of the cephalothorax is segmented, the number of segments varying according to the species, and each segment bears a pair of appendages. These appendages are different in each species, being modified to suit particular functions. Each abdominal segment usually also has a pair of appendages structured for various functions, such as swimming, crawling, respiration, food capture, or reproduction.

The appendages are biramous—that is, each one ends in two jointed branches; they are tubular and jointed and contain muscles that contract to bend the limbs. Crustaceans swim by beating these appendages—some of which have a fringe of bristly setae, to push against the water—and most of the animals also crawl.

Many crustaceans breathe with gills, although some terrestrial species, such as the robber crab *(Birgus latro),* have modified them to become air chambers lined with blood vessels, which absorb oxygen. The gills are also a secondary excretory organ—the primary ones being the antennal and maxillary glands in the segments bearing those structures. The crustacean blood system is open—the blood is pumped by the heart into a hemocoele, where it simply bathes the tissues.

The nervous system of these animals is well developed, and the sensory organs include eyes and various tactile receptors. Most crustaceans have compound eyes in the adult stage. The young, or nauplius larvae, have a median eye composed of three or four ocelli (clusters of photoreceptors), which in some species persist into the adult stage. Other sensory receptors include special tactile hairs (setae), which are scattered over the body surface, but are most concentrated on the appendages and statocysts (balancing organs).

Crustaceans are usually dioecious—that is, they have separate sexes—but some are hermaphroditic and have both male and female sexual organs. The young hatch from eggs that are usually brooded and take the form of free-swimming planktonic larvae with fewer appendages than the adult. However, through successive molts, trunk segments and extra appendages are acquired.

Branchiopods

This subclass of mostly freshwater animals have earned their name (meaning "gill feet") from their thoracic appendages, which are modified for respiration as well as filter-feeding and locomotion. The group consists of four orders: Anacostraca (fairy shrimps), which have no carapace; Notostraca (tadpole shrimps), whose head and front thoracic region is covered by a carapace; Conchostraca (clamp shrimps); and Cladocera (water fleas). The animals in this last group, which include the common genus *Daphnia,* are covered by a carapace that encloses the trunk but not the head. The carapace of these animals is usually transparent, but can appear red or pink, depending on the level of oxygen in the water. *Daphnia,* for example, is transparent in oxygenated water, but turns pink in stagnant water, when it produces hemoglobin as a respiratory pigment.

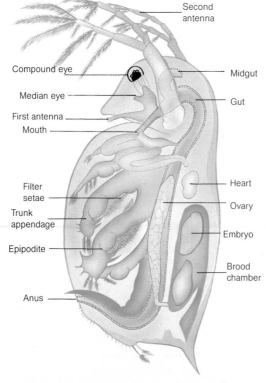

Daphnia, a genus of water flea, is a typical branchiopod. It has five or six pairs of trunk appendages, which have epipodites—extensions that serve as gills. The appendages also have setae on them, which collect food particles. The food is then moved into a food groove and spurts of water push it toward the mouth. Unlike other branchiopods, which use their trunk appendages for locomotion, *Daphnia* uses its large second antennae as paddles to move it in a jerky up-and-down motion. Also, water fleas have a pair of median compound eyes that directs them when swimming.

Second antenna

Compound eye

Median eye

First antenna

Mouth

Midgut

Gut

Filter setae

Trunk appendage

Epipodite

Anus

Heart

Ovary

Embryo

Brood chamber

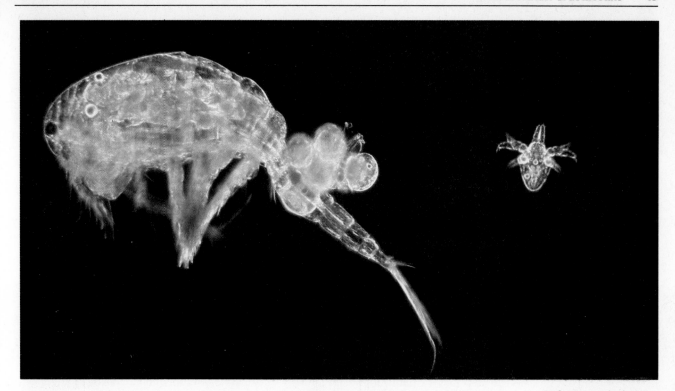

Branchiopods are filter-feeders that collect food particles on the bristles of the trunk appendages. The food is carried to the mouth by streams of water that pass between the trunk appendages as they move back and forth. The first maxillae finally push the food into the mouth.

The sexes are generally separate, and copulation is the means of fertilization, but under favorable conditions the females reproduce parthenogenetically (when the eggs develop without fertilization). The eggs of water fleas hatch into females for several generations until adverse conditions (such as low water temperature or short food supply) induce the production of males, after which eggs are again fertilized by copulation.

Ostracods and copepods

These two subclasses of tiny crustaceans contain freshwater and marine species, and planktonic (shallow-water), as well as benthic (deepwater) types. The ostracods are similar to the conchostracan branchiopods in that they have

a bivalve hinged carapace. The head is more developed than the remainder of the body, and its appendages (especially the antennules and antennae) are modified for crawling, swimming, and feeding. Most ostracods are filter-feeders, but some species are scavengers, predators, or parasites.

Most copepods are marine and occur in huge numbers, making them of great economic and ecological importance, because they form a large part of the diet of many fish. The body is short and tubular, with a trunk that is usually composed of six segments, an abdomen, and—in contrast to the ostracods—a reduced head region. The first antennae are long, whereas the second pair is short and often branched. Rapid locomotion is achieved by the beating of the thoracic appendages, which causes jerky movements, but a slower gliding motion results from the movement of the second antennae.

The planktonic copepods usually live in the upper 650 to 975 feet (200 to 300 meters) of the ocean, but diurnal vertical migrations are common. Light appears to be the trigger for this

Cyclops sp. are freshwater copepods. These animals are remarkable in that they can stagger the development of eggs that are produced from a single mating. After fertilization, one or two ovisacs form on the genital segment of the female—each sac holds up to 50 eggs. A number of eggs are hatched from half a day to five days after fertilization, and a new batch is then brooded. The eggs hatch as nauplius larvae, just as the one shown above, swimming away from the parent.

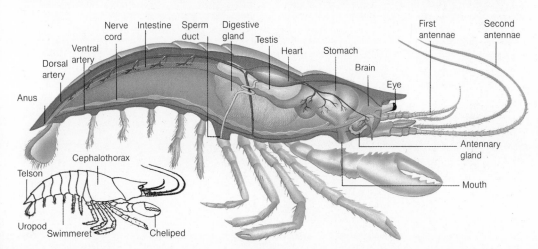

The anatomy of crayfish (*Cambarus* sp.) is similar to that of most decapods, but the male *(left)* and female species differ in some respects. For instance, the female has large swimmerets, on which she carries newly hatched larvae, whereas those of the male are small. Instead, the male appendages are modified for the transmission of sperm.

Barnacles can be stalked, such as the goose barnacle (*Lepas* sp.), which is cemented to the substratum by a peduncle, or non-stalked and attached directly to a surface. The peduncle of the goose barnacle carries the capitulum, or body, which is surrounded by calcareous plates. The dorsal plate is called the carina.

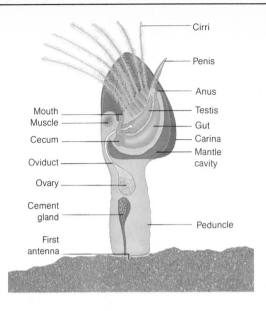

behavior, but its value to the animal is far from certain.

Many copepods are filter-feeders, some are predatory, others are scavengers, and still others are parasitic. The parasitic species feed on freshwater and marine fish, some living on the gill filaments, and others in the intestines.

Neither ostracods nor copepods have gills, and gaseous exchange occurs in the valves (in ostracods), or across the body surface (in copepods). Both groups have an open circulatory system. Median eyes are found in both, and only one group of ostracods has compound eyes. One outstanding feature of these animals is their luminescence. Both are dioecious, and fertilization is generally by copulation, although parthenogenesis is known in some ostracod species.

Barnacles

Barnacles belong to the only group of sessile crustaceans, the Cirripedia. The subclass derives its name from the six pairs of featherlike, two-branched legs (cirri) that protrude from

the shell, which are used for filter-feeding.

All barnacles are marine, and most are found attached to rocks, shells, or driftwood; there are, however, a few commensal and even some parasitic species, which live on other crustaceans. They are surrounded by a carapace of calcareous plates, which develops from a bivalve, clamlike carapace in the young, or cypris, larva.

Most barnacle species are hermaphrodite, but cross-fertilization is common. The young hatch as nauplius larvae, as in other crustaceans, but then develop into cypris larvae that settle on a suitable surface. Finally, metamorphosis takes place, and through a series of molts the animal rapidly adds the carapace and reaches adulthood.

Decapods

The order Decapoda contains most of the larger crustaceans in the subclass Malacostraca; they include lobsters, crabs, crayfish, and shrimps. More than 8,500 species have been described, and most are marine, although some species do live in fresh water. All decapods have eight pairs of thoracic appendages; the rear five are modified for walking and are the origin of the name decapod; the front three pairs serve as feeding appendages (maxillipeds). In some decapods, the first pair of walking legs is heavier and stronger than the others and has chelae (pincers).

The abdomen is composed of six segments and a tail (telson). The abdominal appendages are called swimmerets, and in some species these are reduced. The sixth abdominal segment usually has a pair of appendages called uropods, which together with the telson form a tail fan.

Decapods have compound eyes on jointed movable stalks, and the central nervous system is well developed. Their wide variation in color usually depends on the habitat, and is caused by the pigment-producing chromatophores in the exoskeleton. Aquatic decapods breathe with gills, usually five pairs, which run vertically in the cephalothorax between the endoskeleton and the other organs.

The shore crab *(Carcinus maenas)* is one species in a group that includes scavengers and predators of other large invertebrates, such as the lugworm, *Arenicola marina*. The prey is attacked with the chelipeds and caught up by the maxillipeds, which pass it to the other mouthparts. A portion is bitten off, the rest is torn apart, and the morsels are fed into the mouth. The heavy claw on the right has blunt serrations on the pincers, which are used for crushing. The lighter claw on the left is modified for cutting.

Krill (*Euphausia* sp.) are not decapods (even though they are shrimplike in appearance), but belong to the same class (Malacostraca). Like some shrimps, some species of krill are luminescent. They are well-designed for swimming, but do not have a carapace completely enclosing the gills, as do most decapods. Most krill are filter-feeders, feeding off zoo- and phytoplankton.

Water flows in at the base of the front five appendages, bathes the gills, and flows out through a vent under the second antennae.

An elaborate courtship ritual is typical of many decapods prior to copulation, and odorous chemicals called pheromones play an important role in their sexual behavior. In many species, the eggs are laid soon after copulation and are cemented onto the swimmerets of the female.

Lobsters, like some crabs, have a single huge claw that is used for crushing; the other claw of the pair is much smaller but has sharp edges and is used for seizing and tearing prey. They are scavengers, but also catch fish and break open shelled animals. Crayfish are similar in appearance to lobsters, but most live in fresh water whereas lobsters are marine. Also, like lobsters, crayfish are nocturnal and feed on almost any organic matter, living or dead.

Crabs are probably the most successful decapods, in that they can live on land as well as in water. They are found at all depths of water, in all parts of the world. They have a wide carapace and, unlike lobsters, a small abdomen, which is tucked tightly under the cephalothorax. They do not have uropods, and the female uses its swimmerets only for brooding eggs. They can walk forward, but more usually move sideways; the large front claws (chelipeds) are not used for locomotion.

Crabs range in size from the pea crabs (Pinnotheridae), which live in the tubes constructed by marine annelids, on sea urchins, or in the mantle cavity of gastrophods, to the Japanese spider crab *(Macrocheira kaempferi),* whose body measures about one inch (2.5 centimeters) across, and whose leg span is more than 3 feet (1 meter). Their diversity of form includes the hermit crab, which has no shell of its own and takes over empty gastropod shells for protection.

Crabs are filter-feeders, predators, and scavengers, and their method of obtaining food is usually reflected by the shape of their chelipeds.

Shrimps and prawns are much better designed for swimming than the lobster, being laterally compressed with a well-developed abdomen, but even so, most of them are bottom-dwellers. Their thoracic legs are usually long and slender, and the first three pairs may have claws. The abdomen has long, fringed swimmerets used for swimming; in females, eggs are attached to them.

Isopoda

This order contains the only group of truly terrestrial crustaceans—the wood lice—although most species are marine. The shield-shaped body is flat, has no carapace, and has seven pairs of legs. They have a pair of compound eyes and two pairs of antennae, one of which is vestigial.

Water loss can be a problem to wood lice, as they do not have a waxy cuticle like some other terrestrial arthropods, such as insects. They survive by living in fairly damp habitats and by leading a nocturnal existence. Other behavioral adaptations, such as rolling up into a ball, help to reduce water loss.

Wood lice are the only species of terrestrial crustaceans. They have adapted to the drier conditions by living in moist environments, such as leaf litter and under stones, and by adopting a nocturnal life style. Moisture is essential because these animals still breathe by means of gills. They feed on decomposing organic matter, although some species are carnivorous.

Arachnids

The class Arachnida is a group of mostly terrestrial arthropods that includes spiders, scorpions, mites, ticks, harvestmen, pseudoscorpions, and sun spiders. Many arachnids have highly developed chelicerae (also found in pycnogonids and horseshoe crabs) in the head region, which usually take the form of a pair of pincerlike organs. It is possible that arachnids represent a migration of chelicerates from the sea to the land. In doing so, they have developed a cuticle, which reduces water loss, and their gill-books have become book lungs.

Arachnid anatomy

Like all arthropods, arachnids have a hard, chitinous exoskeleton and jointed appendages, but unlike most of their relatives true arachnids have no antennae. Their bodies are divided into a cephalothorax and an abdomen. The cephalothorax (or prosoma) is usually unsegmented and its upper surface is covered with a carapace. The lower region is usually protected by sternal plates. The abdominal segments of most arachnids, apart from scorpions, are fused, and in ticks and mites both the cephalothorax and abdomen have fused to form a single body.

The chelicerae in the head region of the cephalothorax are used to grasp prey and for feeding. A pair of pedipalpi, which are modified to perform various functions in different species, are also present, along with four pairs of legs. Because arachnids have no jaws, they cannot chew, although most of them are carnivorous. They therefore have to take their food in liquid form. Digestive enzymes are secreted onto or injected into the prey, which is then sucked in.

The respiratory system of arachnids comprises specialized breathing organs, called book lungs, and a network of tracheae (tubes that carry air from the exterior to the internal organs). Some arachnids have book lungs only, others have tracheae only, and some have both. The circulatory system is usually open, that is, arteries carry blood from the heart into a series of blood spaces—the hemocoele. Blood is oxygenated as it flows past the book lungs on its way back to the heart. Some arachnids have hemocyanin—a copper-based oxygen-carrying compound—as the major respiratory pigment of the blood. The excretory system includes a pair of Malpighian tubules, which open into the alimentary canal, and coxal glands, which open to the exterior in the cephalothorax.

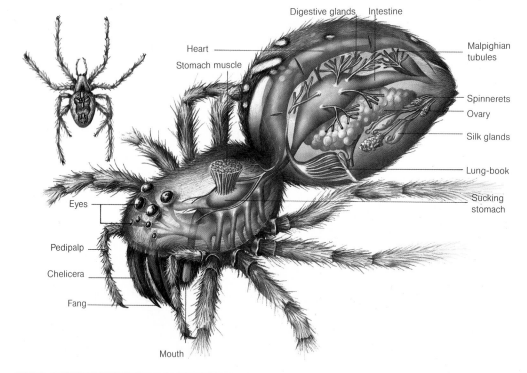

The orange garden spider (*Argiope aurantia*) is a typical web-spinner. Like all spiders, it has eight legs joined to the cephalothorax, which also bears a pair of pedipalpi and fanglike chelicerae. Most spiders have eight eyes. Apart from the brain and sucking stomach (which are in the cephalothorax), most major organs are in the abdomen, including the silk glands and their spinnerets.

Digestive glands · Intestine

Heart

Stomach muscle

Malpighian tubules

Spinnerets

Ovary

Silk glands

Lung-book

Sucking stomach

Eyes

Pedipalp

Chelicera

Fang

Mouth

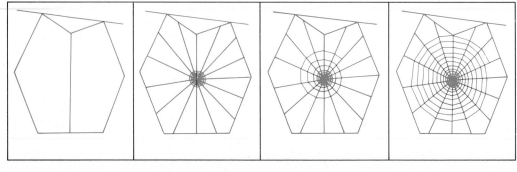

An orb web is spun in stages and takes a spider about an hour to make. Many species spin a new web every day, usually at night or just before dawn. This may be necessary because the web has been damaged, for instance by the struggles of trapped insects. Rain can damage the webs of some species, although others, particularly in the tropics, build webs strong enough to withstand a storm.

Courtship in scorpions involves a curious type of dance. The male grabs the female's pincers in his own (so that she cannot use them) and, with their tails held upright, the pair move backward and forward. After a while, the male drops a packet of sperm on the ground and drags the female over it; she then takes it up into her body.

The brain consists of two ganglia (bundles of nerve cells) above the esophagus, joined to more ganglia below it. Nerves from the ganglia run to various sensory organs, and there are sensory hairs over the body surface. Most arachnids have simple eyes—spiders usually have eight, scorpions have six to twelve; even so, their eyesight is, in most cases, very poor.

Reproductive systems vary in arachnids, but the sexes are generally separate. Fertilization is by copulation, usually preceded by an elaborate courtship ritual. Sperm is often transmitted through a packet of sperm, or a spermatophore, which is picked up by the female. When hatched, most arachnids are small versions of the adults; they do not metamorphose as do many insects. The young molt several times while growing.

Spiders

There are 29,000 known species of spiders, the largest of which are the tarantulas of South America (suborder Orthognatha), some species of which have a body 3 inches (8 centimeters) across with a leg spread of 7 inches (18 centimeters). Tarantulas have poison glands in their chelicerae, but most spiders have them in the cephalothorax, although the poison is administered via the chelicerae. The poison is used to paralyze or kill prey, or in self-defense.

Spiders have abdominal glands that exude silk through organs called spinnerets. The silk threads are used to make webs, to catch prey, and to make cocoons. Not all spiders spin webs, however; trap-door spiders (family Ctenizidae) dig a tunnel often more than 10 inches (25 centimeters) deep, which they line with silk. The tunnel is closed at ground level by a hinged door. When a small animal passes by, the spider jumps out and grabs it. Many wolf spiders (Lycosidae) and jumping spiders (family Salticidae) do not trap their food but stalk their prey and then leap on it.

Spiders perform a courtship ritual before mating. Male wolf spiders, for example, use their pedipalpi as semaphores to attract a female. In many web-spinning spiders, the courting male plucks the threads of the web in a special way that the female will recognize and so not mistake him for prey. Before courtship begins, the male spins a "sperm web," onto which he drops semen, and fills a reser-

Ticks of the species *Ixodes hexagonus,* their bodies swollen with blood sucked from their host—a European hedgehog—remain attached to the skin of their host and feed off it continuously for several days.

voir at the tip of his pedipalp with sperm. During mating, he inserts the pedipalp into a special pouch in the female, in which the sperm are stored. Eggs are not laid until they are ready when sperm is released over them. The fertilized eggs are then wrapped in layers of silk to form a protective cocoon, which is hidden or carried around until they hatch.

Scorpions

Scorpions (order Scorpionida) have remained virtually unchanged for about 450 million years. The largest of the true arachnids, reaching 5 to 8 inches (12 to 20 centimeters) in length, they are nocturnal and live in tropical and subtropical regions. Their pedipalpi are powerful pincers, used to grasp prey. The segmented tail has a sharp sting at the tip with a poison gland, which causes paralysis and death to insects and small mammals.

Other arachnids

Mites and ticks (order Acarina) are small arachnids, usually less than one millimeter in length. Many are parasites, living on blood and tissue fluids, causing skin irritation, and occasionally transmitting diseases to their hosts. Their chelicerae can pierce skin, making ticks, for example, difficult to dislodge. Harvestmen (order Phalangida) are spiderlike animals with long legs and only two eyes. Pseudoscorpions (order Chelonethida), like true scorpions, have pincers (large chelate pedipalpi), but no tail or sting. Sun spiders (order Solufugae), which can be up to 2 inches (5 centimeters) long, have simple elongated pedipalpi that make them look like ten-legged spiders.

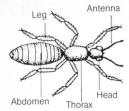

A typical insect has one pair of antennae and three pairs of legs. The body consists of three parts: head, thorax, and segmented abdomen. Many insects also have wings at some stage in their lives.

Insects

No other terrestrial group of animals has as many members as the class Insecta. More than 800,000 species of insects have been described—about 300,000 of these alone are beetles (order Coleoptera)—and there are many thousands more yet to be identified and named. The success of this group is due partly to its tremendous adaptability and huge variation in life styles—insects live in almost every habitat, from steamy tropical jungles to cold polar regions. The ability to fly has allowed them to spread to new, unexploited habitats and, many millions of years ago, to escape from terrestrial predators. It also helped them to disperse and has enabled greater access to food and more desirable environments.

It is possible that the great increase in the numbers and variety of flowering plants during the Cretaceous period also contributed to the enormous success of insects. Most flowering plants are dependent upon them for pollination.

General features

The exoskeleton, which covers the entire insect body, is composed of chitin and hardened by proteins. It is made up of several parts: the tergum, covering the back; the sternum, on the underside; and two pleura, which link the tergum to the sternum. The pleura are considerably thinner than the rest of the cuticle and generally contain spiracles—the openings to air tubes (tracheae).

The body is clearly divided into a head, thorax, and abdomen. The head consists of five or six segments, but they are fused together and are not obvious in the adults. Typically, the insect head bears a single pair of sensory antennae, one pair of compound eyes, which may be color sensitive, and one more ocelli (clusters of light-sensitive photoreceptors).

The thorax is composed of three segments, each bearing a pair of walking legs; this characteristic is unique to insects. The legs are modified in different species for grasping, swimming, jumping, or digging. The winged

insects (subclass Pterygota) also bear a pair of wings on the dorsal surface of each of the second and third thoracic segments, whereas those of the subclass Apterygota are primitively wingless. The abdomen is made up of 10 or 11 segments connected by flexible membranes. The eighth and ninth segments (also the tenth in males) bear the genital appendages.

All insects have a heart that lies dorsally within the thorax and, in most species, in the first nine abdominal segments. The blood circulates in a blood space (called the hemocoele) and bathes all the tissues.

Respiration in most insects takes place by means of a system of internal tubes called tracheae, which open to the exterior via paired spiracles. Oxygen diffusion along the trachea is sufficient to meet the demands of the insect at rest. During activity, however, air is pumped in and out of the tracheal system by expanding and collapsing air sacs (enlarged parts of the tracheae), which are controlled by movements of the body. The spiracles have closing structures for water conservation.

The principal excretory organs of insects are Malpighian tubes, which open into the hindgut and the rectum. Uric acid, dissolved salts, and water are drawn from the hemocoele; the fluid in the tubes then passes into the rectum where useful salts and water are extracted before the waste products are excreted with the feces.

The insect nervous system is much like that of other arthropods, with a brain and a system of linked individual and fused ganglia connected to a ventral nerve cord. Apart from the eyes, sense organs, such as chemoreceptors and tactile hairs, occur all over the body, but are most concentrated on the appendages.

Insect flight

One of the most successful adaptive features of insects is flight. Most pterygotes have wings, although secondarily wingless insects do occur in this group. Various species, such as ants (order Hymenoptera) and termites (order Isoptera), have wings during certain stages only of their life cycle; others have completely lost their wings, for example fleas

The locust (*Locusta* sp.) has the anatomy of a typical winged insect, with a head, thorax, and abdomen. The thorax has three segments, to which the three pairs of legs and two pairs of wings are attached. A chambered heart forms part of the dorsal blood vessel, which pumps blood forward with the aid of valves. Food is taken through the mouth and is digested in the crop, the pyloric ceca, the mid-, and the hindgut. The first ganglion of the ventral nerve cord forms the brain. Spiracles (not shown) open out in the cuticle of each segment. Air passes into them and carbon dioxide is released from them. The air is conducted by tracheae (ducts) to the blood, into which the oxygen diffuses.

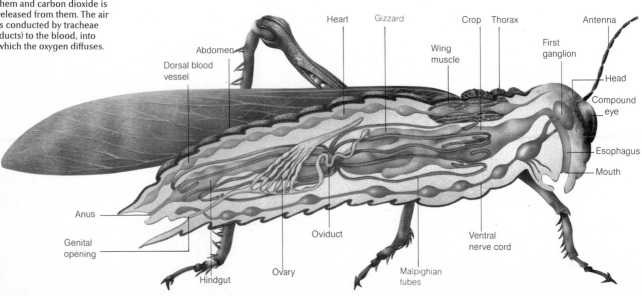

Dragonflies (A) have densely veined, primitive wings that cannot be folded across the back. But more highly evolved insects, such as wasps (B) and beetles (C), have developed structures at the wing base, called sclerites, which allow the wings to be folded across their body, and the wing venation is reduced. The two wings on either side of the wasp's body are hooked by frenal hooks. In beetles, the front pair of wings have hardened and become elytra, to form a wing case. They fly only with the hind wings.

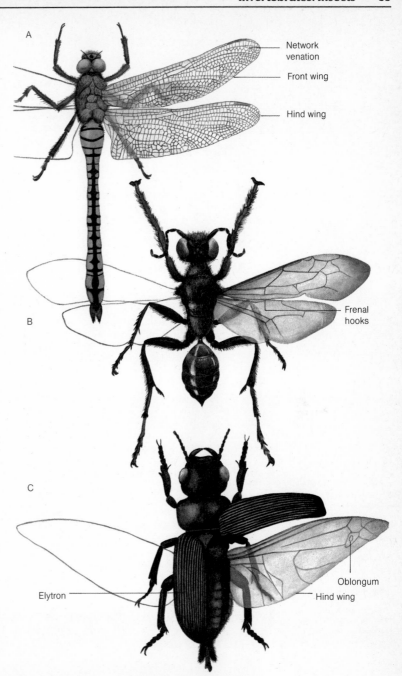

A — Network venation / Front wing / Hind wing

B — Frenal hooks

C — Elytron / Oblongum / Hind wing

(order Siphonaptera), as a result of their parasitic life style.

The earliest insect wing is thought to have been a fan-shaped membranous structure with heavy supporting veins. Modern wings, however, are more highly specialized structures, composed of two pieces of opposing cuticle, which are separated in places by veins. These veins support the wing and provide it with blood. Primitive wings such as those of dragonflies (order Odonata) have large numbers of veins which form a netlike pattern, but subsequent evolution has favored a reduction in venation.

Many insects have two pairs of wings. These may move independently, as in damsel flies (order Odonata), or they can be hooked together so that they move as a single structure, as in many hymenopterans, such as bees and wasps. Coleopterans (beetles) have undergone a further change—the first pair of wings has been hardened to form the wing cases (elytra). These wings form leathery covers that protect the beetle's body. Insects of the order Diptera, which includes all the true flies, have a pair of forewings only. The hind pair has been reduced and modified into club-shaped structures called halteres, which act as organs of balance.

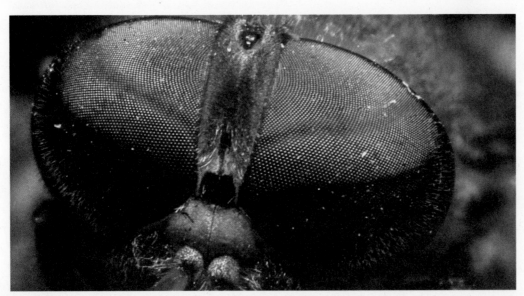

The large compound eyes of insects are multifaceted in those that fly and depend on sight for feeding. The eyes of some flies each consist of about 4,000 lenses packed together, which are not always of equal size—those of the horsefly (*Tabanus* sp.) are larger on the front and upper parts of the eye. Each facet is formed by the cornea of a visual element, called an ommatidium, which contains the cone, iris, and retinal cells necessary for vision.

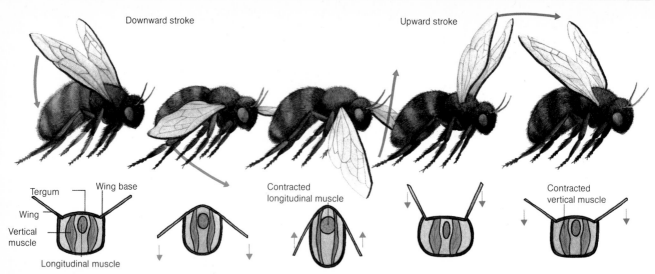

Downward stroke   Upward stroke

Tergum   Wing base   Contracted   Contracted
Wing   longitudinal muscle   vertical muscle
Vertical
muscle
Longitudinal muscle

Insect flight involves a wing movement in the shape of a figure eight. The downward beat results from muscles at the wing base and the longitudinal muscles contracting, which also raises the tergum. An upward beat is achieved by the vertical muscles contracting.

A honey bee colony consists of workers, drones, and a queen, each with distinct roles. The queen controls the colony and lays up to 2,000 eggs a day; drones mate with the queen; and workers forage, build combs, and attend to all other aspects of the colony's life.

The action of flight is fairly straightforward; an upward beat is produced by the contraction of vertical muscles in the thorax; when these muscles contract, the thorax flattens, causing the wings to move up. A downward stroke is produced either by the contraction of muscles attached to the wing base, or by the contraction of horizontal muscles in the thorax the thorax arches upward, causing the wings to move down. This up-and-down movement on its own does not provide enough impetus for flight, however, and the insect's wings must also move back and forth, resulting in a wingbeat that forms a figure eight or an ellipse, which is tilted at an angle to the vertical.

The number of wingbeats per second varies greatly from between 4 and 20 for butterflies (order Lepidoptera) to 190 beats per second in bees, and up to 1,000 per second in a gnat. The mode of flying also varies in different groups. Butterflies tend to have a slow, fluttering style, whereas bees and flies can hover and dart. Flight is controlled by a complex interaction of feedback from sensory hairs on the head, stretch receptors at the

base of the wing, visual cues, and the wing muscles themselves. There is no nervous centers for the control of flight. Flight speed appears to be controlled by the flow of air against the antennae or by sight.

Life cycles and development

Most insects lay eggs. Once hatched, the primitive wingless insects do not metamorphose—they gradually mature through a series of molts. The winged insects, however, do metamorphose. They are divided into two groups: the Endopterygota, such as flies and butterflies, whose larvae do not resemble the adult and whose wing development is internal (the derivation of their name), appearing only in the final stage of metamorphosis; and the Exopterygota, such as cockroaches, grasshoppers, and some bugs, which hatch as miniature versions of the adults, having external wing buds but without being sexually mature, and gradually develop by incomplete metamorphosis (hemimetamorphosis).

The basic life style of insects can be modified by various factors; aphids, for example, exhibit parthenogenesis in favorable weather conditions. Unfertilized eggs laid in the autumn hatch into wingless ovoviviparous females, which do not lay eggs but give birth to broods of similar females. The cycle continues until conditions deteriorate, when one generation produces winged females and males, which mate.

Many insects have complicated life cycles—especially parasitic insects. Parasitic wasps, for example, have a form of reproduction called polyembryony, in which the embryonic cells give rise to more than one embryo. This means that from one egg deposited in the body of a host many larvae can be formed, and the resulting embryos can use the host's body as both a refuge and a food source.

A great variety of parasitic insects exist, from blood-sucking ectoparasites that live permanently on a host during their adult lives to the parasites that visit a host only to feed. Some, such as mud daubers, are parasitic in the larval stage only. The egg-laden female wasp finds a spider, which it paralyzes with its sting; it then builds a nest of mud into which it puts the spider. Finally, it lays an egg and

Description	Number in average colony	Average lifespan
Worker Non-reproductive female	60,000 (approximately)	2 – 6 months
Drone Reproductive male	200 (approximately)	2 – 4 months
Queen Reproductive female	1	up to about 6 years

seals up the nest. When the egg hatches, the larva has a ready source of food until it pupates.

Feeding adaptations

The mouth parts of insects show great variability. In some, they are adapted for sucking; in others, for piercing and biting; and in still others, the mouth parts are modified for chewing, crushing, and tearing.

Chewing mouth parts are found in carnivorous and herbivorous insects. This is regarded as a primitive condition, and is characteristic of insects such as dragonflies, grasshoppers, and beetles, in both the adult and nymphal stages. Butterflies have chewing mouth parts during the larval stage only.

Bees and wasps have mouth parts that are modified for biting and sucking, as well as chewing. In bees, the sucking is done by the highly modified maxillae and labium, whereas the mandibles and labrum have retained their chewing ability, which is necessary for the manipulation of pollen and wax.

The piercing mouth parts of insects that feed on plant juices, such as aphids, penetrate plant tissues, and the insect feeds on the sap. Other insects, such as houseflies, have mouth parts that are modified to form a proboscis, which is used to sponge up liquid food partially digested by enzymes in the saliva.

Social organization

Communal living is developed to the highest degree in termites, ants, bees, and some wasps. The social life of honey bees *(Apis mellifera),* for example, is controlled by a rigid division of labor, and different castes of insects perform different functions within the colony. The nest is made up of a series of vertical wax combs, with hexagonal cells on both sides. Drone cells are larger than those in which workers develop, and the queen cells are more saclike. Some cells are constructed for storing pollen and honey for use during bad

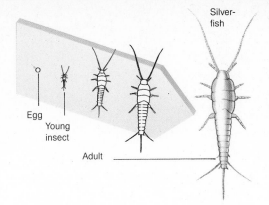

Silver-fish

Egg
Young insect
Adult

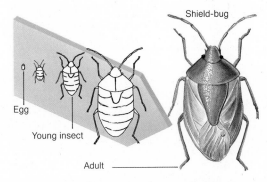

Shield-bug

Egg
Young insect
Adult

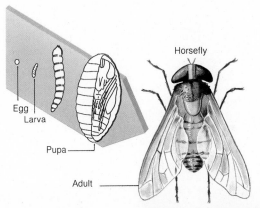

Horsefly

Egg
Larva
Pupa
Adult

Ametabolous insects, such as the silverfish *(Lepisma saccharina),* develop from the egg stage into a small version of the adult. They develop without metamorphosing, in contrast to hemimetabolous insects, such as the shield-bug *(Chlorochroa ligata),* which develops by incomplete metamorphosis into the adult. This insect emerges from an egg, which is shaped like a barrel with an operculum, or lid. The young insects resemble the adult but are wingless up to the sixth and final molt, when the wing rudiments develop. The horsefly *(Tabanus* sp.) is an example of complete, or holometabolous, metamorphosis. Its development occurs in three stages. The first is the feeding stage, when the hatched larva eats continually and increases in size. When it stops feeding, it becomes inactive and constructs a hardened cuticle, or pupa. Inside the pupal case, adult structures develop at this stage from embryonic rudiments. When the period of pupation is over, the adult insect emerges.

Parasitism among insects is illustrated *(left)* by the fate of a large white butterfly caterpillar (family Pieridae). A braconid wasp (family Braconidae) has laid eggs in the caterpillar so that emerging larvae can feed off their host.

The peacock butterfly *(Inachis io) (right)* uses both camouflage and warning coloration for protection. When its wings are closed, their dull undersides are good camouflage. But when disturbed, its wings open to reveal prominent "eye" markings, which frighten a predator.

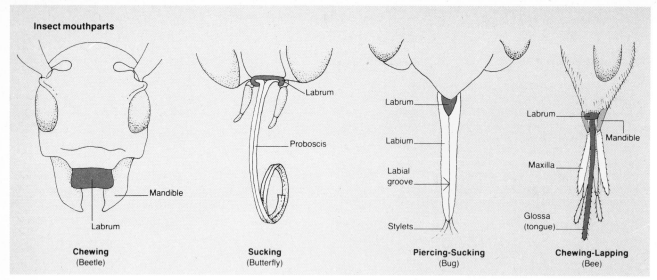

Insect mouthparts

Chewing
(Beetle)

Labrum

Mandible

Sucking
(Butterfly)

Labrum

Proboscis

Piercing-Sucking
(Bug)

Labrum

Labium

Labial groove

Stylets

Chewing-Lapping
(Bee)

Labrum

Mandible

Maxilla

Glossa
(tongue)

Mouth parts differ among insects, according to how the animal feeds. Some insects have mouthparts that are adapted for sucking; in others, for piercing and biting; and in still others, for chewing, crushing, and tearing. Although the two main types of mouthparts are those that are adapted for chewing and sucking, each order of insects has its own variation of one of these types, or a combination of both.

weather or over winter.

A colony consists typically of about 60,000 workers (all sterile females), 200 male drones, and a single queen, whose function is to lay eggs. The main purpose of the drones is to mate with the queen. The duties of the worker bees alter as they become older. Newly emerged workers stay in the hive and clean and feed the queen, drones, and larvae. At this stage the pharyngeal glands of the workers produce "royal jelly," which is fed to very young larvae (for the first four days) and continually to larvae destined to become queens. After about two weeks, when the wax glands have developed, the workers' duties change to cell construction and cleaning, and receiving stores of pollen and nectar from foraging bees. Three weeks later, the worker becomes a field bee with large pollen baskets on the hind legs. Early workers live for about eight weeks, but those emerging in late summer or autumn live over winter. Drones are driven out of the hive by workers in the autumn to con-

serve food stocks. The queen maintains cohesion in the colony by the production of chemicals, called pheromones, which influence the behavior of the bees; these induce the workers to nurse the larvae. When this substance diminishes, as the queen ages, the workers start producing new queens by feeding certain larvae solely on royal jelly. At some stages in the colony's life, the old queen leaves with about half the workers. At this time, a new queen emerges and the other developing queens are usually killed. The new queen mates during a nuptial flight with the drones and returns to head the colony.

One of the most astounding features of bees is their ability to communicate the position of a rich food source to other worker-foragers, which is done by a special dance. On returning to the hive, a foraging bee alights on a vertical surface of the comb and begins to dance in relation to the position of the sun. She moves in a straight line, waggling her body. If she moves upward, the food source

Termite colonies are controlled by pheromones, which are secreted by the queen. She lies in the colony, trapped by the size of her white abdomen—5 inches (12 centimeters) long—from which she releases several thousand eggs a day. The eggs are fertilized by the only sexually active male—visible in the foreground—who is larger than the other termites. Except for her mate, the queen produces all the members of her colony, which are blind, wingless, and sterile. But at certain times of the year, she gives rise to winged, fertile offspring, which leave the colony.

lies toward the sun; downward means that it lies away from it. Moving at angles to the left or right, she indicates that the bees must fly with the sun on their left or right, respectively. The speed of the dance indicates the distance of the food. The other workers follow the progress of the dance by touching her, and then fly off toward the food.

Ant colonies are similar to those of bees; there is usually one queen and many workers, with only a few males. But many ant workers are specialized to perform certain tasks only. Soldier ants, for example, have huge heads and enlarged mouth parts, and their function is to defend the colony. Other ants are workers, tending the larvae and collecting food. Unlike the bees, ant larvae seem to be able to develop into any caste (within the limits of sex), but development hinges on feeding—larger ant larvae develop into queens, for example.

The types of ant colony vary from species to species; they may be groups of hunters, food gatherers, farmers, or even stock-breeders. Army ants are hunters and swarm over victims in enormous numbers, killing them for food. Food gatherers collect plant material and bring it into the nest. So-called dairying ants live chiefly on a sugary liquid called honeydew, which they "milk" from aphids and other plant lice. Many ants are fungus growers; inside their colonies they provide suitable conditions for the growth of particular species of fungi, upon which they feed. Leaf-cutter ants, for example, are fungus growers; the leaf material that they bring back to the nest provides the substrate on which the fungus spores are sown. Other ants keep aphids, which they bring into the nest in winter, and put out again in the spring onto suitable plants.

Some species of ants, called slave makers, (for example, *Formica sanguinea*) take ants of other species, which become slave-workers for the colony. Control of the slaves and the colony is also generally achieved by pheromones. Ants have also been known to mutiny and leave their home nest to raid another, which they move into, keeping its original inhabitants captive as slave-workers.

Economic importance

Many insects are of benefit to humans. The silk moth *(Bombyx mori)*, for example, provides silk. It is obtained from the caterpillars of this moth, which are farmed in huge numbers and fed on mulberry leaves. At pupation, they begin to exude fluid silk and spin a silken cocoon. To extract the thread, the caterpillar must be killed, and the cocoon unwound—each one yields about half a mile of fine silk fibers.

Another beneficial insect is the honey bee, which is often domesticated and kept in specially constructed hives, from which honey and beeswax are obtained.

Fruit trees, shrubs, and flowering plants depend upon insects for pollination, and great care has to be taken when spraying such plants to ensure that insects are not killed by the chemicals. Many other insects are useful because of their function as biological pest controllers. Many ladybugs (family Coccinellidae), for example, feed on aphids, which can

severely damage both ornamental and food plants, particularly citrus fruits.

Unfortunately, there are some insects that are pests; swarms of grasshoppers can lay bare vast fields of crops, and the boll weevil *(Anthonomus grandis)* attacks cotton plants. But some insects are also dangerous because they are the vectors of disease. Malaria, for example, is transmitted by *Anopheles* mosquitoes. Other diseases transmitted by insects include yellow fever, elephantiasis, sleeping sickness, and typhus. In attempting to control these insects and the diseases they cause, the cost of drugs, vaccines, and eradication programs is enormous.

Ants milk aphids for their honeydew, which the aphids collect from plants and release through the anus. But this relationship is not one-sided—the ants build shelters for the groups of aphids and protect their larvae. The ants drink the honeydew in large amounts; they can do this because their cuticle can expand. The ants return to the nest and regurgitate the sweet fluid to the ant larvae or other ants.

Molting—called ecdysis—is an essential process for growing insects because their exoskeleton is rigid and does not permit much growth. The intervals between ecdyses are called instars. The mantid, or praying mantis *(Mantis religiosa)*, has from 3 to 12 instars and takes about a year for complete metamorphosis. The pressure that ruptures the cuticle is achieved by the insect swallowing air or water and contracting muscles. It then wriggles out of the old skin (visible at the bottom of the photograph).

Vertebrates

Despite its appearance, amphioxus is not a fish; it is a lancelet, a chordate animal whose shape reflects the basic vertebrate structure. It has a notochord and segmented muscles.

Animals with backbones, called vertebrates, form only a tiny fraction of all known creatures. In many environments, however, they exert an influence out of all proportion to their numbers, because they are in general larger than invertebrates and in many instances more mobile. Both size and mobility are made possible by a strong internal bony scaffolding, jointed to give flexibility and held in place by strong connective tissue called ligaments.

Structure and development

As vertebrates ourselves, we tend to think that the possession of bones is the great divide between animals. This is not really so, and vertebrates are in fact only part of a larger group, the Chordates (Phylum Chordata). Chordata animals have a stiff jellylike rod, called a notochord, running longitudinally through the dorsal part of the body, and acting as an internal support to a series of muscles or muscle segments (myotomes). Above the notochord is a hollow nerve tube, which is usually folded at the anterior end to form the brain. Below the notochord lies the digestive tract. At some time in their lives all chordates have paired gill slits and a tail.

In true vertebrates the notochord is replaced by cartilage or bone. The latter is a strong, hard substance, formed mainly of calcium phosphate plus collagen and other protein fibers. Bone has great strength for its weight and is well suited to act as the internal support for the body. It is possible that it originated as a waste product deposited in the skin of prehistoric fishlike marine creatures. When these animals began to live in brackish and fresh water, they faced a change in the balance of their mineral environment; this favored the production of bone, because the materials of which it was composed could be recalled if necessary for metabolic use. This role as a reservoir of certain minerals is still an important, although little-considered, function of bone. The early freshwater fishlike vertebrates developed abundant external bone—an enormous store of mineral wealth—which served the additional purpose of protective armor. Such a bony shell is obvious in some contemporary vertebrates, such as tortoises and armadillos. Though less evident, it also exists in all land vertebrates, in which the large and delicate brain is protected by the bony box of the skull.

The only direct descendants of the original bone-clad vertebrates still surviving are the lampreys (Petromyzonidae) and the hagfishes (Myxinidae), although strangely, these have lost all trace of hard skeletal structures. They have a persistent notochord and a gristlelike skull. True fishes, however, have well-developed skeletons and, in most cases, armor made of fine slips of bone (scales) set in the skin. The sharks and their relatives have retained bone-based external armor, but also have an internal skeleton formed of cartilage. In other vertebrates, skeletal cartilage is mainly a juvenile tissue, replaced by hard bone as the animals grow.

Vertebrate types

There are eight classes of vertebrates: the hagfish (Myxini); the lampreys (Cephalaspidomorphi); the shark and other cartilaginous fish (Chondrichthyes); the bony fish (Osteichthyes); the frog and other amphibians (Amphibia); reptiles (Reptilia); birds (Aves); and mammals (Mammalia). The structure of fishes restricts them to water. During the Devonian Period (which began about 408 million years ago), however, some fishes, stranded in drought conditions, struggled toward new pools using large, strong stiltlike fins.

Since that time, vertebrate animals have become less dependent upon a water environment, though all still need water to live (even if they only drink it). First among these terrestrial creatures are amphibians, which must return to the ancient habitat to lay their eggs. Their young generally look like tiny fishes, but the adults are free to colonize the land.

Vertebrates consist of eight classes: the hagfish; the lampreys and their relatives; cartilaginous fish, such as sharks; bony fish, such as carp and bass; amphibians, such as frogs; reptiles, such as the green turtle *(left)*; birds, such as the sacred kingfisher *(above right)*; and mammals, such as the oryx *(right)*.

Next in evolutionary sequence came the reptiles. These developed shelled eggs, enclosing their embryos in their own private pool (the watery white of the egg) during the larval ("tadpole") stage. The egg also supplies the embryo's nutrition, in the form of the yolk, which is the perfect, complete food needed for growth to the hatching point. Hatched reptiles show no trace of gills, and their skin is hard and waterproof. Their metabolic pattern requires external warmth, however, so they are restricted to climatically favorable parts of the world.

In the Triassic Period, which began about 245 million years ago, mammals evolved from reptile species that are now extinct. Activity is the keynote of their being, and mammalian bodies are generally well adapted for easy movement. Such activity must be fueled by abundant food, and the relatively high-energy metabolism of mammals generally requires that the body is maintained at a steady temperature (aided by insulating hair or fur), while regular breathing provides the large amounts of oxygen such metabolism needs. The young of almost all species of mammal are born at a relatively advanced stage of development, because a special maternal organ, the placenta, provides nourishment for the fetus while it grows within its mother's body. The placenta also removes excretory products. After birth, young mammals are fed on maternal milk, which gives them all the nourishment they need at this stage. In many species, important maternal and social ties are formed and cemented during this period of suckling. Most mammals have relatively large and complex brains that enable the young to learn behavior, particularly from their parents.

During the Jurassic period, which began about 208 million years ago, birds—the last of the vertebrate classes—evolved from reptile stock far removed from the ancestors of mammals. They have exploited the possibilities of flight more fully than other vertebrates. To achieve this, they have developed the most energy-intensive metabolic system of all. Birds show many modifications of the general vertebrate pattern, the most obvious being the transformation of the forelimbs into wings. The body is maintained at a high temperature and is insulated by feathers. Reproduction still depends on reptilelike eggs, which are laid individually and at intervals, because of the need to keep weight to a minimum for flight. Many birds care for their young for a prolonged period, which establishes social bonds comparable to those seen in mammals.

Fishes

Most fishes are carnivorous, preying on smaller fishes or other sea creatures, as this grouper feeds on a shoal of dwarf herrings.

Almost three-quarters of Earth's surface is covered by water, in which live about 21,700 known species of fishes. From their earliest jawless ancestors in the Silurian period, which began about 438 million years ago, fishes have diversified to inhabit widely differing aquatic habitats. Sleek, fast-swimming tuna (*Thunnus* sp.) live in the surface waters of the oceans, while the dark abyssal regions are inhabited by lantern fish and other deep-sea forms. Fresh water contains fishes such as trout—able to survive in the violence of mountain torrents—and, at the other extreme, lungfish, which inhabit temporary pools and can withstand several years of drought. Some fishes, like the blind cave characin (*Stygichthys typhlops*), have even more specialized habitats.

Despite their similar basic design, fish forms show considerable variety. One of the smallest fishes—the pygmy goby of the Philippines (*Mistichthyes luzonensis*), which grows to less than .5 inch (13 millimeters) long—is also among the smallest vertebrates. The basking shark (*Cetorhinus maximus*) grows up to 40 feet (12 meters) long, and weighs up to four tons, and the whale shark (*Rhincodon typus*) can reach more than 60 feet (18 meters). Coloration also varies, from the dazzling multicolored fishes of coral reefs to the colorless cave fishes, and the almost totally transparent glass catfish.

Fishes are vertebrates, with a backbone of either bone or cartilage. Among their distinguishing characteristics is the fact that they have fins, mostly in paired sets, and that their bodies are covered in scales. Most fishes breathe using internal gills, to which blood is pumped by a two-chambered heart (mammalian hearts, by contrast, have four chambers). Nearly all fish are cold-blooded animals—that is, they cannot regulate their body temperature, which varies according to the temperature of the water. Tropical fishes, therefore, do not, in fact, have cold blood at all. Most fishes are oviparous (egg-laying), though in some species the eggs are retained in the female until after they hatch (ovoviviparous), and in a few species, such as the Atlantic manta ray (*Manta birostris*), the developing embryos are nourished by internal secretions from the female before being born alive (viviparous).

Fishes are divided into two groups: jawed and jawless. The only jawless species are lampreys and hagfish. Jawed fish are further divided into two groups according to the composition of their skeletons: bony fishes (class

A manta ray *(Manta birostris)* feeds on plankton, which it funnels into its mouth with the two "horns" that are extensions of its snout. Its huge pectoral fins propel it through the water by flapping like wings. This photograph also shows several remoras *(Echeneis naucrates)* attached by their suckers to the manta's large gill openings, where they feed on plankton that the manta leaves behind, and on parasites from the manta's skin.

The streamlined shape and the segmented body muscles of fishes allows them to use sinuous side-to-side movements of the body and tail to move through water.

Osteichthyes) and cartilaginous fishes (class Chondrichthyes).

Adaptations to aquatic life: swimming

Because of its higher density and viscosity, water offers more resistance to movement than air. To minimize drag, therefore, the basic fish shape is streamlined. Backward-pointing scales cover the body, and the skin secretes slippery mucus to cut down water resistance further.

In most fish, propulsion comes mainly from the caudal (tail) fin. Muscle blocks on either side of the backbone contract alternately, thus causing the body to bend and the tail to flex from side to side. The tail fin forces the water backward and this propels the fish forward. Other fins control the direction of movement and help the fish stop. Pectoral fins act as elevators, adjusting the vertical pitch of the fish as it moves. Dorsal and anal fins, which are unpaired, help the fish remain upright. The paired pelvic fins often act like rudders in changing direction.

In some species, the tail has acquired other functions apart from providing propulsion. The sea horse (*Hippocampus* sp.), for instance, uses its tail to cling to weeds; it swims by lateral undulations of its dorsal fin.

Adaptations to aquatic life: buoyancy

Cartilaginous fishes are denser than water and so tend to sink. This is described as negative buoyancy. To overcome this tendency they use their pectoral fins, the front of their head, and their tail fin to produce lift as they swim. When stationary, however, they still tend to sink.

In contrast, most bony fishes can give themselves the same density as water (that is, they achieve neutral buoyancy), and are therefore able to maintain their position in the water even when not swimming. They do this using their swim bladder, a gas-filled, lunglike sac, which can be inflated or deflated to alter the buoyancy of the fish, allowing it to rise or descend in the water. Predacious fish, such as the pike *(Esox lucius)*, exhibit this ability well, remaining stationary as they wait for passing prey, using only small fin movements to maintain their position.

Adaptations to aquatic life: sense organs

Most fishes living in clear waters have good eyesight. The archerfish *(Toxotes jaculator)*, for example, is able to aim a jet of water at insects above the surface and even allows for the

The basic vertebrate shape of a fish is apparent even in a flatfish, where the body appears to have turned onto its side. This computer-colored X ray of a plaice shows the fish's head, skeleton, internal organs, and muscles.

bending of the light rays as they pass from air to water.

In most fish, the olfactory organs (organs of smell) consist of two pouches, one on each side of the snout. Sharks are renowned for their ability to detect blood in the water from as far away as one-third of a mile (one-half kilometer). Many bottom dwellers, such as the catfish *(Siluriformes)*, possess whiskerlike barbels around the mouth, which give them the senses of taste and touch.

Two other sensory systems are found exclusively in aquatic animals, and both relate to water's conducting properties. These are the pressure sense provided by the lateral line system, and an electric sense possessed by some species. In a few species, the latter is also associated with an ability to generate an electrical pulse.

The lateral line system can detect pressure changes caused by disturbances in the water around the fish. In experiments, blinded fishes have been trained to locate a moving glass rod by this method. In the wild, it enables a fish to detect moving food items, approaching predators, or other members of a shoal.

Many fishes that live in muddy water or are active at night also have an electric sense. Electric receptors can be identified in sharks, dogfish, catfish, and mormyrids (Mormyridiformes). Of those species that also possess electric organs capable of generating electrical pulses, some, such as the gymnarchid *(Gymnarchus* sp.), can detect irregularities in the electric field and thus locate objects in the cloudiest water. The electric eel *(Electropho-*

A fish relies on its fins for movement, balance, and position. The dorsal fins on the fish's back help to keep it upright and traveling straight, though some lateral "weaving" inevitably occurs. The pectoral fins at the sides control its horizontal position.

A   Skeleton of a bony fish

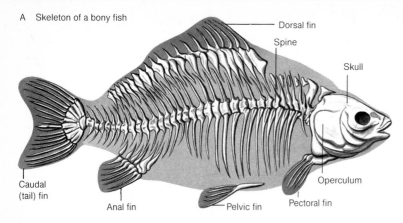

- Dorsal fin
- Spine
- Skull
- Operculum
- Pectoral fin
- Pelvic fin
- Anal fin
- Caudal (tail) fin

B   Internal and external anatomy

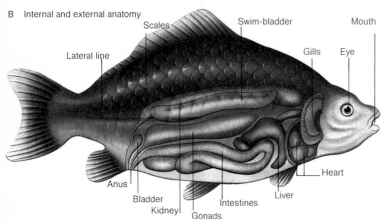

- Scales
- Swim-bladder
- Mouth
- Lateral line
- Gills
- Eye
- Heart
- Liver
- Intestines
- Gonads
- Kidney
- Bladder
- Anus

A typical bony fish (A) has unpaired dorsal, anal, and caudal fins—used for balance and propulsion—and paired pectoral and pelvic fins that help control its direction of movement. Internal organs (B) include the heart, liver, and—in advanced species—a swim bladder. The gills (shown in horizontal section, C) absorb oxygen from water that is taken in through the mouth and pumped out through the gill filaments.

C   Horizontal section through mouth chamber

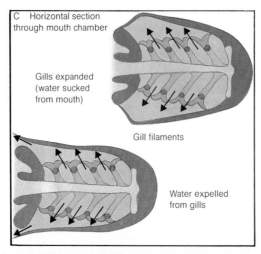

Gills expanded (water sucked from mouth)

Gill filaments

Water expelled from gills

Mudskippers (Periophthalmus sobrinus) have adapted to an amphibious existence by developing sacs in the mouth and gill cavity that are richly supplied with blood, so that they can absorb oxygen directly from the air.

rus electricus) has the well-known ability to produce much more powerful pulses (up to 500 volts) when alarmed, or to stun prey.

Adaptations to aquatic life: gills

The internal gills of fishes have a large surface area over which gaseous exchange between the water and the blood can occur. The gill area is related to the life style of the fish. Active species need more oxygen and so have large gills. Sluggish forms, like the bottom-dwelling toadfish (Opsanus sp.), have smaller gill areas in proportion to their body size. The mouth and gill (opercular) cavities form a mechanism that pumps water over the gills, a one-way flow being ensured by flaps of skin in the mouth. The gills are so arranged that the blood in the gill filaments and the water-carrying oxygen flow in opposite directions, and this counter-current system allows for the most efficient exchange of gases. In some sharks, the respiratory current from the gill slits is strong enough to propel the shark forward.

Certain cells in the gills also help fishes maintain their internal water and salt balance. In freshwater fishes, these cells absorb salts from the water, to keep up the body's salt level; in marine bony fishes, other cells excrete salt to compensate for the high levels of salt swallowed in sea water.

Cartilaginous fishes

Because they lack bony skeletons yet possess gill slits, cartilaginous fishes (class Chondrichthyes) were originally considered a primitive group. They do not appear before bony fish in the fossil record, however, and zoologists now believe that bone has actually been replaced by cartilage in these fishes.

About 600 species of cartilaginous fish have been identified. Most are marine and carnivorous, although the largest representatives are actually harmless filter feeders. They show the complete range of reproductive strategies. Egg-layers lay large yolky eggs: the familiar "mermaid's purse" is the horny egg case of the dogfish. Offshore sharks are often ovoviviparous, the newly-hatched sharks feeding on unfertilized eggs within the female before birth. Some sharks, however, and some rays are viviparous, but in all cases, fertilization is internal. The male fish has a pair of claspers formed from the pelvic fins, which are inserted into the female to transfer the sperm.

Cartilaginous fish are divided into three orders: the chimaeras (Chimaeriformes), rays (Rajiformes), and sharks (Squaliformes).

There are about 30 species of chimaeras, or ratfish. There are short-, long-, and elephant-nosed species. The upper jaw carries tooth plates and is fixed to the brain case, unlike the mobile jaws of sharks. Chimaeras have long, thin tails and swim by flapping their large pectoral fins. They are medium-sized fish with large eyes, and live near the ocean bottom.

Sharks, dogfish, skates, and rays all have gill slits and, usually in front of these, another opening called the spiracle. The mouth, on the underside of the head, is filled with rows of teeth, which are developed from the toothlike structures that cover the body. In sharks, only one row of teeth is used at a time, but as soon as teeth are lost or worn away, others move forward to replace them.

Skates and rays (order Rajiformes) have flattened bodies with the gill slits opening on the underside. Some sharks also have flattened bodies, but the gill slits are always on the side of the head. Many skates and rays are bottom-dwellers, often lying buried in sand with only the eyes protruding from the top of the head. As with chimaeras, the long thin tail is not used for swimming in most species. Instead they move by flapping or forming ripples in the very large pectoral fins. One of the largest rays is the Atlantic manta, measuring up to 23 feet (7 meters) from the tip of one pectoral fin to the other. Like the largest sharks, it is a filter feeder, collecting small fish and crustaceans. Electric rays (suborder Torpedinoidea) use their electric organs (capable of delivering a charge of 200 volts) to stun their prey, or as a means of defense. The stingrays, sluggish bottom-dwellers, have a different defensive strategy—a poisonous spine at the base of the tail.

Most sharks and dogfish (order Selachii) have a streamlined, torpedo shape. Probably the most feared and the most likely to be dangerous to man is the great white shark *(Carcharodon carcharias)*. Specimens up to 21 feet (6.4 meters) have been reported. Stomach content analyses suggest their normal diet is fish, dolphins, sea lions, and seals; but they are also known to attack bathers.

The smallest members of this group are the dogfishes (family Scyliorhinidae), many being smaller than 3 feet (1 meter) in length. Dogfishes live in shallow coastal waters, where they feed on mollusks, worms, and other invertebrates.

Bony fishes

About 95 per cent of living fishes belong to the class Osteichthyes (bony fishes), making this the largest vertebrate class. As their name suggests, at least part of the skeleton is formed from bone, although cartilage often also occurs. Bony fishes can be readily distinguished from cartilaginous fish by the presence of a bony gill cover (operculum). Also, the mouth is usually at the very front of the

head, instead of on the underside, as in cartilaginous fishes.

Reproductive strategies also differ from those of cartilaginous fishes. In contrast to the large yolky eggs of the latter, bony fishes tend to lay numerous small eggs—the number (which can be millions) usually relating to the hazards of the life style. Because the males do not possess claspers to transfer sperm, fertilization takes place externally.

Another typical feature is the air sac, which functions as a lung in the more primitive forms, and as a swim bladder in the rest. Bony fishes are usually subdivided into three groups: lungfishes (subclass Dipnoi), lobe-finned fishes (subclass Crossopterygii), and

Sharks are voracious carnivores, equipped with a large mouth and rows of sharp teeth to tear flesh from their prey. This photograph also shows the shark's gill arches in the sides of the mouth cavity.

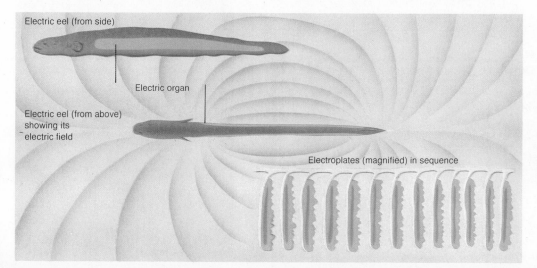

Electric eel (from side)

Electric organ

Electric eel (from above) showing its electric field

Electroplates (magnified) in sequence

Electric fishes can not only sense electric currents in the water but can also generate an electric field and (in some species), strong electric pulses. The organs responsible consist of rows of electroplates that work neurochemically, intensifying what is essentially a nervous impulse. In the electric eel *(Electrophorus electricus),* these organs are located on either side of the body, and produce an electric field that resembles the magnetic field of a bar magnet.

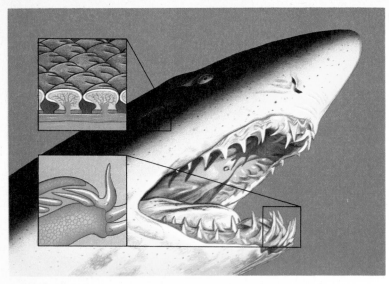

A shark's teeth grow in rows *(lower inset)*. The illustration shows the teeth of a sand tiger shark *(Carcharias taurus)*, which are typical of many shark species. A shark's placoid scales *(upper inset)* have a structure similar to its teeth; this is apparent in the cross section that shows the hard toothlike covering and the soft core of pulp.

ray-finned fishes (subclass Actinopterygii).

Lungfishes and lobefins

Zoologists have studied lungfishes and lobefins with particular interest since it was realized that similar species probably gave rise to the first land vertebrates. Lungfishes possess choanae (nostrils that connect the mouth cavity to the outside air) as in modern air-breathing amphibians. They and lobefins have paired fins containing bony supports and muscles in their bases, from which the weight-bearing limbs of land vertebrates could have developed. Since modern lungfishes have highly specialized jaws with tooth plates, however, they are unlikely to have been the ancestors of tetrapods. Consequently, most zoologists be-

lieve that land vertebrates arose from a freshwater group of lobefins. Today, lobefins are represented by a single species, the coelacanth *(Latimeria chalumnae)*, although more than 50 fossil species are known. This "living fossil" has altered very little since it first appeared in the Devonian period, 400 million years ago.

The lungfishes are also survivors from an earlier period. They were the most numerous fishes in the Devonian period, but there are now only six living species, distributed in Africa, Australia, and South America. All have functional lungs, which allow them to survive in poorly oxygenated waters that occasionally dry up.

Ray-finned fishes

Most freshwater fishes and commercially exploited marine fishes are ray-finned (subclass Actinopterygii). As their name suggests, they have fins supported by bony rays. They have two pairs of nostrils, but these do not penetrate to the mouth. Ray-finned fishes fall into four subdivisions: Polypteri, Chondrostei, Holostei, and Teleostei. The first three are considered primitive forms.

Birchirs, or reedfishes (infraclass Polypteri) occur in African inland waters. They possess a pair of lungs, so like the lungfishes they can survive in oxygen-deficient swamps. Sturgeons (infraclass Chondrostei) include the world's largest freshwater fish, the beluga *(Huso huso)*, which can grow to a length of 14 feet (4 meters) and a weight of over 2,800 pounds (1,300 kilograms). Sturgeons are also the sought-after source of caviar (which is salted sturgeon roe). Their skeletons are made mainly from cartilage, and they have several apparently primitive features, such as spira-

Camouflage is the only means of defense for some fishes. The mottled skin and the flat shape of a plaice *(Pleuronectes platessa)* enable it to merge with the rocks and gravel of the sea bed. Plaice may also try to bury themselves beneath a sandy surface for even greater concealment.

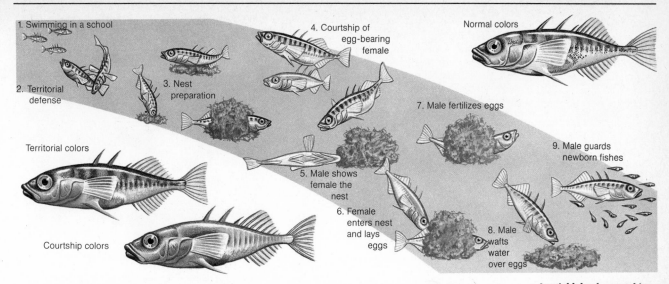

1. Swimming in a school
2. Territorial defense
3. Nest preparation
4. Courtship of egg-bearing female
5. Male shows female the nest
6. Female enters nest and lays eggs
7. Male fertilizes eggs
8. Male wafts water over eggs
9. Male guards newborn fishes

Normal colors

Territorial colors

Courtship colors

cles and an asymmetrical tail fin. They do not have a swim bladder, however.

The North American gar (*Lepidosteus* sp.) and bowfin (*Amia calva*, infraclass Holostei) do have a lunglike swim bladder and can breathe air when necessary. With sharp teeth, both are voracious carnivores, preying on other fishes and often causing damage to commercial nets in the process.

Teleost fishes

By far the most numerous and diverse group of fishes are the teleosts (infraclass Teleostei). Teleost comes from two Greek words meaning *complete* and *bone*. Perhaps more than to anything else, their success can be attributed to their mobility, achieved by the development of the swim bladder, highly mobile fins, and reduced scales.

The swim bladder allows for buoyancy control, and within the group various stages of swim bladder development can be seen. In the carp (*Cyprinus* sp.), the swim bladder is still connected to the gut by a duct and is filled by swallowing air. In the perch (*Perca* sp.) and other advanced teleosts, however, this duct has been lost, and the bladder is filled by gas drawn from the blood at a special "gas gland."

The fins of teleosts also enhance their mobility. The tail fin is symmetrical, giving effective forward propulsion. Another feature that can be observed in this group is the tendency of the paired pelvic fins to move forward to underlie the pectoral fins in more "advanced" species. In the salmon *(Salmo salar),* the paired fins are well separated, whereas in the perch the pelvic fins have moved right forward. Again, this appears to aid mobility, since stopping and turning are easier with this arrangement.

Other teleost features include a reduction of the bone in the scales to a very thin layer. Two types of teleost scale occur: cycloid scales, as in the carp, and ctenoid scales, as in the perch. Both types are considerably lighter than the thick, ganoid scales of primitive bony fish. Scales are of considerable interest to fisheries biologists in temperate regions, because the age of the fish can be determined by counting the growth rings on its scales.

Teleosts are divided into about 30 different orders, of which the most important are eels; salmon, trout, and pike; carps, characins, and catfishes; codfishes, spiny-finned fishes; and flatfishes.

Eels

Characterized by their snakelike bodies and smooth, slimy, often scaleless skin, eels (order Anguilliformes) are easily recognized. They have no pelvic fins, and their anal and dorsal fins have fused to form a fin seam, which is used in swimming.

Eels have an unusual transparent larval form called a leptocephalus (leaf-head), which bears little resemblance to the adult, and was originally considered a completely different fish. In the European eel *(Anguilla anguilla),* the whole reproductive cycle is extraordinary.

In stickleback courtship, the male acquires a red belly as he establishes his territory and prepares the nest. The colors intensify as he identifies a female by her egg-swollen shape, then encourages her to lay her eggs in the nest. Once fertilized, the eggs are tended by the male, who continues to protect the young when they have hatched.

The black marlin *(Makaira indica)* is the largest of the billfish, sometimes exceeding 13 feet (4 meters) and 1,500 pounds (700 kilograms).

Adult eels change from freshwater to saltwater fishes, then migrate from Europe to spawning grounds in the Sargasso Sea, an area of the Atlantic Ocean northeast of the West Indies, more than 3,350 miles (5,400 kilometers) away. Once hatched, the larvae make the return journey, aided by the Gulf Stream. Eventually—possibly after as much as three years—they enter European rivers, often at night, where they grow into freshwater, adult forms.

Most eels are marine, however, like the moray *(Muraena helena)* and conger eel *(Conger conger),* both of which are voracious fish eaters. Garden eels *(Gorgasia maculata),* in contrast, live in tubes and filter tiny zooplankton for food. Despite its name and shape, the electric eel is not a true eel, being more closely related to the carps.

Salmon, trout, and pike

The order Salmoniformes is typified by salmon and trout, both migratory fishes from northern temperate areas, which often use offshore feeding grounds, yet return to fresh water to spawn. Lesser known species include the char *(Salvelinus* sp.), grayling *(Thymallus* sp.), smelt *(Osmerus* sp.), and whitefish *(Coregonus* sp.). All can be recognized by their large mouths and the presence of a small, rayless adipose fin between the dorsal and tail fins. All are popular food fishes.

The pike *(Esox* sp.) is also a member of this order. A large mouth filled with sharp teeth enables a pike to feed on other fish and even small mammals and birds taken at the water's edge or surface.

Carps, characins, and catfish

The majority of the world's freshwater fishes, more than 3,500 species, belong to the same group as carps and catfishes (order Cypriniformes). All possess a swim bladder connected to the gut, cycloid scales, and well-separated pectoral and pelvic fins.

The 2,000 species of carp-like fishes include most European coarse fishes, such as carp *(Cyprinus* sp.), roach *(Rutilus* sp.), bream *(Abramis* sp.), dace *(Leuciscus* sp.), and tench *(inca tinca),*

Moray eels (*Gymnothorax* sp.) are found in subtropical and tropical seas, where they hide among rocks and in crevices, except when hunting for food. Most morays are aggressive; all have sharp teeth; and some species have poison glands in the mouth that pour poison into the wound caused by the moray's bite, and so disable or kill the prey.

plus the non-European goldfish (*Carassius* sp.). Carp lack jaw teeth, but possess teeth on the pharyngeal (throat) bones. In the common carp *(Cyprinus carpio),* these crush the plant material and invertebrates on which it feeds. The mouth can also be protruded, which allows carp to suck up food particles effectively. Originally from central Asia, the common carp has been widely distributed and farmed by man. In 1963, another species, the herbivorous grass carp, was brought to the United States from Asia to help control the overgrowth of certain water plants.

Unlike the carps, characins, which include the piranha (*Serrasalmus* sp.) and tiger fish (*Hydrocinus* sp.), have well-developed teeth. These are brightly colored fishes from South America and Africa, respectively. Many species of characins, however, like the tetra (*Hemigrammus* sp. or *Hyphessobrycon* sp.), have been distributed worldwide to tropical fish enthusiasts.

Catfishes (order Siluriformes), in contrast, are not colorful, being mainly nocturnal bottom-dwelling fishes. Consequently, their eyes are small, but they bear up to four pairs of conspicuous barbels around the mouth, and these are sensitive to touch and taste.

All of this group of carps, characins, and catfishes (superorder Ostariophysi) share two interesting features. The first is that they possess a series of three bones (the Weberian ossicles), which connect the swim bladder to the inner ear. Sound vibrations in the water are picked up and amplified by the gas-filled bladder and then transmitted to the ear, giving these fish excellent hearing. To match this, some catfish can also produce sounds, by drumming on the swim bladder or scraping the spines of the pectoral fins. The second is that they all have a similar "fright" reaction. When one fish is injured, its skin cells release a chemical into the water. Other individuals react to this by either fleeing or hiding, so that if a predator attacks one member of a shoal, the others escape.

Codfishes

Another commercially important group, including the Atlantic cod *(Gadus morhua),* haddock *(Melanogrammus aeglefinus),* and hake *(Merluccius merluccius),* are known collec-

Horse mackerel
(Trachurus trachurus, above) have streamlined bodies and powerful tails. They swim in schools in search of the smaller species on which they prey, and are an important food fish.

Eels *(Anguilla anguilla)* migrate vast distances to spawn *(right)*, and their larvae return slowly to the European rivers. Herrings migrate over short distances—the inset map shows North Sea shoals.

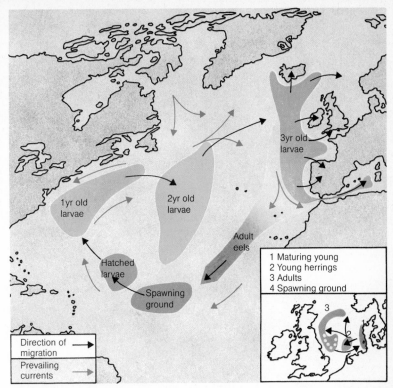

1yr old larvae

2yr old larvae

3yr old larvae

Adult eels

Hatched larvae

Spawning ground

1 Maturing young
2 Young herrings
3 Adults
4 Spawning ground

Direction of migration ⟶
Prevailing currents ⟶

tively as codfishes or gadids (order Gadiformes). They are essentially cool sea fishes, living mainly in the northern waters of the Atlantic and Pacific oceans. Hake, however, also live in deep water, and have invaded subtropical areas. At night, they surface to feed on other fish, such as herring. Growing up to 1 foot (30 centimeters) in length, hake now form the main catch of fishing industries in Europe, South Africa, and South America.

Spiny-finned fishes

The most advanced teleosts have spiny rays in the dorsal, pelvic, and anal fins (as anyone who has handled a perch carelessly will know). Advanced features include ctenoid scales, a swim bladder not connected to the gut, and pelvic and pectoral fins sited close together.

There are more than 7,000 species of perch-like fish (order Perciformes), which include the angelfish *(Pomacanthus* sp.), butterflyfish *(Chaetodon* sp.), mackerel *(Scomber scombrus),* and tuna *(Thunnus thynnus).* They are active, often brightly-colored fishes, with good eyesight and color vision.

The European perch *(Perca fluviatilis)* is an active predator, feeding on other fish—as is the much larger Nile perch *(Lates niloticus)*—but within this group all manner of feeding specializations are found. One family, for example, the cichlids (Cichlidae), are particularly diverse. In Lake Malawi, located in southeastern Africa, 200 different species of cichlids coexist, feeding according to their separate tastes on mollusks, insects, fishes, eggs, plankton, algae, or even the scales of other fishes. In each case, the pharyngeal teeth appear specially adapted to the diet.

Flatfishes

Many teleosts are laterally compressed, but this is taken to extremes in the flatfish (order Pleuronectiformes).

The larvae of flatfish are conventional in appearance, but as they grow they gradually become compressed and turn over on one side. One eye begins to move closer to the eye on the opposite side of the head, and the mouth becomes twisted. The underside becomes white, and the upper surface darkens.

To match this shape, most flatfish live on the seabed in coastal waters, and some—like the plaice *(Pleuronectes platessa)*—possess the ability to alter their coloration to match their surroundings. Commonly eaten flatfish, such as sole *(Solea solea),* are small, although others, such as halibut *(Hippoglossus hippoglossus),* reach weights of 400 pounds (180 kilograms).

The coelacanth *(Latimeria chalumnae),* a "living fossil," may be a link between fishes and amphibians. Once thought to be extinct for 60 million years, it was discovered in 1938 in the waters off southern Africa.

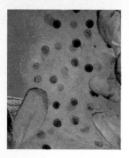

Frogspawn consists of the fertilized eggs of a frog, with the dividing cells surrounded by a gelatinous envelope. The eggs of other egg-laying amphibians, such as toads, newts, and salamanders, look similar.

Amphibians

According to paleontologists, the oldest fossils of amphibians date back to the end of the Devonian Period—more than 350 million years ago. The Devonian Period was a time of great ecological changes, which resulted from massive disruptions of the surface features of the earth. For the evolution of amphibians, the most significant of these were changes that altered the level of the seas.

As water levels rose and then receded, the sea left behind organic materials in which plants could thrive. This tended to encourage the development of areas of lush vegetation in swamplike coastal regions. These conditions favored creatures that could obtain their oxygen from air as well as from water, and it is probable that it was in such an environment that the first amphibians evolved.

In prehistoric times, there were at least six orders of amphibians (class Amphibia), but now only three orders remain: newts and salamanders (Urodela); frogs and toads (Anura); and caecilians (Apoda). Although the majority of amphibians inhabit the tropics, representatives of the class are found throughout the world, except in places where there is no water at all. In cold climates, they hibernate during winter. Like most animals except birds and mammals, they are cold-blooded (poikilothermal), and their body temperature changes with fluctuations in the temperature of their environment.

Amphibians vary in length from an inch or less (for instance, African sedge or reed frogs of the *Hyperolius* genus), to more than 5 feet (1.5 meters), the largest amphibian being the Japanese giant salamander *(Megalobatrachus japonicus)*, although a caecilian from Colombia *(Caecilia thompsoni)* reaches nearly the same length. Amphibians have a wide flat skull attached to the spinal column. The latter may be short, as in frogs and toads, which usually have eight vertebrae in the trunk, or extremely long, with as many as 250 vertebrae in some salamanders and caecilians. The urodeles and anurans have four limbs, with four fingers on each forelimb and five toes on each hindlimb. The apods have lost their limbs. Unlike the urodeles, adult anurans have no tails.

The skin of all amphibians is toughened (cornified) on the animal's upper surface, and smooth on the lower surface. All shed their skin regularly—this molting is under hormonal control. The skin produces slimy or poisonous secretions that make these animals unpalatable to most predators and so afford protection. In many species, the skin color can change, usually for camouflage or mating purposes. The skin also plays a part in respiration.

Respiration

In evolutionary terms, one of the most profound modifications needed for animals to survive the emergence from an aquatic environment was the ability to absorb oxygen from air rather than from water. In amphibians, perhaps reflecting stages in this transition, respiration takes place in the gills, lungs, lining of the mouth, or the external skin, either alone or in combination, depending on the species. The role of the skin in respiration varies, from some species for which it is not particularly important, to others—for example, some lungless salamanders (such as the European Alpine salamander, *Salamandra atra*)—in which the skin is the sole means of absorbing oxygen from the aerated water of the mountain streams in which they live.

Senses

Different amphibians have differing sensory needs. In almost all species the sense of touch is well developed, but the development of organs for sensing things at distance—for sight, hearing, and smell—varies greatly. Cave dwellers, such as the olm *(Proteus anguinus)*, have little need of sight and their eyes are vestigial. Burrowing caecilians have eyes that are either very small or completely absent, although they have another organ similar to a small feeler, which is associated with eye muscles and seems to have a sensory function. In other species, particularly frogs, the eyes are well developed. Underground and cave-dwelling amphibians tend to have a good sense of smell, and this is also important for aquatic species, unless they live in clear water.

A frog is called a tadpole in its larval stage. At the start of metamorphosis tadpoles have an egg-shaped body and head, and a tail. Back legs develop first, by about eight weeks; then front legs emerge from beneath the gill covering (operculum). By about 12 weeks, the larva has lost its gills and gained the legs of the terrestrial adult form, but still has the tail of the aquatic form. Gradually, this tail is reabsorbed as the frog assumes its adult shape.

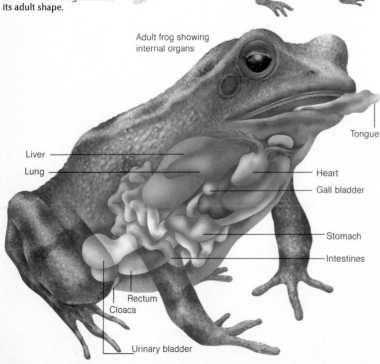

8 weeks

Mouth

Eye

Operculum

12 weeks

Adult frog showing internal organs

Liver

Lung

Tongue

Heart

Gall bladder

Stomach

Intestines

Rectum

Cloaca

Urinary bladder

Lateral line organs are present in aquatic species, although they are less developed than in fishes. They appear as lines of little pits along the head and body, distributed in relation to the lateral line nerves. They respond to vibrations or changes of pressure in the water, enabling the animal to control its equilibrium and posture and to detect predators or prey.

The existence of a sense of hearing in amphibians seems to depend on whether or not the animal has a voice. Urodeles and apods have neither voice nor visible ears, but appear to be able to detect vibrations. Frogs and toads, in contrast, have remarkably loud, even strident voices, and have an eardrum just behind each eye.

Movement

In water, amphibians can both walk and swim. During courtship, for example, newts often walk along the bottom of a pond. Frogs and toads use their hindlimbs for swimming, whereas newts propel themselves with their tails, keeping their hind legs pressed together. Caecilians swim like eels. Although urodeles can walk on land, their tails and short legs restrict their mobility. Frogs and toads crawl on land, but also use their powerful hind legs for leaping—several species can jump 20 times their body length. The limbless caecilians usually burrow below ground; when observed above ground, however, their movements resemble those of a snake.

Feeding

Apart from anuran larvae (tadpoles), amphibians are carnivores, their main sources of food being insects and small invertebrates. Caecilians have a more varied diet, which includes other amphibians, fishes, and even some reptiles, small mammals, and birds.

Amphibian teeth have no roots and grow all the time as they are worn down. Some urodeles have fixed, immobile tongues but others, such as the cave salamander *(Hydromantes genei),* have tongues that can protrude to catch prey. This ability is particularly marked in frogs and toads, in which the tongue is attached to the front of the lower jaw. As the tongue flicks forward, it scrapes the roof of the mouth, collecting a sticky covering that adheres to the prey, so that it can be drawn back

to the anuran's mouth.

From the mouth, food passes to the stomach, where secretions from stomach glands (present in all amphibians, though not in all fishes) start the digestive process. This continues through the intestine, aided by enzymes from the pancreas and bile from the gall bladder, to the rectum and cloaca. Urine also empties from the urinary bladder into the cloaca, from which waste products (urine and feces) are expelled.

Reproduction and life expectancy

Most amphibians lay eggs, and fertilization usually takes place outside the body. The young pass through a larval stage, although in tailed amphibians and caecilians the distinction between this and the adult form is less obvious than it is in anurans. Some species (most caecilians, for instance) bear live young,

Frogs have adapted successfully to many environments. The Costa Rican flying frog *(Agalychnis spurelli)* is a tree frog with webbed feet that enhance its ability to leap to such an extent that it appears to fly.

The fire salamander *(Salamandra salamandra)* protects itself with poison glands in its skin. These secrete an irritant fluid that burns the mouth of any predator that bites the salamander.

Amphibians are carnivorous and some are agile predators. In this photograph a palmate newt (Triturus helveticus) has captured a fish.

others lay eggs that contain partially developed young, and still others (such as the common European frog, *Rana temporaria*) produce spawn in which the whole process of development occurs from the first cell division onward.

In captivity, amphibians have been known to live for 15 years or more, but their life expectancy in the wild is usually much less. Among the longest-lived are some slender salamanders (*Batrachoseps* sp.) and cave salamanders (*Hydromantes geneii*), which live for as long as 10 years in their natural habitat.

The voice of a frog is produced when air is pumped over the vocal cords in the throat. Male frogs of some species—in this photograph the painted reed frog (Hyperolius viridiflavus)—have a vocal sac that can be distended to produce a resonating chamber, which intensifies the sound considerably.

Frogs and toads

The anurans, loosely called frogs and toads, form the largest of the three orders of Amphibia, with some 2,700 species that have adapted to a wider range of habitats than the other orders and live on every continent except Antarctica. Although most are terrestrial

rather than aquatic, some, such as the tree frogs (Hylidae), are primarily if not exclusively arboreal. In some of these species, eggs are laid in water trapped among leaves, but some build nests, and some spawn in ponds and similar locations, then return to their arboreal habitat.

The terms frog and toad are based on appearance and do not relate to actual phylogenetic distinctions. Anuran classification is based primarily on skeletal features, such as the presence of ribs, which distinguishes lower from higher anurans, or the structure of the pectoral and pelvic girdles. Beyond such relatively simple criteria anurans show enormous variety. There are anatomical variations in the extent to which hands and feet are webbed, in the shape of and function of fingers and toes, and in the distribution or arrangement of teeth. Some species have no teeth, others have teeth in the upper jaw only, and one genus (*Amphignathodon*) has teeth in both jaws.

Most anurans are nocturnal, although newly metamorphosed frogs take several days to assume their nocturnal habits. They are mainly dependent on their eyes for catching prey—their visual system responds to small, irregularly moving objects, and they will not react to even a preferred food source unless it moves.

An important feature distinguishing anurans from other amphibians is their voice. Almost all anuran males can increase the volume of the sounds they make by using vocal sacs in the mouth. The mating call of the natterjack toad (*Bufo calamita*), for example, can be heard more than half a mile away. Females, which are generally larger than males, have a quieter call.

In the breeding season the male anuran's call serves to attract females and enables a female to recognize a male of the same species. When a male anuran is ready to mate he will jump upon anything of the appropriate size, and will often clasp a male or some other inappropriate object (even a piece of mud or earth) before managing to find a female.

In most frogs and toads eggs and seminal fluid are emitted at the same time; fertilized eggs are then deposited singly or in clumps or strings. The majority of European and North American anurans lay clusters of hundreds of eggs, each in its own gelatinous envelope; the frogspawn of *Rana temporaria* is the most familiar example. One exception is the North American tailed frog (*Ascaphus truei*), which lays eggs that have been fertilized internally. Internal fertilization also occurs in one genus of toads (*Nectophrynoides*), found in Africa, which do not lay eggs at all but give birth to live young.

Salamanders and newts

The tailed amphibians (Urodela) make up the second largest of the three orders of Amphibia. There are about 330 species of salamanders and newts, most of which inhabit the temperate regions of the Northern Hemisphere. Many are terrestrial, retreating to moist crevices in hot, dry weather. Urodeles live in a wider variety of habitats nevertheless. Some live in trees, some never leave the

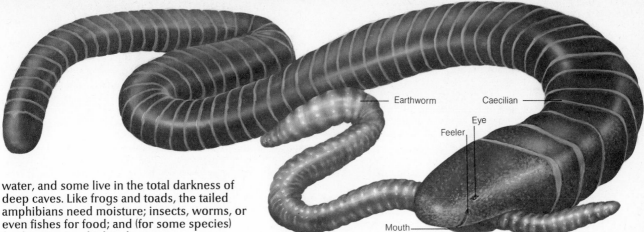

Earthworm   Caecilian

Eye

Feeler

Mouth

water, and some live in the total darkness of deep caves. Like frogs and toads, the tailed amphibians need moisture; insects, worms, or even fishes for food; and (for some species) fresh water in which to lay eggs.

Mating behavior differs from that of anurans. Salamanders and newts have no voice, so mating display is all-important. A male salamander's particular pattern of courtship behavior and coloring elicits a response only from a female of the same species. Male alpine newts *(Triturus alpestris),* for instance, develop crests and striking coloration—blue on the back and flanks, orange on the belly—in the breeding season. Many species indulge in complex courtship rituals, ranging from lashing the tail to waft odorous secretions toward the female, to swimming back and forth in front of her.

During mating the male deposits a spermatophore (sperm packet), which the female takes up into her cloaca. The sperms are then released as the female releases her eggs. When these hatch the larvae resemble adults, although they have gills that disappear during metamorphosis.

Caecilians

The third amphibian order, and the one about which least is known, is the Apoda. Apods, or caecilians, have no limbs and look like large worms or smooth snakes. Lengths vary from just over 2 inches (6 centimeters) to nearly 5 feet (1.5 meters). Nearly all species live in warm-temperate and tropical regions. They usually burrow beneath the ground, seldom being seen above ground in daylight, although it is believed that most come to the surface at night. Eyes are of little use in such a habitat but caecilians have developed a sensitive "feeler" or tentacle that probably helps them search for the worms and insects that are the main constituents of their diet. Reproduction is by internal fertilization, and it is believed that caecilians either lay eggs or retain the eggs until the young hatch.

Caecilians are sometimes mistaken for very large earthworms, but when the two are compared—as in this illustration of a South American caecilian *(Siphonops annulatus)* eating an earthworm—there are obvious differences. Most significant of these are the caecilian's flattened head; its small, almost vestigial eyes; the small feeler located between its eye and nose; and its mouth. Some caecilians are strikingly colored: the species illustrated is blue-black, darker above than below. Others are mottled or striped.

In courtship, many species of newts develop striking coloration. In some species, the crest of the male also enlarges. Both characteristics are evident in this photograph of great crested newts *(Triturus cristatus)* mating.

Reptiles

Reptiles were the first true land-dwelling vertebrates, appearing about 310 million years ago. They dominated Earth from about 225 to 65 million years ago, but today only four reptilian orders remain: the turtles (order Testudinata or Chelonia); lizards and snakes (order Squamata); crocodilians (order Crocodilia); and the tuatara (order Rhynchocephalia).

The most noticeable characteristic of reptiles is their outer covering of scales. They also lay tough, leathery eggs and are "cold-blooded" (that is, they lack an internal means of controlling body temperature). Because of this last feature most of the 6,000 or so reptilian species live in the tropics or subtropics. However, some live in temperate regions, for example, the tuatara *(Sphenodon punctatus),* and the viviparous common lizard *(Lacerta vivipara),* which is found as far north as the Arctic Circle.

The reptilian body

A reptile's body is covered by a dry, relatively thick waterproof skin, which helps to protect the internal structures and prevents dehydration. The scales on the reptilian body are really folds in the skin, composed of a hard, transparent dead material called keratin. In chelonians and crocodilians the outer keratin layer is continually worn away but a new layer always remains underneath. In snakes and lizards, however, the scales are shed at regular intervals. Lizards often shed their scales in strips; but some, like snakes, shed the whole skin in one piece, a process known as sloughing. Lizards and some crocodilians have pieces of bone called osteoderms within their scales, which give the skin additional toughness.

In most vertebrates, including reptiles, the skeleton consists of bone and cartilage. The

The dinosaur Stegosaurus regulated its body temperature by means of the blood-rich skin that covered the diamond-shaped plates on its back. The blood absorbed heat from the sun, carrying it around the body. In the shade, the blood was cooled.

The reptilian skeleton varies greatly. The crocodilians have abdominal and thoracic ribs; the chelonians have their ribs and vertebrae fused to their shell; but the ribs of the snakes extend to the end of the tail.

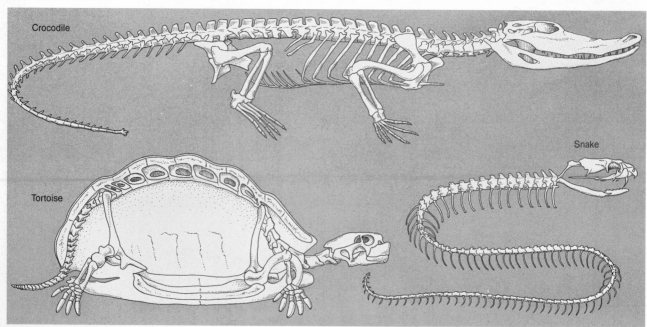

Crocodile

Tortoise

Snake

amount of cartilage in the body is highest in young reptiles, but as the reptile grows and becomes an adult, the cartilage is usually present only over the joints, the shoulder girdle, and parts of the skull. Unlike mammalian bones, those of a reptile continue to grow throughout the animal's life.

The ribs of reptiles extend the length of the body, from the third vertebra of the spine to the beginning of the tail, whereas in mammals they are confined to the chest region. The skull consists of many separate bones. Similarly, the lower jaw is formed from several distinct but joined bones. The teeth are peglike or pointed and are all alike; they are not differentiated as are the teeth of mammals.

The reptilian brain is small in relation to the body—in many, it constitutes less than 0.05 per cent of the total body weight—and reptiles are relatively unintelligent, having very little ability to learn or adapt to new situations. But they compensate for this deficiency by possessing elaborate patterns of instinctive behavior that enable them to survive and reproduce successfully.

Reptiles breathe with the aid of two lungs, one or both of which may be well developed. Some species can also absorb oxygen in the water through the membranes that line the mouth and the genital and waste-eliminating chamber called the cloaca. The cloaca is at the end of the large intestine, and opens under the body in front of the tail. It receives eggs or sperm from the sex glands as well as feces from the intestine and urine from the kidneys. The water needed for elimination of waste products is reabsorbed into the blood through the walls of the large intestine and cloacal chamber. The anal waste is solid or semi-solid, and there is little or no liquid urine. In this way, water is conserved in the body, a feature that is important for those reptiles that live in dry environments.

Senses and sense organs

Most reptiles have good eyesight. The fields of vision of each eye overlap to some extent, so that some of these animals have binocular vision, although in varying degrees. It is particularly highly developed in chameleons (*Chamaeleo* spp.), which must be able to judge distances accurately in order to catch their prey.

Relatively little is known about hearing in reptiles, although this faculty does not seem to be as important as vision. Like birds, mammals, and amphibians, reptiles have a small bone (the stapes), which transmits sound vibrations from the eardrum to the inner ear. Most reptiles, apart from snakes and a few lizards, have external ears with eardrums on the surface or sunk down on a tube at the back of the head. However, they lack earflaps, except for crocodiles. Snakes also lack the middle ear cavity—they "hear" a sound mainly by picking up vibrations from the ground, which are then transferred from the lower jaw bone to the skull.

Smell is an important sense in most reptiles. Snakes and lizards have two tiny cavities known as the Jacobson's organ, which work in conjunction with the tongue as well as with the sense of smell. These organs are found above, and open into, the roof of the mouth

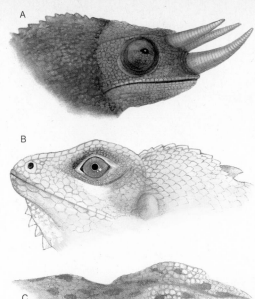
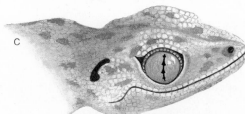

Reptilian eyes are varied. Chameleons' rotating eyes (A) allow them to keep still while watching for prey. Their eyelids cover most of the eye, which sharpens their focus. The round pupils of some lizards (B) contrast with those of the tokay gecko (C), which are vertical and constricted in four places to protect them from dazzle and improve vision. Crocodilian eyes (D) are covered with a membrane that allows them to be submerged in water. Tortoises (E) have round pupils protected by thick, folding eyelids.

Many species of lizard have spines, shields, or frills on their body or head—the Bearded Dragon Lizard (*Amphibolurus barbatus*), for example. These features are either modified scales or skin membranes. They are puffed up to give the lizards an appearance of greater size in displays of aggression or in courtship.

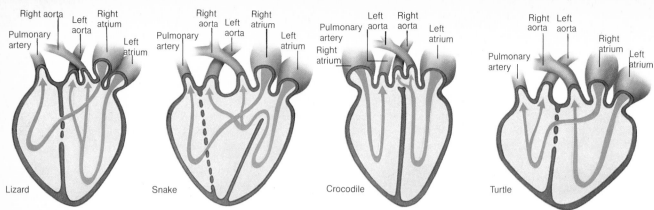

Lizard

Pulmonary artery | Right aorta | Left aorta | Right atrium | Left atrium

Snake

Pulmonary artery | Right aorta | Left aorta | Right atrium | Left atrium

Crocodile

Pulmonary artery | Right atrium | Left aorta | Right aorta | Left atrium

Turtle

Pulmonary artery | Right aorta | Left aorta | Right atrium | Left atrium

The heart system differs among reptiles. The lizards have a perforated septum separating the ventricles. Nonaerated blood flows through it from the left ventricle into the pulmonary artery in the right. In the snakes the pulmonary artery, the aortas, and the right atrium are in the right ventricle. A muscular ridge formed during contraction guides the nonaerated blood into the pulmonary artery. The septum of the crocodiles is whole, and the two aortas come out of each of the ventricles. This is also true for chelonians but, because their ventricles are not perfectly divided, nonaerated and aerated blood flows into the aortas, so a mixing of blood occurs.

and are partly lined with sensitive membranes similar to those that line the nose. As the tongue moves in and out, it picks up minute particles from the air or off the ground, which are carried to the Jacobson's organs.

An additional sense organ—the pineal eye—occurs in the tuatara and many lizards (and was also present in many extinct reptiles and amphibians). It is found at the top of the head and opens, by means of a small hole, into the skull. It is covered by skin, which usually has a lighter color than the surrounding skin. The exact function of this "third eye" is unknown, but it is light-sensitive and probably helps the animal to regulate its exposure to the sun, and thus to control its internal body temperature.

Temperature regulation

The term "cold-blooded" is misleading when applied to reptiles because under certain circumstances a reptile's body temperature may be very high, even higher than the normal body temperature of humans—98.6° F. (37° C). Reptiles are, in fact, poikilothermal—they do not have an internal mechanism to regulate body temperature—and therefore depend on the external temperature. Body temperature is important because it is related to activity.

Under extreme conditions of heat or cold, the body becomes sluggish or even torpid, because vital activities such as heartbeat and breathing slow down. But within a narrow temperature range—which varies from species to species—a reptile reaches its highest level of activity. For most, the optimum temperature is between 77° F. (25° C) and 99° F. (31° C).

Reproduction

Most reptiles that live in temperate and subtropical climates breed in spring. As in most other animals, the urge to mate is triggered by an increase in the hormone levels in the sex glands and other internal organs. These changes are usually a response to changes in the environment, such as lengthening of the day, an increasing abundance of food, and a rise in air temperature. Tropical reptiles may breed several times a year, but even in these species mating usually follows a seasonal cycle.

With the exception of the tuatara, which mates by pressing its cloaca against that of the female, all male reptiles possess a penis through which sperm is introduced into the female's cloaca. Chelonians and crocodiles (*Crocodylus* spp.) have a single penis, whereas

Basking on warm rocks, reptiles such as marine iguanas *(Amblyrhynchus cristatus)* seek to prevent themselves from becoming too cold. They move into shade periodically to stop themselves from overheating. This dependence on external temperature is essential, because they have no internal mechanism to regulate their body temperature. In addition, some reptiles change the color of their skin to make it more or less heat absorbent.

lizards and snakes have two, known as hemipenes, only one of which is used during copulation.

Most reptiles are oviparous—that is, the young hatch after the eggs have been laid. But some species of snakes and lizards, such as adders *(Vipera berus)* and the common lizard, are ovoviviparous (the young hatch while the eggs are still inside the mother's body). In such reptiles, the young may still by surrounded by embryonic membranes when they are born. Exceptions to both these methods of reproduction are found in certain skinks (Scincomorpha) and snakes, in which the relationship between mother and embryo is more intimate, resembling that of mammals. In these reptiles, a type of placenta develops that lies close to the lining of the mother's oviduct.

Tortoises, turtles, and terrapins

Tortoises, turtles, and terrapins (order Chelonia) are differentiated in the following way: tortoises live only on land, turtles live in the sea, and terrapins live in fresh water. In the United States, however, most chelonians are commonly referred to as turtles.

The most striking feature of this order is the presence of a shell. The shell is composed of an outer layer of horny structures called scutes (which are formed from skin tissue), and a thick inner layer of bony plates. The outer, horny layer increases in size with age, but its growth is arrested during hibernation. Each dormant phase produces a ring around the previous year's growth, similar to a growth ring in a tree. Soft-shelled turtles and the leatherback turtle have an outer layer of tough skin rather than scutes. The shell of the hawksbill turtle *(Eretmochelys imbricata)* is the source of the commercial material known as tortoise shell.

Chelonians do not have teeth; instead they have a horny beak on the upper and lower jaws. Tortoises are mainly herbivorous, turtles eat a mixture of plant and animal food, and terrapins tend to be carnivorous, feeding on invertebrates and fish.

There are two suborders of chelonians, distinguished by the way the head is withdrawn into the shell. The Pleurodira are the side-necked turtles, found in South America, Africa, and Australia, and are a small group of two families. An example is the South American matamata terrapin *(Chelys fimbriata),* which has a long snout with nostrils at the end and a long flap of skin behind each eye. It feeds on fish and other small aquatic animals.

The Cryptodira, or hidden-necks—a group that comprises seven families—bend the neck vertically up and down. The family Testudinidae in this group includes the land tortoises, which are some of the most familiar chelonians, with about 40 species. The family Emydidae, with about 80 species, includes terrapins and pond tortoises. The pond tortoise *(Emys orbicularis)* and the red-eared terrapin *(Pseudomys scripta)* are commonly kept as pets.

The family Chelydridae is found in North America, Central America, and northern South America, and is comprised of the musk and mud turtles and the snappers. The common snapper *(Chelydra serpentina)* is a ferocious freshwater turtle that bites sharply when dis-

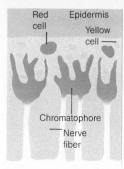

Red cell Epidermis
Yellow cell
Chromatophore
Nerve fiber

The color change in chameleons is due to pigment-containing cells under the skin's surface. When the pigments of these branched cells are concentrated at the cell center *(far left),* the skin is light colored. When the pigments spread into the cell branches *(right),* the skin darkens.

turbed. Unusually, it cannot withdraw its head into its shell, and its tail, legs, and neck are almost completely exposed on the underside. The musk turtles *(Sternotherus* spp.) are exceptional among reptiles in having scent glands on their body; they are often called "stinkpots" because of the musky odor they emit when handled.

The sea turtles (families Cheloniidae and Dermochelyidae) are the most highly adapted to a watery existence. Their legs are flattened and paddle-shaped, and they swim with agility.

Most reptiles lay their eggs on land, usually concealed under a stone or buried in soil or sand. But some, such as the rat snakes *(Elaphe* spp.), lay them in tree hollows. The eggs are protected by a relatively tough, parchmentlike shell.

On land, however, they move clumsily and slowly. It is usually only the females that come ashore, and they do so specifically to lay eggs in a hole in the sand.

The giant tortoises *(Testudo elephantopus)* are found in the Galapagos Islands, Aldabra Islands, and the Seychelles Islands. They may measure up to 4 feet (1.2 meters), and they are known to live to about 100 years of age. They live in the lowlands but venture to the highlands for drinking water, where they wallow for hours.

Lizards and snakes

These reptiles belong to the order Squamata, which is divided into two suborders: the Sauria (lizards), and the Serpentes, also called Ophidia (snakes).

Lizards and snakes form the largest group of reptiles, and are most abundant in tropical regions. Most lizards are small and four-legged with long tails, movable eyelids, and external ear openings. Many can shed their tails to escape from predators. The tail is then regenerated but is never an exact copy of the original, being shorter and with an irregular scale pattern. Members of the family Anguidae have either one or two pairs of short, reduced limbs and some, such as the slowworm *(Anguis fragilis),* are legless.

An interesting feature of some skinks (family Scincidae) is that the eyelids contain a transparent opening, which allows them to see while they close their eyes to protect them against flying debris.

The family Chamaeleonidae contains some 100 species of chameleons. These lizards are exceptionally well-adapted to an insectivorous and arboreal life. Two of the five toes on each limb are opposed to the other three, forming a gripping "hand," and the tail is prehensile. Each eye can move independently or both can focus on the same object. The chameleon can therefore judge distances accurately and aim precisely at the insects on which it feeds, catching them with its long, sticky tongue.

A lizard called the anole is closely related to the chameleon. There are more than 225 species of anoles; they are often called American chameleons.

Only two species of lizards are venomous, with poison glands (in the lower jaw) opening at the base of grooved teeth. These are the Gila monster *(Heloderma suspectum)* and the beaded lizard *(Heloderma horridum),* both of which live in North America.

The snakes, however, contain most of the poisonous reptilian species, although the majority of species are harmless. Venomous species are classed in two main groups—vipers and elapids—according to the position and construction of the fangs. Vipers include rattlesnakes, *(Crotalus* spp.), the adder, and the asp *(Vipera aspis).* When their mouth is opened, the fangs swing down and forward. Elapids include the cobras, mambas, and kraits, in which the front fangs are fixed. Most venomous snakes are front-fanged, but some are rear-fanged. The snakes in the family Boidae, such as the boa constrictor and the pythons (Pythoninae), kill their prey by crushing it.

Unlike lizards, snakes are limbless, although some, such as the boas, have rudimentary hind legs. The tail cannot be regenerated when lost, and the transparent eyelids are fused together to form a protective covering. In addition, most snakes are able to dislocate their jaws, enabling them to swallow prey considerably larger than themselves.

Crocodilians

All the members of the order Crocodilia—crocodiles, alligators, caymans, and gavials—are large amphibious reptiles. Crocodilians use their long, vertically-flattened tail for swimming; their webbed feet are usually kept tucked in at the sides of the body. The ears, eyes, and nostrils are located high on the head, so that the animal can remain virtually hidden under the water and at the same time can hear, see, and breathe. When a crocodilian is totally submerged the eyes are covered by a membrane, and the ears and nostrils are

The venomous snakes are grouped into three families according to the position of their fangs. The Elapidae contain front-fanged snakes, whose fangs are fixed, such as cobras and mambas. The Viperidae also contain front-fanged snakes, such as vipers and adders *(Vipera* spp.), but these snakes have long fangs on a rotating maxillary plate that lie against the palate when the mouth is closed. As they open their mouth, the fangs swing down and forward. Some venomous snakes, such as rat snakes *(Elaphe* spp.), have one to three grooved fangs on the upper jaw in the rear of the mouth. The poison runs down the groove in the teeth and is injected into the victim when the snake bites it.

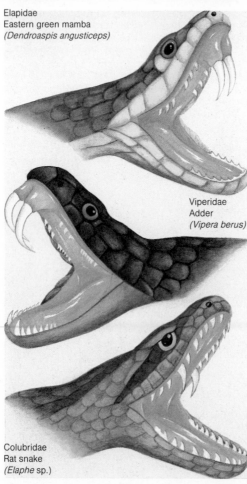

Elapidae
Eastern green mamba
(Dendroaspis angusticeps)

Viperidae
Adder
(Vipera berus)

Colubridae
Rat snake
(Elaphe sp.)

closed by special valves. In addition, a fold of skin shuts off the windpipe so that the animal can open its mouth under water without drowning.

Crocodilians are carnivorous and adults prey on large animals—caught either underwater or on land—occasionally as large as a horse. The prey is eaten whole or first torn apart and then eaten. Large prey is often stored under water until it is sufficiently rotted to be torn apart by the powerful teeth; but since their jaws do not move from side to side, crocodiles often resort to twisting their whole bodies in an effort to detach a piece of flesh from a carcass.

The single species, the false gavial *(Gavialis gangeticus)* makes up the family Gavialidae. Found in India, Bangladesh, Burma, and Pakistan, it is distinguished by its long, thin snout and rather bulbous head. The family Crocodylidae comprises all the other members of the order. These include the Nile crocodile, found widely in Africa; the mugger, which lives in India and Pakistan; and the American crocodile *(Crocodylus acutus),* which occurs in the southeastern United States, south to Ecuador. As in most other crocodilians, the bony plates occur only on the back and tail.

The American alligator and the Chinese alligator are the only two species of alligators. They were once much hunted for their skins and are quite scarce, although in some areas of the United States they are now protected. The caymans of Central and South America are closely related to alligators but are quicker moving. They are mainly distinguished by the scutes, which cover both the upper and lower body.

The tuatara

The tuatara is the only surviving member of the order Rhynchocephalia, a group of reptiles that flourished more than 200 million years ago. This lizardlike animal is found only on a few islands off the coast of New Zealand. It preys on insects and other invertebrates and inhabits the burrows of sea birds such as shearwaters and petrels. It becomes active at night and seems able to function at lower temperatures than most reptiles.

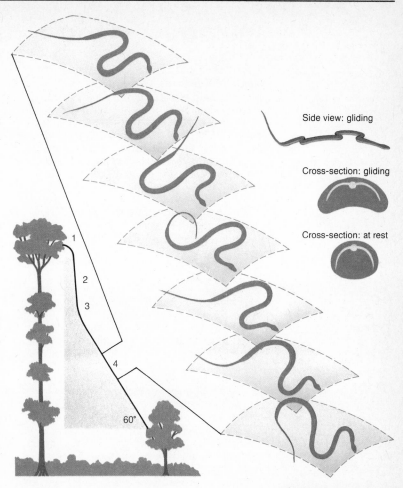

Side view: gliding

Cross-section: gliding

Cross-section: at rest

The flying snake (*Chrysopelea* sp.) glides by projecting itself from a tree (1), falling (2) for several feet while concaving its lower surface (3), and undulating its body in a series of tight S-curves (4) to gain some lift to slow the descent.

Crocodilian teeth are sharp and cone-shaped. In the crocodiles, a tooth on each side of the lower jaw fits into a pit in the upper jaw. This pit is open on one side, and the tooth protrudes when the mouth is closed, giving the characteristic "crocodile smile." One of the most surprising feats, then, is that after the young crocodiles have hatched, the mother carries them gently to safety in her mouth.

Introduction to birds

Birds are relative newcomers to the animal kingdom. The earliest fossil definitely recognizable as a bird, *Archaeopteryx,* lived about 150 to 130 million years ago, during the Jurassic Period. It inhabited a world dominated by cold-blooded reptiles, including the pterosaurs, which evolved powered flight at about the same time but became extinct toward the end of the Cretaceous Period, about 70 million years ago.

The fossil record of birds is very incomplete—their fragile bones and feathers have not preserved well. A mere 850 or so fossil species are known, only a tenth of the number of species alive today. After *Archaeopteryx,* of which a few specimens and a single feather have been found, the next fossil birds come from the Cretaceous Period. *Hesperornis* was a waterbird that lost the power of flight. *Ichthyornis* was a flying seabird that probably had teeth, like *Archaeopteryx.* The first representatives of the modern families of birds did not appear until the Eocene Period, between 65 and 40 million years ago, and species alive today emerged during the Pliocene, between 13 and 2 million years ago.

The key to the success of birds lay in their development of feathers and flight, and of warm-bloodedness. They have now conquered every habitat, from polar ice to tropical deserts. Some have also adapted to life on the water, conquering three environments—something no other vertebrates have been able to do. Several groups of birds have lost the power of flight and developed large size and strong legs to escape enemies.

The lightest skeleton

The bird skeleton is built on the same basic plan as that of other vertebrates, but it is extensively modified for flight. The whole skeleton has become extremely light. The teeth have been replaced by a lightweight horny bill. Many of the bones, like those of the skull, are very thin, whereas others—such as the limb bones—have a honeycomb structure, being hollow with thin internal struts for strength with rigidity and lightness.

The vertebrae in the backbone near the pelvic girdle are fused together to form the synsacrum, which provides firm support for the legs and cushions the bird against the shock of landing. To make up for this rigidity, the neck is extremely flexible, with many more vertebrae (up to 28) than in the neck of a mammal (with only 7).

Although the basic structure of the limb bones is on the general vertebrate plan, they show significant modifications. The femur (thighbone) is normally hidden because it is held up close to the body beneath the feathers. What looks like the thigh of a bird is really the tibiotarsus, formed from the fused shinbones. The equivalent to our shins is provided by the elongated and fused bones of the ankle and feet, forming the tarsometatarsus. Birds walk on their toes. There are usually four of these, each equipped with a claw. The arrangement of tendons and muscles in a perching bird ensures that when it perches, bending its legs, the toes are automatically pulled inward and the foot grasps the perch tightly—even when the bird is asleep.

The collarbones (clavicles) are fused into a V-shape—the furcula, or wishbone. Together with the coracoids (shoulder blades) they form the pectoral girdle; this structure prevents the ribs from being crushed by the powerful wing muscles, which may make up as much as 30 per cent of a bird's weight. The pectoral girdle is attached firmly to the breastbone, or sternum, which is large and keel-shaped, providing a strong anchorage for the wing muscles.

The forelimbs have been modified to form the wings, which articulate with the pectoral girdle. The humerus, the bone of the upper arm, is short and stout and has a large surface area for the attachment of the flight muscles from the sternum. The ulna of the forearm is flattened to accommodate the secondary flight feathers. There are only two wrist bones and three hand bones, two of which are fused together. There are three finger bones; the primary wing feathers are attached to the first of these. A flat membrane of skin on each side of the wing bones, together with the long flight feathers, gives a broad surface to create lift and power.

Unique breathing system

A bird's lungs are connected by tubes to numerous thin-walled air sacs. These can form one-tenth of the volume of the body, spreading into the spaces between the muscles, body organs, and even the hollow bones. The single-direction airflow system allows the bird to extract oxygen from the air even at high altitudes where oxygen is in short supply—some

A reconstruction of *Archaeopteryx,* a prehistoric bird that lived about 140 million years ago, reveals that it had teeth and clawed fingers on the front of its wings. Feathers fringed its long tail, and it was probably capable only of short, clumsy flights from tree to tree. Since that time, birds have continued to evolve and adapt, so that today their representatives occupy nearly every terrestrial and semiaquatic habitat on earth. But above all, they have conquered the air.

birds fly at 25,000 feet (7,625 meters).

Digestive system

Unlike almost all mammals, birds have no teeth and so cannot chew their food. The digestive system features a thin-walled, highly extensible crop at the base of the gullet, where food is stored and moistened. The food then starts to be broken down by enzymes in the first part of the stomach. The second part of

the stomach is modified to form a thick-walled muscular gizzard, which grinds up the food, sometimes with the aid of swallowed grit, before it is passed on to the rest of the digestive system.

Both the digestive and reproductive systems open into one chamber, called the cloaca, with a single opening (the vent). Birds rid themselves of waste in the form of solid uric acid—liquid urine would involve losing too much water.

The red-tailed hawk *(Buteo jamaicensis)* is found in North and Central America. Belonging to the buzzard family, the red-tailed hawk is a superb flier and accomplished hunter, and in many ways represents the pinnacle of bird evolution.

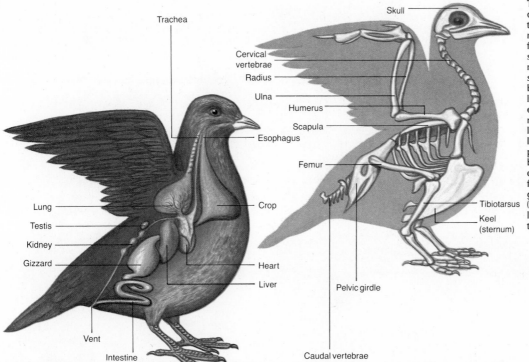

Trachea

Cervical
vertebrae

Radius

Ulna

Humerus

Scapula

Esophagus

Femur

Lung

Testis

Kidney

Gizzard

Crop

Heart

Liver

Vent

Intestine

Skull

Tibiotarsus

Keel
(sternum)

Pelvic girdle

Caudal vertebrae

The skeleton of a bird is designed for lightness and to provide adequate attachment points for the powerful flight muscles. The main supporting structure is fairly rigid, brought about by fusion of some of the vertebrae in the spine. Nevertheless, the whole skeleton is extremely light, because nearly all the bones are hollow. The internal organs follow the broad vertebrate plan, except that in many birds the digestive tract includes a crop, in which hard food is ground or predigested. The urinary tracts (from the kidneys) and the lower intestinal tract come together in the cloaca.

Classification of birds

There are more than 8,600 species of birds alive today, compared with only about 4,000 species of mammals. Apart from the nocturnal species, most are fairly easy to observe. Probably for this reason, bird watching is an increasingly popular pastime. As a guide to the enormous variety in the world of birds, this article outlines the makeup of each of the living orders—although not all taxonomists agree on the exact family groupings that constitute separate orders.

The orders of birds

Birds (class Aves) are classified into two subclasses, Archeornithes (containing the extinct *Archeopteryx*) and Neornithes (containing all other birds). The Neornithes consists of four superorders: Odontognathae, extinct toothed birds; Ichthyornithes, also extinct; Neognathae and Impennes containing all other birds, generally arranged in 28 orders (including some extinct orders), subdivided into 158 families. These orders are described in the summaries that follow. The classification is based only on anatomy, behavior, and life history. Recently, new techniques of analyzing and comparing proteins (albumins) in egg white and examining parasites have led to changes in groupings.

Order Struthioniformes. The ostrich, the largest living bird, is the single species in this order. It is a large, fast-running, flightless bird, found today in the wild only in Africa. Several other groups of birds have also evolved a flightless life style, an example of convergent evolution. All have breastbones that have lost the keel, because there is no longer any need for attachment of flight muscles. Together with the ostrich, they are known as the ratites (from the Latin *ratis,* a raft, referring to the flat breastbone), separated from all other birds, which are called carinates (from the Latin *carina,* a keel). Their wings are very small, and the feathers are loose and fluffy like the down feathers of young birds. They have strong, stout legs for fast running.

Other ratites include the emu of Australia and the cassowaries of Australia and New Guinea (all in the order **Casuariiformes**); the kiwis (order **Apterygiformes**) of New Zealand; and the rheas (order **Rheiformes**) of South America. The two extinct orders, the moas (order **Dinornithiformes**) of New Zealand and the elephant birds (order **Aepyornithiformes**) of Madagascar were also ratites.

Order Tinamiformes. The tinamous are a group of about 50 species of beautifully camouflaged birds that superficially resemble game birds, but are probably related to the rheas. They are restricted to South and Central America.

Order Sphenisciformes. The penguins are found only in the Southern Hemisphere, ranging from near the South Pole to the Galapagos Islands on the Equator. Like the ratites, they have abandoned flight. Superbly adapted for fast underwater swimming, their wings have become stiff flippers, their bodies are stocky and their feet webbed. They eat fishes, squids, and crustaceans and generally breed in huge colonies.

Order Gaviiformes. The divers or loons are a primitive group of five species of water birds

Struthioniformes
Ostrich
Struthio camelus

Rheiformes
Common rhea
Rhea americana

Apterygiformes
Brown kiwi
Apteryx australis

Casuariiformes
Emu
Dromaius novaehollandiae

Tinamiformes
Crested tinamou
Eudromia elegans

Sphenisciformes
Magellan penguin
Spheniscus magellanicus

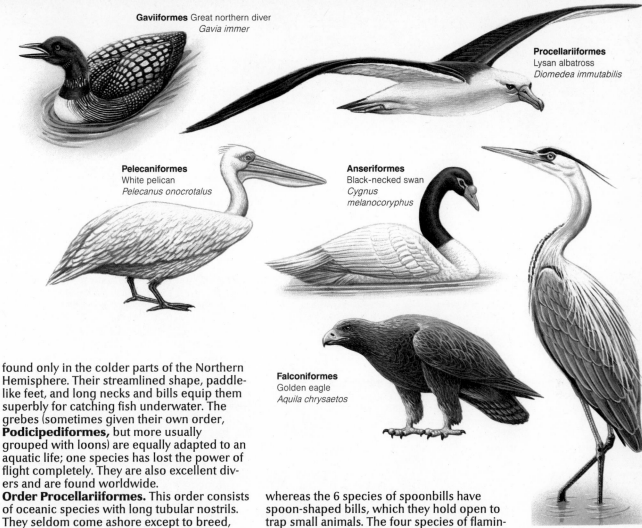

Gaviiformes Great northern diver
Gavia immer

Procellariiformes
Lysan albatross
Diomedea immutabilis

Pelecaniformes
White pelican
Pelecanus onocrotalus

Anseriformes
Black-necked swan
Cygnus melanocoryphus

Falconiformes
Golden eagle
Aquila chrysaetos

Ciconiiformes
Blue heron
Ardea herodias

found only in the colder parts of the Northern Hemisphere. Their streamlined shape, paddle-like feet, and long necks and bills equip them superbly for catching fish underwater. The grebes (sometimes given their own order, **Podicipediformes,** but more usually grouped with loons) are equally adapted to an aquatic life; one species has lost the power of flight completely. They are also excellent divers and are found worldwide.

Order Procellariiformes. This order consists of oceanic species with long tubular nostrils. They seldom come ashore except to breed, and all have webbed feet. Their hooked, plated bills are adapted to deal with a diet of squids, fishes, and other marine animals. Best known are the large albatrosses, among the most impressive fliers in the bird kingdom. Other families are the shearwaters, petrels, and storm petrels; and the diving petrels, which have come to resemble the northern auks closely by a process of convergent evolution.

Order Pelecaniformes. A group of large, fish-eating waterbirds, they are the only birds with all four toes webbed. The pelicans are recognizable by their huge bills and highly extensible throat pouches for scooping fish out of the water. The other families are the gannets, or boobies, which dive vertically into the sea for fish from a height of 100 feet (30 meters) or more; the tropic birds, graceful sea birds with long tail streamers; the 30 or so species of cormorants and shags, which are long-necked, long-billed mainly black diving birds; the anhingas, or darters, which have long, snakelike necks and bodies; and the frigate birds, soarers that frequently pirate food from other sea birds.

Order Ciconiiformes. This order consists of large, long-legged wading birds. The 50 or so species of herons, egrets, and bitterns have daggerlike bills for spearing fish and other prey, as do the 16 species of storks. The 30 species of ibises have slender, downcurved bills with sensitive tips for probing in mud, whereas the 6 species of spoonbills have spoon-shaped bills, which they hold open to trap small animals. The four species of flamingos live in the tropics, and spend their entire life near lakes, marshes, and seas. Their remarkable hooked bills are equipped with comblike plates that strain out tiny organisms from the water pumped through them by the fleshy tongue; the birds hold their heads upside-down in the water to feed.

Order Anseriformes. The swans, geese, and ducks are included in this order, which contains more than 150 species. Predominantly aquatic, they range in size from the mute swan, at 33 pounds (15 kilograms) one of the heaviest flying birds, to the tiny ringed teal, weighing only 10.5 ounces (300 grams). The feet are webbed, and the bill typically is broad and flattened, with fine plates at the edges for straining food from the water. They breed on every continent and major island except for Antarctica.

Order Falconiformes. This order comprises the birds of prey. A large order with almost 300 species, it includes the carrion-eating vultures and condors. All Falconiformes have powerful, sharp, hooked beaks for tearing flesh, and strong feet armed with sharp talons with which they catch their prey. They hunt by day, using their keen eyesight. Some, like the vultures, kites, typical eagles, and buzzards, use soaring or slow flapping flight to spot their prey on the ground. Others, like the falcons, are fast fliers, catching birds and insects on the wing. Still others are specialized for a diet of fish, snakes, snails, and even fruit.

Galliformes
Spruce grouse
Canachites canadensis

Gruiformes
Crowned crane
Balearica pavonina

Columbiformes
White-winged dove
Zenaida asiatica

Charadriiformes
American oystercatcher
Haematopus palliatus

Psittaciformes
Rainbow lorikeet
Trichoglossus haematodus

Order Galliformes. Game birds belong to this order. The 10 species of megapodes, confined to Australia and Indonesia, are medium-sized brownish birds that build huge mounds of soil and vegetation in which they place their eggs to incubate in the heat produced by fermentation. The 18 species of grouse inhabit the temperate and Arctic regions of the Northern Hemisphere. Growing to about the size of a large chicken, they are plump with short bills and legs. There are some 35 species of pheasants, including the red jungle fowl of southern Asia and the East Indies—the ancestor of the domestic hen—the peacock and the smaller partridges and quails. The seven species of guinea fowl live in open country in Africa; and the two species of turkeys are found in the woodlands of North and Central America.

Order Gruiformes. These are ground-nesting, ground-feeding birds. Many are poor fliers, although the migratory cranes are a striking exception. Large, long-legged, and ranging in color from white to dark gray and brown, the 15 species of cranes have long secondary wing feathers drooping down over the tail. Some have ornamental crowns or tufts of feathers on their heads, used in their spectacular mating dances. They inhabit marshy areas in Europe, Asia, North America, and Australia. The rails are among the most widespread of all land birds, found on all continents and very successful at colonizing remote oceanic islands. Most island rails have become flightless. They range in size from species little larger than a sparrow to birds as big as a duck. There are about 130 species of rails. They have long, narrow bodies, short wings and tails, long legs and toes, and include the aquatic coots and gallinules.

Order Charadriiformes. This order consists of the waders, gulls, and their relatives, typically found on or near seacoasts and fresh water. The waders are a huge group of over 200 species, ranging from the crow-sized oystercatchers and larger curlews to the medium-sized plovers and diminutive stints. Most are long-legged, and many have long bills for probing for food in mud. The skuas are dark plumaged gull-like sea birds with webbed feet and most have elongated central tail feathers. They feed on fish, small mammals, birds and their eggs and also chase gulls, terns, and other birds, forcing them to

disgorge their food. There are five or six species. The gulls are a successful and wide-ranging group. There are 43 species, from the large great black-backed gull—30 inches (75 centimeters)—to the little gull—10 inches (25 centimeters). They are typically grayish or brownish when immature and gray-and-white or black-and-white as adults. Most gulls are coastal, but some live inland; many have expanded their range dramatically, benefiting from food thrown away by humans. Terns are slender white, gray-and-white, black, or black-and-white sea birds with short legs, webbed feet, and long pointed bills; they are found worldwide. The auks are short-winged black-and-white diving birds restricted to the northern oceans. Although they can fly, they are most at home in the water, and are the northern equivalent of the penguins, also nesting in huge colonies. Size ranges from the tiny little auk—6 inches (15 centimeters)—to the extinct great auk—30 inches (75 centimeters). The 22 living species include the familiar puffins.

Order Columbiformes. This order contains the pigeons and their allies, including the extinct dodo. The pigeons and doves (300 species) are found throughout the world, except for Antarctica. They live on seeds, fruits, and berries. They are able to drink by a suction action without lifting their heads from the water.

Order Psittaciformes. These are the parrots, the approximately 315 species of which are mainly restricted to the tropics. Varying in size from 3 inches (8 centimeters) to over 3 feet (91 centimeters) long, most are mainly green, although some are brilliantly colored and many have long tails and stout, short, strongly-hooked bills adapted for dealing with fruits, berries, and seeds.

Order Cuculiformes. This order includes the 19 species of brightly colored touracos from the jungles of Africa and the cuckoos, some of which are parasitic breeders. They lay their eggs in the nests of other birds and allow them to rear their young. More than 100 species of cuckoo are distributed worldwide.

Order Strigiformes. Most of the approximately 525 kinds of owls are nocturnal birds of prey, with large eyes at the front of their heads, hooked flesh-tearing bills, razor-sharp talons, and dense, soft plumage, making them almost noiseless in flight. They are subdivided into the 10 species of barn and bay owls (fam-

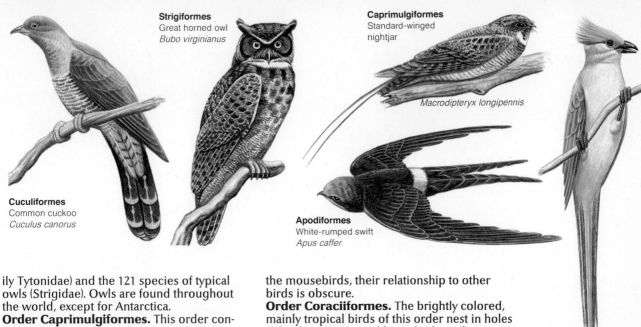

Strigiformes
Great horned owl
Bubo virginianus

Caprimulgiformes
Standard-winged
nightjar
Macrodipteryx longipennis

Cuculiformes
Common cuckoo
Cuculus canorus

Apodiformes
White-rumped swift
Apus caffer

Coliiformes
Blue-naped mousebird
Colius macrourus

ily Tytonidae) and the 121 species of typical owls (Strigidae). Owls are found throughout the world, except for Antarctica.

Order Caprimulgiformes. This order contains about 95 species of nightjars (sometimes called goatsuckers) and their relatives, found worldwide except for Antarctica. Nocturnal birds related to owls, they have long, pointed wings and bills fringed with bristles for trapping flying insects.

Order Apodiformes. All the members of this order are exceptional fliers with pointed, slender but powerful wings and tiny feet that are useless for walking. The swifts are the most aerial of all birds, able to sustain flight for many hours. The 75 or so species are found virtually throughout the world. All of the more than 300 known species of hummingbirds live in the Western Hemisphere. Beating their wings as fast as 70 times per second, hummingbirds can hover and even fly backwards. Most are tiny and the largest is only the size of a sparrow. They feed on nectar and insects.

Order Coliiformes. This order consists of the single family of coly or mousebirds. All six species are African and are small birds with very long, stiff tails and prominent crests.

Order Trogoniformes. This order contains the brightly colored tree-dwelling tropical trogons, which have unusually delicate skins. Like the mousebirds, their relationship to other birds is obscure.

Order Coraciiformes. The brightly colored, mainly tropical birds of this order nest in holes in banks or trees, and have the front three toes partly joined. They include the 87 species of kingfishers, 8 species of motmots, approximately 25 species of bee-eaters, 16 species of rollers, and 8 species of wood hoopoes and hoopoes, as well as the 44 species of huge-billed hornbills.

Order Piciformes. Birds in this order have feet with two toes pointing forward and two backward; they include the approximately 200 species of woodpeckers, which are specialized for feeding and nesting in tree trunks, and about 40 species of fruit-eating toucans of the tropical rain forests of Central and South America.

Order Passeriformes. This order, the perching birds, is the biggest group of all, containing more than a third of all living families and over half the living species. All have feet adapted to perching on or clinging to branches or other supports. The order includes the "song birds" which have developed the ability to sing to the highest degree. It also contains the swallows, wagtails and pipits, wrens, thrushes, warblers, tits, finches, weavers, and sparrows, starlings, and crows.

Trogoniformes
White-tailed trogon
Trogon viridis

Coraciiformes
Common kingfisher
Alcedo atthis

Piciformes
Ivory-billed
woodpecker
*Campephilus
principalis*

Passeriformes
Wood thrush
*Hylocichla
mustelina*

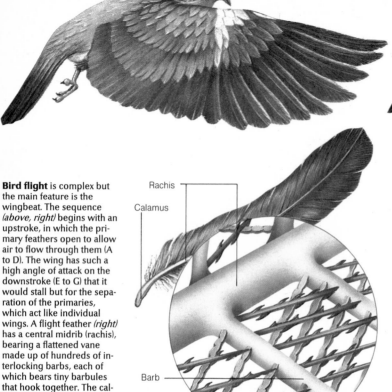

Bird flight is complex but the main feature is the wingbeat. The sequence *(above, right)* begins with an upstroke, in which the primary feathers open to allow air to flow through them (A to D). The wing has such a high angle of attack on the downstroke (E to G) that it would stall but for the separation of the primaries, which act like individual wings. A flight feather *(right)* has a central midrib (rachis), bearing a flattened vane made up of hundreds of interlocking barbs, each of which bears tiny barbules that hook together. The calamus, located at the base of the rachis, is hollow, thus allowing for the passage of nutrients to the feather.

Rachis

Calamus

Barb

Barbule

Physical characteristics of birds

The two factors that set birds as a class apart from nearly all other vertebrates are feathers and flight. Only bats, which are mammals, are also capable of powered flight. Feathers provide insulation and the lifting surface of the wings. The mobility provided by flight has enabled birds to spread and establish themselves in nearly every habitat on earth.

Feathers

Evolved from the scales of their reptilian ancestors, bird feathers are made of the same basic material—the protein keratin—as their horny bills and the scales on their legs. Each feather develops from a knob (papilla) within a feather socket, or follicle. The follicles are arranged in distinct areas called feather tracts over the bird's body. Each follicle produces one, two or even three sets of feathers every year.

There are two main types of feathers—pennae and plumulae. The pennae are the flight and contour feathers. The flight feathers (primaries and secondaries) are directly concerned with flight, whereas the contour feathers have several functions. They give the bird

its streamlined shape, helping it to cut through the air efficiently. They also provide vital insulation; heat is retained by the layer of air trapped close to the skin by the feathers. During hot weather, a bird opens up its contour feathers to allow heat to escape, and in cold weather it fluffs them up to increase the insulating layer of air.

Another function of feathers is to waterproof the bird. They are also the main source of the bird's color, whether for camouflage or for species recognition, sexual display or as warning signals.

The plumulae are the down feathers. They lie beneath the contour feathers, providing extra insulation, and are the only feathers on a newly hatched chick. All other feathers are intermediate between or derived from the two basic types. Down feathers are much simpler than pennae, with a very short midrib and no barbules, so that the barbs are separate, giving them their fluffiness.

The number of feathers varies considerably from one species to another; usually, the larger the bird, the more feathers it has. For example, the tiny hummingbirds may have fewer than 1,000 whereas a large swan may have more than 25,000. The number of feathers also differs from one season to another.

Feathers are subject to great stress, and wear out. All birds molt at least once a year, many twice and some even three times. Most birds molt their feathers gradually, so there is no interference with flight; but ducks, for example, lose all their flight feathers at once (during an eclipse period), when they are flightless and vulnerable.

Despite their proverbial lightness, all the feathers on a bird are, surprisingly, often heavier than its incredibly light, hollow-boned skeleton. In the bald eagle *(Haliaeetus leucocephalus),* for instance, which weighs about 9 pounds (4,000 grams), the feathers account for more than 1.5 pounds (670 grams) but the skeleton for only about 6 ounces (270 grams).

The shapes of birds' bills reflect adaptations for dealing with different types of food. The strong hooked bills of cormorants and eagles tear the flesh of their prey, whereas those of macaws and toucans crack nuts and deal with fruit. A gull's "all-purpose" bill suits its role as a scavenger, and a duck uses its flattened bill to strain food from the water. A blue tit's short bill catches insects and grubs, whereas the extremely long narrow bill of the hummingbird allows it to reach the nectar deep inside tubular flowers.

Flight

Bird flight is governed by the same laws of aerodynamics that control all heavier-than-air flight. There are two opposing forces involved: lift, the upward force that keeps the bird airborne, and drag, the force of the air opposing lift, which is to a great extent the result of air turbulence at the wingtips.

A bird's wing is curved in cross section, rounded above and hollow below, and with the leading edge thicker than the trailing edge—a shape that produces maximum lift. The convex upper surface causes the air flowing over it to travel faster than the air flowing past the undersurface. As a result, the pressure on the underside of the wing is greater than that on the upper surface, producing lift.

The angle the wing makes with the horizontal is called the angle of attack. There is an optimum angle for flight, at which upward lift counteracts the forces of gravity and of drag. The greater the angle of attack, the more the airflow over the wing becomes turbulent, and the more the bird is likely to stall.

Powered bird flight is very complex, and not yet fully understood. The highly flexible primary feathers of the wingtips twist, acting almost like a propeller to produce the forward thrust that drives the bird through the air. The wingtips move faster than the rest of the wing. The main function of the secondary feathers is to provide lift; they move very little as the wing beats. Slow-flying birds, such as herons and eagles, are often in danger of stalling and have large wing slots formed by the separation of the alula, or bastard wing, at the front of the wing. The frequency of wingbeats varies greatly, from about two beats per second in a swan to 50 or more per second in a hummingbird.

To alter the direction of flight, a bird increases the angle of attack of one wing, or beats that wing faster, creating a difference in lift on the two sides of its body. Movements of the tail are also used. To land as gently as possible and minimize the shock to its body, a bird must be on the point of stalling. To achieve this, it pushes its body downward and spreads its wings and tail.

Flight speeds of birds also vary, although typical speeds are between 20 and 35 miles (32 and 56 kilometers) per hour. The fastest bird is probably the peregrine falcon *(Falco peregrinus)*, which dives on its prey at speeds of 180 miles (290 kilometers) per hour or more.

Some birds save energy by gliding instead of flapping their wings. Vultures, for instance, use their long, broad wings to soar in thermals (rising currents of warm air). Albatrosses, with long, narrow wings, tack back and forth low over the waves, using the updrafts produced by the friction of the air with the water to stay aloft.

Hovering in midair, a tiny ruby-throated hummingbird *(Archilocus colubris)* uses its long bill to feed on nectar from sage flowers. The wings beat at more than 70 times a second, requiring its heart to beat 600 times a minute and using five times as much oxygen (per ounce of body weight) than a larger, slow-flying bird.

Blue-eyed cormorant
Phalacrocorax atriceps

Golden eagle

Aquila chrysaetos

Shellduck
Tadorna tadorna

Herring gull
Larus argentatus

Blue tit
Parus caeruleus

Blue-and-yellow macaw
Ara ararauna

Sword-billed hummingbird
Ensifera ensifera

Keel-billed Toucan
Ramphastos sulfuratus

Breeding and behavior in birds

In a courtship display, a male great frigate bird *(Fregata minor)* spreads his wings and inflates his conspicuous scarlet throat-sac. After mating, the female lays a single white egg, which she incubates for six to seven weeks. The young is dependent on its parents for food for at least six months (and sometimes as long as ten), spending the first four or five months in the nest.

Most birds breed within a definite territory, an area that they defend against rivals. In many perching birds, it is about an acre in extent; but in large birds of prey—which obtain food far less frequently over a much wider area—it may be as much as 30 square miles (75 square kilometers) in area. Territory helps birds to survive by parceling out the available habitat into areas capable of supporting a pair of birds, allowing them to feed and breed there.

Courtship

Birds recognize potential mates of the same species and breed with them following courtship. A male and female form a pair bond after a series of courtship displays by the male and a favorable response from the female, which is often another display. The type of courtship behavior varies, as does the type of pair bond formed. Many birds are monogamous and establish lasting bonds, but others are polygamous, successful dominant males mating with several females.

A vital part of bird displays is the emphasis on the colors and patterns that distinguish a particular bird from otherwise similar species. Where several closely related species coexist, the plumage of the males tends to be distinctive, differing strikingly between species (as with ducks of the Northern Hemisphere). On the other hand, in areas with only one species (as with single species of finches on an oceanic island) the plumage can be quite nondescript. In places where birds of different species that look very similar do coexist, as they do with the virtually indistinguishable willow warbler *(Phylloscpus trochilus)* and chiffchaff *(P. collybita)* of European and Asian woodlands, their songs identify the birds.

Another important function of courtship is to encourage the male and female to reduce territorial hostility and accept each other as mates—a process that may take several weeks. For example, the male European robin *(Erithacus rubecula)* sings at the boundaries of his territory, both to warn off rival males and

to attract potential mates. Sooner or later, his song encourages a female to approach him. The male first responds by adopting a threat display, using his red breast as a "flag" to discourage the intruder, just as he would if a rival male was involved. A rival male would either return the threat or flee. But the female does neither, adopting a submissive posture instead. This gradually encourages the male to accept her in his territory, and eventually to mate, nest, and rear a family.

Unlike the robin, some male birds do not display in an individual territory, but come together at communal display grounds, or leks. Game birds, such as the American grouse *(Centrocerus urophasianus)* or the capercaillie *(Tetrao urogallus)* of northern European and Asian coniferous forests, and certain waders, such as ruffs *(Philomachus pugnax),* and birds of paradise *(Paradisaea* sp.), all have leks. The females go there only to pair and mate and take no part in the display, leaving this entirely to the gaudy males.

Not all birds have displays in which the male performs or sings and the female takes on a submissive role. Many species have courtship rituals that involve both partners equally—examples are the strange, complex dances of grebes *(Podiceps* sp.), the elaborate bill-scissoring displays of some albatrosses *(Diomedea* sp.), and the wild dances of many cranes *(Grus* sp.).

Displacement activities

Detailed study of courtship ceremonies has shown that they are usually modified and highly stylized versions of everyday actions, such as preparing for flight, preening, drinking, or feeding. Courtship is a tense period, involving the conflicting emotions of aggression, fear, and the sex drive. A bird may therefore indulge in ritualized behavior that alternates between a desire to flee and a desire to approach the mate—the "fight or flight" situation.

If the conflict is great enough, as when a female behaves aggressively toward a male, the bird may show "irrelevant" behavior, such as beak-wiping; this is called displacement activity. In many birds, displacement activities have become ritualized and form an important part of their courtship display. Other courtship ceremonies originate from the behavior of young birds; for example, female finches and many other birds flutter their wings and beg food from the male before mating.

Mating

Successful copulation, resulting in fertilization of the egg or eggs, depends on the full cooperation of the female; unlike mammals, most male birds do not have a penis. Sperm is transferred from the cloaca of the male to that of his mate. To encourage better contact between them, the female sticks out her cloaca, as well as moving her tail to one side.

Mating takes place mainly during the time when the female is carrying unfertilized eggs. The single egg of the Emperor penguin *(Aptenodytes fosteri)* needs only one fertilization, whereas birds such as songbirds, which lay several eggs, may involve several fertilizations over a period of time.

Nests and nesting

Birds vary enormously in their choice of nest sites, nesting materials, and methods of nest construction. Some penguins and the auks, for instance, build no nest at all. The Emperor penguin incubates its single egg on its feet—where it is warmed by a feathered flap of belly skin—for nine weeks of subzero temperatures and perpetual darkness during the Antarctic winter. Most waders nest in a slight hollow on bare ground, generally lining the hollow with gravel or a few twigs. Some species of gannets, auks, and gulls nest on virtually inaccessible seacliffs where they are safe from mam-

mal predators. The eggs of guillemots (auks), which nest on particularly perilous ledges, are pear-shaped and as a result they roll around in circles instead of over the edge of the cliff.

Many birds, such as owls, woodpeckers, and hornbills, nest in holes in trees; kingfishers, some swallows, and bee-eaters nest in holes in sandy banks. Such birds generally lay white eggs, since there is no need for camouflage in these situations. Others, such as herons, crows, and many birds of prey, nest high up in tall trees, building strong, bulky nests of branches and large twigs. Some of the cave swiftlets *(Collocalia* sp.) of Asia build nests of their saliva alone, which they glue to the walls or roofs of caves; these are the nests collected for making birds' nest soup.

The role of the sexes in nest-building varies greatly. In most birds, both male and female are involved, but in finches and hummingbirds, among others, the female does most of

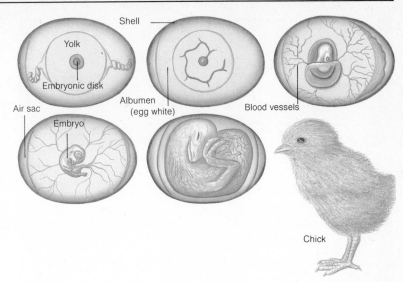

Chick

Development of a bird embryo takes place within the egg during incubation. Most nutrients are contained in the yolk, with calcium (for bones) coming from the shell, which becomes porous and allows the passage of gases, such as oxygen and carbon dioxide.

Contrasts in nest-building are demonstrated by herons and weaverbirds. The great blue heron *(Ardea herodias, left)* lives in Canada and the United States and builds ragged nests of twigs in colonies perched on tall trees and buildings. The black swamp weaver *(Amblyospiza albifrons, right)* builds a delicate nest in reeds by interlacing lengths of grass to form a globular home with an entrance near the top.

Camouflaged coloration is a significant feature of ground-nesting birds and their eggs. During the breeding season, the speckled back plumage of the golden plover *(Pluvialis apricaria)* makes it almost invisible.

A small dunnock, or hedge sparrow *(Prunella modularis),* tries to keep up with the voracious appetite of its enormous "offspring," a cuckoo *(Cuculus canorus),* which has tipped the dunnock's own eggs out of the nest.

the work. In some, such as weaverbirds, the males are the nest-builders.

Eggs and egg laying

After the male's sperm has fertilized the egg in the female's ovary, the egg—now consisting of an ovum (egg cell) plus the yolk—moves down the oviduct. It is covered first by the jellylike "egg white," or albumen, then by two shell membranes, and finally by the shell itself, which consists of several layers covered by a thin cuticle. The pigments that give the egg its color are laid down mainly in the cuticle and outer shell layers. Mixtures of just two basic pigments, red-brown and blue-green, give eggs their great range of colors and patterns. White eggs contain no pigments.

Eggs vary in shape from the almost spherical eggs of owls and kingfishers to the long, pointed eggs of swifts, waders, and guillemots. They also vary enormously in size, from the tiny eggs of hummingbirds (as small as half

an inch long and only 0.2 ounce in weight) to the huge ones of ostriches—8 inches (20 centimeters) and 3 pounds (1.4 kilograms).

Unlike those of fishes and amphibians, the eggs of birds are adapted to allow the embryo to develop on dry land. A bird's egg is a closed system. The large yolk feeds the growing embryo and there is built-in protection in the form of the tough shell, which is porous, allowing air to pass in for the embryo to breathe and letting out excess water. The chick excretes uric acid, which is insoluble and does not dissolve in the body fluids and cause harm. This waste is secreted into the baglike allantois, which is left behind in the shell after hatching.

Incubation

Unless the eggs are kept at a relatively high temperature—about 102° F. (39° C), the chicks will not survive. Responding to hormones, most birds develop naked brood-patches on their abdomen, well supplied with blood vessels, to transfer their body heat to the eggs. Among most species, only the female sits on the eggs. In some birds, both sexes share the task of incubation. In a few, such as cassowaries and the emu, only the male incubates. The Australasian megapodes (brush turkeys, *Leipoa* sp.) do not brood; instead, they build huge mounds of decomposing vegetation that generates enough heat to incubate and hatch the eggs.

Hatching

The chick breaks out of its protective prison by chipping out a series of holes in the middle of the shell with an egg tooth at the end of its upper bill, then cracking it open by pushing in opposite directions with its head and feet.

Chicks are of two basic types. Precocial chicks can walk from the nest within a few hours or days of hatching; some, such as the chicks of plovers, find all their own food from the start. They are well equipped with strong legs and a covering of warm down feathers, their eyes are open, and they are usually superbly camouflaged against predators. Examples of this first type are the young of wild fowl, game birds, and waders. The second type are known as altricial. They hatch at a much more immature stage of development, blind, helpless, and practically featherless. They remain in the nest until almost ready to fly and are totally dependent on their parents. Examples are the young of pigeons, owls, thrushes, hummingbirds, woodpeckers, and all songbirds.

Migration

One of the main reasons birds are so successful is that they are capable of moving far and fast. Many species make long migrations in search of food or breeding sites. True migration involves regular seasonal journeys between a breeding area and a wintering area where the climate is more favorable and the birds can find food. Many insect-eating birds, such as swallows and warblers, breed in temperate regions and migrate to lower latitudes in autumn, to spend winter in the tropics. Oth-

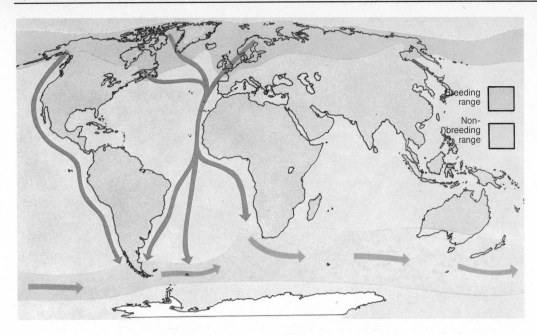

The farthest-traveling migrant bird, the Arctic tern *(Sterna paradisaea),* flies annually up to 22,500 miles (36,000 kilometers) from its breeding grounds in the north to the Antarctic and back again. For much of the year it lives over the oceans, flying along the eastern shore of the Pacific Ocean or across the Atlantic. At the most northerly and southerly extremes of its range, the bird lives in perpetual daylight.

ers, including some wild fowl, waders, and some thrushes, breed in high latitudes and migrate to temperate regions for the winter.

Navigation

Many birds follow well-defined migratory flyways, which often parallel coastlines, mountain ranges and valleys, or ocean currents. It is clear that birds that migrate by day follow various landmarks; they do not need to be taught their route. Young Old World common cuckoos *(Cuculus canorus),* for instance, find their way back thousands of miles to their winter quarters in Africa completely unaided, their parents having returned several weeks before them. But the instinctive following of landmarks cannot explain the phenomenal journeys of seabirds that fly right across the vast Pacific Ocean, where there are no clues to guide them. Nor can they explain the fact that a Manx shearwater *(Puffinus puffinus)* taken

from the coast of Wales and flown in an aircraft to Boston in the United States, found its way back to its nest over more than 3,000 miles (4,900 kilometers) of open ocean in $12\frac{1}{2}$ days—arriving before the letter announcing its release.

Despite many years of research, much remains to be learned about how birds perform such astonishing feats of navigation. According to some experts, it is possible that they possess a sort of internal compass that enables them to use the sun by day and the stars by night to get their bearings. It also seems likely that they are able to respond to the earth's magnetic field and navigate by taking magnetic bearings, especially when the sky is overcast.

Migrating geese fill the sky as they travel southward from their breeding grounds in Arctic Canada. Despite the apparent confusion as they take off together, the geese soon group themselves into a characteristic V-shaped formation *(see inset).* In autumn, the white snow goose *(Anser caerulescens)* and its smaller blue subspecies *(A. caerulescens caerulescens),* both of which appear in the larger photograph, travel 1,700 miles (2,700 kilometers) at an average of nearly 30 miles (50 kilometers) per hour to winter in the marshes fringing the Gulf of Mexico.

Introduction to mammals

The class Mammalia is a relatively small one, especially when compared to the insects (it contains some 4,000 species, whereas Insecta comprises nearly a million). The mammals contain 19 orders, which include rodents (Rodentia)—which make up about half of the mammals—and bats (Chiroptera), which account for about one quarter of mammals. Mammals are one of the most diverse groups, varying remarkably in structure and size, and in the habitats in which they are found. The smallest living mammals are the shrews (family Soricidae); the pygmy shrew *(Microsorex hoyi),* for example, weighs less than an ounce. The largest mammal is the blue whale *(Sibbaldus musculus),* with a weight of over 220 short tons (200 metric tons).

Distinguishing features

The main distinguishing features of mammals are the presence, in the female, of mammary glands (mammae), a body covered in hair, warm-bloodedness, and a large brain.

Mammary glands are found in all species without exception, although there is some variation in form among primitive types, such as monotremes and marsupials. The mammae produce milk for suckling the young and provide them with nourishing food. They also help to maintain the tie between mother and newborn for a considerable period. This dependence of the young on the mother means that there is a period during which it can learn from the experience of its mother, and so become more efficient in dealing with the problems of survival.

In most mammals, hair or fur covers the entire body. Its purpose is to act as an insulator, because mammals are warm-blooded and need a means of preventing the loss of body heat. Body hair is one factor in enabling a mammal to maintain a fairly constant temperature—normally between 96.8° F. (36° C) and 102° F. (39° C). But in addition, a mechanism (the hypothalamus), situated in the brain, regulates body temperature. In most mammals, this mechanism works together with sweat glands that are found in the skin and distributed over much of the body. (Dogs have them only in their feet and keep cool mainly by panting.) Heat induces the hypothalamus to become active, which causes blood vessels to dilate and give off the heat of the blood. The sweat glands exude a liquid onto the skin so that it is cooled by evaporation. When temperatures are low, the blood vessels contract, and the sweat glands dry up. In addition, reflex shivering occurs, which generates heat by the successive contractions of muscles.

Because the body temperature is kept fairly constant, mammals can usually remain active regardless of the external temperature, although in extreme conditions of cold or heat, some may hibernate, or estivate (sleep during the dry season). The body becomes torpid as the rate of heart beat, breathing, and other body processes slow down considerably. The animal then seeks shelter in a burrow or other safe place until the outside temperature increases.

Mammals have a four-chambered heart (also found in fishes, birds, and crocodiles), and a diaphragm that separates the chest and abdominal cavities so that the lungs can work more efficiently and therefore increase the amount of oxygen supplied to the blood. Most mammals have fleshy lips that are initially used in suckling, but as the animal grows, the mouth may become adapted to feed on specialized food.

Habitats

Mammals are regarded as extremely successful animals. One of the reasons for their success is that they are highly adaptable and, as such, have been able to exploit an amazing variety of habitats. Some make their homes in underground burrows, such as moles (family Talpidae) and many rodents, or among leaf litter on the ground (as do shrews); others lead a semiaquatic life in fresh water, such as otters (family Mustelidae) and beavers (family Castoridae), or spend all of their life in the sea,

Suckling piglets typify young mammals, all of which are initially nourished by mother's milk. Unlike most mammals, however, adult domestic hogs have hardly any fur or hair, just a sparse scattering of bristles, although this feature is shown by the fine velvety hair on the piglets. The hog *(Sus scrofa),* bred from the wild hog, often has large litters of between 6 and 14 piglets.

such as whales do (order Cetaceae). Mammals also inhabit the tree canopies in forests (monkeys and others), and some live in the air at least part of the time, such as bats. Certain mammals are able to live in Arctic conditions without having to hibernate, as do Musk oxen *(Ovibos moschatus).* Others live successfully in desert conditions and can withstand the full heat of the sun, such as camels *(Camelus* spp.).

Dentition

Because mammals are warm-blooded, they consume more energy than cold-blooded animals do, and need to increase their food intake to fuel their metabolism. They need teeth in their mouth to break up food at that point so that digestive processes can start earlier and get more out of the food than if the food were processed only in the stomach.

The teeth closely reflect the diet of different mammals. They include incisors, canines, premolars, and molars. Incisors are cutting teeth in the front of the jaws, and are extremely well-developed in the rodents, designed for cutting through tough woody materials. Canines, which are used in tearing and piercing flesh, are highly developed in the carnivores, although their incisors are small. These are used for nibbling, play, and for grooming. The flat-topped premolars and molars are used for grinding non-woody vegetation and are the most important teeth for herbivores, which graze on grasses and other herbs, or nibble on leaves. In carnivores, the last upper premolar and the first lower molar have become bladelike to slice through flesh, and are known as carnassials. These teeth cut meat into bite-sized pieces by their scissor action. Some mammals, such as pangolins and anteaters (which feed on termites and ants) or baleen whales (which feed on shrimplike crustaceans), have no teeth at all and use special mechanisms for collecting and controlling their prey. The giant anteater *(Myrmecophaga tridactyla)* uses its long, sticky tongue to sweep up insects from the ground. Its digestive system includes a gizzard that grinds up the hard exoskeleton of ants.

The thick white fur of the polar bear *(Ursus maritimus)* and its layers of fat insulate it against the bitter Arctic cold. It is able to survive where few mammals do, apart from seals, walruses, and whales. Unlike most animals, the polar bear has fur on its flat feet, apart from the toe and foot pads. This fur gives it extra grip when walking on the ice.

Locomotion

Most mammals are quadrupeds—they move about on four feet. Some walk by placing the whole foot on the ground, in which case they are called plantigrade. This method results in relatively slow locomotion and is seen, for example, in the polar bear *(Ursus maritimus).* Many mammals, such as cats and dogs, lengthen their stride by walking on their toes; this is known as digitigrade locomotion and enables the animals to run at high speeds. Other animals walk on the tips of their toes, which are normally protected by large nails or hoofs. This is called unguligrade locomotion and is found in deer, antelopes, and horses—all of them fast, often long-distance, runners. Humans are the only animals to walk bipedally

The limbs of mammals conform to a basic pentadactylic pattern, sometimes much modified. The lower limb consists of the heavy, weight-bearing tibia and the slighter fibula, and a foot with five toes, containing the ankle bones (tarsals), metatarsals, and phalanges. There are three phalanges on each digit except for the large innermost one. The structure of the foot varies among species. Plantigrade feet are found in humans and bears and are constructed so that the whole foot is placed on the ground. Animals such as dogs and cats, which run fast, have digitigrade feet in which only the part containing the phalanges is used for walking on. Ungulates walk on the tips of the last phalanges. This is called unguligrade locomotion. In horses, the tibia and fibula have fused to form the cannon bone, as have the tarsals to form the pastern; the only remaining toe is the third one. Aquatic mammals, such as seals, have adapted the foot to assume a finlike shape.

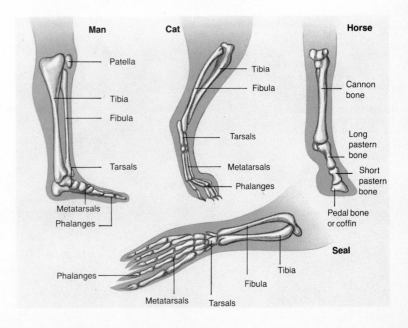

Man
Patella
Tibia
Fibula
Tarsals
Metatarsals
Phalanges

Cat
Tibia
Fibula
Tarsals
Metatarsals
Phalanges

Horse
Cannon bone
Long pastern bone
Short pastern bone
Pedal bone or coffin

Seal
Phalanges
Metatarsals
Tarsals
Fibula
Tibia

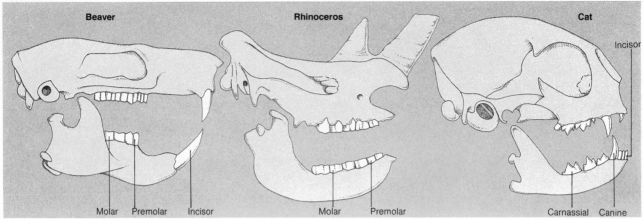

Beaver

Rhinoceros

Cat

Incisor

Molar   Premolar   Incisor

Molar   Premolar

Carnassial   Canine

The dentition of mammals often reflects their diet. The jaws of herbivorous rodents, such as the mountain beaver (*Aplodontia* sp.), have very large upper and lower incisors to gnaw at woody vegetation, and no canines. Their premolars and molars are almost flat, and therefore good for grinding vegetation. Grazing vegetarians, such as rhinoceroses (Rhinocerotidae), usually have no incisors or canines. Carnivores, such as cats (Felidae), have small incisors, but canines for tearing at flesh; their premolars and molars (carnassials) have sharp edges that slice through meat.

(that is, on two feet) in an erect position at all times, but some apes and monkeys move in this way for short periods.

Aquatic mammals have limbs that have evolved into paddlelike flippers, or fins. In some, such as the otter and the platypus *(Ornithorhynchus anatinus)*, a membrane has evolved between the digits on the forelimbs, which aids them in swimming. In seals (Pinnepedia) all the flippers are used for moving through water, whereas in whales, the hindlimbs have completely disappeared; locomotion is powered by movements of the back and tail, whereas the function of the foreflippers is only to steer and balance.

The gibbons, orangutans, and some other arboreal species of the Pongidae family have strong arms that they use to swing from when traveling from branch to branch. Some South American monkeys also have prehensile tails that operate as a fifth limb. The scaly-tailed squirrels (Anomaluridea), which also live in the tree canopy, have folds of skin that extend from the forelimb to the hindlimb and tail, on which they glide from tree to tree. They are sometimes called flying squirrels, but the only

mammals that are true fliers are the bats. Their forearm is the major support of a wing membrane. The hindlimb and the tail often also support the wing.

Classification of mammals

The class Mammalia is divided into two subclasses: the Prototheria and the Theria. The first is a group of primitive mammals and today contains one order only—the Monotremata. It comprises two families: the Ornithorhynchidae (bird-noses), with one species—the duck-billed platypus; and the Tachyglossidae—the spiny anteaters, or echidnas. Monotremes, like reptiles, are oviparous, or egg-laying, and have low, or variable, body temperature. They are toothless, although young platypuses produce three tiny teeth soon after birth, which they lose and replace with horny plates. Also, like reptiles, monotremes have one opening only at the hind end of the body—the cloaca—which serves both the processes of elimination and reproduction. But unlike reptiles, the females have mammary glands, although they do not have mammary organs. Milk secreted

Elephant seals (*Mirounga* spp.) are the largest of the seal group. The males weigh up to 8,000 pounds (3,600 kilograms) and can measure up to 21 feet (6.4 meters) in length. Their name is derived from the bladder on their nose, which can be 15 inches (38 centimeters) long. These animals are polygamous; the bulls become belligerent in the breeding season and challenge each other's dominance to acquire a harem.

by the mammae lies on the surface of the skin either on the abdomen, or, in the echidnas, in the pouch, from where the young lap it up, rather than suckle. Female platypuses also differ from other mammals in that they have only one ovary, located on the left side of the body, whereas other mammals have two ovaries, one on either side.

The subclass Theria contains all other living mammals that give birth to live young. It is divided into two infraclasses: the Metatheria, which has only one order—the Marsupialia, or pouched mammals; and the Eutheria, or placental mammals. The marsupials give birth to live young but they are born at a very early stage of their development, blind and greatly undeveloped, when they are called neonates. As soon as they emerge, they crawl through the mother's fur to her pouch, where they remain attached to the teats for several months before they are weaned.

In the eutherians, or true mammals, the development of the young within the mother is much more complex. Like all mammals, fertilization is internal. Once the egg, or ovum, has been fertilized by sperm it becomes fixed to the wall of the uterus. (Placental mammals have only one uterus, although in some it is divided into two, or is two-horned.) As in birds and reptiles, special structures then develop around the embryo—the amniotic sac, or amnion, which contains amniotic fluid; and the allantois, or respiratory membrane. In addition, a placenta is produced from tissues that arise from both mother and embryo. It is usually attached to the uterus wall and connected to the embryo by the umbilical cord. The purpose of the placenta is to allow the passage of oxygen and nutrients from mother to embryo and waste products from embryo to mother. These substances are carried in the blood, although no blood passes between the two. Rather, they pass through a thin partition separating the two blood systems. This form of development is highly efficient and allows the fetus to remain inside the mother until it is very well developed. Even so, in most mammals the newborn are not fully mobile and are often helpless, as in bats and most rodents.

In most males, two scrotal sacs are found that protrude on the ventral surface of the body just in front of the pelvis. They fuse behind the penis. In marsupials, however, they lie in front of the penis. In many mammals, such as some primates, the sacs descend sea-

Land-dwelling migrating mammals have been greatly reduced in number because of man's population of the globe. Those that still migrate include the caribou and reindeer, which inhabit the northern expanses of Canada and Arctic Europe.

The yolkless egg and the development of the fetus in the uterus are distinguishing features of mammals. The fetus is protected by the amniotic sac and the allantois and is nourished by the placenta, which carries oxygen and nutrients to it and removes waste.

sonally to be retracted when the breeding season is over. They descend because the high body temperatures hinder the process of sperm maturation.

The length of time young mammals remain with the mother varies from group to group. Some are precocious, and able to fend for themselves when they are only a few days old, although they are usually cared for by the mother for several months at least. Others may not become independent for many years. This is particularly true of social mammals, such as elephants, which live in family groups and herds. The young stay with the mother for 12 to 14 years. Elephants and other community animals cooperate in finding food, avoiding danger, and caring for the young. This life style necessitates some sort of code of behavior for herd members, which is learned from the parents and other members of the group.

Monotremes and marsupials

The classic definition of a mammal is an animal that gives birth to fully-formed young that are initially nourished on mother's milk. But there are two groups of mammals that defy this definition: the monotremes and the marsupials.

The monotremes (subclass Prototheria) lay eggs, and the marsupials (subclass Metatheria) give birth to embryonic young that continue their development within the protection of the mother's abdominal pouch. The six species of monotremes and approximately 260 species of marsupials together make up only about six per cent of all mammal species, the remainder of which constitute the placental mammals (subclass Eutheria).

Monotremes

The monotremes are the platypus and the echidnas (spiny anteaters). The most striking difference between them and other mammals is that they lay eggs covered by a leathery shell. This similarity to reptiles is counterbalanced by the mammalian one of feeding the hatched young on milk from mammary glands. These glands do not have teats.

In monotremes, just as in reptiles, the ducts of the excretory system and the genital tract have a common opening known as the cloaca. It is this feature that gives monotremes their name, which means "one hole." The structures of the bones in the lower jaw and middle ear are similar to those of other mammals but the girdle of bones that supports the forelimbs is reptilian in form. In addition, the brain and circulatory systems of monotremes are mammalian but have some reptilian features. This peculiar mixture of characteristics may be an indication of an evolutionary link between the two groups.

There are two families of monotreme: Ornithorhynchidae (bird-noses), which contains a single species *(Ornithorhynchus anatinus),* the platypus, or duckbill; and Tachyglossidae, the echidnas, or spiny anteaters, which consists of two species.

The platypus, which is found only in Australia, is a streamlined animal with a flat snout like a duck's bill. It lives in burrows that it digs in riverbanks or inherits from other animals. It hunts for food underwater, depending largely on the tactile sense organs on the soft edge of its bill to find its prey, which includes small animals such as larvae, earthworms, and crustaceans.

The platypus has webbed feet and dorsal nostrils on the tip of its bill through which it breathes while it floats on the surface of the water. When it dives, a protective skin fold closes over its ears and eyes, and it can stay submerged for up to five minutes. Male platypuses have a venom spur on each hind leg, as do male spiny anteaters.

Spiny anteaters, or echidnas, occur in the sandy and rocky regions of Australia and New Guinea. They have a protective coat of short, sharp spines, rather like a hedgehog. These animals have no teeth but manage to feed on termites, ants, and other insects by picking them up with their long, sticky tongue.

The female spiny anteater temporarily develops a pouch on her abdomen during the breeding season, and transfers her eggs into this pouch after laying. The young hatch about a week later and feed from the milk ducts, which open into the pouch. They stay in the pouch for several weeks, until their spines have developed.

Marsupials

Monotremes are confined to six species but fossil records of the Eocene age, which began

The duck-billed platypus *(Ornithorhynchus anatinus)* inhabits the rivers of eastern Australia. This monotreme feeds off the river beds, probing for small crustaceans and worms with its sensitive bill. Unlike most mammals, its warm-bloodedness is not fully developed. Its body temperature is lower than that of other mammals at 86° F. (30° C), and is not constant, but fluctuates. It has an average life span of 11 to 12 years.

The koala *(Phascolarctos cinereus)* of eastern Australia feeds almost exclusively on eucalyptus leaves and the young bark of the trees. The female of this arboreal species usually produces a single offspring every alternate year, which she carries in her pouch for six months and on her back for six months. Koalas measure from 25 to 30 inches (64 to 76 centimeters) in length and weigh 15 to 30 pounds (7 to 14 kilograms). On their front limb the first and second fingers are opposable with the other three, which aids them in grasping tree trunks and branches.

58 million years ago, indicate that marsupials were once widely distributed and even more common than eutherians are. Now marsupials are restricted to North and South America (70 species) and Australia (more than 170 species). One reason for this reversal could be that marsupials have a smaller, simpler brain than the eutherians do and so stand a smaller chance of survival compared with the more intelligent eutherians.

The marsupials are an extremely diverse group and include arboreal, fruit-eating, grazing, burrowing, insectivorous, and carnivorous types. There are six families of marsupial: opossums (Didelphidae), carnivorous marsupials (Dasyuridae), bandicoots (Peramelidae), rat opossums (Caenolestidae), phalangers (Phalangeridae), and kangaroos and wallabies (Macropodidae).

The most distinguishing feature of a marsupial is the pouch, or marsupium, which contains the mammary glands, and which gives marsupials their name although there are some species in which it is not present. The embryo in some marsupials is supplied with nutrient from the wall of the uterus, whereas in others there is no placental connection between the uterus and the embryo. In all species, the embryo remains in the uterus for a very short period and develops quickly.

At birth, the embryo is tiny—1.2 inches (3 centimeters) long at most, and many are no longer than a grain of rice. Called a neonate, its forelimbs and nervous center are well developed, but the hindlimbs are mere buds. It crawls, unaided, from its mother's birth canal to her pouch where it latches on to a nipple that injects milk into the young animal's mouth. A baby kangaroo, or joey, for example, remains in its mother's pouch for about six months, and will return to feed or seek refuge until it is about eight months old.

The kangaroos, perhaps the best known marsupials, have forward-opening pouches but the form of pouch varies between species. For example, wombats and phalangers, including the koala *(Phascolarctos cinereus)*, have

pouches that open to the rear, an advantage for the young of digging animals, although it means the mother cannot clean the pouch.

The marsupial reproductive system differs from that of eutherians in various other ways: for example, the females have a double uterus and double vagina, and in many species the males have a forked penis, with the testes in front of it. But from the similarities in their reproductive systems, it seems that the marsupials and the monotremes form an intermediate group between the reptiles—which lay eggs covered with shell and do not have mammary glands—and the eutherians—whose young remain in the uterus until they have developed to an advanced stage, when they are born and then fed with milk from the mammary glands.

The young of marsupials are known as neonates. In kangaroos (Macropodidae), a single neonate emerges from the mother's cloaca about 33 days after conception. Its forelimbs are well developed, but its hindlimbs are mere buds. It struggles through the mother's fur to her pouch, where it latches on to one of the teats. About six months later, the joey forays from the pouch.

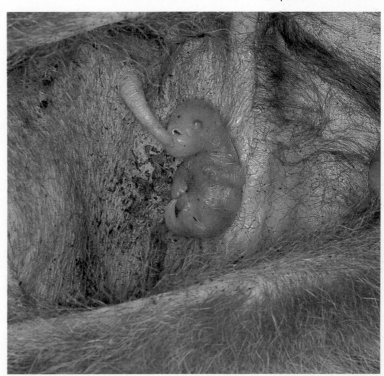

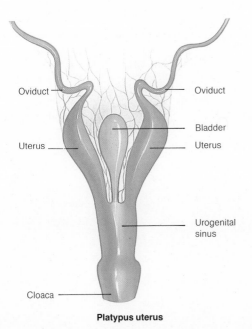

Platypus uterus

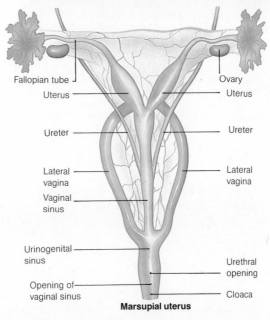

Marsupial uterus

The uteri of monotremes and marsupials are unlike those of eutherians in that they have two uteri and one urinogenital opening. In both, the eggs are fertilized in the oviducts. In the platypus, they are covered with a leathery shell and two eggs are usually produced at a time. In the marsupials, the sperm go up two vaginal canals to fertilize the eggs; the neonates bypass the canals and come down the vaginal sinus. Opossums carry several embryos in both uteri simultaneously, but kangaroos carry only one.

Insectivores

The Insectivora is probably the most ancient order of placental mammals. These insect-eating mammals are known to have lived as far back as 100 million years ago, sharing their world with the dinosaurs. They all share certain basic features, but each species has specialized for a different way of life so that they are superficially dissimilar. With bats (order Chiroptera), which are generally considered to be descended from Insectivora stock, flying lemurs (Dermoptera), anteaters, sloths and armadillos (Edentata), pangolins (Pholidota), and some primates, they form the bulk of a large group of mainly insect-eating mammals.

Insectivore classification

Today, Insectivora is the third largest order of mammals, comprising four suborders and about 380 species. The suborder Lipotyphla contains most of the insectivores, and includes creatures such as solenodons, tenrecs, moles, desmans, golden moles, hedgehogs, moonrats, and shrews. The related water shrews, or otter shrews, have been placed in their own suborder—Zalambdodontia—because their teeth differ from the rest of the insectivores. The elephant shrews have also been separated—into the suborder Macroscelidea—for the reason that they hop on their back legs. The suborder Dermoptera contains the flying lemur—the most accomplished of gliding mammals.

Insectivores occur throughout the world. Typically, they are small, nocturnal mammals with elongated narrow snouts. They are distinguished from other small mammals by the fact that they have five digits on each limb—most rodents, for example, have four or less. Each digit has a distinct claw. The body is covered with short, dense fur; in some species, such as hedgehogs and tenrecs, some of the hairs are developed into spines. They have small ears and small eyes with poor vision; their senses of smell and hearing, however, are usually sharp. The brain has a primitive structure and the placenta is simpler than that found in most other mammals. Insectivores have up to 44 teeth—the largest number normally found in placental mammals. These usually have sharp cusps that enable them to slice their prey. Insectivores include ground-living, burrowing, climbing, and even semiaquatic species. They feed on insects, grubs, and snails and, occasionally, on helpless vertebrates, such as the young of ground-nesting birds. Many insectivores are extremely active and therefore need to be refueled constantly by large quantities of food—sometimes equaling the animal's total body weight each day.

Habitats and life styles

Of the two species of solenodon, one was last seen in Cuba in 1909 and is now thought to be extinct. The other lives on Haiti—*Solenodon paradoxus.* This animal is about the size of a rat and looks like a shrew, with its pointed, almost naked, snout. It uses this sensitive snout to root about on the ground for invertebrates and plant material; it also eats lizards, frogs, and small birds—like some other insectivores, it produces a toxic saliva from a gland in the lower jaw.

The tenrec family (Tenrecidae) includes about 20 species, all found on Madagascar and the Comoro islands. They are primitive animals and retain some reptilian features, such as the cloaca—a common opening for urogenital and anal systems—but are most interesting in that they have adapted to fill a wide range of habitats in Madagascar. Some resemble shrews; those of the genus *Setifer* resemble hedgehogs and have sharp spines; others are similar to mice and moles. Their main diet consists of small invertebrates and plant material.

The family Talpidae consists of about 29 species of mole, shrew-mole, and desman,

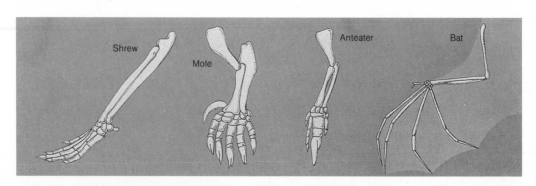

The diversity of insectivores is reflected in their limb structures. All have basically pentadactyl (five-toed) limbs, modified to suit their life styles. Shrews walk on their toes, whereas a mole's digits form a broad spade for digging. Anteaters have an enlarged third digit with a curved claw for breaking open ant and termite nests. Bats have four elongated digits on the forelimbs, which support the membranous wing.

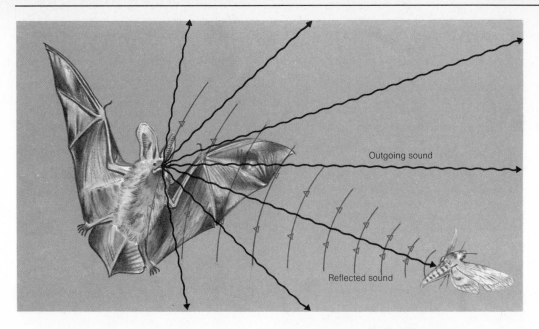

Outgoing sound

Reflected sound

Most bats *(far left)* eat insects and, like this noctule *(Nyctalus noctula)*, hunt their prey at night using echolocation *(left)*. While flying through the air at up to 18 miles (24 kilometers) per hour, they generate high-frequency sounds and detect prey or obstacles by the echoes they reflect. The range of detection is, however, limited to 3 feet (1 meter) or so, but is sufficiently discriminating to enable some bats to catch fish by detecting the ripples they make on the water surface.

which occur widely in the Northern Hemisphere. Most are burrowers and are highly modified for an underground existence with powerful spadelike front feet, minute eyes with poor vision hidden in the fur, and no external ears. The short fine hairs on the body can be brushed in any direction, enabling them to reverse easily in their tunnels. The desmans, which are the largest of this group, lead a semiaquatic life in, or near, ponds and streams and feed on aquatic invertebrates and fish. They use their long noses as snorkels, turning them up so that they stick out of the water.

Golden moles, which resemble true moles, form the family Chrysochloridae and are found in a range of habitats in Africa, from desert to forest. They have a blunt snout covered with a leathery pad, the eyes are vestigial, and the front feet are armored with powerful claws that are used for efficient burrowing. Golden moles are diurnal—that is, active during the day—and feed on a range of underground invertebrates. Some desert-dwelling, sand-burrowing types, such as the desert golden mole *(Eremitalpa granti),* even capture and kill burrowing reptiles.

The hedgehog family (Erinaceidae) includes the familiar hedgehogs, with their covering of sharp, tough spines, and the more rodentlike, long-snouted moonrats *(Echinosorex gymnurus).* There are 17 species in all, found in Europe, Asia, and Africa. They are nocturnal, feeding on a range of invertebrates, but also on carrion and small mammals.

The shrews of the family Soricidae are the most successful insectivore group in terms of numbers; there are about 250 species living almost everywhere in the world. Most are small—the pygmy shrew *(Microsorex hoyi)* is the smallest and weighs less than 0.08 ounce (2.5 grams). Seldom seen, shrews forage on the ground, moving under logs, plant debris, and into crevices in search of invertebrate prey. Some are able to subdue larger animals such as mice and frogs because, like solenodons, they also have a highly toxic substance in their saliva. The prey is rendered helpless by just a few bites from these venomous ani-

mals. Shrews communicate by high-pitched squeaks and by noises of too high a frequency for the human ear to hear.

The water shrews—also known as otter shrews—of the order Zalambdodontia are different from other insectivores in that they have four-cusped molars, the cusps being arranged in a W-shape. This formation is known as zalambdodont dentition, and is almost identical with that of the earliest placental mammals. They lead a semiaquatic life in streams, rivers, and swamps, feeding on fish, crabs, and frogs. The giant otter shrew *(Potamogale velox)* is the largest living insectivore, with a length of about 24 inches (60 centimeters). With its sleek dense coat and powerful tail it resembles a small otter.

The elephant shrews differ from other insectivores in that their hindlimbs are adapted

Hedgehogs are mainly nocturnal animals and predominantly insectivorous, although they have been known to feed on carrion and small mammals. When food is scarce in winter, they hibernate.

for hopping. There are about 18 species, found in Africa, in habitats ranging from semi-desert to forest. They have large eyes and ears and are further distinguished by their extremely long, narrow snout. It is the supposed resemblance of this snout to an elephant's trunk that led to the origin of its common name. These animals forage on the ground using their mobile snouts and long-clawed front feet to search for small invertebrates.

Flying lemurs

The two surviving species of flying lemur (also known as colugos) represent an early specialized development of the basic insectivore type. These Southeast Asian tree-dwelling mammals are not really able to fly, but glide among the treetops by means of membranes at the sides of the body. These membranes extend from the neck to the front feet, the hind feet, and the tip of the tail. Normally held folded in at the sides, the membranes become parachutelike when the animal extends them by stretching out its limbs. Flying lemurs are excellent climbers and spend the day hanging by their clawed feet from a branch. At night, they glide from tree to tree feeding on leaves, buds, flowers, and fruit. Their jaw is unusual among mammals in that its lower incisors have become "comb teeth." Used for grooming the fur, the teeth are similar to those of the lemurs—an example of convergent evolution from two separate family groups.

Bats

Descended from the insectivores, but far more successful, the bats are second only to rodents in terms of numbers. More than 900 species are known from almost all parts of the world. The order is divided into two suborders: Megachiroptera contains one family, known as fruit bats, which feed primarily on fruit; Microchiroptera contains the other 17 families, most of which are largely insect-eating.

The main reason for the enormous success and diversity of bats is their use of an otherwise unoccupied ecological niche—that of nighttime flying mammals. No other mammal can actively fly, and no other creatures, even birds, can surpass the bats' mastery of the night skies, achieved by their use of a sonar sensory system for navigation and prey-finding.

To enable them to fly, bats have evolved extensive wings that consist of thin skin flaps stretched between the enormously elongated fingers of the hands and between the forearm and the much smaller hind legs. In most species, the skin flap also extends backward from the legs to the tail. The skin is an extension of the back and belly. In flight, bats are exceptionally maneuverable; when they alight, they

The three-toed sloth *(Bradypus tridactylus)* is found in the Amazonian forests, where it feeds on leaves and rarely descends to the ground. Its three digits are bound for almost their entire length by skin and have long, curved claws.

The tamandua, or collared anteater *(Tamandua tetradactyla),* is a mainly nocturnal, arboreal species found in South America. Its body length reaches 23 inches (58 centimeters). This animal walks on the outside of its hands to prevent the tips of its curved claws from digging into its palms.

hang upside down from perches with the aid of clawed hind feet.

Skill in flight and echolocation has enabled Microchiropteran bats to adapt to a wide range of feeding strategies apart from the most important one of capturing night-flying insects. Some feed on the nectar and pollen of night-flowering plants and are important pollinators of those plants. Others feed on small invertebrates and mammals, and even capture fish in swoops to the water surface. The vampire bats (Desmodontidae) have very sharp, triangular-shaped front teeth that cut a narrow groove into the skin of sleeping mammals and birds, and sever capillaries, which bleed freely. They lap up the blood that flows from these wounds, consuming about 1 tablespoon (15 milliliters) of blood a day.

Armadillos, anteaters, and sloths

The order Edentata today contains about 30 species in three families: armadillos (Dasypodidae), anteaters (Myrmecophagidae), and sloths (Bradypodidae). All have a reduced number of teeth, or none at all.

The 20 species of armadillo of the Western Hemisphere are nocturnal and feed primarily on insects, as well as other small invertebrates and vertebrates and, in some cases, carrion. Their bodies are protected by a protective shell made up of bands of bony plates, leaving only the limbs and underside vulnerable to attackers. Some species of armadillo curl up into a ball to protect these parts of the body. They have simple, cylindrical teeth that are gradually shed with age. Their limbs are sturdy and powerful, with large strong claws.

Also living in the Western Hemisphere—in Central and South America—are four species of anteater, all of which are highly specialized for feeding on ants and termites. The anteater has a long snout and no teeth, but a long sticky tongue that is flicked out to capture insect prey. The giant anteater *(Myrmecophaga tridactyla)* is ground-dwelling, but the other species spend at least some of their time in the trees.

The five species of sloth are so adapted to life in the trees that they can barely move on land. These creatures have earned their name from their slow movements. For this reason, they rarely descend to the ground, as they would make easy prey. They live in forests in Central and South America and spend much of their time hanging upside down from their large hooklike claws. There are two genera—Bradypus, the three-toed group, and Choloepus, which are two-toed. The three-toed species tend to be slower than the two-

toed, and their grooved hairs carry algae, which give them a green color.

Pangolins

The pangolins (order Pholidota), or scaly anteaters, of Asia, Indonesia, and Africa lead a similar life to the American anteaters. They have no teeth and feed largely on termites, ants, and other insects, which they capture with deft movements of their long tongue. The largest of them can protrude its tongue 16 inches (40 centimeters) out of its mouth. Like anteaters, pangolins have a gizzardlike stomach that grinds down the hard exoskeletons of the insects they eat.

Scaly anteaters, or pangolins *(Manis* spp.), are distinguished by their scaly skin, which resembles the bracts of a pine cone. These arboreal mammals have a prehensile tail and a flexible body that can roll into a ball. Like the anteaters, they have no teeth, but have strong claws for tearing open termite nests.

Fact entries

Echolocation is a means of establishing the position of objects by monitoring the sound waves that bounce back off them. Some bats that cannot see well in the dark use echolocation to navigate. These animals emit ultrasound—high energy pulses or whistles of

sound at frequencies of up to 150 kHz, which are far above the upper frequency limit of the human ear, which is around 20 kHz. Bats produce the sounds with their large, specialized larynx and project them either through the open mouth or through the nose, which is

designed as a transmitter, with leaflike appendages. While they are in flight, they emit these sounds in a rapid series of squeaks, each lasting for only about $\frac{1}{500}$ of a second, at a rate of about 50 per second. Ultrasound bounces off objects in a similar manner to light. Bats

receive these reflected noises with their large, highly modified ears like dish radio telescopes, which receive in a similar way. The returning sound signals are analyzed by the bat's inner ears, and enable it to estimate with extraordinary accuracy the range, di-

rection, nature, and speed of objects flying through the air. Bats are thus able to avoid danger and, just as important, locate food.

Primates

Man and his closest relatives in the animal kingdom belong to the order Primates. The name, which means "first ones," is apt because early members of this group were contemporaries of the dinosaurs, although they were not the earliest placental mammals. The primates began to diverge from the other mammalian orders about 80 million years ago, at which time they differed from them very little in appearance and behavior; however, they bore the evolutionary potential whose expression since that time has produced the diverse forms of their descendants today.

The present order is divided into two suborders: the Prosimii, including tarsiers, lemurs, indris, aye-ayes, galagos, pottos, and lorises; and the Anthropoidea, consisting of the New World monkeys (tamarins and marmosets, and cebid monkeys), the Old World monkeys (including the macaques, baboons, and colobus monkeys), the lesser apes (gibbons and siamangs), and the great apes (orangutans, chimpanzees, and gorillas). Among the smallest primates is the pygmy marmoset (*Cebuella* sp.), whose body length measures about 5.5 inches (14 centimeters); the largest is the gorilla *(Gorilla gorilla),* which stands at about 6 feet (1.8 meters) high and weighs about 450 pounds (204 kilograms).

Distribution

The prosimian group is dominated by the lemurs and their relatives, which are concentrated in Madagascar and the nearby Comoro Islands. This is because about 50 million years ago, the earliest lemurlike prosimians on Madagascar were separated from Africa by the Mozambique Channel. There were few predators on Madagascar and so they were able to diversify. Those that remained on the mainland were forced to live a nocturnal life by the more versatile Old World monkeys and apes that developed. These nocturnal prosimians include galagos (*Galago* spp.)—sometimes called bush babies—in tropical Africa, and lorises (Lorisidae) and tarsiers (Tarsiidae) in tropical Asia. Prosimians failed to reach Australia because it was isolated in the Pacific well before their evolution. Tarsier and lemurs once existed in North America, but were ousted by the New World monkeys that evolved there. The success of the primates meant that some species increased in size and moved from the ancestral forest habitats. Today, the largest primates spend little time in the trees. Primates, whatever their way of life, have remained essentially animals of the tropics, rarely being found where warmth and food are not con-

Lemurs, such as the ring-tailed species *(Lemur catta),* inhabit Madagascar. They were revered by the people of the islands as the home of the spirits of the dead, but since the imposition of Christianity by European colonists they have been killed for food.

The Primates consist of two suborders: the Prosimians, which include tree shrews and lemurs, and the Anthropoids, which contain New World monkeys, Old World monkeys, and hominoids.

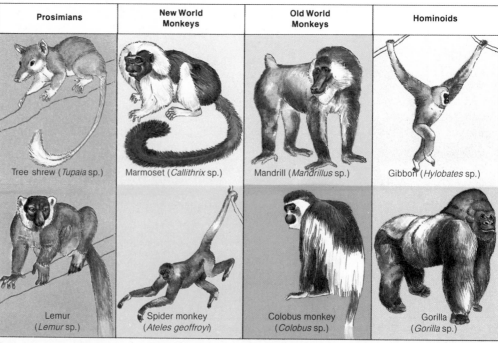

Prosimians	New World Monkeys	Old World Monkeys	Hominoids
Tree shrew (*Tupaia* sp.)	Marmoset (*Callithrix* sp.)	Mandrill (*Mandrillus* sp.)	Gibbon (*Hylobates* sp.)
Lemur (*Lemur* sp.)	Spider monkey (*Ateles geoffroyi*)	Colobus monkey (*Colobus* sp.)	Gorilla (*Gorilla* sp.)

stantly available.

Evolutionary trends

The earliest primates are thought to have fled from their large neighbors by scrambling into the trees. This arboreal tendency and its adaptations has remained with the primates throughout their evolutionary history.

The more distinctive developments among the primates include the evolution of hands and feet equipped with grasping fingers and toes. This involved the separation of the digits and the development of musculature that enabled them to fold around a branch or other objects. The first digit (thumb or big toe) became widely separated from the others, but could, in many cases, be folded across the palm of the hand, providing a manipulative grasp. The tips of the digits became flattened, and nails—rather than claws—developed on their dorsal surfaces. Friction pads of deeply folded skin developed to maintain a hold on smooth or slippery surfaces.

Another important development was the reduction in the size of the snout, which allowed greater room for the eyes to move forward and evolve stereoscopic vision. This was particularly important for judging distances when leaping among the trees.

High activity levels and manipulative skills require enlarged brain centers, and the primates tended to develop big brains in comparison with their body bulk. In general, this leads to a higher level of intelligence, but is not an absolutely rigid ratio.

In addition, the development of the embryo in the womb becomes more complex in primate evolution, and takes longer. This correlates with a prolongation of parental care. Most primates are highly social animals, leading a life of complex interactions between members of a group. With social safety and prolonged care, education of the young can develop. Strong links are forged between an infant and its mother in the early stages of life.

The slow loris (Nycticebus coucang) is, as its name implies, a slow-motion climber. The opposable thumbs and big toes of this animal give it a powerful grip as it pulls itself along, hand over hand, suspended under branches. It catches by stealth and eats birds' eggs, fruit, and insects.

Later, bonds are made with playmates and other members of the group.

Each of these (and other) trends has progressed to different points in different primates but is generally less advanced in the prosimians than in the higher primates, the anthropoids.

Prosimians

The inclusion of the predominantly ground-dwelling tree shrews (Tupaiidae) in the primate order is debatable because they have few primate characteristics. Even so, these animals, which inhabit the forests of tropical eastern and southeastern Asia, are thought by some zoologists to be the earliest relative of primates. The Latin name Tupaia is derived from the Malay word for a squirrel, which tree shrews resemble in size and, to some extent, in appearance. They are small, often bushy-tailed, clawed creatures, but they differ greatly from the rodents in their dentition, which is adapted to a diet of insects, fruit, and worms, rather than the specialized gnawing and chewing teeth possessed by squirrels. Unlike squir-

The prototype primates began to separate from the other mammalian orders about 80 million years ago. Today the order contains about 170 species—54 among the prosimians and 117 in the anthropoids.

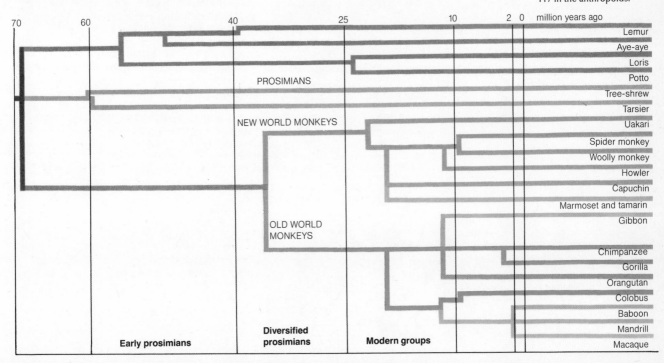

| 70 | 60 | | 40 | 25 | 10 | 2 0 | million years ago |

Lemur
Aye-aye
Loris
Potto
Tree-shrew
Tarsier
Uakari
Spider monkey
Woolly monkey
Howler
Capuchin
Marmoset and tamarin
Gibbon
Chimpanzee
Gorilla
Orangutan
Colobus
Baboon
Mandrill
Macaque

PROSIMIANS

NEW WORLD MONKEYS

OLD WORLD MONKEYS

Early prosimians

Diversified prosimians

Modern groups

Foot	Hand	Grip

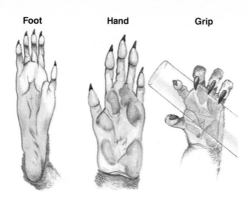

The digits of the tree shrews have long, sharp claws and poor grasping power. The thumbs are not opposable with the fingers even though they are longer than them. The soles of the feet are naked and have thick friction pads.

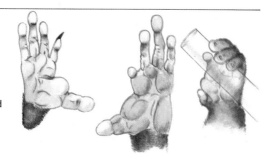

The African potto *(Perodicticus potto)* has short digits with nails, except on the second toe. The index finger is a mere stub, and has no nails or joints. The digits lie at an angle of almost 180° to the thumbs and big toes.

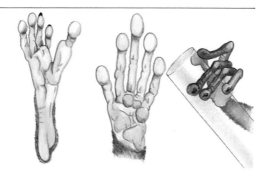

The tarsier's long digits with flattened tips and large friction pads contribute to its superior grasping power. It also has flattened nails rather than claws, except on the second and third toes.

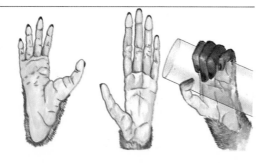

Most brachiating monkeys and apes have short thumbs and long fingers. A gibbon's thumb is longer, but is folded out of the way across the palm when the animal uses its arms to swing through the trees.

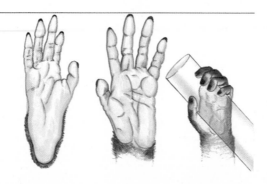

The hands and feet of macaques grasp well, having opposable thumbs and big toes with flattened nails. In the larger, less active primates, the friction pads provide large areas of skin for tactile nerve endings.

rels, they are nocturnal and have highly light- but not color-sensitive eyes. These are situated on each side of the head so that there is no stereoscopic vision. But like squirrels, they have prominent snouts and depend heavily on their good sense of smell. In their favor as primates, however, tree shrews have moderately large eyes, the sockets of which are encased in bone; they have bony ridges (postorbital bars) surrounding the eye sockets, and have primatelike ears.

Tree shrews are among the few primates that generally produce twins. Each of the twins develops in one of the two long branches of the bicornuate uterus common to the primitive placental mammals. Gestation lasts about six weeks and parental care is minimal.

The status of the tarsiers (*Tarsius* spp.) as primates is certainly less controversial than that of the tree shrew. These arboreal animals inhabit the forests of the East Indies and the Philippines, and one of their most notable features is the greatly flattened tips of their digits. These allow the tarsiers to be able to jump and support themselves even on smooth vertical surfaces. The ability to grasp and climb among smooth branches, which is where most trees produce their most succulent buds and leaves, enabled the early primates to colonize forest habitats unused by other mammals.

Travel between high fruit-bearing branches was made possible by the development of leaping as a means of progression. The tarsier gets its name from its means of leaping—its greatly elongated ankle bone, or tarsal bone, allows it to jump at least 6 feet (2 meters).

The tarsier has a relatively flat face and forward-facing eyes with stereoscopic vision, which aids it when jumping. Its enormous, fixed, bulging eyes are the tarsier's most remarkable feature. Unable to move them, it can swivel its head a full 180° to the left or right. The size of its eyes may contribute to its good night vision, but a more important factor is the abundance in the retina of rods—which operate well at low light intensities—and absence of color-sensitive cones. This arrangement is typical in nocturnal vertebrates because color vision and fine resolving are less useful in the dark. Its eyes lie in eye sockets completely encased by bony ridges.

The largest number of prosimians are found among the lemurs. These animals, which are superficially monkeylike, are arboreal, have forward-facing eyes with less well-developed binocular vision than other primates, but with a tapetum (a reflector at the back of the retina), which allows them to see at night. Like the tarsier, they have nails rather than claws on their digits (with the exception of the clawed second toe), which allow them to grip more easily. Unlike the tarsier, however, they have pseudo-opposable thumbs. Their nose is foxlike in shape, although not as pointed as the tupaia's. Scent—an important feature in the life of these animals—is secreted from scent glands to convey a complex language of signals—in aggression and marking territory, for example. The lower incisor teeth are modified to form a comb, which is used for cleaning the fur (as is the claw on the second toe).

Related to the true lemurs and also found in Madagascar are the indris and the aye-aye (*Daubentonia madagascariensis*). The aye-aye was once thought to be a rodent, mainly because its curved, chisel-like incisors continue to grow throughout its life. But if they did not, the teeth would be worn away because the aye-aye tears at rotten wood and gnaws at tree branches for hidden grubs detected by their sensitive ears; it then dislodges the prey with its extraordinarily long, thin, hooked middle finger. The finger is twice as long as the others, and has a sharp claw.

In Africa, the prosimians are most represented by the galagos—sometimes called bush babies. These animals are fast-moving with tremendous jumping power, and are nocturnally active on the ground or in the shrub layer of the forest. Their eyes are large and forward-pointing, and the snout is reduced, giving them good binocular vision. They have the curious habit of urinating on their hands and feet, probably for territorial claim, spreading their scent as they leap about. Bush babies are unlike the lorises and pottos which, although similar in appearance, travel differently. They exert a vicelike grip on a branch with their hands and feet while they move slowly upside down along the branch.

New World monkeys

Most of the primate group inhabiting the New World are considered to be more primitive than the other anthropoids. They include two families—the Callitrichidae, which consists of the 21 species of marmosets and tamarins, and the Cebidae, which contains 26 species, including howlers (*Alouatta* spp.) and capuchins (*Cebus* spp.). They are confined to tropical forest areas and are, in general, diurnal animals. Only the douroucouli, or owl monkey (*Aotus trivirgatus*), is nocturnal.

New World monkeys are termed platyrrhine, because they have flat noses, with widely spaced nostrils. They have better stereoscopic vision than the prosimians and also have relatively sophisticated grasping faculties. These two complementary developments may explain, in part, why they displaced the prosimians.

The callitrichids are the smallest of the New World monkeys, measuring usually not more than 10 inches (25 centimeters). They have curved, clawlike, keeled nails on all their digits except for the big toe (which has a flattened nail). These claws give them sufficient grip as they travel along branches on all fours. Unlike the cebid monkeys, they have nonopposable thumbs and grasp objects between the fingers and the palm of the hand. Like the tree shrews, the female marmosets usually have twins. They are carried and cared for by their father, who hands them over to his mate to be suckled.

All the cebid monkeys have better manipulation than the callitrichids—the capuchins being the most skillful. Larger and heavier than the marmosets and tamarins, they have to hold on to branches rather than merely balance on them. Like the callitrichids, some cebid monkeys live in family groups; others, however, are found in large, multi-male groups. In a few species, the males carry and care for the young, but they are generally tended entirely by the females.

The prehensile tail

In addition to their manual dexterity, some of the South American monkeys are further supported by a prehensile tail. This tail is possessed only by the howlers, the spider monkeys (*Ateles* spp.), woolly monkeys (*Lagothrix* spp.), and the woolly spider monkey (*Brachyteles arachnoides*). In howler and woolly monkeys, the tail is used as an extra hand, although it reaches its fullest development in the spider monkey, which can support its whole weight

The tarsiers (Tarsiidae, left) are small, nocturnal animals, which can rotate their heads by 180° in order to see because their eyes are fixed. This curious feature led local Borneo inhabitants to believe that if they saw a tarsier while warfaring, they would be successful in taking many enemy heads.

The tiny marmosets of the New World often have large tufts of fur that conceal their ears, such as this golden lion tamarin (*Leontideus rosalia*). Unlike the rest of the New World monkeys, marmosets and tamarins have long, keeled claws on their digits, and their thumbs are not opposable.

from the tail. The end of the underside of the tail is naked and has ridged skin, which provides a better grip. It is also very sensitive and can pick up even tiny objects.

Anatomy and the senses

The spider monkeys are typical of New World monkeys in that they move through the trees by jumping from branch to branch as well as swinging from their arms. This latter method of locomotion is called brachiation, the supreme exponents of which are the Old World apes, the gibbons (*Hylobates* spp.). Like many brachiators, spider monkeys have hooklike hands with reduced thumbs, and arms that are much longer than the legs. Senses such as the olfactory one are important to these monkeys. Marmosets and tamarins mark their territory and points of reference with scent released from glands in the scrotal and anal regions. Capuchins rub their chest glands on branches for the same purpose and also urinate into a cupped hand with which they anoint a foot before moving along their territory.

Color vision and visual acuity are also significant to the New World monkeys (apart from the nocturnal douroucouli). The bald uakaris (*Cacajao* spp.), for example, have brilliant red faces set off by their white or red-brown fur. As well as species recognition, color also plays a role in food recognition—those with color vision can estimate by looking at it the ripeness of fruit or the freshness of foliage.

The brains of the New World monkeys are much larger and more complex than those of the prosimians. The greater weight of the brain is largely attributable to the expansion of the cortex, which coordinates sensory and motor functions and controls memory and intelligence. This overall trend in the dominance of the cortex (corticalization) is more advanced in the cebid than in the callitrichid monkeys.

Males are, in most cases, larger than the females. Like most other animals, they are territorial—the male howlers are most notable for the method in which they proclaim their dominance over their territory. They have an enormous hyoid bone that makes a cup-shaped sounding box in the throat. This air sac is inflated to resonate sounds that carry a distance of about 2 miles (3.2 kilometers).

Few New World monkeys show evidence of menstrual cycles; actual menstruation is rare and minimal, and swelling of the female external genitals is minor. Their uteri have no uterine horns, unlike the prosimians. Gestation lasts about 18 to 32 weeks, and their infantile, juvenile, and adult phases are longer than those of the prosimians. The extension of the postnatal phases is a clear trend further developed in the higher primates and is critical to learning and social behavior.

Prehensile tails are particular to only a few of the New World monkeys, such as this howler (*Alouatta* spp.). These are the largest of the American monkeys, having a body length of about 24 inches (61 centimeters) and weighing 12 to 20 pounds (5.4 to 9 kilograms). They therefore can use their tails only as an extra hand, whereas the spider monkeys, which are slighter, can hang their whole body from the tail.

Coloration is important in displays among many monkeys. The red uakari (*Cacajao rubicundus*) is most notable for its bright red face and almost bald head. The uakaris are the only New World monkeys with short tails. They inhabit the upper layer of the Amazonian forest in troops and rarely descend to the forest floor.

Old World monkeys

The monkeys of the Old World are found in Africa and the warmer parts of Asia and, with human help, the Barbary apes survive in Gibraltar. Old World monkeys live across a wide range of habitats and are far more varied in their ways of life than are the cebids or marmosets. Some inhabit semiarid areas beyond forest boundaries, where they are forced to hunt on the ground for any food they can find.

These monkeys are all grouped in one family—the Cercopithecidae. This family is divided into two subfamilies—the Cercopithecinae, which includes the macaques (*Macaca* spp.), the African baboons (*Papio* spp.), and the guenons (*Cercopithecus* spp.); and the Colobinae, which includes the langurs (*Presbytis* spp.), the Colobus monkeys (*Colobus* spp.), and the proboscis monkey *(Nasalis larvatus)*. The subfamily divisions reflect different eating habits. Most colobine monkeys are vegetarian, whereas the cercopithecine monkeys, most of which are ground-dwelling, are generally more omnivorous and greater opportunists, eating what they find. They have cheek pouches, in which they store food that they do not eat immediately.

The most obvious difference between Old and New World monkeys is that the nostrils of the former are closer together and point downward rather than sideways. They are therefore known as narrow-nosed, or catarrhine, monkeys. Another distinguishing feature of all catarrhine monkeys is the presence of bare patches of hardened skin on the rump, called ischial callosities. These patches have neither nerve nor blood supply and allow the monkeys to remain in a sitting position for long periods without serious discomfort—while sleeping, for example.

Hands, limbs, and locomotion

Many Old World monkeys have fine manipulative skills that are associated with true opposability of the thumb—its tip can be placed opposite any of the other fingers on the same hand. True opposability depends on the movement of the carpo-metacarpal joint and development of the thenar muscles at the base of the thumb, rather than on the movement of the next joint up in the thumb, the metacarpo-phalangeal (which confers pseudo-opposability, as in New World monkeys). The predominantly ground-dwelling baboons and mandrills (*Mandrillus* spp.) have relatively long, highly opposable thumbs and use them to good effect in pulling up grass and other plants. Colobus monkeys, in contrast, grip between their fingers and the palms of their hands because, like the spider monkeys of South America, their thumbs are very short, or absent. This

Tree shrew

Lemur

Squirrel monkey

Macaque

One of the first adaptations of the early primates to an arboreal life was the reduction of the long snout found in the tree shrews (tupaia) which, despite their name, are mostly ground-dwelling. This reduction enabled the eyes (which are on the sides of the tupaia's head) to move closer together and achieve binocular vision—essential for judging distances accurately when leaping. The lemurs are more arboreal than the tupaias are, but still spend time on the ground. Their muzzle is reduced to a foxlike snout, and their eyes are closer than are the tupaia's, but their vision is not as well-developed as that of the squirrel monkey *(Saimiri sciureus)*. As with all New World monkeys, these are platyrrhine because their faces are flattened, their nostrils are set wide apart and face sideways. In contrast, the Old World monkeys, such as the macaques, are catarrhine—their nostrils are close together and point downward. The great apes, such as the gorilla, have developed heavy, jutting jaws and a large brain case.

Gorilla

Limb lengths of primates vary. The woolly spider monkey and the gibbons brachiate, and their arms are longer than their legs, although more so in the gibbons, which rely solely on their arms, whereas the spider monkeys also use their prehensile tail. Gorillas' arms are slightly longer than their legs.

keys are very different in appearance—a phenomenon called sexual dimorphism. An average female, for example, is only one-third the weight of a male. In the patas and the olive baboon *(Papio anubis),* the female is only about half the weight of the male.

Male physical prowess is important both inside and outside the group—in determining the social pecking order and in defense of the troop. Many of the open-country monkeys are at risk from predators and their social organization helps them to minimize the danger.

The powerfully built male baboons, geladas, and mandrills possess fearsome canine teeth, whose display rather than actual use is often enough to discipline troop members or to frighten off predators or strangers. Their teeth are housed in prognathous jaws, but the monkeys still have good binocular vision, because the muzzle forms a shelf over which the eyes can focus well.

The visual cortex is necessarily well developed in higher primates because their recognition of and communication by color is extremely important to them. Mandrills, among the Old World monkeys, have brilliant blue and red facial and genital markings.

Reproduction

Female reproductive behavior is much the same in Old and New World monkeys, in that it is seasonal. Many cercopithecoid females, however—mandrills, some of the macaques, and colobus monkeys—clearly advertise their peak of fertility to the males by pink, swollen genitalia. They also menstruate more heavily than the American primates and have regular menstrual cycles. Gestation and the postnatal phases are longer in the Old than in the New World monkeys.

feature is the derivation of their name, which means "maimed." Also like the spider monkeys, they brachiate, or swing by their arms, through the forest.

The wooded savannas and open dry grasslands of subsaharan Africa are the home of primates that tend to move on all fours. The patas monkeys *(Erythrocebus patas)* have exceptionally long limbs relative to their trunk, enabling them to sprint through the grass with long, bounding strides, faster than any other primate.

Anatomy and behavior

The males and females of cercopithecine mon-

The apes

The last group of the primates, the superfamily Hominoidea, includes the great apes. The main characteristic that distinguishes apes from monkeys is their lack of an external tail

Macaques are the most widespread of monkeys. The Japanese macaques *(Macaca fuscata)* are some of the few Old World monkeys found in areas where heavy frosts and snow are frequent. They have adapted by growing long beards and thick fur. These animals show remarkable ingenuity and exercise of choice in their eating habits. This mother and her infant are washing sweet potatoes in seawater because they prefer salted potatoes. They are also known to throw rice grains into the water to wash away the husks.

(although as with man, there are small internal tail bones). Like the brachiating monkeys, those apes that brachiate have very long arms, which exceed the length of their legs.

The gibbons and the siamangs *(Symphalangus syndactylus)* are often referred to as the lesser apes because they are smaller than the others. They are both Asian species; the gibbons populate the tropical forests of southeastern Asia, Malaysia, and Indonesia, whereas the siamang is confined to those of Sumatra and mainland Malaysia. The other Asian ape is the orangutan *(Pongo pygmaeus)* of Borneo and Sumatra; together with the gorilla *(Gorilla gorilla)* and the chimpanzee *(Pan* spp.), of the African tropical forests, they constitute the great apes.

Locomotion and anatomy

The Asian apes are the most accomplished brachiators of all the primates. The light siamang, which may weigh up to about 28 pounds (13 kilograms), and the still lighter gibbons are tremendously agile in the trees and rely almost exclusively on swinging to move about. Effective brachiation, or swinging, requires the smooth rhythmical transfer of the body weight from one arm to the other, as the hands alternately curl around and release a branch. But this method of locomotion is not without its dangers, because many animals fall at some time and a high proportion of skeletons studied show evidence of broken bones. The brachiating apes have retained their thumbs, unlike the spider and colobus monkeys, even though these are short in relation to their fingers and the rest of the hand. The hand assumes the shape and function of a hook during brachiation, when the thumb plays no role at all, but is folded across the palm. On the ground, gibbons and siamangs can run upright, holding their long arms out of the way and to balance themselves.

In contrast to the lesser apes, the great apes do not brachiate. The orangutan walks on branches while holding on to branches above with its hands; gorillas and chimpanzees walk on the knuckles of their hands, and on the curled toes of their feet. The gorillas have better opposability and make greater manipulative use of their thumbs than do the other apes, but it is the chimpanzee that makes and uses tools.

Whereas the monkeys use color for purposes of display and threat, the apes use their size and, in the orangutan, the fatty deposits around their face. These "blinkers" contain reserves that are drawn upon in times of food shortage.

The vertebral column and the skull

All monkeys carry their slender bodies horizontally on four limbs, and the chest is deeper front-to-back than it is across. But apes walk erect or semiupright. They have fewer vertebrae in their trunks, which are wider than they are deep. They thus characterize the evolutionary trend toward the reduction of trunk length in the more recently evolved primates.

Instead of a flattening of the face, the great apes have developed prognathic jaws. Such heavy jaws and high cranial capacity are associated with increased brain size, and result in a heavy skull. The forward position and the weight of the skull make the head fall toward the chest. This feature and an enlarged crest, which runs from front to back across the top of the head, is characteristic of many great apes. The crest is twitched in displays of aggression, but its height also serves to attract females.

Long fringes of white fur are the dominant feature of the black-and-white colobus monkeys *(Colobus* spp.) of Africa, and have led them to be hunted for the fur trade. These forest-dwellers are leaf-eaters and have a complex digestive system to deal with foliage.

Brachiation, the method of movement under branches by swinging from hand to hand, has been perfected by the gibbons *(Hylobates* spp.). The males also use this swinging and dropping action as a territorial display to neighbors.

Reproduction

The female chimpanzee alone among the apes exhibits external genital swelling as an indication of estrus. Female ape reproductive behavior is characterized by light menstrual bleeding, and the sexual cycles last about a month. Gestation lasts about 30 weeks in gibbons (compared to 27 weeks in the much larger baboons) and up to 36 weeks in gorillas and orangutans.

Homo sapiens

Evidence from fossils has convinced most scientists that human beings developed over millions of years from ancestors that were not completely human. The fossil record does not, however, provide enough information to trace human development in detail. As a result, not all experts agree on how humans developed. Man is, however, classified by scientists as a primate, and a survey of the living primates reveals that humans are most closely related to the apes and resemble them in a number of ways. Those trends that are preeminent in the evolution of the primates, such as the development of grasping hands, good stereoscopic eyesight, elaboration of the cerebral cortex and other parts of the brain, and longevity, are far advanced in the modern apes but have progressed furthest in human beings. But humans are vastly different from the apes in that their hands no longer perform a locomotory function, the brain is more than twice the size of that of any other living primate, and humans are bipeds—that is, they walk on two feet.

Hominid ancestors

Hominid fossils so far recovered from paleontological sites around the world have been classified into two genera, *Australopithecus* and *Homo.* The australopithecines of southern and eastern Africa lived from about 4 million to 1 million years ago. Gracile australopithecus *(A. africanus)* was about the same size as the modern male chimpanzee and had a similar

Gorillas are highly social animals and live in groups consisting of about six families. Each group is ruled by one large silver-backed male. Their life is one of complex interactions between the members of the group, the rules of which are taught at an early age and upheld by the dominant males. The two subspecies of gorillas (*Gorilla* spp.) live on the floor of the lowland and montane forests of central Africa. They rarely climb and then only when young. Gorillas sleep on the ground on nests constructed from flattened foliage.

In an African tropical forest, the layers occupied by different primate species are discrete. Boundaries are observed carefully to avoid confrontations and to reduce competition for the same food. The red colobus *(C. badius)* feeds in the upper layer of the forest, or canopy, which reaches about 150 feet (45 meters). The black-and-white colobus *(C. polykomos),* however, feeds in the understory at heights of about 100 feet (30 meters). Pottos and bush babies eat among the upper branches of the understory, whereas the patas monkeys feed in the lower trees and on the ground. Gorillas inhabit the floor of the denser parts of the forest and eat ground vegetation, as do the baboons, which live in the open savanna.

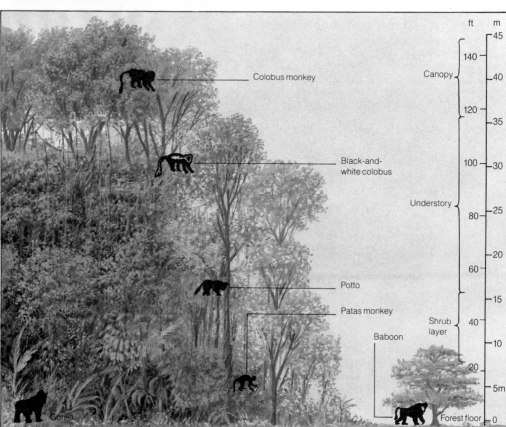

cranial capacity of 24 cubic inches (400 cubic centimeters). In australopithecines, the hole in the skull through which the spinal cord runs up to the brain (the foramen magnum) is relatively far forward and vertical. This suggests that the spinal cord must have entered the brain perpendicularly and the skull on the vertebral column would have faced forward rather than slightly downward, in contrast to the great apes. The australopithecine pelvis is bowl-shaped with short, stout hipbones that extend backward; their high surface area permitted the attachment of powerful gluteal (buttock) muscles, and their long iliac crests allowed the anchorage of strong abdominal and back muscles. In these and other respects, many of their skeletal elements approximate those of modern man; the australopithecines were undoubtedly bipedal and walked upright.

Other hominids—*Homo habilis,* for example—shared parts of Africa with the australopithecines. But whereas the australopithecines may have used very simple tools—usually stone fragments—which they found but did not make, *Homo habilis* the toolmaker definitely made them. With his somewhat superior cranial capacity of about 30 to 50 cubic inches (500 to 800 cubic centimeters) and less massive jaws, *Homo habilis* resembled modern man more than did the australopithecines. *Australopithecus* became extinct about 1 million years ago; *Homo habilis* may have overlapped with *Homo erectus,* modern man's immediate predecessor at about 1.5 million years ago. These early bipedal hominids were neither very large nor particularly strong, nor could they run fast. It is very likely then that cooperation based on communication and sign language, in food-gathering, and group defense would have been vital for their survival.

Homo erectus had, except for *H. sapiens,* the largest brain of all the primates, accommodated in a cranium with a capacity of 42 to 75 cubic inches (700 to 1,250 cubic centimeters). Despite the evolutionary tendency within the primates for the skull to become dome-shaped with increasing cephalization, *H. erectus* still had a sloping forehead with heavy, bony brow ridges and jutting jaws without a chin. But the brain's external casing has little to do with its efficiency.

H. erectus ushered in Acheulian stone technology, which featured a wide range of carefully manufactured tools for the killing or butchering of game, and preparation of food. He was perhaps a good hunter: bone deformations caused by his excessive vitamin A intake as a result of eating too much raw meat have been diagnosed in some fossil remains. Fossil remains of this hominid, in East Africa, Europe, China, and Java, point to his northward and eastward expansion out of his native Africa.

Modern *Homo sapiens*

According to scientific theory, modern man, *Homo sapiens,* began to emerge from 450,000 to 100,000 years ago. His earlier fossil remains have been found across Europe into Asia. He gradually spread from western and eastern Eurasia to America and Australia, helped by land bridges created by lower water levels during cold world climates. Human beings, at

this stage, basically resembled *Homo erectus,* but had a larger brain and smaller jaws and teeth. As time passed, *Homo sapiens* began to look like today's human beings.

Although the *Homo sapiens* face displays a highly differentiated musculature, humankind, nevertheless, relies primarily on symbolic language to express and communicate most aspects of its culture. Among primates, this characteristic is unique. Certain animals, including apes and monkeys, communicate by making a wide variety of sounds. These sounds express emotion and may communicate simple messages, but they apparently do not symbolize any object or idea. Language therefore distinguishes human culture from all forms of animal culture.

Bones of *Homo erectus* were found in 1974 on the western shore of Lake Rudolf (Lake Turkana) in Kenya, Africa. Discovered between two layers of volcanic ash, the remains were dated by scientists as being about 1.5 million years old, making them among the oldest *Homo erectus* finds. Because the skeletal remains are so nearly complete, have not been chewed by scavenging animals, and display no evidence of disease, scientists feel that future study of this find will provide valuable insight into the anatomy, growth, and development of these early hominids.

Rodents and lagomorphs

The order Rodentia is the largest mammalian order and is divided into three suborders: Sciuromorpha, which contains the squirrellike rodents; Myomorpha, or mouselike rodents; and Hystricomorpha, or porcupinelike rodents. The word rodent means "gnawing animal"; these mammals were perhaps so named because their large incisors and their manner of eating are their most obvious characteristics. Lagomorphs were once thought to constitute a suborder of Rodentia because of their long, large incisors but they are now treated as a separate order (Lagomorpha). The order contains two families: the Leporidae, the hares and rabbits, of which there are some 50 species; and the Ochotonidae—pikas, or mousehares—with 14 species. Rodents and lagomorphs are similar in appearance and habits, but differ in certain aspects of anatomy. They are all relatively small animals and are found in most parts of the world.

General features of rodents

The two long pairs of chisel-shaped incisors in each jaw, characteristic of all rodents, project from the mouth and are used to gnaw on hard foods, such as nuts and wood. These teeth, which are segments of a circle, grow continuously and must be constantly worn down at the tips. Rodents have no canines.

Because these animals feed on tough materials that are difficult to break down, they have a highly developed cecum (a branch of the gut at the junction of the small and large intestines), which aids digestion. A bacteria culture is maintained in the stomach that breaks down cellulose, which can then be absorbed by the stomach.

The limbs of rodents are constructed for plantigrade locomotion. There are usually five digits on the forelimbs and three to five on the hindlimbs. The digits on the forelimbs are extremely manipulative and are used for holding food. Hindlimbs may be adapted for running, jumping, climbing, or swimming (in which case the three to five toes are webbed).

The females are capable of bearing numerous young and usually do so at one time; some species can reproduce almost uninterrupted throughout the year. The uterus is usually divided, although in some species it is double. Most newborn rodents emerge both blind and naked and are entirely dependent on the mother for several days. But the guinea pigs (Caviidae), spiny mice (*Acomys* spp.), and nutria, or coypu (*Myocastor* spp.), have precocious young that are active at birth and can soon take care of themselves.

Squirrellike rodents

Squirrels, marmots, gophers, and beavers make up the suborder Sciuromorpha, in which there are seven families. These animals are found everywhere except in Australia, Asia, Madagascar, and parts of South America. They have a variety of habitats: some, such as the squirrels, are arboreal; others, such as the mountain beaver *(Aplodontia rufa)* and gophers, burrow underground; still others live a semiaquatic existence, such as beavers (Castoridae).

The squirrels (Sciuridae) are particularly noticeable for their bushy tails, and large eyes and ears. They are agile and graceful, and move equally well on the ground and in trees. The ground squirrels, such as prairie dogs *(Cynomys ludovicianus),* generally make complicated underground tunnels and chambers, some of which extend for hundreds of feet. The nest or burrows are sometimes used for storing food, which is eaten when food is scarce. The marmots and woodchucks (*Marmota* spp.) are also ground-dwelling species of squirrels. Like the prairie dogs, they live in large social groups. They hibernate during the winter in their underground chambers and

Rodent incisors grow continuously from roots which extend deep into the jawbone. Rodents gnaw at any hard surface to keep the teeth in order. If their erosion is prevented, the tips of the teeth may grow past each other and those of the lower jaw may perforate the palate or grow out of the mouth into the eyes. The front of the incisors only has a hard coating of enamel, which acts like a blade as the dentin behind it is worn down. The jaws that work these powerful incisors are operated, among others, by the masseter muscles. These muscles allow the lower jaw to pull back farther than in most mammals, enabling the cheek teeth to grind together. But they also bring the incisors together for gnawing.

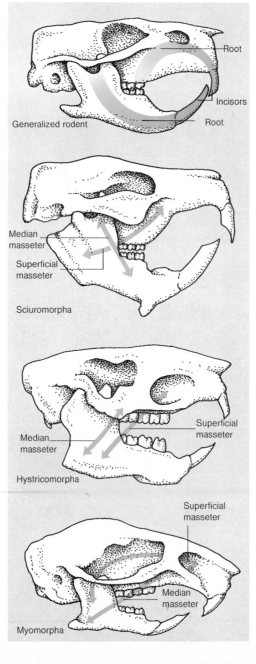

Generalized rodent — Root, Incisors, Root

Sciuromorpha — Median masseter, Superficial masseter

Hystricomorpha — Median masseter, Superficial masseter

Myomorpha — Superficial masseter, Median masseter

live off reserves of fat built up during summer feeding.

The beavers (*Castor* spp.) are the only members of the family Castoridae and are distributed throughout the Northern Hemisphere. Primarily water-dwelling rodents, they have dense underfur that is covered in coarse guard hairs. They are excellent swimmers and use their broad flat tails as a rudder while they paddle with their webbed feet.

The springhaas, or Cape jumping hare *(Pedetes capensis),* is the only species of the family Pedetidae. In most respects, it looks like a small version of the kangaroo, except that it has a bushy tail. Its long hind legs are used for jumping, but it can also move quadrupedally like a rabbit. Like the jumping hare, the kangaroo rats in the family Heteromyidae are nocturnal and burrowing, and their hindlimbs are also modified for jumping.

The brightly colored scaly-tailed squirrels (Anomaluridae) are the only airborne rodents. They glide from tree to tree by means of a patagium, a membrane that joins their limbs.

Mouselike rodents

The suborder Myomorpha contains more than 1,000 species, arranged in nine families. Their mouselike appearance and lack of premolars distinguish them from the sciuromorphs. About 570 species belong to the family Cricetidae, and include hamsters, lemmings, voles, and New World rats and mice. They are mainly terrestrial, although some burrow, and there are some semiaquatic species. Many have a short tail and legs, and a thickset body.

The puna mouse *(Punomys lemminus)* is the only mammal to live at altitudes of 16,500 feet (5,000 meters). It is found in the altiplana region of the Andes and is about 6 inches (15 centimeters) in length. The more familiar common hamster *(Cricetus cricetus),* which occurs across Europe into the Russian steppes, is a nocturnal species and may hibernate for a short period during winter. It stores food throughout the summer, some of which it carries to the winter burrow in its cheek pouches. This burrow is divided into separate compartments, for nesting, food storage, and body wastes. Each food, such as corn or potatoes, is stored in a different food compartment. They may store up to 200 pounds (90 kilograms) of food to see them through the winter. In summer, another burrow is made, which is used for nesting. The golden hamster *(Mesocricetus auratus)* is found today only as a pet or laboratory animal.

The red tree squirrels (*Sciurus* spp.) of Europe, Asia, and the Americas inhabit large conifer forests as well as mixed woodland and parks. The digits on their forelimbs are dextrous and used for holding food, at which they gnaw. They learn to crack open nuts only through practice and trial and error. Eventually, by chiseling deeply with their incisors into the natural grooves of the shell, they crack it easily.

Another member of this family, the true lemming *(Lemmus lemmus),* lives in the Northern Hemisphere, particularly in Arctic regions. It is stocky, with very short ears and tail, and burrows in the soil during summer and under the snow in winter. When food supplies are plentiful, lemmings breed rapidly. But every four to five years, their population reaches a peak when there are too many individuals for the available food. The lemmings then start to migrate in search of new food sources. In Norway, the migrating lemmings keep moving until they reach the sea. This water barrier

Beavers (*Castor* spp.) are known for their building techniques. They not only build complex lodges *(below)* but also engineer dams and cut streams through woodland. The dams and lodges consist of a foundation of mud and stones on which brush and poles are stacked and plastered with soggy vegetation and mud. The lodges are about 3 to 6 feet (91 to 180 centimeters) high with a diameter at the base of about 40 feet (12 meters).

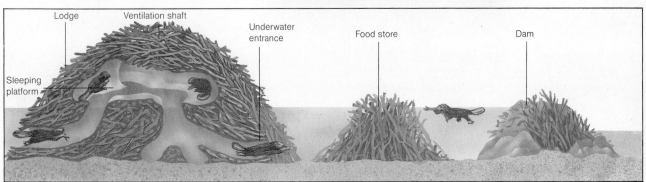

Prairie dogs *(Cynomys ludovicianus)* inhabit the North American plains in underground colonies called towns. These towns can contain about 1,000 animals and are divided into coteries, which have one male, three to four females, and several offspring. Sentries are posted at the entrance to the burrows, where they keep watch with a characteristic stance, standing upright on their hindlimbs. If an intruder is spotted, they bark a warning—the source of their name. They are known to clear the surrounding land of plants they do not like in order to allow those they prefer to grow.

does not stop them and they plunge into the sea, where most of them drown. In the following three to four years, the numbers return to a similar level and the cycle continues. Lemmings compete for the same food as reindeer and caribou and, at the peak of their population numbers, they deprive the large ungulates of food and cause many of them to starve.

Some voles are also prone to similar cyclical fluctuations in numbers. The peak of population is known as a "vole year," during which there is a marked increase in the voles' predators, such as birds of prey.

Apart from the mole rats (Spalacidae), bamboo rats (Rhizomyidae), and jumping mice (Zapodidae), there are also the Old World rats and mice of the family Muridae. Many of them, especially the rats and the house mouse *(Mus musculus),* have been introduced accidentally to all parts of the world, although they originated in the Old World. Most have long snouts and a long, naked, scaly tail. The black rat *(Rattus rattus)* probably originated in southeastern Asia, but like the house mouse, it is now found throughout the world. Like other rats and mice, the black rat lives in close association with humans, inhabiting buildings and

living off human food and refuse. These close associations often mean that the rats carry disease to humans.

The suborder also contains the dormice (family Gliridae) and spiny dormice (Platacanthomyidae). They are mainly arboreal and squirrellike, with a bushy tail. Like other leaf-eating rodents, they start to consume large amounts of berries, grains, and nuts in autumn to accumulate as much fat as they can. This energy reserve enables them to hibernate throughout the winter, during which they may lose half their body weight.

Porcupinelike rodents

Sixteen families comprise the suborder Hystricomorpha, and include porcupines, guinea pigs, and coypus. The porcupines make up two families: the Hystricidae, or Old World porcupines (found in Africa, Italy, and southern Asia); and the Erethizontidae, the New World porcupines. In addition to hair on the body and tail, they have long, sharp, black-and-white quills on their back and flanks. The spines are loosely attached to the skin, and when the rodent attacks, it lunges sideways,

Unlike most rodents of the temperate forests, dormice (family Gliridae) hibernate. This period of sluggish heartbeat and circulation can last from October to April and begins when the temperature drops consistently below 61° F. (16° C). The dormouse's body temperature drops from its normal 98.6° F. (37° C) to 39° F. (4° C). It wakes occasionally when the outside temperature rises, to nibble at the food it has stored, then hibernates again when the temperature drops.

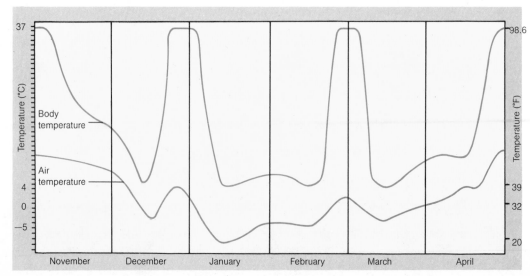

then immediately withdraws, so that some of the quills or spines may become lodged in the victim.

The New World porcupines have shorter spines and some of them are barbed. They are arboreal and their feet are modified for climbing. The sole is widened, and the first toe on the hind foot is replaced by a flexible pad. This group is represented in South America, among others, by the family Caviidae—the cavies and guinea pigs—the capybaras (Hydrochoeridae), and the family Chinchilladae, the chinchillas and vizcachas.

Lagomorphs

The members of the order Lagomorpha differ from rodents in that they have an additional pair of sharp incisor teeth in the upper jaw, which are situated behind the normal pair. In addition, these animals have a curious method of making the best use of plant food. To extract the maximum nutrient from their food, they first digest it in the stomach with the aid of bacteria and excrete it in the form of pellets. These pellets are eaten and pass through the digestive system once more—a process known as refection. After the second excretion, they are left.

The family Ochotonidae consists of the pikas, or mousehares (also called cony, conie, little chief hare, or calling hare), found in North America and Asia. Of the Asian species, one lives on Mount Everest at an altitude of 5,780 feet (1,750 meters). Others live in deserts, on grasslands, rocky regions, and in forests. Most of them inhabit areas with hard winters but they do not hibernate. They do, however, store food for winter and during the summer they dry vegetation in the sun, piling it up in "haystacks."

The remaining lagomorphs, the rabbits and hares, make up the family Leporidae. They are native to most countries except Australia and New Zealand, although some have been introduced there by humans. These animals are distinguished by their very long ears, short upturned tail, and their hind legs, which are usually longer than their forelimbs, allowing them to leap. Most are active at night or at twilight.

Hares (*Lepus* spp.) are solitary except in the breeding season. They do not burrow as rabbits do, but make a depression in the grass called a form, in which they rest during the day. They are most active after dusk, but are alert to potential danger. To escape predators they either run swiftly or lie prone and very still on the ground.

The European wild rabbit *(Orycolagus cuniculus)* has also been introduced to most countries. It is extremely prolific—females become fertile at about six months of age and usually have five to seven litters a year, each with two to nine young. They are capable of becoming pregnant within 12 to 15 hours after giving birth. They are also voracious feeders, and these two facts make them serious agricultural pests when they are not controlled.

Rabbits live together in large groups of about 150 individuals. They inhabit lowlands and hills, generally where the soil is sandy.

Old World porcupines, such as the Indian porcupine *(Hystrica indica),* have longer spines than their New World counterparts. This species has a short tail which, as well as being covered with sharp quills, has a cluster of hollow quills. These quills are shaken in warning and produce a sound similar to that of a rattlesnake. Porcupines attack in self-defense and usually run backward toward their attacker, releasing the quills in its face.

Hares (*Lepus* spp.) are notable mostly for their very long ears. Like rabbits, they eat bark, root crops, and grasses, but, in contrast to them, newborn hares are covered with hair, have developed eyesight, and teeth. They are also solitary animals, whereas rabbits are social.

Cetaceans

The cetaceans—whales, porpoises, and dolphins—have the most highly evolved brain of all aquatic animals and include some of the most intelligent animals on earth; indeed, they are sometimes considered to be as intelligent as humans. Although they are descended from land-dwelling mammals, they have nevertheless become so well adapted for an aquatic life that they cannot now leave the water.

Except for a few species of dolphins that live in rivers and lakes (family Platanistidae), all cetaceans are marine mammals. The order Cetacea divides into two main types of whales, according to their method of feeding. The first type includes the toothed whales (suborder Odontoceti), which has seven families. The second type includes the baleen whales (suborder Mysticeti), which has three families.

The common naming of these animals is confusing; most large species are called whales and most of the smaller ones, dolphins. The killer whale *(Orcinus orca),* however, is a member of the dolphin family (Delphinidae), and there are several species of whales considerably smaller than it.

A further inconsistency is that in the United States, most dolphins are called porpoises, whereas in Europe, this name is reserved for six species of small, blunt-faced dolphins (family Phocaenidae).

The bottle-nosed dolphin *(Tursiops truncatus)* occurs in all the world's oceans, but is most common along the Atlantic coast of the United States. It eats fish and, like other true dolphins, can often be seen swimming alongside or in front of ships.

Anatomy and physiology

Whales and dolphins are the mammals best adapted for a life in water. The outline of their body has become very streamlined and the forelimbs have become broad flippers used for steering and balance. These flippers still have all the bones of the vertebrate forelimb, although they have been modified. The hindlimbs have disappeared, but a reduced pelvis is retained and supports (in the male) part of the reproductive apparatus. The dorsal fin and the tail are not supported by any skeletal elements, but are just folds of skin. The smooth outline is partly due to the disappearance of hair or fur. Propulsion is achieved by up-and-down movements of the broad horizontal tail flukes. The body is protected by layers of fat, or blubber, which act as an efficient insulator to keep the body warm and as an energy store. The presence of large amounts of fat in the surface tissues allows subtle variations in the animal's shape, which reduce drag and make deep diving easier.

Cetaceans usually show only a small part of their back when they come up to breathe, although even the largest ones can leap clear of the water. The nostrils are on the top of the head, forming a single blowhole in toothed whales, and two blowholes in baleen whales. As a cetacean surfaces, it blows, sending up a distinctive spout of watery spray. This jet is a cloud of droplets caused by water vapor in the breath condensing as the pressure suddenly drops when the animal shoots up to the surface.

Cetaceans carry a relatively small proportion of their oxygen intake in their lungs, which are surprisingly small. There is evidence to suggest that the lungs are emptied before a deep dive and that oxygen is stored elsewhere, most of it combined with hemoglobin and myoglobin in the blood and tissues. Because there is not enough oxygen to supply all body functions during a long dive, cetaceans compensate by directing oxygen-rich blood toward the brain and nerves, where it is most needed.

These animals have also evolved some muscles that can work for short periods of time anaerobically (without oxygen), although they must be replenished with oxygen soon afterward. The problem of nitrogen coming out of solution as bubbles in the blood when these animals return to the surface is reduced because of the small amount of oxygen they take down with them, and also because the rate of blood flow to the tissues is diminished.

Cetaceans have very little sense of smell,

A baleen whale filters plankton from seawater using baleen plates that hang down from the upper jaw, shown in the section of the jaws *(right,* A). An example is the blue whale (*Sibbaldus musculus, far right,* B); it is the largest mammal that has ever lived, although now in danger of extinction.

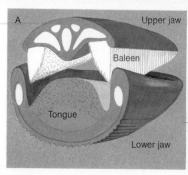

and a variable ability to taste. Whales and dolphins have no sense of smell. Many species have good eyesight, but vision is not of much use because little light penetrates the depths of the sea. Sound, however, travels well in water, and hearing is their main sense, as well as that of touch.

Whales and dolphins are able to produce a range of different noises, with which they communicate and find their way. Schools of dolphins chatter continually to each other, using clicking and whistling sounds, and the "songs" of the humpback whale (*Megaptera novaeangliae*) are known to carry hundreds of miles. Such calls inform the cetaceans of the identity and mood of their fellows. Distress calls, for instance, seem to summon other cetaceans to an injured individual.

Some species of toothed whales, especially dolphins, are known to use echolocation. Like bats, they emit streams of high-frequency clicks and ultrasonic squeaks and use the returning echoes to locate prey and to orient themselves. There is evidence that dolphins and killer whales have a language, and an ability to reason, to learn and remember information.

Feeding and dentition

The whales of the suborder Mysticeti have no teeth. Instead, they have a series of baleen plates (comblike keratin) hanging down from the upper jaw, or palate. Their food consists of swarms of tiny crustaceans known as krill, and also sometimes of small fish. Water containing the food is drawn into the whale's mouth and then squirted out through the baleen plates, which act as a filter, keeping behind the food.

Toothed whales include all nonbaleen whales and have numerous conelike teeth. But some toothed whales, such as the sperm whales (family Physeteridae), have teeth in their lower jaw only, and the beaked and bottle-nosed whales (family Ziphiidae) usually have only one or two pairs of teeth showing, but even these may not erupt. The male nar-

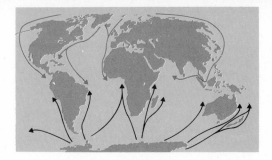

whal (*Monodon monoceros*) has a single tooth that has become a long, twisted tusk on one side of its head.

The teeth of most toothed whales are adapted for holding prey but not for chewing; food is consequently swallowed whole. Most feed on fishes, squid, and cuttlefish, but the killer whale will attack and eat any available prey.

Reproduction

Cetaceans breed seasonally, mating during spring and early summer. They produce single offspring, and birth takes place from 10 to 12 months after conception in most species, although sperm whales have a very long gestation period of some 16 months.

Calves are born under water and may be as much as a third of the mother's size at birth. A calf emerges tail first and is pushed to the surface by its mother to take its first breath and to suckle from the teats, which lie in the folds of blubber on each side of the reproductive opening. The milk contains 50 per cent fat and is very rich in protein and minerals.

Baleen whales seem to breed only every two years; as a result of this, the numbers already severely depleted by the commercial whaling industry will take a long time to recover. In addition, large whales start to reproduce only when they are about 12 years old, which obviously affects the replacement of individuals in nature.

A young humpback whale (*Megaptera novaengliae*) swims above its mother. It is fed on mother's milk for five to ten months after birth, but does not grow to full size until it is 10 years old. These whales migrate annually from Arctic and Antarctic waters (*see map, left*) to spend their respective winters in warm tropical seas.

Carnivores

The carnivores (order Carnivora) are the chief flesh-eating mammals, although hunting as a way of life is shared by others, such as seals and some whales. But this characteristic of the group can be misleading, because a few species (such as some bears) do not eat flesh. The group, which contains seven families and more than 100 genera, is distributed throughout the world, apart from some islands and the Antarctic. Most carnivores are terrestrial or arboreal, but there are also aquatic species, such as the sea otter. Social patterns vary widely, according to the species, although most are fiercely territorial. The two most prominent groups, the cats and their relations, and the dogs and related species, have developed different hunting techniques—dogs, which are usually social and hunt in packs, tend to run down their prey, whereas most cats are solitary ambushers.

Carnivore anatomy

The long, flexible body of the hunting animals and their way of life are adapted to their predatory existence. Terrestrial carnivores are sure-footed and agile, as well as swift runners. Most species naturally stand on the tips of their toes with four or five toes touching the ground, and many have claws. Some species, such as dogs, cats, and hyenas, have a dewclaw on each forefoot, which represents a toe that no longer touches the ground. The claws help to grip the ground and prey as well as being useful for digging and scratching.

One of the distinguishing features of carnivores is their long, pointed, canine teeth, which they use for stabbing and holding prey. The skull of a carnivore is strong, and powerful muscles work the jaws. In some species, there is a ridge of bone on top of the cranium (a sagittal crest), which serves to increase the anchorage for the upper end of the jaw muscles. The lower jaw is articulated only for open and shut action, with little facility for sideways grinding movements of the teeth.

In proportion to their body size, carnivores have a large and well-developed brain that controls the intelligent behavior needed for hunting. Their senses are efficient, enabling the animals first to locate prey at a distance and then to guide the attack. Carnivores have a fine sense of smell, important both for trailing prey and for communication. Scent released from the anal and other glands conveys information about an animal's identity, sex, and territorial ownership. Vision is also vital for directing attacks, and these animals have forward-facing eyes that help in judging distance accurately when they spring on prey. The eyes of many carnivores have an internal reflector, the tapetum, which increases its sensitivity at night; it is the lucidum that causes the eyes to shine when a light is directed at them.

Most carnivores breed only once a year—although a few species reproduce twice a year, such as some weasels. Litters vary in size from single offspring in bears to 12 or more in skunks. The young are usually blind at birth and are necessarily dependent on parental care for some time. In captivity, some carnivores have been known to live for more than 30 years.

The flesh-eating mammals *(Carnivora)* are thought to have evolved from insectivore stock some 60 million years ago. By the end of the Eocene epoch, two lines with distinct doglike and catlike characteristics had emerged, although fossils showing features of both have been found. The development of pinnipeds (walrus and seals) and their relationship with carnivores is difficult to ascertain because of the lack of fossil evidence.

65—56 million years ago **Paleocene**	55—41 million years ago **Eocene**	40—27 million years ago **Oligocene**	26—15 million years ago **Miocene**	14—1.75 million years ago **Pliocene**	25—10 thousand years ago **Pleistocene**	**Holocene**

Walrus (Odobenidae)
Eared seals (Otariidae)
Raccoons (Procyonidae)
Bears (Ursidae)
Dog (Canidae)
Weasels (Mustelidae)
True seals (Phocidae)
Viverrids (Viverridae)
Hyenas (Hyaenidae)
Cats (Felidae)

Insectivore ancestor
Dog-like mammals
Cat-like mammals

Carnivores have four kinds of teeth: incisors, canines, premolars, and molars. Incisors are for biting off flesh, canines for stabbing and grasping prey. The premolars and molars for slicing and chewing show considerable modification, according to diet. Bears chew their food thoroughly and have flat cheek teeth to crush vegetable matter. Cats (except for lions) and dogs have more pointed cheek teeth called carnassials, which slice and tear meat into chunks.

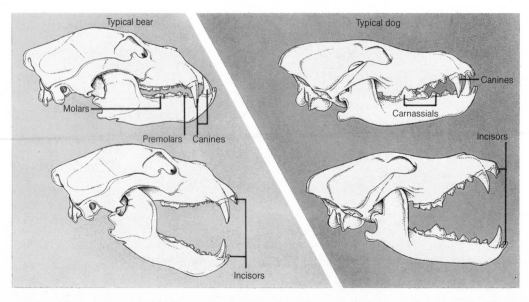

Typical bear
Molars
Premolars Canines
Incisors

Typical dog
Canines
Carnassials
Incisors

The dogs

The dogs (family Canidae) are generalized hunters. They are the most vocal of the carnivores, having a variety of barks, howls, and whines. Those members of the family that hunt in packs can bring down large animals, but the solitary hunters usually live on small rodents, insects, or birds.

The wolf *(Canis lupus)* looks like a heavily built German shepherd dog. Until persecution by humans drove it from much of its former range, it could be found over most of the Northern Hemisphere. The basic unit of wolf society is a female with her offspring. When the cubs mature, they stay with the mother and hunt with her. The male stays with his family and helps to feed the cubs. Lone wolves eat anything they can obtain, from mice upward, but most wolves form packs of 8 to 20 animals, which are highly efficient hunting groups capable of bringing down prey as large as an elk.

The coyote *(Canis latrans)* resembles a small wolf. It is found throughout North and Central America and lives in pairs or family groups that feed on anything from deer to refuse.

There are about two species of jackals living throughout Africa and southern Asia, which usually live in pairs that cooperate in hunting; however, they may gather in packs to prey on large animals or to scavenge.

The red fox *(Vulpes vulpes)* has as extensive a range as the wolf, and has been introduced into Australia as a quarry for hunters (an interference with the natural balance that Australians now regret). Unlike the wolf, the fox has survived continuous persecution and has even taken to living on the fringes of towns and cities, where it scavenges on domestic refuse. Some adult foxes are wanderers without a permanent home, but most live in pairs in territories, although they hunt separately.

The Arctic fox *(Alopex lagopus)* has two forms of seasonal color change. It has either white fur in winter, which turns brown in summer, or a blue-gray winter coat that becomes darker in summer. This variation seems to reflect the harshness of the climate and the environment.

The hot, dry parts of Africa are the home of

the bat-eared fox *(Octocyon megalotis)* and the fennec *(Fennecus zerda)*. Both species have outsize ears that act as radiators to help to keep the animal cool, and as sound receivers to increase the sensitivity of hearing.

The Cape hunting dog *(Lycaon pictus)* of the African savanna is exceptionally social. It lives in packs of up to 20 that cooperate to hunt zebras and antelopes. The members of the pack share the food and, when a female has pups, the other dogs bring food back to the den.

The bears

The bears (family Ursidae) are the largest members of the carnivore order and are found in the Northern Hemisphere and in parts of South America. They are heavy-bodied and most species live in forests; those that live on

The foxlike fennec *(Fennecus zerda)* lives in the African desert, feeding on a varied diet of rodents, reptiles, and insects; it also eats fruit, such as dates. It rarely drinks, but relies instead on the body fluids of its prey to provide it with moisture.

Cape hunting dogs *(Lycaon pictus)* live in the open on the grasslands of southern Africa, forming packs to hunt herbivores such as wildebeest and antelopes.

Bears are grouped with the carnivores and they do sometimes eat meat when it is available, like this Alaskan Kodiak bear, a type of brown bear *(Ursus arctos)*, which has caught a salmon. Most of their diet, however, consists of fruit and grasses, and so they can properly be regarded as omnivorous.

The hindlimbs of a dog *(below)* and a bear *(below, right)* reflect their ways of walking. Dogs are digitigrade: they walk on their fleshy toe pads. Bears are plantigrade: they walk on the sole of the foot with the heel in contact with the ground. A dog has blunt claws on its four toes, whereas a bear has sharp curved claws on each of its five toes.

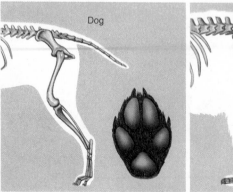

Dog

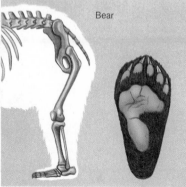

Bear

mountains have probably been forced there by humans. Bears are usually omnivorous and have blunt teeth. They eat a variety of plant foods, such as fruit and grass, but fish and other small animals are also eaten when they are available. Bears are solitary animals, although several may gather around a good source of food such as a garbage dump or a shallow salmon-run. The cubs are extremely small at birth, weighing less than $\frac{1}{350}$ of their mother's weight. The species that live in cold places spend most of the winter asleep in a den, but do not really hibernate.

The brown bear *(Ursus arctos)* weighs over 1,500 pounds (680 kilograms). It lives in the northern forested areas of North America, Europe, and Asia. The grizzly bear is a large subspecies of the brown bear, but is less common. Another North American bear is the black bear *(Euarctos americanus)*, which is smaller than the brown bear; it is an agile climber even when adult. Other bears include the spectacled bear (the only true bear in the Southern Hemisphere), moon bear or Asiatic black bear *(Selenarctos thibetanus)*, which is characterized by a white mark on its chest, and the sloth bear *(Melursus ursinus)* of India and Sri Lanka, which has a long snout with mobile lips that it uses to suck out termites from their nests. The female carries her young on her back when they are first ready to leave the

den. But the smallest and most arboreal bear is the sun bear *(Helarctos malayanus)* of Burma, Malaysia, and Borneo; another characteristic is its short coat, which is less shaggy than that of other bears.

The polar bear *(Ursus maritimus)* is different from other bears, being forced by its habitat to be almost exclusively a flesh-eater. It lives in the Arctic and spends most of its time on pack ice, where it preys mainly on seals. It is a strong swimmer but never hunts in water; seals are either pulled out of the water (as are fish) or caught on the ice. Birds, hares, and berries are also eaten at times. The thick white fur of the polar bear covers even the soles of its feet, giving added grip on the ice as well as insulation from the cold.

The raccoon family

The raccoon family (Procyonidae) includes the raccoons, cacomistles, kinkajous, ringtails, and pandas. Most are small animals which spend much of their time in trees. Apart from the two pandas, they live in temperate and tropical areas of the Americas and eastern Asia.

Most procyonids have long ringed tails; that of the arboreal kinkajou *(Potos flavus)* is prehensile. Their diet includes a variety of small animals, although the kinkajou and olingo *(Bassaricyon gabbii)* eat mainly fruit. Most procyonids are nocturnal, except for coatis *(Nasua* spp.), which are usually diurnal. Most are also found in pairs or groups, except for the giant panda *(Ailuropoda melanoleuca)*, which is solitary. The coatis are the most social of this group, living in large bands.

The raccoon *(Procyon lotor)* is found throughout North America and in parts of Central America. Like the fox, it has adapted to living in built-up areas and scavenges in trash cans, but in wilder regions frequently feeds along the water's edge on shellfish, crayfish, and frogs.

The question as to whether the giant panda is a near relative of the bears or of the raccoons remains debatable. Answering it has not been made easier by the remoteness of the animal's habitat in the bamboo and rhododendron forests of southwestern China and eastern Tibet. Its diet is almost exclusively bamboo shoots, and a feature characteristic of pandas is a sesamoid bone that rises from the wrist and acts as a sixth finger on the fore paw, used to hold the shoots. Pandas have broad teeth for chewing tough shoots into a pulp, and a muscular stomach for aiding digestion. The lesser or red panda *(Ailurus fulgens)* also lives in bamboo forests, from China to Nepal. It has a similar sixth finger for handling bamboo but frequently also eats acorns, roots, fruit, and small birds.

The weasel family

The family Mustelidae, with 67 species, is the largest and most varied of the carnivores. Most mustelids resemble the European weasel *(Mustela nivalis)*, with long, slender bodies and short legs, and are unspecialized hunters of earthworms, frogs, lizards, snakes, and warm-blooded prey. From this basic pattern they have developed a variety of life styles: the martens *(Martes* spp.) are tree-climbers; the minks and otters are aquatic; and the badgers are stocky digging animals. The diet also varies among species. For example, the tayra *(Tayra barbara)* of Central and South America eats fruit, small animals, and birds; the larger wolverine or glutton *(Gulo gulo)* is a powerful scavenger of the high northern latitudes that can also kill deer and cattle weakened by hard weather.

Weasels are lithe, very fast-moving animals. The European weasel and the American least weasel *(Mustela rixosa)* are closely related (the latter is the smallest carnivore). Weasels are small enough to follow mice and voles down their burrows, so do not compete directly with their larger relation, the stoat *(M. erminea)*. In the northern parts of their range (North America, Europe, Asia, and Indonesia) stoats and weasels grow a white coat in winter, which makes them inconspicuous in snow.

Minks and polecats are larger members of the family, and the black-footed ferret *(M. nigripes)* is one of the rarest carnivores. It lives in the North American prairies and preys almost exclusively on prairie dogs (a type of squirrel). Its numbers have declined because prairie dogs have become scarce, having been reduced in numbers by farmers.

Most carnivores have anal glands that secrete a fluid used for marking territory. But the best-known example is the skunk, also a mustelid, which uses the fluid for defense. The glands have also been modified for the same purpose in the Asian stink badger *(Mydaus javanensis),* the African striped weasel *(Poecilogale albinucha)* and the African zorille *(Ictonyx striatus).*

The badger *(Meles taxus)* of Europe and Asia is one of the few social mustelids—and one of the largest—and lives in family groups called clans. The clan territory centers on their burrows, or setts, which may form an extensive underground network. Badgers are nocturnal and feed mainly on earthworms and insects. The American badger *(Taxidea Americana),* however, is more solitary and its diet is mainly rodents. The honey badger, or ratel *(Mellivora capensis),* is known for its association with the honey guide, a bird that attracts honey-eating mammals to beehives. The ratel opens the nest to devour the contents, and the honey guide feeds on the scraps.

Some of the largest mustelids are the otters, of which 18 species live in fresh water, but some river otters and the sea otter *(Enhydra lutris)* frequent the sea and shoreline. Otters swim with powerful undulations of their

A striped skunk *(Mephitis mephitis)* raises its tail as a warning (A) when threatened. Before spraying, it gives warning by stamping its front feet or hissing and growling. It arches its back and may raise itself on its front paws (B). If the threat persists, the skunk turns and ejects two jets of foul-smelling fluid from its anal glands (C).

The raccoon *(Procyon lotor)* is an opportunist, feeding in the wild on frogs and fish or on the fringes of towns scavenging in trash cans and garbage.

The stoat *(Mustela erminea),* or ermine as it is often called when in its white winter coat, can run extremely fast, chasing down its prey of small rodents or even rabbits and squirrels.

Eggs form part of the diet of the banded mongoose (*Mungos mungo*) of Africa, together with insects, snails, and mice; it also eats small reptiles and fruit. Mongooses roam in bands, taking temporary shelter in the abandoned nests or burrows of other animals.

otter civet *(Osbornictis piscivora)* and crab-eating mongoose *(Herpestes urva)* hunt in water.

Viverrids prey mostly on small animals, although some also eat fruit. Mongooses are known to attack snakes, using their speed and agility to confuse the snake and avoid its counterattacks. They have been introduced to several parts of the world to destroy poisonous snakes and rats, but cause destruction among native wildlife and also raid poultry pens (mainly for eggs). Most viverrids are solitary and active by night, because although they are well armed, they are small enough to be attacked by birds, such as eagles, which hunt by day. Some of the diurnal species live in troops and cooperate to watch for danger and drive away large predators.

The hyenas

Hyenas (family Hyaenidae) have had a bad reputation as cowardly scavengers, but are now known to be fierce predators as well as eaters of carrion. The three species that live in Africa and southwestern Asia are strong runners and hunt in packs, chasing herds of antelopes or zebras until a victim can be caught and pulled down. Their powerful jaws and large sharp teeth can crunch even the largest bones. Hyenas have a big head and well-developed forelegs. They have a characteristic trot, but are also able to run at high speeds. Spotted hyenas *(Crocuta crocuta)* are as noisy as many dog species, making howling and "laughing" sounds.

The African aardwolf *(Proteles cristatus)* is a type of hyena and, in contrast, has weak jaws, small teeth, and lives mostly on termites and other insects.

The cats

bodies and broad tails and steer with their webbed feet. They can dive for several minutes in search of fish and other aquatic animals, closing their ears and nostrils while submerged. The sea otter, which lives off the western coast of North America, feeds on crabs, sea urchins, and shellfish. It smashes them open by banging them on a stone, which it carries on its chest while floating on its back. It also carries and nurses its young in this position. Unlike most marine animals, sea otters do not have a heavy insulating layer of fat; instead, they rely on the protection of a layer of air trapped by their long soft fur.

The mongoose family

The mongooses and civets (family Viverridae) resemble weasels and, indeed, occupy similar ecological niches in Old World tropical regions. Many have spotted coats and ringed tails. Some, such as the genets (*Genetta* spp.), are agile, catlike tree climbers, whereas the

The family Felidae consists of six genera and 36 species. The main genus *Felis,* with 25 species, includes the mountain lion, or puma *(F. concolor),* the largest of the genus; the ocelot *(F. pardalis);* the serval *(F. serval)* and many species of smaller wild cats, as well as the domestic cat *(F. domesticus).* The other main genera are *Lynx,* which contains four species, includ-

Tiger *Panthera tigris*

Lion *Panthera leo*

Leopard
Panthera pardus

Young cheetahs (*Acinonyx jubatus*) feed on an antelope that has been run down and killed by their mother. The fastest of all mammals, cheetahs can run at speeds of up to 70 miles (110 kilometers) per hour over short distances (up to several hundred yards), and often chase their prey for 450 yards (415 meters) or more before springing on it.

ing the caracal *(L. caracal)* and the bobcat *(L. rufus),* and *Panthera,* which also has four species—the jaguar *(P. onca),* the leopard *(P. pardus),* the tiger *(P. tigris),* and the lion *(P. leo).*

Compared with other carnivores, the cats have a short muzzle and a broad, rounded head. With the exception of the lion, the fur is soft and often marked with spots or stripes. Cats are specialized hunters having lithe, compact bodies and large, sharp, scissorlike cheek teeth, called carnassials. The whiskers are developed and cats have acute sight, hearing, and sense of smell. There is a wide variation in the size and appearance of the members of this family; the smallest wild cats are much the same size as the domestic cat, whereas the largest species, the tiger, has a body length of up to 9.2 feet (2.8 meters), or 10.5 feet (3.2 meters) including the tail.

Most cats are nocturnal and all, except the lion, hunt alone. Lions live in prides of several females and their cubs, with one or more males. Several members of the pride usually hunt together. They lie in ambush or sneak forward slowly toward their prey until they are close enough to leap up and catch it, bringing it down with their claws and a bite that breaks the victim's neck.

Unlike most carnivores, cats have retractile claws that are extended to help grasp and slash prey, and when not in use are retracted into sheaths. The exception is the cheetah *(Acinonyx jubatus);* its blunt, nonretractile claws give it a good grip on the ground as it sprints at up to 70 miles (110 kilometers) per hour. Its light build and flexibility help it to turn fast, and its long tail provides steering and balance.

Among the big cats, one feature of some species is the roar, which is heard at night. These cats—the lion, tiger, leopard, and jaguar—have an additional ligament in the throat that is attached to the hyoid bone.

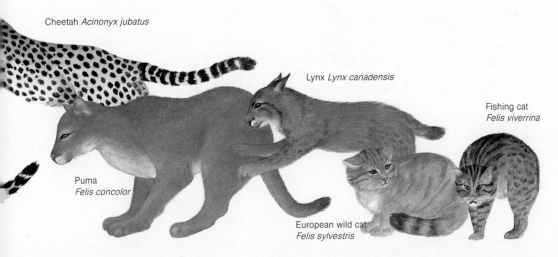

Cheetah *Acinonyx jubatus*

Lynx *Lynx canadensis*

Fishing cat *Felis viverrina*

Puma *Felis concolor*

European wild cat *Felis sylvestris*

Enormous variety in size and build of the cats becomes evident when species are compared. The head and body of a lion is about 8 feet (2.4 meters) long, and a tiger is even larger at up to 9 feet (2.8 meters) long. The leopard, cheetah, and mountain lion are similar in size—5 feet (1.5 meters)—whereas the lynx and European wild cat are slightly smaller. The body length of the fishing cat is about 28 inches (70 centimeters). With the exception of the cheetah, these cats stalk their prey or spring from ambush.

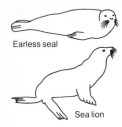

Earless seal

Sea lion

An earless seal cannot turn its hind flippers forward and so is much less mobile on land than the sea lion.

Pinnipeds

The seals (order Pinnipedia) are marine mammals which, together with the carnivores, insectivores, whales, and humans, comprise the flesh-eating animals of this earth. The order is divided into three families which, in turn, fall into two superfamilies—the earless seal family (family Phocidae), the sea lions and fur seals, also known as the eared seals (family Otariidae)—and the walrus (family Odobenidae). Pinnipeds are found along most coasts but some of the biggest concentrations are in Arctic and Antarctic waters.

General features

Pinnipeds spend most of their lives in water, although they come on to land or ice to bear and rear their pups, and to molt. Like the cetaceans, they are well adapted for an aquatic life; their bodies are streamlined and torpedo-shaped, and padded with fatty blubber that acts as an energy store and provides insulation; the limbs have been modified into flippers for swimming. Earless seals are clumsy on land, whereas in water they are very graceful, swimming with side-to-side movements of the hind flippers, the foreflippers being used for maneuvering at low speed. Pinnipeds have either tiny external ears or none at all, and slit-like nostrils. The ears and nostrils are closed when the animals are submerged, but the eyes, which are well cushioned, remain open

and are efficient under water. Whereas walruses are almost bare-skinned, most pinnipeds have a covering of short hair.

All pinnipeds are well adapted for diving; when they plunge, the heart rate immediately drops from 50-100 beats per minute to 10 or less—the remaining bloodflow is directed mainly to the brain. Like whales, they can survive without breathing for much longer periods than land mammals; the record for diving is probably held by the Weddell seal (*Leptonychotes weddelli*), at a depth of some 2,360 feet (719 meters) and for up to 43 minutes.

An adult pinniped usually eats about 11 to 15 pounds (5 to 7 kilograms) of food per day. The diet consists mainly of fish but eared seals also eat crustaceans and marine mollusks such as squid and octopus. Others, such as the leopard seals (*Hydrurga leptonyx*), also eat seal pups, and a genus of sea lion (*Neophoca*) occasionally eats penguins.

A few days after a cow seal has given birth, she mates again, but the implantation is delayed for a few months; this allows the female to recover from the strain of feeding her pup. It also means that pups are always born at about the same time of year, which is an important consideration for colonial or migratory species. Cow seals give birth to one pup a year, usually at a traditional breeding place where large colonies of seals gather. The bull seals at these breeding grounds are usually polygamous—one bull mates with several cows—and arrive there before the cows do to establish territories, keeping out other males by fighting.

After a gestation period of about 12 months, the pup is born. Earless suckle their pups for a short time—the harp seal (*Phoca groenlandica*), for example, suckles its young for only nine days after birth. The pups develop very rapidly and during this period the cow does not feed, drawing on her reserves of blubber to produce milk. The pups of some species are able to swim within hours of birth, whereas others take several weeks. Eared seals, however, rear their pups very slowly—Galapagos fur seals (*Arctocephalus galapagoensis*), for example, are not weaned until they are two or three years old.

Male pinnipeds are much larger than the females: a large bull southern elephant seal (*Mirounga leonina*) weighs up to 8,000 pounds (3,600 kilograms), four times more than the cow. The life span varies according to species, from about 25 years to 40 years or more, in captivity.

Elephant seals (*Mirounga angustrirostris*) breed in large colonies. The females (cows) feed the young (pups) on milk, living themselves on reserves of body fat, while the males (bulls) aggressively defend their harem of females.

The hindlimbs of earless seals are contained within the body; the small forelimbs are placed well forward. They move with difficulty on land, hunching onto the front flippers (A) and wriggling forward (B); they haul themselves up (C) and then collapse into a new position (D).

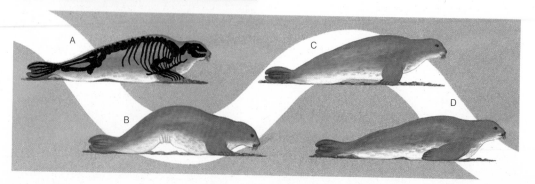

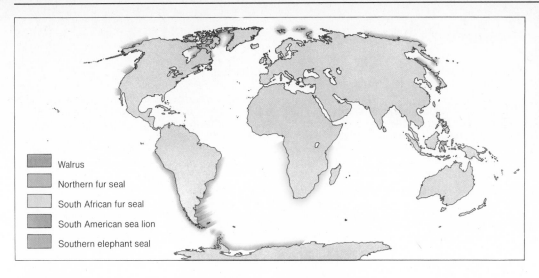

Walrus
Northern fur seal
South African fur seal
South American sea lion
Southern elephant seal

Some seals migrate. Walruses live in open Arctic waters, migrating south in winter before the ice closes in. Northern fur seals gather to breed at islands in the North Pacific, Okhotsk Sea, and Sea of Japan, then disperse south. South African fur seals, South American sea lions, and southern elephant seals are not really migratory, although the latter have been sighted as far north as Saint Helena.

The true seals

The 18 species of earless seals live mostly in the Arctic and Antarctic, but some inhabit temperate waters. The main exceptions are the monk seals (*Monachus* spp.), which live in warm seas, and some seals that inhabit freshwater lakes, such as the Baikal and Caspian seals *(Pusa subirica* and *P. caspica),* which live in these inland waters.

Pups of most species are born with a soft, dense, woollike white coat, which is replaced by the stiffer adult coat before they start to swim. The white coat serves as camouflage on the ice and its thickness provides good insulation. Common seal pups *(Phoca vitulina),* however, are born with their adult coat.

The crabeater seal *(Lobodon carcinophagus)* is the most abundant of all earless seal species, with a population of 15 million. Despite its name, it feeds on shrimplike crustaceans that it strains from the water through its teeth. Young crabeaters are hunted by leopard seals and many bear large scars from these attacks.

The eared seals

There are 16 species of eared seals, five of which are sea lions and eleven of which are fur seals; they are found in polar, temperate, and subtropical areas. They get their name because of their tiny cartilaginous earflaps, which earless seals do not possess. They are long and slender, with short but developed tails, whereas earless seals have only vestigial tails.

Fur seals have a thick undercoat of soft fur, protected by longer, coarser hair, whereas sea lions have one layer only of coarse hair. Sea lions are the biggest of the eared seals, have a heavier muzzle and head, and also a greater disparity in size between the sexes than other seals.

The eared seals and the walrus swim at high speeds by undulating their bodies, with their foreflippers tucked well back. The northern fur seal (*Callorhinus* sp.), for example, is able to swim at 10 miles (16 kilometers) per hour. Eared seals are more agile on land than are earless seals because they can turn the hind flippers forward; they thus lift the body off the ground, and move forward.

The walrus

The single species of walrus *(Odobenus rosmarus)* lives in the Arctic Ocean; it migrates south in winter, riding on the ice floes, and returns in the spring. It has a thick body and a tough, hairless skin that covers a layer of blubber 1 to 6 inches (2.5 to 15 centimeters) thick. Both sexes have a pair of tusks, which are long upper canines, to stir up food from the seabed, to fight, and to clamber up on to the ice. Walruses feed on bivalve shellfish. The bulls can measure 10 to 13 feet (3 to 4 meters) long and weigh as much as 3,000 pounds (1400 kilograms). Despite their size, they can swim at about 15 miles (24 kilometers) per hour.

Adult walruses *(Odobenus rosmarus)* have long powerful tusks—canine teeth—which the males brandish in threat displays when competing for females.

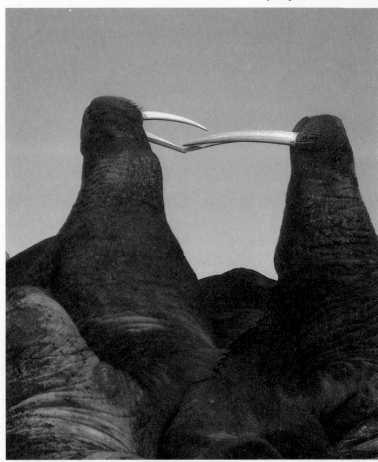

Aardvarks and subungulates

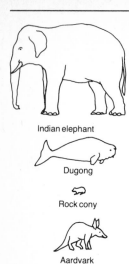

Indian elephant

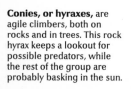

Dugong

Rock cony

Aardvark

The subungulates, shown here to the same scale, have a wide variety of forms and sizes, but are classified together mainly because of their dentition. An aardvark is included for comparison.

Plant-eating mammals that possess hoofs are referred to as ungulates. But many nonhoofed animals have evolved from primitive ungulate ancestors and have similar features to the ungulates; consequently, they are called subungulates. These include the aardvark, elephants, manatees, and conies, or hyraxes. Of these, the last three groups are herbivorous and have well-developed grinding molar teeth.

Aardvarks

As the only surviving species of primitive ungulates, zoologists place the aardvark *(Orycteropus afer)* in an order by itself—Order Tubulidentata. The name relates to the unusual molar teeth that the aardvark has, which contain many tubular pulp cavities. Aardvark means "earth pig" in Afrikaans, referring to its appearance and burrowing habits. These animals are stocky and powerful, weighing up to 140 pounds (64 kilograms). They have large ears that flatten to keep out the soil when they are burrowing, and which can move independently of one another. They have strong limbs and a thick, muscular tail. Aardvarks resemble the anteaters of South America in several ways, having an elongated snout, no teeth, and a long, protrusible tongue. These features, however, reflect parallel adaptations to a similar diet, rather than a close phylogenetic relationship.

Aardvarks feed mainly on ants and termites, using their strong claws to break open the sun-baked ant and termite hills. They also collect the insects as they swarm across the ground. An aardvark's tongue can be protruded up to 18 inches (46 centimeters) and is covered with sticky saliva, to which the insects adhere. Their thick skin appears to protect them from the painful bites of soldier termites.

Aardvarks are found in the savanna regions of Africa. They are nocturnal, traveling up to 19 miles (30 kilometers) a night in search of termites. During the day, they sleep in their burrows, and so are rarely seen. They usually have single offspring, but occasionally produce two.

Elephants

The present order of elephants (Proboscidea) is a mere remnant of its former size. In the Ice Age, numerous species, which included the mammoths, were spread throughout the world. Today, only one family remains (Elephantidae), containing two species—the African elephant *(Loxodonta africana)* and the Asiatic, or Indian elephant *(Elephas maximus)*. They are easily distinguished from each other, because the African species has larger ears than its Asian counterpart and grows to a greater size. The African elephant is the largest living land animal, weighing up to 6 tons. To support their weight, the limbs of elephants have become pillarlike, with each bone resting directly on the one below. The feet contain elastic pads to cushion its weight as the elephant moves.

Elephants often consume more than 770 pounds (349 kilograms) of vegetable matter per day, and may spend up to 16 hours a day feeding. Food and water are collected using the trunk, which is an extension of the nose and upper lip. At the trunk tip are fingerlike projections (one in the Asiatic elephant and two in the African one), which allow the trunk to pick up objects as small as groundnuts. Most of their food is woody and fibrous, which is broken down by very large molar teeth with jagged ridges. Each jaw has six molar teeth per side, but normally only one tooth is present at a time. As the tooth wears away, another one erupts from the back of the jaw. Once the last tooth (the size of a small brick) is lost, elephants have difficulty feeding, and may starve. The much sought-after ivory tusks of elephants are not canines, as is often thought, but rather well-developed upper incisors. Tusks of more than 10 feet (3 meters) long are known to have been taken from African bull elephants.

Conies

Conies, or hyraxes, resemble large, gray-brown guinea pigs. But they are more closely

Conies, or hyraxes, are agile climbers, both on rocks and in trees. This rock hyrax keeps a lookout for possible predators, while the rest of the group are probably basking in the sun.

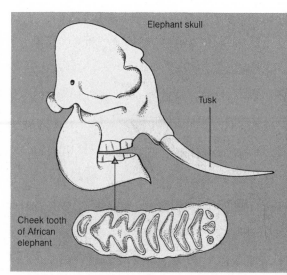

Elephant skull

Tusk

Cheek tooth of African elephant

related to elephants than to rodents, particularly in the arrangement of their teeth. The members of this group (order Hyracoidea) have well-developed grinding cheekteeth, and upper incisors that grow continually and curve, protruding from the mouth. These teeth are equivalent to tusks in elephants. The cony digestive system is unusual in that it has two appendixes.

Rock conies (*Procavia* sp. and *Heterohyrax* sp.) are highly sociable animals and live in large colonies. They are diurnal and often bask in the sun, when older members of the colony act as lookouts, giving a shrill alarm call if a predatory animal, such as a leopard, bird of prey, or rock python, approaches. Tree conies (*Dendrohyrax* spp.) are less sociable and are nocturnal, spending the day in tree holes or thick foliage.

All conies are highly vocal and use a wide range of croaks, cries, and alarm calls. All species also have a gland on the back, which is marked by a patch of different colored hair. When they are frightened, or during the mating season, this gland is exposed when the surrounding hairs are erected.

Manatees, dugongs, and sea cows

Despite their large, blubber-filled bodies, this group (order Sirenia) are thought to have been the origin of the mermaid stories. These aquatic mammals are found in coastal waters and large river systems in tropical and subtropical areas. Weighing up to 1,500 pounds (680 kilograms) and ranging in size from about 6 to 14 feet (2 to 4 meters) long, they do not venture ashore, even when giving birth. Today there is one genus of manatees *(Trichechus),* which contains three species, and one genus of dugongs and sea cows (Dugong), of which only dugongs exist.

Sirenians are herbivorous, feeding on seaweeds or freshwater plants. In Guyana, manatees have been used to control water weeds, which would otherwise choke up the rivers. The dugong has tusklike incisors and three cheekteeth on each side, whereas the manatee has no incisors, but up to 10 cheekteeth on each side, which are replaced and moved forward continually.

African elephants roam in herds consisting mainly of females and juveniles. After a gestation period of 18 to 23 months, pregnant females leave the herd to give birth. Like other mammals, the newborn young are fed on milk; the female has two nipples, located between her front legs.

The forelimbs of manatees form paddles, as in many other aquatic mammals. There are no hindlimbs, and the tail has a horizontal fluke like a whale's (but unlike seals and sea lions). Manatees can remain submerged for up to 15 minutes before having to surface to breathe.

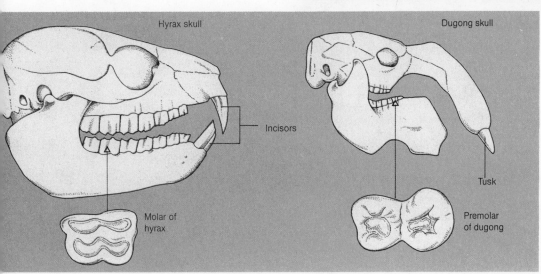

Hyrax skull

Dugong skull

Incisors

Molar of hyrax

Tusk

Premolar of dugong

Elephants, conies, and dugongs all eat plants and have batteries of cheek teeth for grinding plant material. A cony, or hyrax, has rodentlike incisor teeth, but in elephants and dugongs the upper incisors are modified into tusks. A manatee has neither incisors nor tusks.

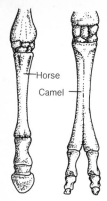

The horse represents the odd-toed ungulates (Perissodactyla), and the camel the even-toed ungulates (Artiodactyla).

Ungulates

The ungulates are hoofed, herbivorous mammals, although some are omnivorous. The group is composed of several unrelated species of mammals that have evolved hoofs. They have been grouped together into two orders—the odd-toed hoofed mammals (Perissodactyla), which comprise about 15 species, and the even-toed ungulates (Artiodactyla), which consist of approximately 170 species.

The characteristics, common to all ungulates, are concerned either with the problems of extracting energy, during digestion, from the plant food they eat (a process called rumination), or with defense. They are the only horned animals, and those that do not have horns use their long canine teeth as weapons.

General features

The dentition of ungulates allows them to cope with a herbivorous diet, the constituents of which need to be thoroughly chewed. The sharp, pointed cheekteeth found in primitive mammals are unsuitable for this diet; instead, ungulates have developed large, flattened cheekteeth with good grinding surfaces. In those animals whose diet consists of highly abrasive vegetation such as grass, molars with high crowns have evolved, which can be ground down a considerable distance before they are worn out. The cheekteeth have complex ridges composed of dentin, which are adjacent to areas of enamel, and are filled with cement. As the vegetation is ground down, the cement, enamel, and dentin are worn away to different degrees, producing a rough, self-sharpening surface.

Any animal unable to defend itself well against predators needs to be able to run fast, and most ungulates have evolved an efficient type of movement known as unguligrade locomotion. In fast-running animals, the upper bones in the limbs are short, but the lower bones are long, allowing lengthy strides. In addition, the bones in the feet are elongated, and by running on its toes the animal effectively adds a third functional segment to its limb. The toes themselves are lifted until they only touch the ground at the tips. Hoofs have developed, replacing the stability that the ungulates lost by not having the whole foot flat on the ground. These hoofs are composed of keratin, which makes them light, resilient, and extremely tough.

Because the ungulates lift the backs of their feet to run on their toes, the short side-toes cannot reach the ground; without a function, these toes have become reduced in many ungulates or have disappeared altogether.

It is this feature that divides the ungulates into the two orders. In the odd-toed perissodactyls, the functional axis of the leg passes through the third or middle digit, and species with only three digits (or even just one) have evolved. Where the axis falls between the third and fourth digits, animals with either four or two toes have evolved—these are the even-toed artiodactyls.

The antlers of the red deer stag *(Cerbus elaphus)* are a typical feature of those herbivores whose dentition has been so modified for a herbivorous diet that they cannot use their teeth for protection or offense. Instead, these animals have developed horns or antlers with which they defend and assert themselves.

Dentition among the ungulates is varied. The grazing horse (A, *Equus caballus*) has high-crowned cheekteeth with self-sharpening grinding surfaces. The tapir *(Tapirus* spp.), which nibbles at low shrubs (B), has relatively low-crowned cheekteeth and its nose extends into a short mobile proboscis. Among the artiodactyls, the peccaries *(Tayassu* spp.) have tusklike upper canines (C) and a long snout. The camels *(Camelus* spp.) have spatulate incisors (D) that project forward.

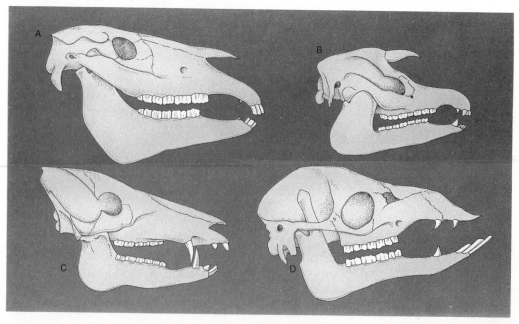

Ungulates breed usually once a year, with single offspring, although some species breed once every two years. The females come into estrus several times a year and, if not mated, can continue on heat for several months. The gestation period is usually 11 to 12 months, and the life span from 25 to 40 years or more.

Rumination

Most mammals are not able to digest cellulose, but herbivores have evolved a method of extracting nutrition from their food by breaking down the cellulose. This is achieved by microorganisms that live symbiotically in some part of the digestive system and dissolve the cellulose.

In ruminating animals, such as camels and chevrotains, the stomach has three compartments, but in true ruminants—giraffes, deer, antelope, sheep, goats, and cattle—it consists of four: the rumen, the reticulum, the omasum, and the abomasum. Food, mixed with saliva, is fermented in the rumen and reticulum, where bacteria and protozoa break it down. To ensure that the food is well broken down, it is regurgitated and chewed once more (this is called chewing the cud). After it has been remasticated, or rechewed, the food bypasses the rumen and enters the omasum. Here the mixture is fermented further; the liquid is pressed into the abomasum, where it is subjected to the action of digestive enzymes; the rest is absorbed and the waste is passed out.

Perissodactyls

The odd-toed ungulates have not been very successful. In the early days of mammalian history they were numerous, but today only three of the original twelve families remain: the horses (Equidae), the tapirs (Tapiridae), and the rhinoceroses (Rhinocerotidae). The tapirs and rhinoceroses are greatly reduced in numbers and, apart from the zebra, the Equidae would probably also be greatly reduced in numbers had they not been domesticated. Their natural range today is Africa and the steppes of Asia.

The perissodactyls have three toes (if only on the hind feet, as in tapirs) or one single toe, as in the equids. They are browsers and grazers, and the structure of their lips facilitates the collection of plant material. Their flat-topped cheekteeth and high-crowned molars enable the breakdown of coarse vegetable food. They have simple stomachs, with a large cecum and no gall bladder. Horns composed entirely of dermal material may be present, and the skin is often very thick, with little hair.

The family Equidae contains only one living genus, *Equus,* which includes horses, the ass, and zebras. All species are highly specialized for swift movement and for grazing. Only the third digit remains on the limb and the second and fourth toes have been reduced to splints. In their native states they live in migratory herds, as do many herbivores that live on plains.

The wild horse is now represented by only one species—the Mongolian wild horse, or

Wart hogs *(Phacochoerus aethiopicus)* are typical of the hoglike artiodactyls in that their canines form tusks, which they use in defense. The nyala *(Tragelaphus angasi)*—like many other antelopes—has developed, instead, sharp horns with which it can defend itself.

The well-developed canines of the hippopotamuses are used as powerful weapons. These animals live in large herds, the males of which are territorial and use their lower canines in fights during the mating season.

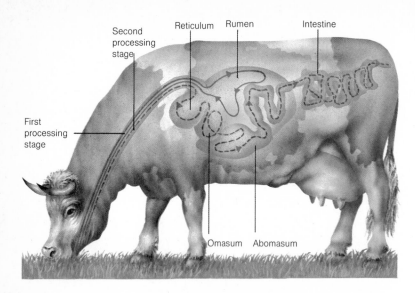

Second processing stage

First processing stage

Reticulum   Rumen   Intestine

Omasum   Abomasum

Cattle are true ruminants. They have a four-chambered stomach composed of a rumen, a reticulum, an omasum, and an abomasum. Food is swallowed with salivary enzymes and is fermented in the rumen, where the enzymes and bacteria in the digestive juices break it down. It is regurgitated and chewed again. The food is swallowed once more, this time passing into the other chambers, where it undergoes further enzyme action. It is absorbed and the waste is passed out.

The horse is the fastest, strongest runner of the ungulates, because in it the development of the unguligrade limb is most advanced. As a migratory animal it is adapted to sustaining speed for long periods.

Przewalski's horse. They used to roam the steppes of central Asia in large herds but there have been no sightings of them for many years and they probably no longer exist outside captivity. The wild horse is shorter than the domestic one, with a stiff, erect mane, small ears, a low-slung tail, and a shrill voice.

The ass, native to Africa and Asia, is found most frequently on plains sparsely covered with low shrubs. It was the first animal in the genus to be domesticated.

Zebras, now the most common member of the genus in the wild, are found only in eastern, central, and southern Africa. They were once called horse tigers because of their stripes. The stripes of the plains zebra are wide apart, with shadow stripes in some species. The rare mountain zebra has wide stripes with a transverse gridiron pattern on the lower back. The largest zebra, Grevy's zebra, has narrow, close-set stripes.

The tapir, whose natural range is restricted to the Malay Peninsula, Java, Sumatra, and Central and South America, has only one living genus *(Tapirus)*, with four species. The tapir's forefeet have four toes, whereas the hind feet have three.

The three genera of rhinoceros are found in Africa, Asia, Sumatra, Java, and Borneo. They inhabit savanna and moist wooded areas, often near water, feeding on shrubs, leaves, and fruit, and are mainly nocturnal. These massive animals—they reach 6 to 15 feet (2 to 4.6 meters) in length—have short, pillarlike limbs with three digits. They have thick, sparsely haired skin with characteristic folds and one or two horns on the nose, or nasal plate com-

posed of solid fibrous keratin. Their hearing and sense of smell are well developed, although their vision is dull.

Artiodactyls

In the early days of ungulate development, artiodactyls were not as common as perissodactyls. But they have become increasingly prominent and today are one of the most successful groups of mammals, native throughout the world, except in Australia and New Zealand, where they have been introduced.

There are nine families of artiodactyls: the hoglike species contain the pigs and hogs (Suidae), the peccaries (Tayassuidae), and the hippopotamuses (Hippopotamidae). The camels and llamas are contained in the family Camelidae, and the chevrotains in the family Tragulidae. The rest of the artiodactyls are true ruminants and are grouped into the infraorder Pecora. This group contains the giraffes (Giraffidae), the deer and their allies (Cervidae), the cattle, antelope, goats, and sheep (Bovidae), and the pronghorn (Antilocapridae).

The hoglike artiodactyls are in many ways the most primitive of the group. They are still four-toed (although the side-toes are reduced), and their limbs are not greatly elongated, which means that they cannot move quickly. They are omnivorous and have large, canine tusks. Their two-chambered stomach is not as developed as that of the ruminants.

The most typical of the five genera of wild hogs is the wild boar *(Sus scrofa),* from which the domestic hog was probably derived. The hog is typically a nocturnal forest dweller and

The zebras (*Equus* spp.) are the most common equid in the wild. No two individual zebras are alike in the pattern of their stripes. It is thought that the stripes serve a purpose in social recognition. Out on the open plain they seek safety in numbers and move in vast herds of males and females. This characteristic contrasts with many of the other plains herd animals, such as antelope, which move in herds of separate sexes.

travels in groups of up to 50 individuals. But some species, such as the wart hog *(Phacochoerus aethiopicus),* are diurnal and travel singly or in family parties. The males have upper and lower canine tusks that curve upward. They eat roots, plants, birds' eggs, and small mammals. The young number up to 12 per litter.

Peccaries are distantly related to wild hogs. There are three living species of peccaries: the collared peccary, or javelina; the white-lipped peccary; and the tagua, or Chacoan peccary. The tagua lives in the Gran Chaco region of Paraguay, Argentina, and Bolivia. Scientists discovered the tagua in 1975. They had previously thought that this species had become extinct more than 10,000 years ago.

There are two genera and two species of hippopotamuses, both found in Africa. These large, heavy animals are adapted for both aquatic and terrestrial life. They have a broad muzzle that is suitable for taking in large masses of pulpy water plants. Their eyes and ears are situated high up on the skull, enabling them to function well while almost totally submerged. They are expert swimmers and can stay submerged for more than five minutes. These animals live in herds of 5 to 30, usually near the water.

The camelids can be split into two groups: camels (*Camelus* spp.), which are native to the Old World, and llamas (*Lama* spp.), found in South America. There are two species of camels, both desert dwellers, although only one is still found in the wild. They are able to conserve water by reducing evaporation and concentrating their urine, and can lose up to 25

The tapir (*Tapirus* sp.) is a solitary animal found in damp forests or swamps, and is nocturnal or crepuscular. It feeds on leaves, shoots, and fruit that it collects with its short proboscis.

per cent of their body weight by desiccation. Possibly because of this characteristic they are unique among mammals in that their red blood cells are oval rather than spherical.

The hoofs have disappeared on all camelids and have been replaced by a nail and a large pad, which enables them to walk on soft or sandy ground. They have two digits on each limb, the third and the fourth. The camelids are ruminants but have a less complex system than the Pecoras, with no separation of the omasum and abomasum.

The South American camelids live in a variety of habitats, from cool plains to mountains of permanent snow. The llamas *(Lama glama)* are smaller than camels, have no humps, and

In a transverse gallop, such as this (below), a horse's body is supported by at least one limb on the ground, except during one short phase in the cycle.

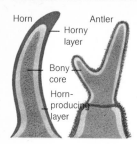

Horns are a feature of most bovids. They are firmly attached to the skull and are not shed. In contrast, the antlers of most cervids, which are bony growths from the skull covered by a layer of velvety skin, break off every year.

Camels (*Camelus* spp.) are well adapted for walking on sandy ground. Their digits (two on each limb) splay as they walk, revealing a cushionlike pad in between that provides a larger surface area for them to walk on and helps them not to sink into the sand.

A stag's antlers are grown and shed every year, each time developing more points, until the animal reaches about its fifteenth year. They are shed in early spring, and six weeks later new ones develop. By the end of May they are fully grown.

are covered with a thick coat of wool. Two wild species of South American camelid are the vicuña (*Vicugna* sp.) and the guanaco *(Lama guanacoe).*

The chevrotains, or mouse deer, are timid forest browsers, not much bigger than a rabbit, found in the tropics of the Eastern Hemisphere. They have no horns and use their large, tusklike upper canines as weapons. They resemble deer in the white patterning of their red-brown coat. With a three-chambered stomach, the chevrotains—like the camels—lie between the non-ruminants and the true ruminants.

The rest of the artiodactyls, all of which are true ruminants, contain the most successful and numerous of the ungulates. As well as the possession of a rumen, almost all of them have horns or antlers, and the side-toes of their limbs have disappeared, leaving two functional digits, although lateral ones may be represented by imperfect dew claws. The incisors have been lost from the upper jaw, and the lower teeth bite against a hard upper gum.

The giraffes (*Giraffa* spp.) and okapis (*Okapia* spp.) are browsing animals now restricted to tropical Africa. Their long necks contain seven vertebrae only, which is the usual number in mammals, but each vertebra is greatly elongated. The neck of the okapis is shorter than that of the giraffes. Horns are found in both sexes and are ossified knobs that grow continually although slowly. Whereas okapis are solitary, giraffes usually move in family herds.

The deer, or cervids, which are mainly forest dwellers, are essentially temperate zone animals, although some are found in southern Asia. The males have antlers, which are bony growths from the skull. They are shed each year and form progressively more branches as the animals age. The older the cervid, the larger are the antlers.

Cervids are divided into four subfamilies: Moschinae, Muntiacinae, Cervinae, and Odocoileini. Moschinae contains only one genus, the musk deer (*Moschus* spp.). Restricted to Asia, this genus is thought to be the most primitive of the cervids and, with the water deer (*Hydropotes* spp.), is the only type with no antlers. The male has an abdominal gland that exudes musk. Because of the demand for musk by the perfume trade, resulting in it being extensively hunted, the musk deer has died out of most of its former range.

Muntiacinae, or muntjacs, contains two genera that are also restricted to Asia. They are small deer, and although they have antlers they also have well-developed upper canines. They are solitary crepuscular animals.

The subfamily Cervinae includes the red deer and wapitis (*Cervus* spp.), axis deer (*Axis* spp.), and fallow deer (*Dama* spp.). They are found in Asia, Europe, and North America. The Odocoileini is the most widely distributed subfamily and includes such species as white-tailed deer (*Odocoileus* spp.), moose or elk *(Alces alces),* and caribou and reindeer *(Rangifer tarandus).* The caribou and reindeer are the most northern species of cervid.

The bovids are the largest group of ungulates found throughout the world. They include most of the animals that man depends on for food, such as cattle, sheep, and goats,

Eighteen months old

First set

Two and a half years old

Second set

Four and a half years old

Fourth set

Fifteen and a half years old

Fifteenth set

Giraffes (*Giraffa* spp.) are the tallest of all animals, the males reaching a height of 18 feet (5 meters) and the females 15 feet (4.5 meters). Because rising from a lying position is so difficult for these animals, they usually sleep while standing. They have massive hearts, needed to force the blood up their long necks to the brain. An advantage of their height is that they have little competition for the leaves on high branches on which they feed.

as well as other animals such as antelopes and gazelles. There are nine subfamilies: the cow-like Bovinae, the duikers (Cephalophinae), the reedbuck and their relatives (Hippotraginae), antelopes and gazelles (Antilopinae), and the sheep and goats (Caprinae).

All bovids have bony horns which, unlike antlers, are never shed. The horns, which are firmly attached to the skin, are not branched, although they can be compressed or twisted. Bovids are usually found in herds, and most inhabit grassland, scrubland, or deserts, but goats and sheep are generally found in rocky mountainous or desert areas. They feed by twisting vegetation around the tongue and cutting it with the lower incisors.

Domestic cattle, sheep, and goats have been bred from European and Asian species. There are six species of wild sheep found in North Africa, Canada, and mountainous areas of Asia and the Mediterranean. None has as woolly a coat as the domestic sheep. Together with rats and hogs, wild goats or goats that have escaped domestic captivity are among the most destructive of animals because they eat anything in sight. In destroying vegetation they have been instrumental in the extinction of other animal species, such as some birds.

The pronghorn *(Antilocapra americana)* is the only remaining species of its family, peculiar to North America. Herds of about a thousand animals used to be common, but their numbers are greatly reduced, and today they live in herds of about 50 to 100. Like cattle, their horns consist of a bony core that is never shed, although the horns' covering is. The horns are branched, as are those of the cervids.

Impalas *(Aepyceros melampus)* gather in large herds, often in groups of hundreds of individuals, which affords them some safety from predators; while a few sentries keep watch, the others can eat reasonably peaceably. Impalas can run very fast when threatened and are known to leap as far as 30 feet (9 meters).

Animals in danger

The great auk (Pinguinus impennis), a large flightless bird, lived in similar habitats in the Northern Hemisphere to those occupied by penguins in the South. It became extinct in 1844; now only stuffed museum specimens remain.

In a world that did not change physically and in which new species of animals and plants did not evolve, extinction would be unknown. Each available niche in the world's ecology would be filled by a steady population of various animals—the predators and the prey—in an unchanging, balanced life cycle. The real world does not correspond to these ideal conditions, however, in a number of significant respects. The population of a given species increases in a period when conditions are advantageous, and decreases when adverse conditions predominate (for example, when there is a particularly cold or long winter). The natural ecological balances that do exist are dynamic in character, and tend to change with time. In fact, such changes are an inextricable part of the mechanism of evolution: if evolution takes place, extinction is inevitable.

Physical changes and extinction

The conditions for the existence of life on earth are dependent on a narrow band of acceptable criteria, and only small variations in such factors as the local rainfall, temperature range, or chemical pollution levels can lead to the extinction of a variety or a species. And this extinction in turn inevitably has some effect on all the local species as the ecological balance readjusts to compensate and regain stability.

A larger climatic or other change can have even more dramatic effects. For example, strong evidence now exists to show that the sudden and total disappearance about 65 million years ago of the dinosaurs (then the dominant life-form) and many other species resulted from catastrophic climatic changes caused by a collision between the earth and an asteroid. Ice ages (which might have been caused by variations in the sun's activity) had a

dramatic effect on flora and fauna—leading to the reduction or extinction of some species and the increase or evolution of other better adapted ones.

Effects of one species on another

The gradual evolution of better adapted life-forms causes the reduction in numbers and possibly the eventual extinction of less well adapted species trying to occupy the same ecological niche. In addition, certain species develop an interdependence on other species of flora or fauna in areas of reproduction, habitat, or food requirements. Any external event that affects the numbers or habits of one of these species may therefore have disastrous effects on the survival of the other dependent species. Such interdependence reduces the chances of survival of the species concerned. And disease—particularly the evolution of new virus strains—threatens certain species with extinction while leaving others relatively unaffected.

In each ecological environment one dominant species is likely to evolve, and it has a major influence on the ecological balance, affecting the numbers and survival of other species. For example, some scientists believe that dinosaurs became extinct because they were unable to compete successfully with mammals for food. The dominant species is most likely to be the predator at the top of the food chain. It will be challenged and replaced in this position only by the evolution of a better adapted species, or by a physical change in the environment.

Man and his activities

The evolution of humans as an intelligent and highly adaptive species has led to an ecology in which they have a position of dominance over all other species on earth. This fact, linked with human ability to modify or even totally alter the environment, has placed many species in danger of extinction. Pressures of food production for a rapidly expanding human population have meant that there is probably no natural habitat that is not now threatened. Humans are the first species to have the ability to make all life forms extinct—including themselves.

The threat of humankind to other species is apparent in a number of ways. The development of domesticated strains of plants and animals to improve the efficiency of food production (for example, wheat and domestic cattle) demand the creation of specialized environments that remove large areas of habitat from the native ecology. Indeed, positive action is taken to exclude the naturally occurring plants and animals from these areas with such things as weedkillers, traps, and fences. Increased requirements for living accommodation remove land from the natural ecology as new towns

The North American bison (Bison bison), or buffalo as it is also known, was relentlessly hunted throughout the nineteenth century so that by the 1880's its numbers had fallen alarmingly. The animal has been brought back from the edge of extinction by careful management, but like its European cousin the wisent (Bison bonasus), is today found only on reserves.

and cities are built. Relocation of water courses and the physical manipulation of the landscape remove further natural habitats. In addition, overgrazing of domestic animals can cause soil erosion, reducing previously fertile land to new desert, again changing the local ecological balance.

The overexploitation of a species for food, clothing, or ornament can reduce its numbers to below that necessary to maintain a viable population. The collecting of animals from the wild for study or to populate zoos can threaten scarce animals. Wars between various human groups can result in animals confined to a small area being threatened as they become incidental casualties, whether of bomb, bullet, fire, or from the use of defoliants—or more indirectly by the lack of food that often accompanies war.

Human activities such as farming and industry create pollution by releasing poisonous chemicals into the atmosphere, soil, and water. Species with little tolerance to such pollutants may be threatened. Sometimes catastrophic accidents that release large amounts of oil, toxic gases, or radioactive waste can have immediate and disastrous effects on wildlife. The burning of wood and fossil fuels to produce energy may have long-term effects on the carbon dioxide content of the atmosphere—possibly affecting the climate in an adverse way. Other experiments in climate control might have unpredictable effects on the world's ecology.

The introduction of species from different parts of the world into an ecology—either accidentally or deliberately—can have a disastrous effect on local species and may result in the extinction of those that are unable to compete or those that become predated upon.

Wherever a species is present in only a limited geographical area, or occupies only a particular type of habitat, or has only one kind of food, it must be considered to be in potential danger. But ironically for some species whose numbers have fallen below a certain level, only the direct intervention of humans can now save them from total extinction.

Unique to the Galapagos Islands, the land iguana *(Conolophus subcristatus)* is being threatened by introduced predators—particularly rats—which destroy and eat its eggs and young.

Uncontrolled hunting and poaching still bring the threat of extinction to some of the world's large animals. Despite international agreements, whales are still being overhunted. Fast catcherboats armed with explosive harpoons take the dead whales to large factory ships *(above)*, where they are processed. In Africa, the killing can be even more wasteful. The rhinoceros is killed by poachers only for its valuable horn *(left);* the carcass is left for the vultures and hyenas.

Endangered lower animals

Increasingly, people are becoming aware that various species of birds and mammals have become in danger of extinction, and commend or actually help in the steps being taken to conserve such animals. But many other creatures—the less glamorous animals such as mollusks and insects, fishes, and reptiles—are also endangered. Colorful tropical butterflies are caught by the thousands so that their wings can be used in jewelry and ornaments. Some species of snails, crabs, and crayfish are caught and eaten as delicacies in restaurants around the world without any thought about the preservation of breeding populations and their future survival. Fishes continue to suffer from the effects of overfishing and increasing pollution of the seas and oceans.

Nearly all such lower animals are part of the food supply of an interdependent chain of higher animals such as birds and mammals. Eventually, some of these may also become threatened as their food supply diminishes. And ultimately, the threat may extend to the food supplies of man himself. Yet it is nearly always the activities of man that have brought the animals to the point where their survival is in question.

Man-made hazards

The greatest of the threats to lower animals is pollution of all kinds—from the testing of nuclear weapons to the dumping of sewage and industrial waste. For example, the komodo dragon *(Varanus komodoensis),* the largest of all the lizards, now survives on those tiny Indonesian islands that as yet offer nothing for man to exploit.

Land reclamation, industrialized agriculture, and the wanton and greedy destruction of the world's large forests will continue to cause havoc among wildlife unless it is halted—and with some urgency. In some areas of the world, there is little hope that present governments will realize that it is to the advantage of their own people and traditional ways of life that each and every species is conserved, including the lower life forms. An animal would not have evolved naturally if there was not some reason for its existence in the delicate interrelationships of nature.

In the sea

An instructive example of the threat to lower animals is provided by the myriad array of fishes and other creatures that depend for their existence on Australia's Great Barrier Reef. Since the 1960's, some parts of the coral reef have died off as a result of pollution and a plague of large, dark, spiny starfish known as the crown-of-thorns *(Acanthaster planci).* These starfish, often as many as 15 of them on each square yard of reef, prey on the depleted coral polyps. The large increase in the number of crown-of-thorns is due in part to the removal from the reef of their chief natural enemies—and population stabilizers—the large marine snails. Called tritons (Cymatiidae) and helmet shells (Cassididae), their ornamental shells were much prized as souvenirs by tourists. The sale of the shells has now been halted to allow the coral to revive, so that a healthy balance of species is restored to the reef.

Concentrated fishing (and pollution) has resulted in shortages in the world's fish population. Since the 1940's, so intensive has the fishing of some species become that even common fishes such as flounders, ocean perch, lake herring, tuna, and others are presently in danger. Often the fault lies not merely with the tonnages of fish that are taken, but with the

The living corals whose skeletons accumulate to form the Australian Great Barrier Reef are the chief food of a spiny starfish *(below)* called the crown-of-thorns *(Acanthaster planci).* The reef is a habitat for a whole range of interdependent creatures, which are therefore also threatened by the demise of the coral.

Butterflies have long been collected indiscriminately, mainly because they are so decorative. This New Guinea species, the Victoria birdwing *(Ornithoptera victoriae),* has been hunted almost to extinction, as have other birdwing species and the iridescent blue South American butterflies, such as those of the *Morpho* genus.

fact that, by using nets with a very small mesh, fishermen are catching young immature fish before they have a chance to breed. Also, there is a need for international restrictions on the sale of highly valued tropical fish for home aquariums.

On the land

Most of the major species of endangered lower animals on the land, and in its associated freshwater lakes and rivers, are reptiles. In the Americas, two tortoises, the Mexican gopher tortoise *(Gopherus flavomarginatus)*

and the giant Galapagos land tortoise *(Geochelone elephantopus),* are at risk, and the population of the Cuban crocodile *(Crocodylus rhombifer)* has been estimated at fewer than 500 individuals. The short-necked tortoises *(Pseudemydra umbrina)* of western Australia probably total only half that number. And on the small islands off the North Island of New Zealand the unique primitive lizardlike animal called the tuatara *(Sphenodon punctatus)*—the sole remaining species of a whole order of reptiles that has remained virtually unchanged for 20 million years—is finally in danger of joining the dinosaurs.

Large land reptiles continue to suffer from the spread of man's activities and introduced predatory species. The Galapagos land tortoise *(Geochelone elephantopus, above left)* and the Indonesian komodo dragon *(Varanus komodoensis)*—at 10 feet (3 meters) long, the world's largest lizard—are both endangered.

Israel painted frog
Discoglossus nigriventer
Possibly extinct

Italian spade-footed toad
Pelobates fuscus insubricus
Almost extinct

Desert slender salamander
Batrachoseps aridus
250—500

Orange toad
Bufo periglenes
5,000—10,000

Santa Cruz long-toed salamander
Amblystoma macrodactylum croceum
About 10,000

Illinois mud turtle
Kinosternon flavescens spooneri
Fewer than 20

False gavial
Tomistoma schlegelii
About 100

St Croix ground lizard
Ameiva polops
About 150

Watling Island ground iguana
Cyclura rileyi rileyi
200

Indian gavial
Gavialis gangeticus
450

Endangered amphibians *(far left)* include various species of frogs, toads, and salamanders, many of which suffer from the drainage or pollution of the waters in which they breed. Among reptiles *(left),* turtles and crocodiles are threatened mostly by being hunted for their shells and skins. The numbers given refer to the estimated survivors in the early 1980's.

Endangered birds

Ever since the last dodo (*Raphus* sp.) disappeared from the island of Mauritius in 1681, about 80 species of birds have become extinct. A few of them may have died out naturally, but most have succumbed as a result of human destruction, competition, or other interference.

As well as these birds that can never be brought back, there are today about 210 species and subspecies in danger of extinction. The main threats are to large birds that are conspicuous and easy to kill, as well as suffering from the disadvantage of breeding slowly. Birds that are confined to islands are particularly at risk.

Direct threats

There are various kinds of direct threats. The most obvious is hunting—for food, feathers, or sport. Although a significant threat to birds in many parts of the world, uncontrolled hunting is declining in northern Europe and North America, with more enlightened attitudes about conservation. But controls have come too late for some species, such as the Eskimo curlew *(Numenius borealis)*. Once seen in huge migratory flocks numbering thousands of birds, it has not been sighted for several years and may well already be extinct.

The California condor *(Gymnogyps californianus)* is another seriously endangered American bird. One of the world's heaviest flying species, with an 8-foot (2.4-meter) wingspan, this majestic Western Hemisphere vulture was once scarce but widespread over much of North America; but today there are only about 30 birds in one small area of southern California. The primary reason for its decline was land cultivation (it needs huge hunt-

ing areas in which to find animal corpses), and the small population has been further depleted by illegal shooting.

Another example of such a large, slow-breeding bird is the Steller's, or short-tailed, albatross *(Diomedia albatrus)*. Japanese plume traders slaughtered more than 5 million of them in 17 years, so that it is now reduced to a small colony on Torishima Island, near Japan.

To this day, hunting in areas such as the Mediterranean accounts for many thousands of birds killed. In Italy, for instance, about 100 million songbirds such as robins and thrushes are killed every year. Such pressures can result in local extinctions or near extinctions, as with the threatened European population of the great bustard *(Otis tarda)* or the extermination of the Arabian race of the ostrich *(Struthio camelus syriacus)* in the 1960's as a result of elaborate hunting expeditions. An indirect hazard of hunting is that birds eat, with their food, the waste lead shot scattered over the ground from shotguns. It is a particular threat to swans, geese and ducks.

Rare species are threatened by unscrupulous egg collectors and taxidermists. Illegal collecting of live birds is also a problem. Exotic tropical birds suffer most; huge numbers are captured for the pet trade and for the less reputable zoos, and many birds die crammed in packing cases in aircraft. For example, about 50 of the beautiful cock of the rock *(Rupicola peruviana)* die in transit from South America for every one that survives.

Another direct threat occurs when birds are killed because they are thought, often wrongly, to be a pest. The only North American parrot, the Carolina parakeet *(Conuropis carolinensis),* once was common, but by 1904 had been hunted to extinction because of its fondness for fruit, especially the citrus fruit in the settlers' orchards (which had replaced much of the original forest habitat). In New Zealand, the kea *(Nestor notabilis),* a parrot with a hooked,

In the early 1980's, more than 20 species of birds had fallen in numbers to fewer than 50 each. Indeed, some of those illustrated here have not been sighted for several years and may by now have become extinct.

A   Cuban ivory-billed wood-
    pecker
    *Campephilus principalis
    bairdi*
    Fewer than 12

B   Mauritius kestrel
    Falco punctatus
    About 12

C   White-breasted silver
    eye
    Zosteros alcogularis
    Fewer than 20

D   Madagascar sea eagle
    Haliaeetus vociferoides
    About 20

E   Pink pigeon
    Nesoenas mayeri
    About 20

F   Chatham Island pigeon
    *Hemiphaga
    novaeseelandiae
    chathamensis*
    Fewer than 25

G   Lord Howe currawong
    *Strepera graculina
    crissalis*
    30—50

H   Seychelles magpie robin
    *Copsychus
    seychellarum*
    Fewer than 40

I   Californian condor
    *Gymnogyps
    californianus*
    About 30

J   Western tragopan
    *Tragopan
    melanocephalus*
    About 50

The nene, or Hawaiian goose *(Branta sandvicensis, left),* was so reduced in numbers in its island habitats that small breeding colonies have been established in wildfowl reserves. The fate of the monkey-eating Philippines eagle *(Pithecophaga jefferyi, right)* is less certain because, due to its specialized diet, it is extremely difficult to keep in captivity.

hawklike bill, has been wrongly accused of killing game birds and attacking sheep.

Indirect threats

The main damage to birds is being done indirectly by habitat destruction or alteration, or pollution. The most serious threats are to birds of tropical rain forests and wetlands. The Cuban and American race of the ivory-billed woodpecker *(Campephilus principalis),* for example, was for many years feared to be extinct. Logging had destroyed most of its habitat. In 1986, at least two ivory-billed woodpeckers were sighted in Cuba. The diminutive Kirtland's warbler *(Dendroica kirtlandii)* struggled to survive in its extremely specialized habitat in central Michigan, United States, helped by careful management and strict protection. There are about 1,000 of these small yellow-breasted birds, which nest only in areas of forest that have been burned.

Wetland species such as the Japanese crane *(Grus japonensis)* and the whooping crane *(Grus americana)* are similarly threatened as drainage, pollution, and acid rain from factory emissions destroy their habitats. Oil pollution accounts for the deaths—often slow and miserable—of countless thousands of seabirds, such as puffins, razorbills, and other auks, divers (loons), and waterfowl. Such birds are particularly vulnerable because they spend a considerable proportion of their time swimming on the surface of the sea.

Other indirect threats to seabirds include fishing nets. Danish fishing boats off Greenland are thought to have killed an estimated 500,000 of the auks called Brünnich's guillemots *(Uria lomvia)* in their salmon nets.

Pesticides have had a devastating effect on many birds, such as the peregrine falcon *(Falco peregrinus).* In the 1950's, the peregrine was almost wiped out in North America and severely reduced in Europe because it ate prey that had been feeding on crops sprayed with DDT and other pesticides. Other birds that have suffered similarly include the American bald eagle *(Haliaetus leucocephalus),* the osprey *(Pandion haliaetus),* various species of pelicans, and the bald ibis *(Geronticus eremita).*

Overhead power cables kill or maim many migrating birds, especially at night. Light-houses are also a threat to night migrants, as are some skyscrapers; oil and gas flares can kill huge flocks at once. Cars and trucks also take a great toll of birds worldwide.

One of the worst of all indirect threats comes from animals introduced by man, especially on islands where there are no indigenous mammalian predators. Cats, rats, dogs, and hogs have helped to wipe out many species. Rats, for instance, have caused the extinction of at least nine species of flightless island rails, and cats introduced in 1931 to Herokapare Island, New Zealand, have wiped out six species and reduced the total bird population from an estimated 400,000 to a few thousand. On tiny Saint Stephens Island, New Zealand, the entire population of the unique wren that lived there was killed in a single year (1894) by a single cat belonging to the lighthouse keeper.

A male osprey *(Pandion haliaetus)* swoops down to a female before mating. The decline of this fish-eating bird has resulted mainly from poisoning with pesticides, although even its eggs are vulnerable to theft by unscrupulous human "collectors."

Prosimian primates are among the most highly evolved animals on the endangered list, particularly those confined to islands, where they cannot escape from intensive hunting or introduced predators. The sifaka *(Propithecus verrauxi)* is native to Madagascar, where some of the animals are protected on reserves.

Endangered mammals

Almost every year for the past 80 years, at least one species of mammal has become extinct. Of the 4,000 or so living species of mammals, 375 are currently listed as endangered, and are given protection by international law from hunting and exploitation. Less adaptable than lower forms of life and usually less mobile than most birds, mammals are in the front line of the fight for survival.

Humans have considerable commercial interest in mammals and have long been dependent on them for a variety of purposes. Whales are killed for their oil and meat, monkeys are snatched from forests for medical research, leopards and cheetahs are killed for sport and the profit from the sale of their furs. It is estimated that two million deer are killed by hunters each year in the United States. Other mammals—the giant panda and tiger, for example—are threatened by the destruction of their natural environments, caused by concentrated exploitation of valued natural resources or through land reclamation. Chemicals and liquid waste being discharged into lakes and rivers are another hazard.

Special parts of some mammals are sought by the fashion and jewelry trade. Rhinoceros horn is a highly prized ingredient in Oriental potions; ambergris—a substance exuded by sperm whales—is used as a base for perfumes; elephant and walrus ivory is lucrative; and crocodile skin is still in demand, often on black markets. Even when animals are protected by law, poachers will go to great lengths to obtain them.

Sea mammals

The whale is a potent symbol of endangered aquatic mammals, and of the need for international management and regulation. In the last century, the herds of whales that congregated in the plankton-rich waters of the Antarctic were extensively hunted and killed. Modern intensive hunting has left many species at the edge of extinction. A hundred years ago, the blue whale—the world's largest mammal—numbered nearly 250,000; by 1965 there were a mere 2,000 left, and some experts believe that the animal is now beyond saving.

International concern over the blue whale caused Antarctic whalers to "mass hunt" smaller species. As a result, all of the eight species of whales are now in danger. The gray whale of the Pacific is near to extinction; the humpback whale has been reduced to an estimated 1,000; fin and sperm whales, as well as sei and Minke whales, are also threatened.

Protection is given to other mammals in the sea. Restrictions on hunting have saved the polar bear and various species of seals. The Arctic fox is also given limited protection.

European mammals

The fate of the European bison, the largest of Europe's mammals, was determined by a high demand for the land they roamed. By the beginning of the twentieth century, the bison was almost extinct, as were the wolves and bears that occupied the same habitats. National parks throughout Europe now offer sanctuary not only to the bison but also to the elk deer, beaver, otter, and other mammals. Bears are protected in special reserves.

Once found over most of the northern half of the world, the wolf is now becoming scarce in many countries. It is rare in western Europe and extinct in 11 countries, killed for a variety of reasons. Conservation groups lobby for controls and for finance to research the wolf's environment. One scientific project in Italy resulted in the government granting complete protection to the species—there are only 100 wolves remaining there. Once common in Europe and northern Asia, the European lynx is now scarce, although government protection is helping to stabilize the population.

African mammals

The African continent is inhabited by a spectacular range of mammals—rhinoceroses, gorillas, elephants, and hippopotamuses, to name but a few. The colonization of Africa over the last two centuries sparked off a mass slaughter of many of the large mammals. During the 1880's, for example, nearly 80,000 elephants were killed for their ivory. Today, the elephant is protected on many special reserves.

Many of Africa's familiar mammals are now seriously at risk. A list of threatened African mammals includes the Madagascar lemurs, okapi, gorilla, Grevy's zebra, eland, and white rhinoceros. These animals have been given complete protection, and the giraffe, chimpanzee, and some of the big cats—the cheetah most of all—are guaranteed a limited safety. There is, however, still much poaching in the large game reserves.

American mammals

Like the polar bear of northern America, the brown grizzly bear of the Rocky Mountains

and the spectacled bear of the Andes in the south are endangered mammals. Other American mammals in danger include the puma, pronghorn antelope, tapir, pampas deer, chinchilla, and vicuña. (The sale of vicuña wool has been banned in some countries to make the killing of the animals less profitable.)

National reserves have made a beginning in halting the slaughter. In a Peruvian park on the slopes of the Andes, for example, the puma, jaguar, ocelot, agouti, peccary, tapir, sloth, and bush dog are among the endangered species given some protection to maintain their dwindling populations.

The United States contains some of the world's largest and best equipped natural animal reserves. On these, woodland bison, alligators, antelopes, bears, and white-tailed deer are among some of the animals protected.

Australasian mammals

In Australia, the marsupials are of unique scientific interest as they are found nowhere else in the world; yet these same animals are being threatened by the spread of mechanized agriculture and the search for minerals.

Special efforts are, however, being made to preserve the koala bear and the egg-laying duck-billed platypus and echidna. Nearly 3 million square miles (8 million square kilometers) of Australian territory now lie in the boundaries of a number of excellent national parks. Some areas protect the red kangaroo. In 1965, for example, 1.5 million kangaroos were killed for their skins and meat (used for pet food). Some states do not regulate hunting, and the kangaroo is still in danger. One mammal, the striped wolflike thylacine of Tasmania, is now thought by scientists to be extinct.

The Pampas deer *(Ozotoceras bezoarticus, above left)* clings to a precarious existence in the grasslands of northern South America. A white rhinoceros and its young *(Ceratotherium simum)* have to be equally alert as they break cover to go down to a water hole to drink. Hunting poses a major threat to both species.

Cuban solenodon
Atopogale cubana
Fewer than 20

Eastern cougar
Felis concolor concolor
About 20

Greater bilby
Macrotis lagotis
About 20

Northern hairy-nosed wombat
Lasiorhinus krefftii
Fewer than 40

Southern bearded saki
Chiropotes satanus satanus
Fewer than 50

Vancouver Island marmot
Marmota vancouverensis
Fewer than 100

Golden marmoset
Leontideus rosalia
Fewer than 100

Buff-headed marmoset
Callithrix flaviceps
About 100

Lower Californian pronghorn
Antilocapra americana peninsularis
About 100

Volcano rabbit
Romerolagus diazi
Fewer than 200

The most endangered mammals range in size from the Cuban species of the shrewlike solenodon to the cougar and pronghorn antelope from the eastern United States. Once the numbers of a particular species fall below about 50—the numbers given here were estimated in the early 1980's—it is extremely doubtful whether a viable breeding population can be maintained without special protective measures being taken.

Conservation successes

Despite the number of animal species that have become extinct, the conservation movement has had many successes. One achievement has been the establishment of national parks and reserves. An international conference in Paris in 1968 established that such parks should be at least 1,920 acres (800 hectares) in extent, with strict prohibitions on mining, cultivation, stock raising, hunting, and fishing. There are now about 1,200 reserves in the world, covering a total of 6,700,000 acres (2,800,000 hectares). Protection is also given to animals in their natural environments.

Conservation in the sea

One success story involving a natural environment is the preservation of the polar bear. In 1955, the International Union for the Conservation of Nature recommended that all Arctic countries should curb the hunting of bears. In 1965 the Soviet Union banned the killing of polar bears and established a special reserve for them on Wrangle Island. Norway has set up a similar sanctuary. In Canada, only license holders and indigenous Eskimos are permitted to hunt bears. Despite safari hunts outside territorial waters, the population of the animals is now increasing.

Successful treaties and special reserves have also ensured the survival of the northern fur seal, a species that lives and breeds around the islands of the Bering Sea. During the nineteenth century, the seal population was reduced to a precarious level to obtain skins for the clothing industry. Protected by law, the population of seals is currently multiplying.

On the land

Some species of deer are now ensured survival, some after a dramatic rescue. Père David's deer is named after the French missionary Armand David who, in 1865, discovered 120 of the animals living in a walled royal park in China and took some to European

Conservation measures have succeeded in increasing the numbers of two northern mammals: the Alaskan, or northern, fur seal *(Callorhinus ursinus, below)* and the once rare saiga antelope *(Saiga tatarica, below right)* of the Asian steppes.

The scimitar-horned oryx *(Oryx dammah)* was in danger of the same fate as its Arabian cousins until, like them, it was bred in captivity. Here a pair of these graceful animals feed contentedly in the protection of a European wildlife park, far away from their native Africa.

zoos. Successful breeding brought about a slight increase in numbers. But because of wars this initial success was mitigated so that by 1920 the only specimens survived at Woburn Abbey, England. Postwar breeding has swelled their numbers and Père David's deer are now in zoos throughout the world—to reduce the risk of one disease destroying them all—and more have been released in national parks.

The oryx has also been brought back from the edge of extinction. There are three different species. One is the beisa oryx, gemsbok, or fringe-eared oryx. A second is the scimitar-horned oryx, whose natural habitat is on the fringes of the Sahara. The Arabian oryx is the third.

By 1960, there were only an estimated 50 Arabian oryxes from those hunted using machine guns and jeeps. All survived in the Empty Quarter of the Arabian peninsula. Three were captured in 1962 and taken to Phoenix Zoo in Arizona, where they bred successfully with other oryxes, forming the world's herd of this animal.

Captive breeding programs are successful also in ensuring the survival of a variety of rhinoceroses. The white rhinoceros of Uganda has been saved when only 50 remained.

Many national parks in Africa offer protected sanctuary to rhinoceroses and other animals. Kruger Park in South Africa covers nearly 2,500,000 acres and contains many different habitats, ranging from humid tropical forest to near desert, hot savanna to bamboo forests. Apart from animals such as the wildebeest, Kruger Park harbors groups of other animals, such as zorils, that would otherwise be extinct.

National parks now safeguard such animals as the otter and beaver. In Asian Soviet Union, for example, the kiang (a wild ass) and the saiga (an antelope) have been rescued from extinction; indeed, so successful has been the saving of the saiga that permits can now be obtained for limited hunting. The Ussuri tiger and Himalayan bear are also preserved on Russian reserves.

Birds

European national parks and wilderness guarantee the conservation of several varieties of eagles and owls, the peregrine falcon, and other birds, such as the rose flamingo. The Camargue, a swampy wilderness in France, is one of many wetlands that has preserved a great number of the 150 species of migrating water birds. In Africa, similar sanctuaries have conserved the secretary bird, ostrich, maribou stork, pelican, and many small birds that migrate the length of the continent.

There are many examples of species of endangered animals whose complete extinction has been averted yet that cannot be described as successfully conserved in the full sense. It is a testimony to the conservation movement that even this much has been achieved. From a small beginning, it is hoped that such successes will eventually lead to species being taken off the endangered list and add extra momentum to the movement that preserves wildlife. And will the saving of wildlife ultimately mean the saving of humankind?

Chinese animals saved from extinction in Britain, the Père David's deer *(Elephurus davidianus)* introduced into zoos and animal parks throughout the world, were all bred from a small group that had survived on the grounds of an English country house.

Growling defiance from its solitary perch on the ice, a polar bear *(Ursus maritimus)* represents one of the major conservation successes.

Animal taxonomy

The Animal Kingdom

Kingdom	Phylum	Subphylum	Class	
Protista	Protoza	Sarcomastigophora	Phytomastigophora	Zoomastigophora
			Rhizopodea	Actinopodea
		Ciliophora	Kinetofragminophora	Oligohymenophora
			Polyhymenophora	
		Sporozoa	Sporozea	Piroplasmea
		Cnidospora	Myosporidea	Microsporidea
Metazoa	Porifera		Calcaria	Hexactinellida
			Demospongiae	Sclerospongiae
	Cnidaria		Hydrozoa	Scyphozoa
			Anthozoa	
	Ctenophora		Tentaculata	Nuda
	Platyhelminthes		Turbellaria	Trematoda
			Cestoda	
	Entoprocta			
	Rhyncocoela		Anopla	Enopla
	Gnathostomulida			
	Gastrotricha			
	Rotifera		Digononta	Monogonta
	Echinorhyncha			
	Nematoda		Aphasmida	Phasmida
	Nematomorpha		Gordioidea	Nectonematoidea
	Acanthocephala			
	Annelida		Polychaeta	Oligochaeta
			Hirudinea	
	Echinodermata		Asteroidea	Ophiuroidea
			Echinoidea	Holothuroidea
			Crinoidea	
	Mollusca		Gastropoda	Bivalvia
			Cephalopoda	Monoplacophora
			Polyplacophora	Aplacophora
			Scaphopoda	
	Arthropoda	Chelicerata	Merostomata	Pycnogonida
			Arachnida	
		Crustacea	Cephalocarida	Branchiopoda
			Ostracoda	Mystacocarida
			Copepoda	Branchiura
			Cirripedia	Malacostracas
		Uniramia	Insecta	Chilopoda
			Diplopoda	Pauropoda
	Tardigrada			
	Linguatulida			
	Echiura			
	Bryozoa			
	Priapulida			
	Phoronida			
	Brachiopoda			
	Sipunculidea			
	Pogonophora			
	Chaetognatha			
	Chordata	Hemichordata	Pterobranchia	Enteropneusta
		Urochordata		
		Cephalochordata		
		Vertebrata	Agnatha	Elasmobranchiomorphi
			Osteichthyes	Amphibia
			Reptilia	Aves
			Mammalia	

Largest Animal Classes

Class (or Subclass)	Superorder (or Infraclass)	Order		
Arachnida		Scorpiones	Pseudoscorpiones	Solifugae
		Palpigradi	Uropygi	Schizomida
		Amblypygi	Araneae	Ricinuclei
		Opiliones	Acarina	
Malacostraca (Phyllocarida)		Leptostraca		
(Eumalacostraca)	Syncarida	Anaspidacea	Bathynellacea	
	Hoplocarida	Stomatopoda		
	Eucarida	Euphausiacea	Decapoda	
	Peracarida	Mysidacea	Cumacea	Tanaidacea
		Thermosbaenacea	Spelaeogriphacea	Isopoda
		Amphipoda		
Insecta (Apterygota)		Protura	Thysanura	Collembola
(Pterygota)		Ephemoroptera	Odonata	Orthoptera
		Isoptera	Plecoptera	Dermaptera
		Embioptera	Psocoptera	Zoraptera
		Mallophaga	Anoplura	Thysanoptera
		Hemiptera	Homoptera	Neuroptera
		Coleoptera	Strepsiptera	Mecoptera
		Trichoptera	Lepidoptera	Diptera
		Hymenoptera	Siphonoptera	
Osteichthyes (Actinopterygii)	Chondrostei	Acipenseriformes	Polypteriformes	
	Holostei	Lepisosteiformes	Amiiformes	
	Teleostei	Elopiformes	Anguilliformes	Notacanthiformes
		Clupeiformes	Osteoglossiformes	Mormyriformes
		Salmoniformes	Cetomimiformes	Gornorynchiformes
		Ctenothrissiformes	Cypriniformes	Siluriformes
		Percopsiformes	Batrachoidiformes	Gobiesociformes
		Lophiiformes	Gadiformes	Atheriniformes
		Beryciformes	Zeiformes	Lampridiformes
		Gasterosteiformes	Channiformes	Synbranchiformes
		Scorpaeniformes	Dactylopteriformes	Pegasiformes
		Perciformes	Mastocembeliformes	Pleuronectiformes
		Tetradontiformes		
(Sarcopterygii)		Crossopterygii	Dipnoi	
Aves (Neornithes)	Neognathae	Struthioniformes	Casuariiformes	Apterygiformes
		Rheiformes	Tinamiformes	Sphenisciformes
		Gaviiformes	Podicipediformes	Procellariiformes
		Pelecaniformes	Ciconiiformes	Anseriformes
		Falconiformes	Galliformes	Gruiformes
		Charadriiformes	Columbiformes	Psittaciformes
		Cuculiformes	Strigiformes	Caprimulgiformes
		Apodiformes	Coliiformes	Trogoniformes
		Coraciiformes	Piciformes	Passeriformes
Mammalia (Prototheria)		Monotremata		
(Theria)	(Metatheria)	Marsupalia		
	(Eutheria)	Insectivora	Edentata	Pholidota	Chiroptera
		Primates	Rodentia	Lagomorpha	Cetacea
		Carnivora	Tubulidentata	Hyracoidea	Proboscidea
		Sirenia	Perissodactyla	Artiodactyla	

Glossary

In the following glossary, small capital letters (e.g., NUCLEUS) indicate terms that have their own entries in the glossary.

A

allantois A membrane in the EMBRYO of TETRAPODS. It carries a large number of blood vessels that connect the blood system of the mother's PLACENTA with the embryo and, in reptiles and birds, allows gas exchange between the SHELL and the embryo.

allele A GENE with a pair member, both occupying the same loci on homologous CHROMOSOMES. They pair during MEIOSIS and can MUTATE one to the other.

alternation of generations Found in lower plants and some animals, especially coelenterates, it involves organisms of distinctly different body form, such as POLYPS and MEDUSAS, each of which gives rise to the other.

alula Also known as a "bastard wing," this small bunch of feathers is attached to the thumb-bone of a bird's wing. At low flight speeds it can be raised to form a "slot" that controls air flow over the upper surface of the wing, reducing the stalling speed.

ametabolous Describes those insects that hatch from eggs as miniature replicas of their wingless parents and simply grow in size between each molt, without METAMORPHOSIS. The process occurs in the subclass Apterygota, a group of primitive wingless insects, such as silver fish.

amino acid A member of a group of organic acids containing an amino group and a component of DNA molecules in the CELL NUCLEUS. About 25 are known to be found in PROTEINS, of which they are the building blocks, combining in different orders to form the proteins.

amnion A fluid-filled sac and the innermost membrane in which the EMBRYOS of TETRAPODS develop.

asexual reproduction The formation of a new individual from a single parent. This may be by PARTHENOGENESIS, by budding, or by fragmentation.

B

bacterium A microscopic uni- or multicellular organism. Bacteria vary in shape (the basis of their classification) and motility. They are generally considered to be plantlike although they lack CHLOROPHYLL. They feed on plant and animal tissues (as well as inorganic matter), decomposing it and thus releasing in water and soil the nutrients which support larger and more complex organisms.

baleen Plates of horny material hanging from the palate of toothless whales. The inner edge is fringed and forms a filter. Seawater drawn into the open mouth is squirted out through the baleen, food contained in the water is kept behind.

bastard wing *See* ALULA.

benthic Describes organisms that inhabit the bed of a lake or the sea.

bilateral symmetry The symmetry of most active animals with an elongate body. At one end is a head in which the main sense organs and BRAIN are assembled; behind it the body carries paired organs such as limbs, which are mirror images of each other.

bilharzia Also known as schistosomiasis, this parasitic disease, widespread in the tropics, is carried by flukes of the genus *Schistosoma*. It is transmitted in water when the LARVA of the fluke burrow through the skin. Like most parasitic diseases, it is debilitating and may be fatal.

binary fission Reproduction of a CELL by splitting into two equal parts, common in many single-celled organisms.

binomial classification The system of classifying plants and animals by which each SPECIES is given a unique combination of two names: the genus, or group name, and the species name. The genus name always begins with a capital letter, the species with a small letter; e.g., *Panthera leo,* the lion.

blubber Fat lying beneath the skin of seals and whales. Consisting of oil-filled cells, it is a poor conductor of heat and helps to preserve body warmth. It also acts as a food reserve.

bone Vertebrate skeletal material, formed largely from COLLAGEN, phosphates, and calcium salts. It is hard, but flexible to some extent.

brain The forepart of the main nervous system in BILATERALLY SYMMETRICAL animals. It is housed in the head, close to the principal sensory organs, such as the EYES, ears, and nose. To a greater or lesser extent the brain coordinates the activities of the entire body.

C

carnassial In carnivores, the first lower molar tooth and the last upper premolar teeth. Together they form large shearing blades and are used for slicing flesh.

cartilage A skeletal tissue in vertebrates containing COLLAGEN fibers in a matrix composed largely of carbohydrates. It is softer and more flexible than BONE.

cell The basic unit of organic tissues. Cells are bounded by a cell wall or membrane and contain a NUCLEUS, which is derived by division from a previous cell nucleus and holds the CHROMOSOMES and CYTOPLASM. Some organisms are unicellular but most comprise many specialized cells.

cellulose A complex carbohydrate material, with a fibrous structure that makes the cell walls of plants rigid.

cephalothorax The fused head and forebody found in arachnids and some crustaceans.

chiasmata The crossing-over or exchange of genetic material between CHROMOSOMES during MEIOSIS. It can lead to the production of new varieties within a SPECIES.

chitin The tough, fibrous EXOSKELETON of arthropods. It is relatively inelastic and therefore dictates the jointed limb and body structure of arthropods and their system of growth by molting.

chlorophyll A green pigment found in most plants, contained in the CHLOROPLASTS. It absorbs light from the sun and by photosynthesis converts it into chemical energy used to build up carbohydrates (sugars and starches).

chloroplasts Small, pigment-containing bodies found in plant CELLS. They contain CHLOROPHYLL as well as other pigments which give plants their color.

choanocyte A collar CELL found in some sponges, in which a flagellum arises from a PROTOPLASMIC collar. The beating of the flagella moves water containing food and oxygen through the sponge's body.

chromatid One of two long filaments of GENETIC material on a duplicated CHROMOSOME, visible during MITOSIS and MEIOSIS.

chromatin The nucleoprotein material of which CHROMOSOMES are made.

chromatophore A pigment-containing cell found in many animals, such as squids, chameleons, and flatfish. The pigment level can be altered rapidly, which enables the animal to change color.

chromosome Found in the NUCLEUS of every plant and animal CELL, chromosomes are composed of CHROMATIN, and carry the GENES, which are the units of inheritance. The number of chromosomes varies in different SPECIES, but in all, the sex cells (GAMETES) contain half of the normal complement. In fertilization, the chromosomes from the male and female gametes come together to give the new individual its complete inheritance pattern, received in part from each parent.

clavicle The collarBONE found in vertebrates. The clavicles have been lost in many mammals, but are found in birds as a single, fused element called the furcula, or wishbone.

cleavage The subdivision of a fertilized ZYGOTE during its development to form a hollow sphere of small cells called the blastula.

clitellum A saddlelike structure found in some sexually mature annelids. It produces a mucous sheath around mating animals and binds the cocoon round the fertilized eggs.

cloaca The end of the gut in vertebrates (except for nonmarsupial mammals) into which the digestive and reproductive tracts open.

cnidocil The trigger hair of a NEMATOCYST, or stinging cell.

coelenteron The body cavity of coelenterates. It has one opening only and through it food enters and waste products and sperm or eggs are ejected.

coelom The main body cavity of many complex animals.

collagen A PROTEIN which forms intercellular fibers in the skeletal tissues of vertebrates. Collagen fibers have great tensile strength, but little elasticity.

commensalism The association of two different organisms where mutual advantage may result, although the partners may also be capable of independent existence.

compound eye Found in crustaceans and insects, compound eyes consist of a number of separate lens systems (more than 10,000 in each eye in some insects), each of which accepts information from a very small part of the surroundings. They may be color-sensitive, but lack visual acuity compared with cephalopod or vertebrate EYES.

conjugation The partial fusing of two individual ciliate protozoan cells, when nuclear material is exchanged, during the process of SEXUAL REPRODUCTION.

coracoid This strutting bone in the PECTORAL GIRDLES of primitive land vertebrates lies between the sternum and the outer ends of the CLAVICLES. They have been totally lost in mammals, but are present in birds.

cornea The clear, tough, protective layer of connective tissue that covers the lens of the EYE in vertebrates.

corona The ciliated "crown" of rotifers. The activity of the CILIA is the means of locomotion and food collection in these creatures.

crop A thin-walled, distendable sac in the esophagus of many birds, which functions as a food store.

crystalline style A rod of PROTEIN containing a starch-digesting ENZYME found in the gut of some mollusks. The free end projects into the stomach and is worn away as the enzyme is mixed with the gut contents.

cuticle The protective surface layer that covers plants and animals.

cypris The fully developed LARVA of a barnacle, when it is ready to settle on a surface.

cytoplasm The watery substance that surrounds the NUCLEUS of a CELL and which contains bodies such as mitochondria and Golgi bodies. Together with the nucleus they form the PROTOPLASM of the cell.

D

delayed implantation A pause in the development of the EMBRYO of some mammals which, after early CELL division, remains unattached to the wall of the UTERUS for a period of up to several months. It probably allows courtship and mating, as well as birth of the young, to occur at times when food supplies are abundant.

deoxyribonucleic acid See DNA.

dewclaws The toes of a DIGITIGRADE or UNGULIGRADE animal that do not normally touch the ground. In carnivores, such as dogs, the first toe of the forelimb forms a dewclaw; in many deer, the second and fourth digits of all feet are dewclaws.

diaphragm A sheet of tissue that separates the chest cavity from the abdomen, found in mammals. It can be arched or flattened to improve the efficiency of breathing.

digitigrade The method of TETRAPOD locomotion in which an animal walks on its toes, thus increasing its stride by the length of the hand or foot bones. Dogs and cats are digitigrade.

dioecious A term applied to plants and animals that have separate sexes.

displacement activity An inappropriate form of behavior performed as a result of conflicting drives. It usually appears as an exaggerated form of normal activity.

DNA (deoxyribonucleic acid) A compound found in plant and animal CELLS, formed from nitrogenous bases arranged in a double helical form and capable of self-replication. It carries GENETIC information in the arrangement of these bases. Each sequence of three bases forms the code for one AMINO ACID.

E

ecdysis The shedding of the EXOSKELETON in arthropods, necessary in this group to allow growth. Under HORMONAL control, the body covering is split off, allowing a new one, already produced beneath the old, to expand and then harden.

echolocation A method of short-distance navigation and sometimes food-finding, used by some nocturnal and aquatic animals. Short bursts of sound are produced by the animal which, if they encounter an obstruction, return an echo which is detected by the animal. Bats and whales echo-locate using ULTRASONIC sound.

eclipse period A dull-colored, post-mating plumage phase in many birds. In ducks and geese this phase is accompanied by a simultaneous molt of the flight feathers, so that they are temporarily flightless.

elytron The thickened and stiffened forewing in beetles.

embryo The pre-birth or pre-hatching stage of a developing animal.

endoskeleton The body support that lies within the muscular structure. It is best developed in vertebrates as a SKELETON, but is also seen in some other groups.

enzymes Proteinaceous substances that are produced by living CELLS, vital to the processes of METABOLISM.

epidermis The outermost layer of CELLS of plants and animals. In vertebrates it is several cells thick and in land-living forms the outer layers are often dead and horny. In invertebrates it is one cell thick and often secretes a CUTICULAR protection.

estivation Dormancy during hot dry seasons.

estrus The period of greatest sexual receptiveness in a female mammal, normally coinciding with ovulation.

exoskeleton The bodily support that lies outside the muscular structure. It is best developed in arthropods and mollusks.

eye An organ for light-reception, varying from a simple cluster of light-sensitive CELLS, such as the OCELLUS or the COMPOUND EYE, to a complex system with one or more light-gathering lenses focusing on special cells sensitive to light intensity and color.

F

fetus A mammalian EMBRYO in the later stages of its development.

filter-feeding A method of feeding used by many marine invertebrates in which minute organisms are removed from large quantities of water that is strained through GILLS or some other sifting mechanism.

food vacuole A fluid-filled space found in single-celled animals, created when food is engulfed. The fluid contains ENZYMES which digest the food. The waste flows out from the vacuole into the CELL CYTOPLASM.

frenal hooks Tiny hooks along the edges between the two wings of hymenopterans (bees and wasps, etc.), which hold the two wings on each side of the body together so that they beat as a single unit.

furcula See CLAVICLE.

G

gamete A reproductive CELL with half the number of CHROMOSOMES normal for the SPECIES (haploid). It is either a mobile male cell (sperm) with reduced CYTOPLASM, or an immobile female cell (ovum) with hugely increased cytoplasm. They fuse during fertilization when a diploid cell (ZYGOTE), with a full complement of chromosomes, is formed.

ganglion A small knot of nerve tissue from which nerve cords arise. In invertebrates it may form the BRAIN. In vertebrates ganglia occur in the peripheral nervous system and as some of the nerve connections of the brain.

gastrulation The movement of CELLS in the early stages of the development of an EMBRYO to the positions in which they will form the internal organs of the animal.

gemmule A bundle of CELLS that are capable of developing without fertilization into a new organism. They may be a means for an individual, the major part of

whose body dies in adverse circumstances, to survive until the environment is suitable for further activity.

gene The basic unit of heredity, formed from a sequence of bases on a DNA chain. Each gene has a definite position of the CHROMOSOME and may occur as an ALLELE.

genotype The GENETIC (hereditary) constitution of an individual.

genus See BINOMIAL CLASSIFICATION.

gestation The period of development between conception and birth in mammals.

gill The RESPIRATORY organ of aquatic animals. Gills are usually projections from the body wall or gut and are often complex in shape, so that they offer the maximum surface area for gas exchange between the blood which flows through them and the water which flows round them.

gill-book Found in some aquatic arachnids, these plates of tissue resemble the pages of a book; they are set in a cavity where they can be bathed in water from which they extract oxygen and in which they release carbon dioxide.

gizzard The muscular stomach of birds and some other animals, which breaks up food prior to digestion, sometimes aided by swallowed stones.

grooming This care of the body surface, usually by scratching or licking, may be performed by a pair of animals on each other when it may be an important force in pair bonding or maintaining social cohesion within a group.

guard hairs The thick hairs which overlie the fine underfur in many mammals. In cold or wet conditions air is trapped close to the skin, and the guard hairs (which are often greasy and waterproof) clamp down and prevent the escape of this warm blanket.

H

halteres The hind wings of flies (Diptera) which have been reduced to tiny, club-shaped structures, used in flight as gyroscopic balancing devices.

heart The strong, muscular pump that drives blood through animals. In mammals and birds it has a complex of chambers which separate out deoxygenated blood and send it to the lungs from which it returns oxygenated to supply the body with its needs. In lower vertebrates the oxygenated and deoxygenated blood is mixed and in invertebrates it plays little or no part in the distribution of oxygen throughout the body.

hemimetabolous Describes insects with an incomplete METAMORPHOSIS. When they hatch, they resemble the parents, although they do not develop functional wings until mature. They grow by a series of molts.

hemocoele A closed body cavity containing blood. It is well-developed in arthropods and mollusks. Unlike the true COELOM, it never contains reproductive cells.

hemocyanin A RESPIRATORY pigment containing copper, found in the blood of most arthropods and mollusks. It gives the blood of these animals its green color.

hemoglobin An iron-containing RESPIRATORY pigment found in the blood of most vertebrates and some invertebrates.

hermaphrodite An animal possessing both male and female sexual organs. These organs are usually functional at different times, preventing self-fertilization.

hibernation A state of torpor which POIKILOTHERMAL animals enter when the surrounding temperature drops below a certain critical point. A few mammal and bird SPECIES also hibernate, but they do so for long periods (up to 7 months in some rodents). Their temperature, heartbeat, and breathing rates fall dramatically and they use very little energy in staying alive.

holometabolous Describes insects that undergo a complete METAMORPHOSIS from an egg to a LARVA, a PUPA, and finally an adult.

homeothermal Describes animals that are "warm-blooded," with an internal thermostat that keeps their body temperature within very narrow limits, whatever the temperature of their surroundings.

hormones Substances produced by glands, in animals, and released into the bloodstream where they have an important role in body functions, such as growth, reproduction and digestion.

host An individual on which a PARASITE feeds.

hybrid The result of successful cross-fertilization between members of different SPECIES. Hybrids among animals are rare in nature and are almost always sterile.

hydrostatic skeleton The body support found in some invertebrates, which depends on the movement of liquid inside the cells to maintain body shape or to change position.

hyoid A system of small bones in the base of the tongue in TETRAPODS, derived from a GILL arch in fish ancestors. In some SPECIES they have become enlarged to support a long insect-catching tongue, as in woodpeckers, or a resonating voice box, as in howler monkeys.

hypothalamus A part of the BRAIN of vertebrates, which is thought to contain, among other things, the mechanism of body temperature control.

I

iliac crest The expanded upper part of the ilium, which is part of the PELVIC GIRDLE of TETRAPODS. It is particularly important in humans as the area of attachment of the muscles which allow them to stand and walk upright.

imprinting The process by which many animals learn to recognize their own kind. It occurs at an early stage of development as a response to a narrow range of stimuli to which the young individual is normally exposed.

incubation The period between the laying and hatching of eggs, when they are kept warm, either by the Sun, rotting vegetation, or the warmth of the parent's body.

instinct Nonlearned or innate behavior patterns, often very complex, usually triggered by specific stimuli.

K

keratin A tough, fibrous PROTEIN material found in TETRAPODS. It forms the outer layer of the skin, and hair, hoofs and horny structures in mammals, feathers in birds, and SCALES in reptiles.

L

larva The young stage of many OVIPAROUS animals that have a distinctly different body form from the adult, usually related to a specialized way of life. For example, in insects the larvae may be the feeding stage, in many crustaceans, the dispersal phase. At the end of the larval life, they rapidly METAMORPHOSE to the adult state.

lateral-line system A series of sense organs on the flanks and sides of the head in agnatha, fishes and amphibians. Each nerve ending, housed in a bony pit, is sensitive to pressure changes, so that the animals can detect, through water movement, the presence of potential enemies or prey.

lung The RESPIRATORY organ of land-living vertebrates and some mollusks. Air is drawn into a cavity, the skin of which is well-supplied with blood vessels, so that gas exchange can take place there.

lung-books The breathing organs of some arachnids. They consist of a series of thin flaps of tissue, like the pages of a book, projecting into a cavity in the body wall. Blood flows through them and gas exchange takes place at their surface.

M

macronucleus In Ciliophora, a large NUCLEUS which divides MEIOTICALLY and disappears during CONJUGATION.

Malpighian tubules Excretory glands found in the hindgut of insects, arachnids, and some other arthropods.

mammary glands MILK-producing glands of female mammals. Their state usually varies with the ESTRUS cycle and their growth and milk production is controlled by various HORMONES.

mandible The lower jaw of vertebrates, and in some invertebrates (such as insects) the major pair of crushing mouthparts.

maxilla In vertebrates, this forms part of the upper jaw; in invertebrates, it forms one of the pairs of mouthparts that lies behind the MANDIBLES.

medusa A free-swimming, jellyfishlike coelenterate which reproduces sexually. In many cases, however, the eggs of medusas give rise to POLYPS that form further medusas by ASEXUAL division.

meiosis Two stages of CELL division that result in the formation of GAMETES. (*See also* MITOSIS.)

mesogloea A jellylike substance found between the ectoderm and endoderm (the outer and inner tissue layers) of coelenterates.

metabolism Life processes which involve both the breakdown (catabolism) of organic compounds to liberate energy for various activities, and also the build-up (anabolism) from simple materials of the complex tissues of an organism.

metamorphosis The change that occurs between the immature, LARVAL stage of an animal's life and its mature, reproductive phase. Complete metamorphosis involves a major change in form and takes place within the shelter of a PUPAL case. Incomplete metamorphosis is more gradual until wing growth and sexual development are accomplished.

micronucleus A small nucleus found in Ciliophora which divides MITOTICALLY and provides the nuclear material for CONJUGATION. After conjugation, the MACRONUCLEUS is reformed from the ZYGOTIC (micronuclear) material.

milk Produced in the MAMMARY GLANDS of female mammals, milk contains fats, sugars and PROTEINS and is used to feed the young.

mitosis Normal CELL division in which CHROMOSOME material is doubled, so that daughter cells carry the same GENETIC information as the parent cells.

mutation A spontaneous, irreversible GENETIC change. It normally occurs during CELL division and can affect any cells of the body. Most mutations are harmful and kill the organism, but those that are not lead to variation in the SPECIES.

myoglobin An oxygen-carrying pigment, related to HEMOGLOBIN, contained in the muscles of mammals, especially those such as seals and whales, which hold their breath for long periods.

N

nectar guides Brightly colored lines or patches on petals that lead insects toward the nectar which usually lies at the center of the flower. In their search the insects brush against pollen which they carry to other flowers to effect pollination.

nematocyst The stinging cell of a coelenterate. Thickly scattered on the tentacles, nematocysts consist of a poison cell in which a long, barbed, hollow tube lies coiled, and above which lies a CNIDOCIL, or hair. When this hair is triggered, the hollow tube shoots out and cuts the skin of the prey, allowing the poison to affect the nervous system.

nidifugous Describes young birds which leave the parental nest shortly after hatching, such as ducks and game birds.

notochord An internal rod, made of a stiff, jellylike substance, found in the LARVAE or EMBRYOS of vertebrates. It lies beneath the nerve cord and above the gut and supports the muscle blocks of the body in all chordates.

nucleus The controlling center of all cellular activity, containing the CHROMOSOMES, the nucleolus, and the nucleoplasm.

O

ocellus A simple EYE—a cluster of photoreceptors—with a single lens system, found in arthropods and some other invertebrates.

ommatidium A single element of the COMPOUND EYE of insects and crustaceans.

operculum A cover used in many animal structures, such as the lid of a NEMATOCYST; the horny cover with which some gastropods close their shell opening against desiccation or enemies; and, in bony fishes, the large bony plate which protects the GILLS.

ovary The egg-forming structure in a female or HERMAPHRODITE organism.

oviduct The tube connecting the OVARY to the UTERUS in female mammals, and carrying eggs out to the body in other vertebrates.

oviparous Describes animals that lay eggs that hatch once they are laid.

ovoviviparous Describes animals in which the EMBRYO develops in an egg membrane until it hatches inside the mother.

P

parasite An organism that lives on another at its expense. Ectoparasites, such as fleas, live on the surface of their HOST; endoparasites live internally, and include tapeworms and hookworms.

parthenogenesis The development of an unfertilized ovum into a new individual. In some animals this is the usual method of reproduction, but the pattern is often broken by a sexual generation which allows a recombination of GENETIC material within the population.

pectoral girdle The BONES supporting the forelimbs in TETRAPODS, consisting of shoulder blades (scapulas), collar bones (CLAVICLES) and, in some cases, CORACOIDS.

pelvic girdle The hip girdle of TETRAPODS composed, in most cases, of the ischium, the pubis, and the ilium. It supports the abdomen, the base of the tail, and the upper part of the leg.

pentadactyl Meaning "five fingered," this term refers to the limbs of early land vertebrates, which had five digits on each. This number has been reduced in many modern vertebrates, but the basic pattern is the same, so the term is still used.

peristalsis Waves of muscular contraction moving along tubular organs, moving and mixing the contents.

phenotype The physical form of an organism.

pheromone A chemical, usually a scent, secreted by an organism which stimulates a particular response in another individual. Pheromones play a large part in the courtship and mating behavior of many animals.

photosynthesis The process by which green plants transform the light energy from the sun into chemical energy and use it to build carbohydrates. It occurs in the CHLOROPLASTS.

phytoplankton The plant component of the PLANKTON. These unicellular organisms are the basic food for all ocean-dwelling animals and, through their PHOTOSYNTHETIC activity, they provide much of the free oxygen in the atmosphere.

placenta A temporary organ that develops in the UTERUS of most pregnant mammals through which the EMBRYOS are nourished, receive oxygen, and eliminate waste.

plankton The term covers all floating aquatic organisms. Many planktonic animals are LARVAL forms, but some are permanent members of the plankton. Most are microscopic, but a few, such as jellyfish, are large.

plantigrade The style of locomotion in TETRAPODS where the whole length of the foot is placed on the ground, as in man, most insectivores, and some reptiles.

pneumostome The RESPIRATORY pore of terrestrial mollusks, which is found behind the head, on the right side of the body.

poikilothermal Describing animals that are "cold-blooded." Their body temperature is not low, but matches that of their surroundings, fluctuating with the time of day or year.

polyembryony The formation of more than one EMBRYO from a single ZYGOTE by fission at an early stage.

polyp The fixed stage in the life of many coelenterates. In some, such as sea anemones and corals, it is the only adult form; but, in others, such as hydrozoa, it is the ASEXUAL reproductive phase.

proglottid A single reproductive segment of a tapeworm. In its early life it is connected to a chain of similar segments. When mature and full of ripe eggs, it breaks away and leaves the HOST's body with the feces.

prognathous Projecting jaws, as found in baboons, apes and some early humans.

protein A complex organic compound, formed from large numbers of AMINO ACIDS. Proteins play an important part in the formation, maintenance, and regeneration of tissues.

protoplasm The contents of a cell containing the CYTOPLASM and the NUCLEUS.

pseudopodium A temporary extension of a CELL caused by the directional flow of PROTOPLASM within it. It is the method of locomotion and feeding in ameboid cells.

pupa The stage between the LARVAL feeding form and the adult reproductive form in HOLOMETABOLOUS insects. During the pupal stage, the body tissues are almost completely broken down and reconstructed round a group of special CELLS.

R

rachis The main part of the shaft of a feather, which carries the vane made of barbs and barbules.

radial symmetry A circular body form in which there is no "head end" to the body and no concentration of BRAIN or nervous tissue. It is usually found among inactive animals.

radula The "tongue" of mollusks. It carries large numbers of horny teeth, which are used to rasp food.

reflex An involuntary, unlearned, stereotypic response to a stimulus.

respiration The method by which an organism oxygenates its tissues and rids itself of unwanted carbon dioxide. In invertebrates, gases may diffuse through the whole of the outer surface or via TRACHEAE to the tissues. In larger animals specialized organs have evolved, including GILLS for aquatic animals and LUNGS for terrestrial species.

retina The light-sensitive layer at the back of the EYE of vertebrates and cephalopods. It includes two types of cells—rods, which are sensitive to dim light, and cones, which are concerned with the perception of colors.

ribonucleic acid *See* RNA.

RNA (ribonucleic acid) The material in a CELL, composed of a single nucleotide chain, that organizes and governs PROTEIN synthesis.

royal jelly A highly nutritious secretion from the pharyngeal glands of young worker honey bees. It is fed to all the LARVAE in the colony for the first few days of their lives, after which most of them are switched to a pollen diet. Larvae which are to become queens continue to be fed solely on royal jelly.

rumination The method of digestion used by cud-chewing ungulates. They swallow their food unchewed, which goes into the rumen where it is partly broken down by BACTERIA. Later it is returned to the mouth to be masticated completely and when swallowed it by-passes the rumen.

S

scales In bony fishes, scales are fine slips of bone formed in the dermal layer of the skin and overlapping like tiles; they may be smooth-edged (cycloid), serrated-edged (ctenoid), or bony (ganoid). Scales in reptiles are made of KERATIN and on the wings of insects they are composed of CHITIN.

scolex The head of a tapeworm, which is armed with hooks, by which it attaches itself to the wall of the HOST's intestine. The PROGLOTTIDS grow from the scolex.

sedentary Describes animals that remain in the same living area, such as nonmigratory birds which, even so, move through several acres of territory. Among the invertebrates, it describes animals such as oysters or barnacles which are fixed to one point of the substrate.

segmentation Repetition of a structural pattern along the length of an animal's body or appendage, seen most clearly in annelids and arthropods. Each unit is referred to as a segment.

sesamoid A BONE developed within a tendon, especially in mammals, such as the kneecap, and the "thumb" bone of the giant panda.

sessile Describes animals that are attached to the substrate, as are barnacles or oysters.

sexual dimorphism The differences between the male and female form of SPECIES. Often the differences are slight but sometimes they are so great that the male and female have been thought to be of unrelated species.

sexual reproduction The formation of a new individual from a fertilized ovum, or SYNKARYON. At conception, a male GAMETE fuses with a female gamete. Because during MEIOSIS there is considerable shuffling of GENETIC material, each gamete differs from all others. The individual formed as a result of sexual reproduction is genetically unique and even the offspring of the same parents differ from each other.

shell The protective armor of many animals, including some vertebrates such as tortoises, or the outer covering of the egg of a reptile or bird. The term mainly refers to the strong EXOSKELETON of invertebrates, particularly crustaceans, mollusks and brachiopods.

shoaling In fishes, the habit of forming large, tightly knit groups composed of individuals of the same age and size. The purpose may be safety—predators may think the group to be one large animal, too big to attack safely, and if an attack is made the large number of individuals may bewilder the predator.

skeleton The BONY internal support of vertebrates. It consists of the vertebral column, which supports the head at the anterior end, a PECTORAL GIRDLE, to which the forelimbs are attached, and a PELVIC GIRDLE, which carries the hind limbs. Fishes have fins instead of girdles.

sonar *See* ECHOLOCATION.

species The basic unit of animal classification consisting of populations of organisms sufficiently similar to permit free interbreeding in the wild. (*See also* BINOMIAL CLASSIFICATION.)

spermatophore A packet of sperm produced by the males of some species in which there is internal fertilization but in general no intromittant organ. In many cases complex mating behavior patterns have evolved to ensure that the female is correctly positioned to pick up the spermatophore in her CLOACA.

spicules The skeletal support of sponges. They may be of a horny material as in bath sponges, silicaceous in glass sponges, or chalky as in calcareous sponges.

spinnerets Small raised organs at the hind end of a caterpillar or spider, through which silk is produced. Each one contains minute outlets through which the silk is forced in liquid form, in chains of molecules. The silk polymerizes on contact with the air.

spiracle In cartilaginous fishes, this small opening lies in front of the GILLS. In bony fishes, it is dorsally situated and is used to take water into the gill chambers. It is also a breathing pore found on the sides of insects which opens into the TRACHEAL system.

spore A dormant form that many protozoans adopt allowing them to withstand long periods of extremes of heat or cold which would be lethal at other times. They return to a normal, active form when conditions are appropriate.

stapes One of the three small BONES of the mammalian inner ear. Reptiles, amphibians and fishes have a comparable bone, but are lacking the other two.

statocyst A more or less spherical organ of balance which contains a granule of hard material which stimulates sensory CELLS as the animal moves.

sternum The breastbone in land vertebrates, to which the ribs, CLAVICLES, and CORACOIDS (if any) are attached.

suspension feeder An animal which feeds on minute food particles strained from the water in which it lives.

swim-bladder A gas-filled sac in the abdominal cavity of bony fishes which enables them to achieve neutral buoyancy. Its presence means that the animal need not spend energy in maintaining its level in the water, but rather can use all of its locomotive power in moving forward.

symbiosis An association of two or more different organisms which are mutually interdependent and cannot live alone.

synkaryon The diploid ZYGOTE NUCLEUS, formed by the fusion of GAMETIC nuclei.

synovial capsule A bag of connective tissue surrounding any free-moving joint such as a shoulder, elbow, or wrist. It contains synovial fluid, which lubricates the CARTILAGE coverings of the ends of the BONES.

T

tapetum A reflecting layer at the back of the EYE of some vertebrates, particularly those that are nocturnal. It enables the eye to make the fullest possible use of any available light.

taxon A classificatory unit, such as a SPECIES, GENUS, or family.

tergum The thickened CUTICLE on the upper surface of a segment of an insect or crustacean.

testis The sperm-forming structure in a male or HERMAPHRODITE organism.

tetrapod Literally meaning "four feet," this term is used to denote any land vertebrate.

torsion The twisting of the visceral mass through 180°, which takes place in the LARVAL stage of gastropods, bringing the anus from its original posterior position into an anterior position above the head. The advantage appears to be that the mantle cavity then provides space into which the animal can retract its soft parts, within the protection of the SHELL, closed in many cases by the horny OPERCULUM.

trachea A breathing passage in insects and some arachnids. It conducts air from the SPIRACLES on the skin into the body, where it branches to form fine tubes called tracheoles, where gas exchange takes place. In higher vertebrates, the trachea is the windpipe.

trochophore A planktonic LARVA of polychaetes and some mollusks. Roughly spherical in shape, it has a ring of cilia round the body, the beating of which stabilizes the animal in the water and brings food to its mouth.

U

ultrasonic Describes high-frequency sound waves above the hearing of human ears, used by bats and whales in ECHOLOCATION.

unguligrade A method of mammalian locomotion in which the animal walks on the tips of its toes, which are generally protected by horny hoofs. Each stride is lengthened by the length of the hand or foot plus the toe bones, which are often greatly elongated. Many long-distance runners such as horses and antelopes are unguligrade.

uric acid A waste product formed from the breakdown of AMINO ACIDS. It is produced by animals such as insects, snails, reptiles, and birds, which need to conserve water rather than lose it in excreta.

urine Liquid waste produced by the kidneys (and stored in the bladder) which contains mainly the breakdown products of AMINO ACIDS.

uterus The muscular organ in female mammals and some other vertebrates in which the EMBRYOS develop.

V

vector A blood-feeding insect, such as a mosquito, which transmits parasitic organisms, for which it is the intermediate HOST, to another host in the PARASITE's life cycle.

veliger The LARVA of gastropods and some other mollusks, which develops from the TROCHOPHORE. The CILIATED region is drawn out into an enlongated velum, which supports the animal like water skis. During the veliger state TORSION takes place.

viviparous Describes the development of an EMBRYO inside and nourished by the mother, until it is born, when it is a smaller version of the adult.

Z

zooplankton The animal members of the PLANKTON. Many are LARVAE but some, such as jellyfish, include the largest members of the plankton.

zygote The fertilized ovum before it begins further development.

Index

Credits

The following have provided photographs for Part 6:
Michael Abbey/Okapia 15; Kurt Amsler/Seaphot 62;
Heather Angel 12, 19, 20, 25, 26, 35, 37, 40, 41, 43, 44,
50, 53, 57, 60, 64, 71, 72, 73, 78, 88, 91, 96, 98, 114, 115,
116, 143; Anthony Baventock/Seaphot 39; James Bell/
Science Photo Library 9; S. C. Bisserot FRPS/Nature Photographers Ltd 103, 105, 113; Frank V. Blackburn/Nature
Photographers Ltd 18; P. Boston/Natural Science Photos
109; Brinsley Burbidge/Nature Photographers Ltd 142;
N. A. Callow/Nature Photographers Ltd 59; Peter D. Ca-
pen/Seaphot 136; Dick Clarke/Seaphot 62; Colour Library International 43, 89, 90; Conor Craig/Seaphot 68;
Richard Crane/Nature Photographers Ltd 135; Bill Curt-
singer/Okapia 125; Martin Dohrn/Science Photo Library
55, 72; Georgette Douwma/Seaphot 67; Friskney Essex/
Natural Science Photos 140; Douglas Faulkner/Okapia
127; Geoscience Features 33; Finnish Tourist Office 95;
Ron and Christine Foord 51; Gower Medical Publishing
30, 53, 70, 95; Dr Steve Gull/Science Photo Library 63;
Eric Gravé/Science Photo Library 17, 20, 32, 36; James
Hancock/Nature Photographers Ltd 126, 135; Margaret
Hayman/Seaphot 57; A. Hayward/Natural Science Photos
74, 80; Jan Hirsch/Science Photo Library 24; J. Hobday/
Natural Science Photos 101, 102; David Hosking 25;
James Hudnall/Seaphot 117; Alan Hutchinson Library
123; Masao Kawai/Orion Press/Bruce Coleman Ltd 108;
Edgar T. Jones/Aquila Photographics 91; Nicholas Law
11, 133; Hugo van Lawick/Nature Photographers Ltd
119; J. Lawton Roberts/Aquila Photographics 90; Mi-
chael Leach/Nature Photographers Ltd 142; Ken Lucas/
Seaphot 23, 31, 137; John and Gillian Lythgoe/Seaphot
122; R. L. Matthews/Seaphot 141; C. Mattison/Natural
Science Photos 77; L. C. Marigo/Bruce Coleman Ltd 106;
Nature Photographers Ltd 47; Peter Newark's Western
America 134; Okapia 58, 97; W. S. Patou/Nature Photographers Ltd 139; J. M. Pearson/Biophotos 19, 132; How-
ard Platt/Seaphot 94; K. R. Porter/Science Photo Library
15; Jurge Provenza/Seaphot 106; W. J. von Puttkamer/
Alan Hutchinson Library 100; Ian Redmond/Seaphot 59,
110; Brian Rogers/Biofotos 89; Rod Salm/Seaphot 76;
Scala III; Peter Scoones/Seaphot 68, 69; Jonathan Scott/
Seaphot 22, 27, 28, 29; Seaphot 44, 46, 47, 51; David Se-
well/Nature Photographers Ltd 139; Silvestris/Meyers
120; Silvestris/Wothe 121; Dr Nigel Smith/Alan Hutchinson Library 100, 131; Sinclair Stammers/Science Photo
Library 46; Tony Stone Associates 6, 8, 10, 34, 61, 66, 71,
79, 81, 92, 93, 96, 105, 119, 121, 128, 129, 131, 133, 141,
143; Soames Summerhays/Biofotos 12, 124, 139, 142;
Herwarth Voigtmann/Seaphot 65; John Walsh/Science
Photo Library 13, 38, 49; P. H. and S. L. Ward/Natural
Science Photos 77, 115, 127; Gary Weber/Aquila Photographics 75; Curtis Williams/Natural Science Photos 87;
Robin Williams/Gower Medical Publishing 95; York Museum 135.

Auguste Rodin's "The Thinker"—*Homo sapiens sapiens.*

**Part
7**

The
Human Body

Acknowledgments

Consultant Editor   Ann Kramer

Consultants and Contributors

Charlotte Austin
Iris Barry
Arthur Boylston
Gill Clark
Michael Day
Helen Dziemidko
Graham Ellis-Becker
Loraine Fergusson
David Lambert
Gail Lawther
Gwyneth Lewis
Keith Lye
Clare Openshaw
John Payne
Theodore
    Rowland-Entwistle
Caroline Shreeve
Gillian Sparrow
Robert Stewart
Bruce Welsh

Artists and Designers

Stephen Bull
Eric Drewery
Pauline Faulkes
Bob Freeman
Mick Gillah
Nicki Kemball
Aziz Khan
Janos Marffy
Jim Marks
David Parker
Rodney Paull
Colin Salmon
Mick Saunders
Alan Suttie
Lisa Tai
Shirley Willis

Creative Team

Bull Publishing Consultants Ltd
Harold Bull
John Clark
Eric Drewery
Kate Duffy
Nicola Okell
Martyn Page
Polly Powell
Hal Robinson
Sandy Shepherd

Part 7 Contents

Preface

The Human Body, like the other parts in this series about the sciences, deals with a specific scientific area. The human body is introduced through its anatomy and physiology. Growth and development and the causes and treatment of illness extend this study. Finally, it describes the characteristics of adaptation, socialization, and the ability to modify or control the environment, which make human beings the dominant species of our planet.

The editorial approach

The object of the publication is to explain for an average family readership, adults and children alike, the many aspects of science that are not only fascinating in themselves but are also vitally important for an understanding of the world today. To achieve this, the material has been made straightforward and concise, accurate in content, and is clearly and attractively presented. They are also a readily accessible source of scientific information.

The often forbidding appearance of traditional science publications has been completely avoided. Approximately equal proportions of illustrations and text make even the most unfamiliar subjects interesting and attractive. Even more important, all of the drawings have been created specially to complement the text, each explaining a topic that can be difficult to understand through the printed word alone.

The application of these principles thoroughly and consistently has created a publication that encapsulates its subject in an interesting and stimulating way, and that will prove to be an invaluable work of reference and education for many years to come.

The advance of science

One of the most exciting and challenging aspects of science is that its frontiers are constantly being revised and extended and new developments are occurring all the time. Its advance depends largely on observation, experimentation, and debate, which generate theories that have to be tested and even then stand only until they are replaced by better concepts. For this reason, it is difficult for any science publication to be completely comprehensive. It is possible, however, to provide a thorough foundation that ensures any such advances can be comprehended—and it is the purpose of each part in this series to create such a foundation, by providing all the basic knowledge in the particular area of science it describes.

How to use this material

This material can be used in two ways.

The first, and more conventional, way is to start at the beginning and to read through to the end, which gives a coherent and thorough picture of the subject and opens a resource of basic information that can be returned to for re-reading and reference.

The second allows this set to be used as a library of information presented subject by subject, which the reader can consult piece by piece as required.

All articles are prepared and presented so that the subject is equally accessible by either. Topics are arranged in a logical sequence, outlined in the contents list. The indexes allow access to more specific points.

Within an article, scientific terms are explained in the main text where an understanding of them is central to the understanding of the subject as a whole. Fact entries giving technical, mathematical, or biographical details are included, where appropriate, at the end of the article to which they relate. There is also an alphabetical glossary of terms at the end of each part, so that the reader's memory can be refreshed and so that the material can be used for quick reference whenever necessary.

All articles are relatively short, but none has been condensed artificially. Most articles occupy two pages, but some are four pages long.

The sample two-page article *(right)* shows the important elements of this editorial plan and illustrates the way in which this organization permits maximum flexibility of use.

(A) **Article title** gives the reader an immediate reference point.

(B) **Section title** shows the section in which a particular article falls.

(C) **Main text** consists of approximately 850 words of narrative information set out in a logical manner, avoiding biographical and technical details that might tend to interrupt the story line and hamper the reader's progress.

(D) **Illustrations** include specially commissioned drawings and diagrams and carefully selected photographs, which expand, clarify, and add to the main text.

(E) **Captions** explain the illustrations and make the connection between the textual and the visual elements of the article.

(F) **Annotation** of the drawings allows the reader to identify the various elements referred to in the captions.

(G) **Theme images,** where appropriate, are included in the top left-hand corner of the left-hand page, to emphasize a central element of information or to create a visual link between different but related articles.

(H) **Fact entries** are added at the foot of the last page of certain articles to give biographical details, chemical or mathematical formulas, or additional information relating to the article but not essential to an understanding of the main text itself.

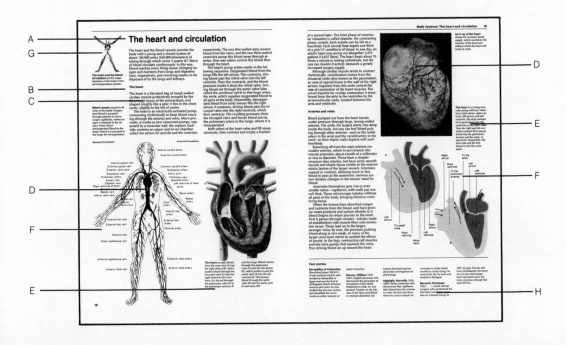

Introduction

The human body is a marvel. It starts out as a single cell and in time develops into a body consisting of trillions of cells that can perform an astonishing variety of physical and mental activities. The human body can also replace certain worn-out parts and defend itself against hundreds of diseases. The outer layer of the skin, for example, our first line of defense against disease, is entirely replaced every 15 to 30 days.

The human brain, the most remarkable part of the human body, is what distinguishes people from all other living things. It enables them to delve into the secrets of the living cell, create beautiful poetry and other works of art, and send sophisticated spacecraft to the moon and beyond. Nothing else—no other animal, no machine—can think like a human being.

The human sciences, as they are sometimes called, attempt to encompass an approach to humankind that includes the study of our ori-gins, our structure, our functioning, our inherited characteristics, and our behavior, both as individuals and as members of human society. Taken together, these broad areas of knowledge form the basis of the humanitarian applied science of medicine—which itself forms the focus of a modern caring society in which the young are nurtured, the adult kept strong and healthy, and the elderly and the sick given relief and rest.

The need for knowledge of ourselves becomes increasingly apparent as medicine becomes more specialized and our world becomes more complex. To be a survivor in this modern age demands judgments from all of us about such things as what to eat and drink, how much exercise to take, how many children to bear, or how much stress to accept. Such judgments can be made easier by the knowledge about ourselves revealed in this book.

The human body gives off heat through the skin. This thermograph shows how the temperature varies over different parts of the body surface.

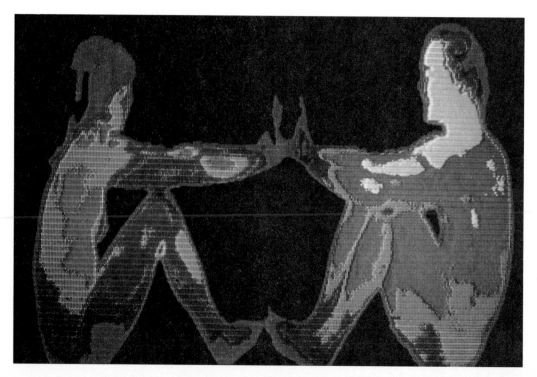

The basic human sciences

The oldest of the human sciences is anatomy, the study of human structure, which was founded on the basis of observation at Alexandria in about 300 B.C. (although the embalmers of ancient Egypt had acquired a rudimentary knowledge of human anatomy). Herophilus of the Alexandrian School studied the brain and spinal cord, identified tendons and nerves, and discovered that the nerves and brain direct movements. He was probably the first anatomist who learned by carrying out dissections of cadavers rather than by merely reading ancient texts.

The most famous anatomist of the Middle Ages was Leonardo da Vinci. His enquiring mind and his skill as an artist have left us an unrivaled collection of anatomical drawings. Unfortunately, his notebooks were lost for two centuries, but now we can see that Leonardo—the artist and engineer—was perhaps the father of scientific anatomy. Traditionally, this title goes to Andreas Vesalius, a Flemish anatomist who studied at Louvain in 1537. It was commonly held at that time that nothing could be added to the conclusions of the Greek physician Galen, who died at the end of the second century A.D., and whose theories combine anatomical and medical observation with a belief in the existence of "humors" that influence the body and its health. When Vesalius was appointed professor at Padua, he carried out dissections in public and wrote his masterpiece *On the Fabric of the Human Body,* or *Fabrica,* which established the scientific basis of anatomy.

Knowledge of physiology was increased at about the time that the Englishman William Harvey went to study at Padua in 1598. When he returned to Britain he taught anatomy and surgery at St. Bartholomew's Hospital in London, and in 1628, published his book on the circulation of the blood. This work refuted Galenic doctrine and continued the scientific revolution in our understanding of human anatomy and physiology. The modern era of physiology expanded with the use of the experimental method, while in anatomy, the invention of the microscope led to an appreciation of cellular theory and tissue structure and function. The modern basic sciences include relative newcomers, such as biochemistry, which developed out of physiological chem-

Growing up is a physical and mental process that relies on diet and activity, the care of other people—especially the parents—and the environment, from which all things are learned.

Human beings are set apart from other animals by their ability to use intellect and tools (the combination we now call technology) to conquer or modify the environment. Humans have learned to make wheeled vehicles to improve their mobility on land, build boats to cross oceans, and construct aircraft—from hang gliders to supersonic jet planes—to fly through the air.

istry, and pharmacology (the study of drug actions), which developed out of pharmacy and materia medica (the branch of medical study that deals with drugs, their sources, preparations, and uses).

The latest additions to these basic human studies are human genetics, psychology, and sociology. Human genetics as a science has led to a greater understanding of the mechanisms of inherited characteristics and disorders and to the ability to counsel prospective parents on their chances of having normal babies even if there is a history of genetic problems in the family. The study of psychology has allowed a better understanding of the functioning of the mind and human behavior, which in turn is the basis of our appreciation of mental illness and mental subnormality. And advances in sociology, the study of human societies in towns and cities or in the countryside, may lead to better use of our human resources, with reduced conflict between societies' divisions and classes.

Human adaptability

Divisions of mankind are obvious in the differing physical features of the populations in various parts of the world. Some of these racial characteristics are the result of useful environmental adaptations during the later stages of human evolution. Other physical characteristics, such as physiological adaptations to high altitude in mountain-dwelling peoples, show more immediate examples of physical adaptability.

Human culture, however—with the use of clothes, fire, travel, warfare, and so on—has tended to blunt the edge of the selective processes that led to evolutionary differences, and marriages across racial groups have blurred the boundaries in many parts of the world. Racial mixtures are diffuse in South America, for example.

When the human machine breaks down

There are thousands of separate disorders listed in medical dictionaries, but there are just a few basic categories into which nearly all illnesses can be classified. These are deficiencies (of diet, vitamins, hormones, and so on), infections (by bacteria, viruses, or fungi), tumors (such as cancers resulting from uncontrolled growth), allergies (such as hay fever and asthma), and lastly, the degenerative processes that affect the heart, arteries, and joints of older people.

The Western system of medicine is based on the attempt to understand the human body by means of science and then to apply this knowledge to the alleviation—or, better, prevention—of the disorders that physicians are called upon to treat. Thus, deficiency diseases are diagnosed and then treated by replacement therapy; infections are treated using antibiotics that kill the invading microorganisms; allergies are treated by desensitization; and tumors by surgery to remove the tissues whose growth has gotten out of hand. Degenerative processes cannot be completely halted, but some of their effects can be relieved, by the replacement of worn-out joints and blood vessels, for example.

The whole apparatus of science is brought to bear on the diagnostic and therapeutic work of the modern physician. Computerized X rays, radioactive scanning techniques, and automated biochemical investigations all help in diagnosis. In treatment microsurgery, joint replacement and kidney transplants are now commonplace, and new drugs are continually being developed to help in the battle against infection, pain, and allergy.

In the large teaching hospitals and research institutes, medical research workers continue the search for new understandings and methods to help physicians treat the sick. Modern electron microscopes allow researchers to visualize particles and structures within cells, to analyze their contents, and to identify even single elements such as pollutants from the environment. Scanning methods and multiple trace recordings provide new insights into the workings of the brain. Transplant surgery of the heart is now emerging from the experimental stage.

The future

The future of mankind is as unanswerable a question as the one with which we began, but some problems face us still and our future depends on their solution. The world's population and the world's food supply are not always in balance, and distribution problems lead to the scandals of starvation and waste still coexisting on this planet. Space for living is not always wisely used, and squalor and overcrowding in towns and lack of services in rural areas still exist widely in the world. Our social systems do not always produce contentment or allow for the aspirations of the people, and our technology does not always respect the environment in which we have to live. But perhaps most important of all is that on our shrinking world we must achieve a cultural and social understanding between peoples so that conflicts among races, religions, and nations will fade and die forever.

Perhaps only through a realization of the unity of humankind, through the study of the human animal, can this respect for each other be made a reality.

Man has progressed from merely sheltering in caves to making weatherproof dwellings and building cities, so that people can now live almost anywhere on earth. Combined with a detailed knowledge of the workings of the human body and medical science based on it, this technology has effectively accelerated human development in terms of adaptability, and, properly used, should ensure continued survival.

Body systems

The human body is made up of over 10 million million cells. Most are smaller than a pinpoint, yet each is a living entity, receiving nourishment from, and ejecting waste into, the fluid in which the cell is bathed. Hundreds of millions of cells die every minute, but many millions more are being born as cells divide and multiply.

Under a low-powered microscope, a typical cell may look like a blob of jelly. Higher magnification reveals that it includes some strange and complex structures. Between them, these support and repair the cell and help it reproduce.

Most cells contain a clearly demarcated control center called a nucleus, which is embedded in the jellylike cytoplasm that makes up most of the rest of the cell. The major constituent of the nucleus is the complex of protein and DNA called chromatin. When a cell divides, chromatin forms into threadlike chromosomes, each of which contains genes, the hereditary factors determining the characteristics of the new cells produced by cell division. The nucleus also includes at least one nucleolus—a granular unit rich in ribonucleic acid (RNA) that helps to manufacture protein molecules according to "instructions" given by the DNA. The nuclear envelope around the nucleus and its nucleoli is a thin membrane serving as a sieve that regulates the flow of nutrients and wastes both in and out of the nucleus.

Extending from the nuclear membrane through the cytoplasm are paired membranes pleated like a half-closed concertina and called the endoplasmic reticulum. These membranes help to regulate the flow of chemicals. The outside surfaces of the endoplasmic reticulum in many cells are covered with tiny granular structures called ribosomes, where ribonucleic acid builds amino acids into protein, both for the cell itself and also for other uses.

Cytoplasm also contains a variety of tiny specialized structures, including Golgi bodies, mitochondria, lysosomes, and centrioles. Golgi bodies consist of groups of flattened parallel sacs derived from the endoplasmic reticulum. Their function seems to be to take in newly made protein and add carbohydrate to produce mucoprotein (the main constituent of mucus). Lysosomes are sacs containing enzymes that digest large molecules so that the products can be oxidized. Mitochondria resemble minute hollow sausages (some cells have thousands of them). These are the power plants of the cell, for here its respiration occurs, and its energy is stored as a chemical compound, adenosine triphosphate (ATP). Centrioles appear like cylindrical bundles of tiny rods or fibrils. They play a part in cell division.

Cytoplasm also contains many other structures, some with functions yet to be discovered.

The whole cell is surrounded by a plasma membrane made up of fat molecules sandwiched between two protein layers. Small molecules pass in and out of this cell wall by diffusion; larger molecules, such as those of glucose, may be brought inside by specialized receptor molecules that lie within the membrane.

Tissues and organs

By no means are all cells identical. Their form reflects their function, and cells may be specialized in many ways. For instance, neurons (nerve cells) act like minute cables, conveying messages. Long, slim muscle cells contract. And cells lining much of the respiratory system have projecting whiplike threads that help to move mucus.

Similar cells performing a similar task form a mass of tissue. Examples are muscular tissue;

The human body is a complex combination of systems—circulatory, lymphatic, digestive, urinary, nervous, endocrine, and reproductive—supported by the skeleton and musculature, which also give the body its shape. The whole body is enclosed within skin.

Brain

Spinal cord

Muscles of the neck, shoulder and chest

Sternum

Heart

Ribs

Humerus

Stomach

Large intestine

Small intestine

Radius

Ulna

Femoral artery

Femur

Great saphenous vein

Patella

Tibia

Fibula

Great cephalic

Lung

Brachial artery

Liver

Radial artery

Bones of the hand

Bones of the foot

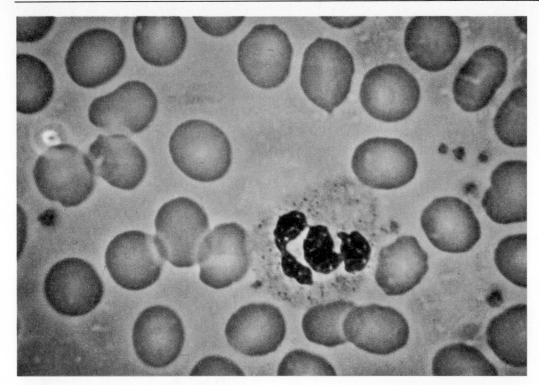

Cells occur in many forms, which reflect their function. Blood cells, for example, include erythrocytes—atypical cells without nuclei (here shown as the globules)—and more typical leukocytes, in which the nucleus is large and lobular (the darker, more fragmented object).

A typical cell contains many microscopic structures within its cytoplasm and nucleus. Most are so small that they can only be observed with the aid of an electron microscope.

nerve tissue in the brain; the epithelial tissue of the skin and of internal body linings; connective tissue, which serves to support or pack other types of tissue or body organs (themselves made of specialized tissues); and skeletal tissue, which supplies the body's framework.

Different tissues grouped together for a common purpose form an organ, such as the stomach, heart, or lung. Cooperating groups of organs, in turn, build up body systems.

Body systems

The human body is built up of nearly a dozen major interrelated systems, each designed for a special function. The skeleton provides a strong framework. Muscles are the engines of the body. Bones (with tendons, ligaments, and fibrous sheaths linking joints and muscles) provide the system for translating muscular contractions into bodily movements. The fuel and oxygen that keep muscles working travel through thousands of miles of tubing in the circulatory system, which in turn depends upon the respiratory system to supply the blood with oxygen, and the digestive system, where food is broken down into nutrients that can be used as fuel. The urinary system gets rid of processed body wastes. The endocrine system and the nervous system control bodily activities. And the senses, extensions of the nervous system, keep us aware of our surroundings. All these interlocking systems are contained neatly by the skin.

Though many body systems parallel systems in a complex machine, the body is no ordinary mechanism. Its lymphatic and circulatory systems can prevent or minimize damage and replace worn components. The reproductive system enables human beings to reproduce themselves. And no machine has yet learned how to think.

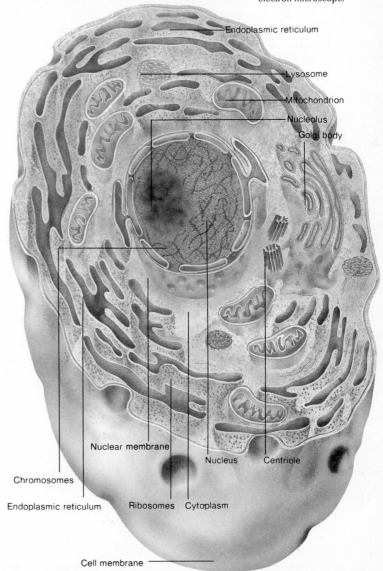

Endoplasmic reticulum
Lysosome
Mitochondrion
Nucleolus
Golgi body
Nuclear membrane
Nucleus
Centriole
Chromosomes
Endoplasmic reticulum
Ribosomes
Cytoplasm
Cell membrane

The skeleton is the framework around which the body is built.

The skeleton

The human skeleton comprises more than 200 strong, bony rods, blocks and plates buffered by cartilage and linked by joints. Between them, different bones provide internal scaffolding, muscle-operated levers, and shields protecting vital organs. Bones also contain marrow, which manufactures blood. Furthermore, despite a popular misconception, bone is a living substance and, like the brain, needs nourishment.

Bone types and structures

Some anatomists classify bone into four types: long, short, flat, and irregular. Long bones form the levers of the limbs. Short bones, as in the wrist and ankle, provide strong, compact structures. Flat bones, such as those of the skull and shoulder blades, protect other structures or provide broad surfaces for muscle anchorage. Irregular bones, such as the bones of the spine, are those too peculiarly shaped to be grouped with any of the rest.

There are two main types of bony tissue.

The hard, solid, heavy walls are made of dense tissue called compact bone. Inside is a mesh of spongy, or cancellous, bone. The two combined give bones their strength and relative lightness. Bone's hardness comes from layers of crystals of compounds of calcium, phosphorus, and other elements. Bone's resilience depends upon pliable threads of the fibrous protein collagen, which has high tensile strength and forms a network within which the hard crystals are laid down. Strength, hardness, and limited flexibility combine to help bone resist forces that would otherwise crush or bend it.

If you cut through a typical long bone you find first a thin covering of tough tissue, the periosteum. Then comes the hard compact bone built up of so-called Haversian systems: concentric rings with central canals carrying the blood vessels that supply oxygen and nutrients to the bone. Beyond the compact bone, a network of spongy bone occupies the bone's interior and its bulging ends. The inside of the shaft and spaces between the "struts" of spongy bone, however, are filled with pulpy marrow, of connective tissue, blood vessels, and red blood cells. As long bones mature, fatty yellow marrow takes the place of red.

The ends of long bones are covered with cartilage, a dense, flexible connective tissue that is a precursor of bone in children and serves to protect bones from friction against other bones and from damage from jarring within the joints.

Axial skeleton

The axial skeleton of skull, vertebrae, and ribs provides the body's structural core, supporting the appendicular skeleton of limb bones and providing the frame for the internal organs.

The skull's 22 bones include 8 interlocking cranial bones, forming a dome that holds and shields the brain, and 14 facial bones, forming the basis of the face and jaws: a rigid maxilla (upper jaw) and hinged mandible (lower jaw). Air-filled cavities, called sinuses, lighten certain facial bones, and bony basins support and protect the eyes. The nasal cavity and mouth provide openings for the respiratory and digestive systems. The skull rests on the topmost of the 33 or so short, strong irregular bones called vertebrae. (Their numbers vary slightly in some individuals.) These and the fibrous disks between them form the spine. This flexible, weight-bearing column with a double bend supports the upper body's weight; bony arches at the backs of vertebrae sheathe the fragile spinal cord. From top to bottom, the spine's five sets of vertebrae comprise typically: 7 cervical (neck) vertebrae; 12 thoracic vertebrae at the back of the chest; 5 lumbar (lower back) vertebrae; 5 fused vertebrae forming the sacrum; and the 4 fused vertebrae of the coccyx, a vestigial tail.

The ribcage consists of 12 pairs of flat, curved bones projecting forward from the thoracic vertebrae. Pairs 1-7, the true ribs, meet the sternum, or breastbone, at the front of the chest. Pairs 11-12, the floating ribs, stop short. Ribs and breastbone protect the heart and lungs inside the chest cavity and work with the diaphragm during breathing.

Bones link together to form the skeleton, which is symmetrical about a vertical, central plane. The illustration shows the skeleton seen from the front on one side, and from the back on the other. Bones in the center of the body have been shown cut in half.

Front view

Cranium
Maxilla
Mandible
Clavicle
Humerus
Sternum
Radius
Ulna
Pelvic girdle
Carpals
Metacarpals
Phalanges of the hand
Femur
Patella
Tibia
Fibula
Tarsals
Metatarsals
Phalanges of the foot

Back view

Cervical vertebrae
Scapula
Thoracic vertebrae
Lumbar vertebrae
Sacrum
Coccyx
Calcaneus

Appendicular skeleton

Limb bones are anchored to the axial skeleton by frameworks known as girdles. The pectoral or shoulder girdle has two clavicles (collarbones), which help muscles hold the shoulders back, and two scapulae (shoulder blades), which lie at the back of the chest. A humerus (upper arm bone) fits into a socket in each scapula. Each forearm has two bones (radius and ulna) that are articulated so they can twist, allowing hand rotation. Each hand has 27 bones comprising carpals (wrist bones), metacarpals (palm bones), and phalanges (fingers). The pelvic or hip girdle has two sets of three bones (ilium, ischium, and pubis) that flank and join the sacrum and, with it, form a bony, pelvic basin. This pelvis supports and protects internal organs, and each side of it has an acetabulum, a cup-shaped cavity, serving as a socket for a femur (thighbone). Below the femur are two other leg bones, the tibia (shinbone) and fibula. The tarsals, metatarsals, and phalanges form the bones of the back of the foot, the forefoot, and the toes, respectively.

Joints, ligaments, and tendons

Bones can transmit body weight and help muscles move limbs and other parts of the body only because they are linked at joints— that is, where bone meets bone. Different types of joints serve different purposes. At fibrous joints, like those between the cranial bones, fibrous tissue knits bones almost rigidly together. At cartilaginous joints, like those between the vertebrae, however, springy cartilage buffers bone ends, and between these lies a fibrocartilage pad. Much greater movement occurs at synovial, or movable, joints, such as those of the ankle, elbow, and shoulder. Some are gliding joints, others are pivot, hinge, or ball-and-socket joints. Many are superbly designed to combat friction and the stress induced by sudden jolting. In each synovial joint, opposing bone ends are capped by cartilage and separated by a cavity walled by ligaments—bands of flexible tissue that give the joint stability and strength. The inner lining of the joint capsule surrounding the cavity consists of smooth, slippery synovial membrane producing syrupy synovial fluid that lubricates joint surfaces. Active movement of many joints would be impossible without tendons—the strong, tough, plaited fibers forming the cords that attach bone or cartilage to muscle.

Teeth and nails

Tooth enamel resembles bone in that it is made of mineral crystals in a mesh of protein, but enamel has a higher mineral content than bone and so is even harder. Tooth enamel, however, is not part of the skeleton: with the substance of toenails and fingernails, enamel forms the nearest human equivalent to an insect's exoskeleton.

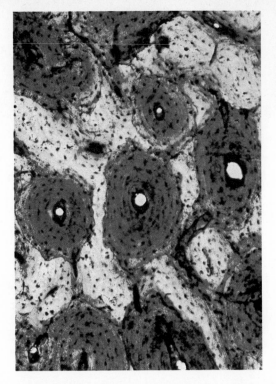

Compact bone, which forms the outer part of bones and gives them their strength, is made up of many columns—shown here in cross-section—of cells called osteoblasts, arranged concentrically around central Haversian canals.

The hip joint consists of a moving bone, the femur, attached to a group of fixed bones, known collectively as the pelvic girdle. Ligaments and muscles hold the femur in place and make it move. The head of the femur and the socket (acetabulum) into which it fits are lined with cartilage. Synovial fluid, produced by the enveloping synovial membrane, allows these two surfaces to move against each other without friction. The femur is a typical long bone, with a thick layer of compact bone around its shaft, and with spongy bone inside. The latter allows bones to be both strong and relatively light; it also contains a rich supply of blood vessels and the blood-forming tissue called marrow (not shown). The shafts of long bones contain yellow marrow, which is also a store of fat cells. Red marrow is found in the head of the femur, as well as in the flat bones of the body—among them, the bones of the pelvic girdle.

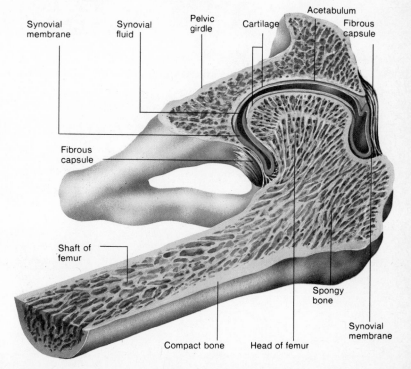

Muscles

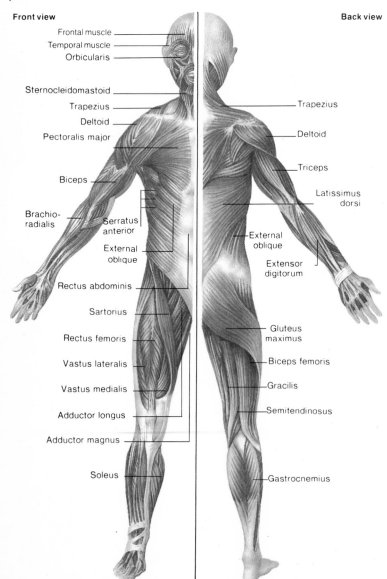

Muscles hold and move the skeleton and give the body its shape.

Muscles involved with movement are arranged symmetrically—like the bones to which they are attached—about a vertical, central plane. In addition to the surface muscles shown, there are many "deep" muscles, which play equally important roles.

Muscle makes up nearly half the body weight of an adult. More than 600 muscles cover the skeleton and give the body bulk and form. But their main task is to move limbs, push food through the gut, make the heart beat, and control blood flow around the body.

A typical skeletal or voluntary muscle comprises thousands or millions of fibers whose coordinated contractions cause the whole muscle to contract. The energy for muscular contraction comes from chemical reactions involving fuel and oxygen brought to the muscles through a rich supply of blood vessels. Besides mechanical energy, muscle action produces heat and chemical wastes, which leave through capillaries leading to veins that carry spent blood from the muscle.

There are three main types of muscle: skeletal, smooth, and cardiac.

Skeletal muscle

Skeletal muscles are joined to bones and make them move. Groups of skeletal muscles operate the arms, legs, torso, neck, and face. They range in size from tiny muscles rotating the eye to the large, powerful thigh muscles. Each skeletal muscle consists of long, slim muscle fibers from less than .25 inch (a few millimeters) to more than 1 inch long, in bundles bound together by connective tissue. Each fiber has a number of nuclei. Fiber bundles are organized according to the tasks they must perform. Thus, parallel bundles capable of strong contractions form the muscle felt at the side of the neck. And the deltoid muscle—the topmost muscle on the outside of the arm—has short fiber bundles arranged like the barbs of a feather that produce limited but powerful movements.

The basic units of each fiber are thick, dark filaments and thin pale ones. Seen under the microscope, these give skeletal muscle a striped appearance so that it is also called striped or striated muscle. Because we can usually move skeletal muscles at will, they are also known as voluntary muscles, although they are capable of involuntary reflex movements, too, as when a hand jerks away from a source of heat.

Skeletal muscle contracts when it is stimulated by an electrochemical signal from the central nervous system. This acts on nerve endings linked to the muscle fibers. How much a whole muscle contracts depends on how many of its fibers have been activated.

In order to work, a typical skeletal muscle needs to have both its ends connected to the skeleton—either directly or via tendons or fibrous sheets called aponeuroses. The fixed muscle end, closest to the body's center, is called the origin. The other end—called the insertion—is attached to the bone that actually moves.

Many muscles have names that indicate their function. For instance, flexors bend joints, extensors straighten them. Abductors pull a part of the body away from its central axis, adductors do the opposite. The to-and-fro action of a limb or jaw or eyeball depends upon pairs of muscles acting in opposition to each other. Muscles have to work in opposing pairs because each muscle acts in just one direction. It can pull or squeeze, but then simply relaxes, for muscles cannot push.

Skeletal muscles can be grouped in four main categories according to their general function: prime movers contract to cause active movement; antagonists act in opposition to prime movers; fixation muscles hold steady such parts as the shoulder blade to provide a base for movements involving other muscles; and synergists combine with prime movers to keep joints still.

Coordinated signals from the central nervous system ensure that opposing muscles do not contract simultaneously to cancel out one another. So when the triceps muscle of the upper arm contracts to straighten the arm, the opposing biceps muscle relaxes. The triceps is then acting as a prime mover and the biceps as the antagonist. But when the elbow is bent, the biceps contracts, the triceps relaxes, and their roles are reversed.

Powerful skeletal muscles moving long bones make these act as levers so that a short

Front view

- Frontal muscle
- Temporal muscle
- Orbicularis
- Sternocleidomastoid
- Trapezius
- Deltoid
- Pectoralis major
- Biceps
- Brachio-radialis
- Serratus anterior
- External oblique
- Rectus abdominis
- Sartorius
- Rectus femoris
- Vastus lateralis
- Vastus medialis
- Adductor longus
- Adductor magnus
- Soleus

Back view

- Trapezius
- Deltoid
- Triceps
- Latissimus dorsi
- External oblique
- Extensor digitorum
- Gluteus maximus
- Biceps femoris
- Gracilis
- Semitendinosus
- Gastrocnemius

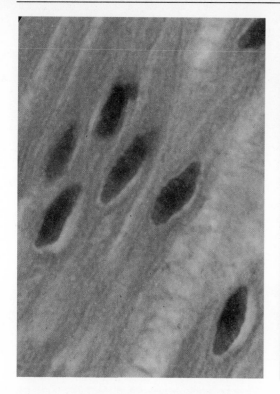

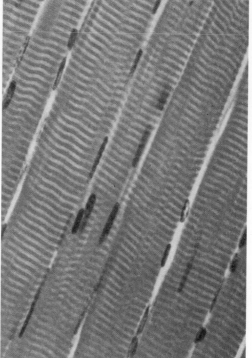

Smooth muscle *(far left)*—which consists of elongated cells, each with its own nucleus—is found in tissues such as the stomach and the intestines.

Skeletal muscles *(left)*, also called striped or voluntary muscles, are controlled directly by the motor nerves of the central nervous system, and are chiefly concerned with movement. They consist of long, thin, striped fibers, each with several nuclei.

muscle movement produces a large limb movement. For example, a muscle contraction of less than 3 inches (8 centimeters) moves the fingers through an arc that is 12 times greater, although the force involved is correspondingly diminished.

Smooth muscle

Smooth muscle occurs in the digestive tract, urinary tract, blood vessels, bronchial tree, and other internal structures. Unlike skeletal muscle, a fiber of smooth muscle lacks stripes and has one nucleus instead of many nuclei. Also, it contracts more slowly than a skeletal muscle fiber, tends to contract rhythmically, and is not under direct control of the brain. By contracting or relaxing, smooth muscle narrows or enlarges the diameter of blood vessels to control the blood flow passing through. Similarly, alternate contraction and relaxation of smooth muscle forming stomach and intestine walls drives food through the gut in the action called peristalsis. The rate at which smooth muscle contracts depends on hormones and the autonomic nervous system. Because we cannot normally control its action, smooth muscle is also called involuntary muscle.

Cardiac muscle

Cardiac muscle is striped like skeletal muscle, but contracts automatically like smooth muscle. Its fibers surround the ventricles—the heart's main pumping chambers—and contract rhythmically at intervals regulated by the sinoatrial node, the "pacemaker," and by the autonomic nervous system.

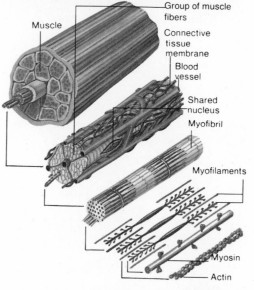

Muscle
Group of muscle fibers
Connective tissue membrane
Blood vessel
Shared nucleus
Myofibril
Myofilaments
Myosin
Actin

A striped muscle consists of muscle fibers with shared nuclei, enclosed in a connective tissue membrane through which the fibers receive their blood and nerve supply. The fibers are composed of myofibrils, which contract or relax as filaments of myosin and actin that they contain move against each other.

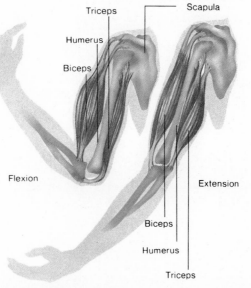

Triceps
Scapula
Humerus
Biceps
Flexion
Extension
Biceps
Humerus
Triceps

Muscles can only contract or relax, which enables them to pull or to be stretched. They cannot push. So to move bones at a joint, there must be opposing muscles or sets of muscles. In the arm, the biceps bends the elbow joint and is called the flexor. The triceps straightens the joint and is called the extensor.

The heart and circulation

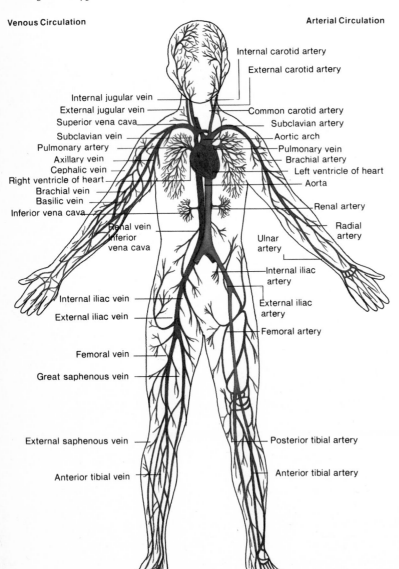

The heart and the blood circulation are the major elements of the body's internal transportation system.

Blood vessels extend to all areas of the body. Oxygenated blood is pumped through arteries to microscopic capillaries, where oxygen is released to the tissues. Veins return deoxygenated blood to the heart, where it is pumped to the lungs for reoxygenation.

The heart and the blood vessels provide the body with a pump and a closed system of about 100,000 miles (160,000 kilometers) of tubing through which some 5 quarts (4.7 liters) of blood circulate continuously. In this way, blood reaches every living tissue, bringing oxygen and nutrients from lungs and digestive tract, respectively, and removing wastes to be disposed of by the lungs and kidneys.

The heart

The heart is a fist-sized bag of tough-walled cardiac muscle protectively encased by the thin, tough tissue of the pericardium, and shaped roughly like a pear. It lies in the chest cavity, slightly to the left of center.

The heart is an electrically-activated pump, contracting rhythmically to keep blood coursing through the arteries and veins. More precisely, it works as two connected pumps, separated by a muscular wall, the septum. Each side contains an upper and lower chamber called the atrium (or auricle) and the ventricle,

respectively. The two thin-walled atria receive blood from the veins, and the two thick-walled ventricles pump this blood away through arteries. One-way valves control this blood flow through the heart.

The heart's pump action works in the following sequence. Oxygenated blood from the lungs fills the left atrium. This contracts, driving blood past the mitral valve into the left ventricle. Then this contracts, and the blood pressure inside it shuts the mitral valve, forcing blood out through the aortic valve (also called the semilunar valve) to that huge artery, the aorta, which supplies oxygenated blood to all parts of the body. Meanwhile, deoxygenated blood from body tissues fills the right atrium. It contracts, driving blood past the tricuspid valve into the right ventricle, which then contracts. The resulting pressure shuts the tricuspid valve and forces blood out via the pulmonary artery to the lungs, where it is reoxygenated.

Both valves of the heart relax and fill simultaneously, then contract and empty a fraction

Venous Circulation

Arterial Circulation

Internal carotid artery

External carotid artery

Internal jugular vein

External jugular vein

Superior vena cava

Common carotid artery

Subclavian artery

Subclavian vein

Aortic arch

Pulmonary artery

Pulmonary vein

Axillary vein

Brachial artery

Cephalic vein

Left ventricle of heart

Right ventricle of heart

Aorta

Brachial vein

Basilic vein

Renal artery

Inferior vena cava

Renal vein

Radial artery

Inferior vena cava

Ulnar artery

Internal iliac artery

Internal iliac vein

External iliac vein

External iliac artery

Femoral artery

Femoral vein

Great saphenous vein

External saphenous vein

Posterior tibial artery

Anterior tibial artery

Anterior tibial vein

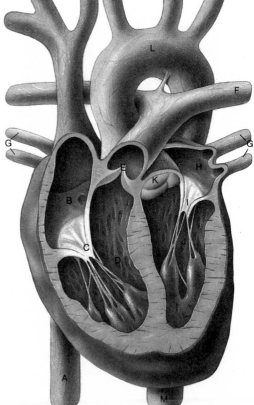

The heart accepts blood from the vena cava (A) into the right atrium (B), which pushes blood through the tricuspid valve (C) into the right ventricle (D). From here, it is forced through the pulmonary valve (E) to the pulmonary arteries (F) and the lungs. Blood returns through the pulmonary veins (G) into the left atrium (H), which pushes it past the mitral valve (I) into the left ventricle (J). This pumps blood through the aortic valve (K) into the aortic arch (L) and aorta (M).

of a second later. The brief phase of ventricular relaxation is called diastole, the contracting phase, systole. Each systole can be felt as a heartbeat. Each normal beat expels one-third of a pint (17 centiliters) of blood. In one day, an adult's heart may pump out altogether 3,475 gallons (13,637 liters). The heart beats about 70 times a minute in resting individuals, but the rate can double if activity demands a greatly increased oxygen supply.

Although cardiac muscle tends to contract rhythmically, coordination comes from the sinoatrial node (also known as the pacemaker), an area of special tissue in the wall of the right atrium. Impulses from this node control the rate of contraction of the heart muscles. The actual impulse for cardiac contraction is transferred from the atria to the ventricles by the atrioventricular node, located between the atria and ventricles.

Arteries and veins

Blood pumped out from the heart travels under pressure through large, strong-walled arteries. The aorta, the largest artery, lies deep inside the body, but you can feel blood pulsing through other arteries—such as the radial artery in the wrist and the carotid artery in the neck—as their elastic walls expand with each heartbeat.

Branching off from the main arteries are smaller arteries, which in turn branch into minute arterioles, about a tenth of a millimeter or less in diameter. These have a simpler structure than arteries, but have some smooth muscle and elastic tissue similar to the internal elastic lamina of the larger vessels. Arterioles expand or contract, allowing more or less blood to pass as the autonomic nervous system dictates changes in the tissues' need for blood.

Arterioles themselves give rise to even smaller tubes—capillaries, with walls just one cell thick. These microscopic tubules infiltrate all parts of the body, bringing blood to every living tissue.

When the tissues have absorbed oxygen and nutrients from the blood, and have given up waste products and carbon dioxide to it, blood begins its return journey to the heart. First it passes through venules—tubules made of endothelium with muscle fiber and connective tissue. These lead on to the larger, stronger veins. By now, the pressure pushing blood along is very weak, so many of the larger veins have valves to combat the effects of gravity. In the legs, contracting calf muscles provide extra pumps that squeeze the veins, thus driving blood on up toward the heart.

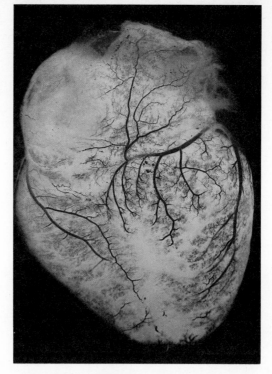

An X ray of the heart shows the coronary blood supply, which nourishes the muscles of the heart and without which the heart will cease to work.

The heart is a strong muscular pump with four chambers: right atrium, right ventricle, left atrium, and left ventricle. The atria contract (A) to push blood into the ventricles as the latter relax. Then the right and left ventricles contract (B) to pump blood into the pulmonary arteries and the aorta, respectively. Meanwhile, the atria relax and fill with blood to start the cycle again.

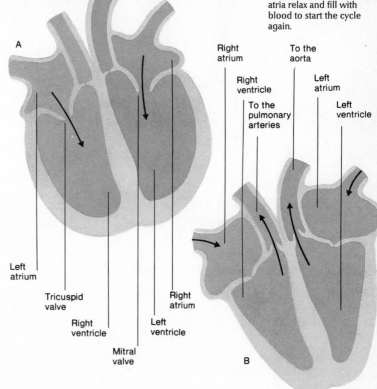

A

Left atrium

Tricuspid valve

Right ventricle

Mitral valve

Right atrium

Left ventricle

Right atrium

Right ventricle

To the pulmonary arteries

To the aorta

Left atrium

Left ventricle

B

Fact entries

Herophilus of Chalcedon (flourished about 300 B.C.), Greek medical teacher who worked at Alexandria in Egypt and was the first to distinguish clearly between arteries and veins. He also studied the nervous system and identified the nerve trunks as either sensory or motor branches.

Harvey, William (1578-1657), English physician who discovered the principles of circulation of the blood. Published in 1628, *An Anatomical Treatise on the Motion of the Heart and Blood in Animals* abolished old beliefs that had long hindered the development of physiology.

Malpighi, Marcello (1628-1694), Italian anatomist who discovered that capillaries take blood from the arteries to veins. He first saw them when he used a simple microscope to study blood vessels in a frog's lung. For most of his life he lived and worked in Bologna.

Barnard, Christiaan (1922-   ), South African surgeon who performed the first heart transplant operation on a human being. In 1967, he gave 55-year-old Louis Washkansky the heart of a 25-year-old woman. Such operations later became common, though Barnard did few.

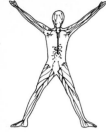

Lymphatic ducts drain body tissues, returning intracellular fluid to the circulatory system. Lymph nodes are found where ducts converge.

The lymphatic system consists of small, thin-walled vessels containing lymph. These drain into larger ducts and ultimately into the large thoracic duct that runs near the aorta and the spine.

Blood and lymph

Coursing ceaselessly through arteries and veins, blood is vital for the life of every tissue in the body. This complex fluid contains the foods and fuel that provide energy and the materials for repairing damaged cells and building new ones. Blood also helps demolish and remove worn-out cells, other wastes, and harmful foreign bodies. It also takes heat from the body core to the extremities. And blood brings to wounds the materials that minimize blood loss and promote healing.

A man weighing about 155 pounds (70 kilograms) contains about 1.3 gallons (5 liters) of blood; a child half his weight has only half that quantity. Most blood is manufactured in bone marrow, although some components come from the lymphatic system. The four main ingredients of blood are plasma, red cells, white cells, and platelets.

Plasma

This pale yellow fluid accounts for 55 to 65 per cent of blood by volume, and it is in this that the blood cells are suspended. Plasma is 90 per cent water and 10 per cent dissolved substances, chiefly salts and proteins. Most salts are ionized and can diffuse out from capillaries into the surrounding tissues, but the proteins are too large to escape. The resulting difference of concentration inside and outside capillaries creates osmotic pressure, which helps maintain a healthy balance between the fluid in the capillaries and in the tissues.

Important plasma proteins are albumin, globulin, and fibrinogen. Albumin (a substance also found in egg white) helps maintain blood volume and pressure. Globulin contains various antibodies—each kind combining chemically with a specific kind of foreign body such as a bacterium or virus—which help to neutralize disease-inducing germs. Fibrinogen plays a crucial part in blood clotting. Plasma deprived of clotting factors forms the watery liquid known as serum, which often oozes from a minor injury to the skin.

Red blood cells

These account for more than 99 per cent of the total volume of all blood cells. A mature red blood cell is a disk with concave sides, and is only 7 microns in diameter. Erythrocytes, as red cells are also known, perform the vital task of bringing oxygen from the lungs to tissues. They can do this because red cells contain the oxygen-attracting compound hemoglobin, which picks up oxygen molecules from the lungs. These oxygen molecules transform hemoglobin into oxyhemoglobin, a compound that colors the erythrocyte bright red. When erythrocytes surrender oxygen to tissues in exchange for carbon dioxide, blood becomes more purple in color, which explains the general color difference between bright red arterial blood and the duller-colored blood in veins.

Typically, a normal human body contains about 25 billion red blood cells; each microliter of blood contains from four to six million red blood cells. Bone marrow produces over 100 million every minute to make up for the millions destroyed. Each erythrocyte loses its nucleus before it leaves the marrow, then survives about 120 days before it is broken down in the spleen, liver, or blood vessels.

White blood cells

White blood cells, or leukocytes, are larger than red blood cells but far less plentiful—a mere 4,000 to 10,000 per microliter compared to 5 million red blood cells. White blood cells protect and scavenge, many of them moving actively to sites of danger. There are three main types of leukocyte: granulocytes, monocytes, and lymphocytes. These account, respectively, for 70 per cent, 10 per cent, and 20 per cent of all white blood cells. The first two come from bone marrow, the third comes from lymph glands.

Granulocytes—cells that have a granular appearance when stained and viewed under the miscroscope—include cells that swarm upon infected tissue and devour bacteria by a process called phagocytosis. Monocytes produce macrophages that settle primarily in the spleen and liver, where they engulf old red cells and

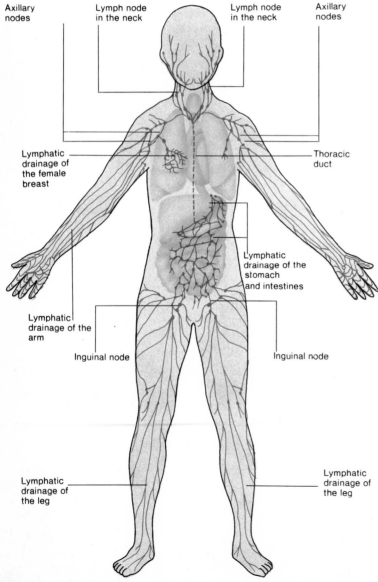

Axillary nodes

Lymph node in the neck

Lymph node in the neck

Axillary nodes

Lymphatic drainage of the female breast

Thoracic duct

Lymphatic drainage of the stomach and intestines

Lymphatic drainage of the arm

Inguinal node

Inguinal node

Lymphatic drainage of the leg

Lymphatic drainage of the leg

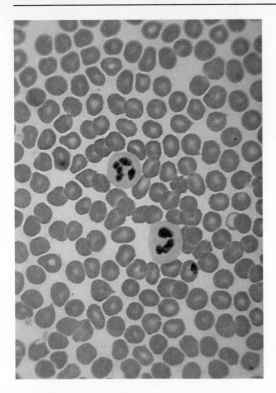

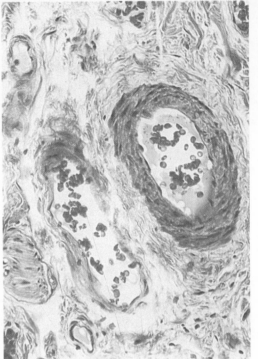

Blood consists principally of red cells in plasma. Microscopic examination of a blood sample *(far left)* also shows white cells (leukocytes) and the very small platelets.

Arteries and veins, shown in cross-section *(left)* appear quite different, although they are composed of similar tissues. Arteries are subject to greater blood pressure than veins and are much thicker, with more smooth muscle in their walls. This also enables them to control the blood flow by constricting or dilating in response to stimuli such as temperature or the presence of epinephrine in the blood.

foreign bodies. Lymphocytes are the core of the body's immune system: some kinds "remembering" specific types of foreign body and recognizing fresh invasions by them, others producing antibodies that coat these foreign bodies and make them easy prey for granulocytes and macrophages.

Platelets

These smallest blood particles, of which there are from 150,000 to 400,000 per microliter of blood, play a crucial part in clotting. They collect where an injured blood vessel is leaking blood, then stick together, thereby partly plugging the hole in the vessel wall. Platelets also react with clotting factors to convert the soluble fibrinogen in blood plasma into a mesh of fibrin threads, creating a net that traps other cells, to plug the gap completely.

Lymph and the lymphatic system

While blood circulates through arteries and veins, the blood-based fluid lymph flows through the lymphatic system.

Lymph is colorless, like plasma, but with little protein and no blood cells. Leaking from capillaries, lymph bathes the body's cells and drains into the lymphatic system, taking with it waste matter, dead cells, and bacteria. Tissues pressing on the smaller thin-walled tubes (the larger ones have one-way valves) drive lymph into two major ducts that drain ultimately into broad veins at the sides of the neck. On the way, lymph flows through lymph nodes that filter out wastes and produce bacteria-destroying lymphocytes and other defensive cells. During illness, node activity increases, producing enlarged lymph glands that can be felt in armpit, neck, and groin.

Besides the lymph nodes, the tonsils, adenoids, intestines, spleen, and the thymus gland all generate protective lymphocytes.

Composition of blood

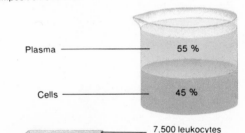

Plasma — 55 %

Cells — 45 %

Blood contains plasma and cells. The latter constitute about 45 per cent of the total volume of blood.

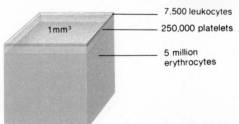

1mm³ — 7,500 leukocytes

250,000 platelets

5 million erythrocytes

A cubic millimeter of blood contains about 5 million erythrocytes, about 7,500 white cells (leukocytes), and about 250,000 platelets.

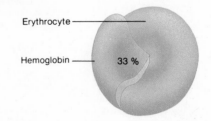

Erythrocyte

Hemoglobin — 33 %

Erythrocytes are red because they contain the red pigment hemoglobin, which makes up about one-third of their weight.

Incidence of ABO blood types

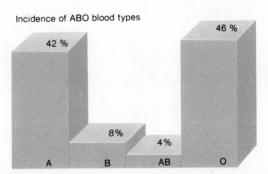

A 42 %   B 8%   AB 4%   O 46 %

Blood types are most commonly classified according to the ABO and the Rhesus (Rh) systems. ABO classifies blood by the presence of A-proteins (A), B-proteins (B), both (AB) or neither (O). The presence or absence of the Rhesus factor is indicated by Rh+ or Rh−.

Lungs and respiration

The lungs draw air into the body through the mouth and nose so that oxygen can be absorbed into the bloodstream.

The air around us provides our body tissues with the oxygen they need for oxidizing nutrients derived from food to provide energy for the processes of living. Respiration is the process by which the body gets that oxygen and expels waste carbon dioxide. External respiration involves air flow in and out of lungs. From the lungs, blood supplies tissue cells with the oxygen they need for the energy-releasing chemical reactions collectively called internal respiration.

Parts of the respiratory system

Some tiny, primitive animals allow oxygen to reach all their cells by diffusing it in and out through openings in the body wall. A human's much larger body needs an active pump to supply oxygen to the lungs where the gas can be absorbed into the blood for transportation throughout the body. This system consists basically of two bellows (the lungs) that fill with air, then empty, as muscles make them open and close.

Seen from the outside, lungs appear as two roughly pyramidal spongy structures that almost fill the conical thoracic (chest) cavity, walled by ribs and backbone, with the diaphragm—a sheet of muscle—as the floor. The left lung is smaller than the right, to make

room for the heart. The left lung is divided into two main lobes, the right into three; each lobe is subdivided into segments. Both lungs and the cavity in which they lie are lined by the pleura—a thin, smooth membrane that secretes a lubricating fluid that prevents friction between lungs and ribcage.

The lungs and passages supplying them with air form complex structures that parallel the trunk and branches of an inverted tree. This bronchial tree's internal surface provides an area for gaseous exchange more than 40 times larger than the body's surface.

The "tree trunk" is the windpipe or trachea—a wide, flexible tube stiffened by up to 20 broad bands of cartilage and roughly 4.5 inches (11 centimeters) in length. Some tracheal bands can be felt at the front of the throat. Inhaled air reaches the top of the trachea via the nasal cavity or mouth and the pharynx—all of which are lined with mucous membranes that warm the air and moisten it. From the pharynx, air passes through a slim aperture, the glottis. When swallowing, this is closed automatically by a flap (the epiglottis) that prevents food from entering the lungs. From the glottis, air flows down through the larynx (the voice box), the position of which can be identified by the tracheal cartilage called the Adam's apple, at the top of the tra-

The respiratory system within the lungs—illustrated here by a model made from a resin cast—consists of a closely interlinked system of air passages, arteries, and veins. Deoxygenated blood, shown in blue, is pumped from the heart through a treelike arrangement of pulmonary arteries and arterioles until it flows through capillaries in and around the alveoli, which are the terminations of the bronchial "tree," shown in white. Oxygen is absorbed and carbon dioxide is released before the blood, now oxygenated and shown in red, returns through a similar arrangement of pulmonary veins to the heart. The model is seen from the front so the left side of the chest appears on the right. The heart lies in the left side of the chest, and to accommodate it, the two-lobed left lung is smaller than the three-lobed right lung.

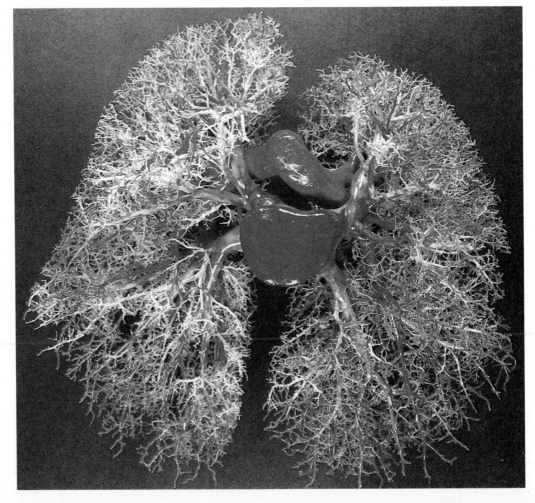

chea below the chin. Changing the length and tension of the vocal cords—elastic bands of tissue stretched across the top of the larynx—changes vocal pitch.

At its lower end, the trachea forks into two hollow branches known as bronchi. Each supplies air to a different lung. In each lung, the bronchus divides into subbranches. The smallest subdivisions of a bronchus are bronchioles, less than one millimeter in diameter and walled by smooth muscle. The bronchial tree's outermost "twigs" are more than 250,000 tiny respiratory bronchioles about half a millimeter in diameter. Sprouting from these are some 6 million "leaves": tiny alveoli that resemble minute, clustered, air-filled bubbles. It is here that gaseous exchange takes place as you breathe in and out.

Breathing in, breathing out

When you breathe in, the muscles of the dome-shaped diaphragm contract. This pulls the dome down, thereby lowering the floor of the chest cavity. Meanwhile, the ribs' intercostal muscles contract, pulling the ribs up and out. These actions expand the chest cavity, creating a vacuum that causes air to flow into the lungs as they expand.

When you breathe out, the muscles of the diaphragm relax, and it rises in the chest cavity. The intercostal muscles also relax, and the elasticity of the chest wall causes the ribs to sink down and inwards, expelling air from the lungs. When breathing out forcefully, muscles of the abdomen contract to increase the pressure, which pushes the diaphragm upwards and forces air from the lungs.

At rest you may breathe in as little as .25 pint (57 centiliters) of air with each breath. During exercise, however, when the body's need for oxygen increases, each breath may draw in as much as 2 pints (4.5 liters).

Normally, about one-third of breathed-in air gets no farther than the bronchi or bronchioles. The rest fills alveoli. Oxygen molecules are absorbed by fluid lining each alveolus's thin wall, then pass to blood cells in a thin-walled capillary—part of a mesh that surrounds each alveolus and carries deoxygenated blood from the pulmonary artery. Oxygen molecules attach to the hemoglobin molecules of red blood cells. Meanwhile, carbon dioxide molecules, dissolved in the blood plasma, pass out from the capillaries into the alveolus. Expired air also contains water vapor from the moisture lining alveolar walls.

How fast we breathe depends on the carbon dioxide level in the bloodstream. The higher the level the more acid the blood. Cells in the brainstem and elsewhere monitor changes in the acid level and, as it rises, stimulate the breathing reflex.

Respiratory defenses

The body has various means of preventing and combating disease or injury in the delicate respiratory system. Mucous membranes warm and moisten inspired air to prevent it from chilling or drying the bronchioles and alveoli. Cough and sneeze reflexes expel food or other particles that find their way into the respiratory passages and the bronchial tree. Inside al-

veoli, cells called phagocytes swallow bacteria and dust, and tiny whiplike cilia projecting from the inner walls of the bronchial tree lash these foreign bodies up toward the trachea in blobs of mucus, which are coughed up as "phlegm."

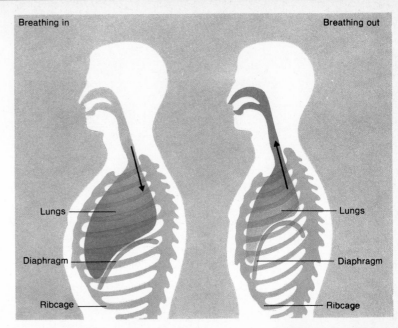

Breathing in   Breathing out

Lungs — Lungs
Diaphragm — Diaphragm
Ribcage — Ribcage

Breathing is accomplished by lowering the diaphragm and raising the ribcage, to expand the lungs and breathe in, then by relaxing the diaphragm and lowering the ribcage to breathe out.

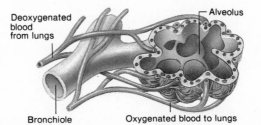

Deoxygenated blood from lungs
Alveolus
Bronchiole
Oxygenated blood to lungs

Alveoli, the extremities of the bronchial "tree," allow air to come into close contact with blood in capillaries, so that gas exchange can take place.

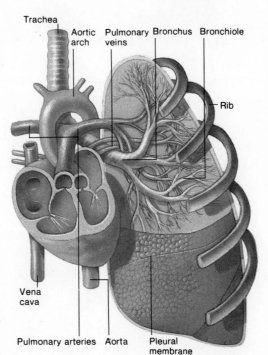

Trachea
Aortic arch   Pulmonary veins   Bronchus   Bronchiole
Rib
Vena cava
Pulmonary arteries   Aorta   Pleural membrane

Lungs are composed of spongy tissue in which are thousands of tiny branches of veins, arteries, and bronchioles. Surrounding each lung is a thin membrane, the visceral pleura, which permits the lungs to move smoothly within the pleural cavity—the space occupied by the lungs in the chest.

Food and digestion

The digestive system consists of a long and convoluted tube, in which food is broken down physically and chemically so that the nutritional elements it contains can be absorbed.

The digestive system is a biological mechanism that dismantles foods into their chemical components—some destined to form muscle, bone, blood, skin, or other tissue; some producing energy to power the processes of life.

The main part of the digestive system is the gut, or alimentary canal, a convoluted muscular tube measuring about 30 feet (9 meters) if extended, with an opening at each end. One opening, the mouth, admits unprocessed food. The other opening, the anus, releases food wastes. Between these two lie specialized organs like the teeth, stomach, and pancreas. These break down proteins, fats, and carbohydrates into molecules small enough to filter from the gut into the blood supply. In this way, nutrients are absorbed into the body.

The process is principally one of chemical reactions speeded up by biological catalysts called enzymes. During digestion, starches and complex sugars break down into simple sugars. Fats become fatty acids and glycerol. Proteins break down into amino acids. But water, minerals, and vitamins enter body tissues undigested.

Inside the mouth

The first stages of digestion take place inside the mouth. Each mouthful of solid food is cut up and crushed by the teeth. An adult normally has 32 teeth of four kinds, designed for different purposes. Two sets of four somewhat chisel-shaped incisors at the front slice food with a scissorlike action. Four strong canines flanking the incisors have a pointed chewing surface and help to tear up large chunks of food into smaller pieces. Next come eight premolars, each with two cusps (pointed chewing surfaces) that crush food into still smaller pieces. The twelve molars at the back of the jaws are strong, broad-crowned teeth that grind food into small particles.

While teeth are masticating food, the tongue and cheek muscles push the food around so that all of it is subject to the chopping, grinding process. Reflex action ensures that the tongue itself does not get trapped between the teeth and bitten.

Meanwhile, saliva is entering the mouth cavity from three glands on each side of the face. These are the sublingual gland below the tongue, the submandibular gland below and behind the sublingual gland, and the parotid gland in front of and below the ear. Saliva is rich in ptyalin (salivary amylase), an enzyme that starts the conversion of starches into simple sugars. The lubricating, mixing action of

The digestive system begins with the lips, teeth, mouth, and tongue, which form a chamber in which food is moistened and crushed before it starts its passage through the stomach and intestines. Most absorption occurs in the long, narrow, "small" intestine.

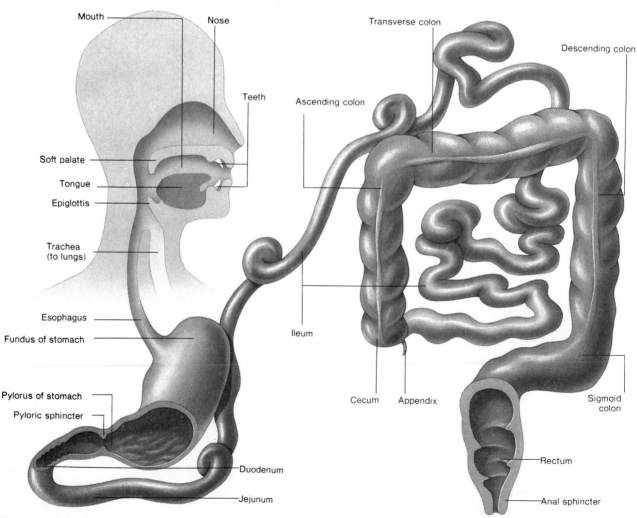

Mouth
Nose
Teeth
Soft palate
Tongue
Epiglottis
Trachea (to lungs)
Esophagus
Fundus of stomach
Pylorus of stomach
Pyloric sphincter
Duodenum
Jejunum

Transverse colon
Descending colon
Ascending colon
Ileum
Cecum
Appendix
Sigmoid colon
Rectum
Anal sphincter

saliva helps to shape each mouthful of food into a ball (bolus) that can be swallowed easily and will not stick in the throat.

Swallowing involves coordinated reflexes that stop food from entering the nasal cavity or windpipe. As the tongue throws the bolus back into the pharynx, the soft palate automatically rises to protect the nasal cavity, and the epiglottis—a flap of cartilage and membrane—helps to shut the windpipe. Meanwhile, the top of the esophagus, or gullet, relaxes and receives the bolus, which now starts its journey through the gut.

Inside esophagus and stomach

The esophagus is a short length of tube between the lower pharynx (throat) and the stomach. Like other sections of the gut, its inner surface is lubricated by mucus. The tube's thin walls consist of both skeletal and smooth muscle, which contract in waves (peristalsis) that move down through the esophagus, each wave taking about ten seconds from top to bottom.

The lower end of the esophagus is usually kept closed by a ring of muscle called the cardiac sphincter and by external pressure. The sphincter opens to release food into the stomach, then shuts again, preventing food from escaping back up through the esophagus.

The stomach is an enlarged section of the gut shaped rather like a letter J and closed by sphincters at the top and bottom. Three muscle layers, each with fibers aligned in a different direction, form the stomach walls.

The stomach serves partly as a place to store swallowed food before this passes on into the small intestine. As eating fills the stomach, its elastic walls relax and allow it to expand.

The stomach also acts to mix the swallowed food. Its muscles contract in a coordinated fashion that sends waves sweeping through the stomach, churning up its contents. This mixes the food with gastric juices secreted by glands and cells in pits in the mucous lining of the stomach wall.

Each day, the stomach yields about 6 pints (3 liters) of secretions. Among these is the stomach's chief digestive enzyme, pepsin, which starts to break down proteins. Pepsin needs acid if it is to work, and the stomach obliges by manufacturing hydrochloric acid. This also helps to kill bacteria that might otherwise cause intestinal infections. Stomach acid is strong enough to burn skin, but the stomach's walls are protected by their mucous coating.

Food mixed with and partly broken down by gastric juices forms a homogeneous mixture known as chyme. From this mixture, water, glucose, salts, and alcohol can pass directly to the bloodstream.

Every minute, however, about one per cent of the stomach's contents spurts out through the pyloric sphincter, the stomach's lower opening, into the small intestine, where the last all-important stages of digestion and absorption occur.

The intestines

Below the stomach food passes into the con-

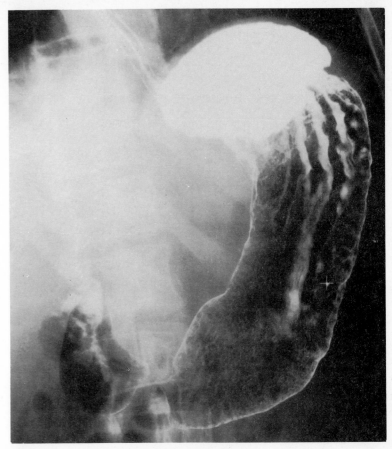

An X ray of the stomach taken after a radiopaque substance—called a "barium meal"—has been swallowed shows most of the barium in the fundus of the stomach. Some remains in the esophagus, however, and some is beginning to move through the rest of the stomach as a result of the stomach's muscular action.

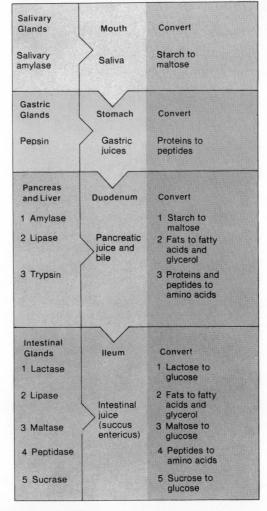

Salivary Glands	Mouth	Convert
Salivary amylase	Saliva	Starch to maltose
Gastric Glands	Stomach	Convert
Pepsin	Gastric juices	Proteins to peptides
Pancreas and Liver	Duodenum	Convert
1 Amylase		1 Starch to maltose
2 Lipase	Pancreatic juice and bile	2 Fats to fatty acids and glycerol
3 Trypsin		3 Proteins and peptides to amino acids
Intestinal Glands	Ileum	Convert
1 Lactase		1 Lactose to glucose
2 Lipase		2 Fats to fatty acids and glycerol
3 Maltase	Intestinal juice (succus entericus)	3 Maltose to glucose
4 Peptidase		4 Peptides to amino acids
5 Sucrase		5 Sucrose to glucose

Digestion is accomplished by the actions of digestive juices, which are secreted by glands into different parts of the alimentary canal. The table shows some of the main glands and the enzymes they produce, in the left column; the part of the alimentary canal and the medium in which they act, in the center column; and their effect, in terms of the main chemicals they act on and produce, in the right column.

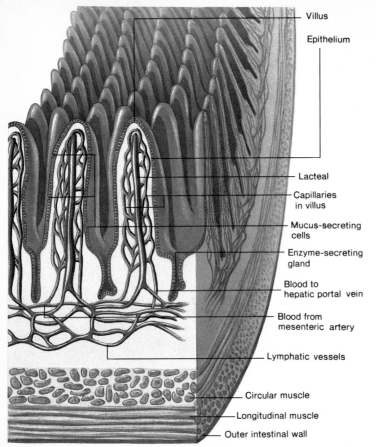

Villus

Epithelium

Lacteal

Capillaries
in villus

Mucus-secreting
cells

Enzyme-secreting
gland

Blood to
hepatic portal vein

Blood from
mesenteric artery

Lymphatic vessels

Circular muscle

Longitudinal muscle

Outer intestinal wall

The ileum, where most absorption of nutrients occurs, is a narrow tube formed by layers of smooth (involuntary) muscle around numerous fingerlike villi projecting into the lumen of the tube. These villi give the ileum an enormous surface area and so maximize the quantity of dissolved nutrients that can be absorbed through the epithelial cells. Amino acids, glucose, and some fatty acids enter the blood capillaries and are carried through the hepatic portal vein to the liver. Other fats pass into the lymphatic system via the lacteals, and ultimately return to the circulation and reach the liver by this route. Digestive enzymes are produced by the enzyme-secreting cells at the base of the villi. Mucus-secreting cells on the villi help lubricate the ileum's contents.

voluted intestines: the long, narrow small intestine and the shorter, broader large intestine. The small intestine is supplied with juices that help complete the breakdown and absorption of most proteins, fats, and carbohydrates. The large intestine turns undigested wastes into feces for expulsion from the body.

The small intestine

This longest section of the gut forms closely-packed loops through which waves of muscular contraction force chyme—food mixed with gastric juices. Anatomists divide the small intestine into three sections: duodenum, jejunum, and ileum.

The duodenum, a curved, short length of tubing, leads from the stomach and receives ducts from the pancreas and liver. This makes the duodenum chemically very active, for digestive pancreatic juice flows in from the pancreas, while the liver yields bile, a digestive juice made up of salts and pigments produced by chemical breakdown. Much of the bile reaches the small intestine via a storage depot, the gall bladder. The flow of bile and pancreatic juice varies with hormone output that is stimulated by chyme arriving in the duodenum from the stomach.

The alkaline pancreatic juice and bile counteract gastric acid from the stomach and make the duodenum strongly alkaline, which helps to activate its digestive enzymes and neutralize digestive juices from the stomach. When duodenal ulcers form, this happens at the duodenum's upper, stomach end, where unneutralized acid chyme makes contact with the duodenum wall.

Inside the duodenum, carbohydrates, fats, and proteins are broken down. Bile salts and the churning action of the duodenal walls break large fat droplets into smaller ones. These offer a large surface area to be attacked by lipase—a fat-splitting enzyme that indirectly helps bile salts to create still smaller droplets called micelles. Meanwhile, the enzyme amylase is breaking down carbohydrates to simpler compounds, the sugars dextrose and maltose. The enzymes trypsin and chymotrypsin found in pancreatic juice break down proteins into their component amino acids.

From the duodenum, chemically dismembered particles of food continue through the jejunum—the first two-fifths of the remainder of the small intestine. The jejunum is a major transfer station where nutrients from digested food are absorbed into the bloodstream. This absorption is facilitated by the structure of the small intestine's inner surface, pocked with pits and lined with millions of tiny, fingerlike projections known as villi, each supplied with a network of capillaries around a central lymph channel. Some villi in their turn form bases for millions of even smaller microvilli. The mass of villi and microvilli produce a surface like fine velvet pile: its total area may exceed that of the complete body surface by five times. This enormous area permits the mass transfer of digested particles of food from the small intestine into the bloodstream. Digestion is carried out by glands at the bases of the villi, which release enzymes that complete the breakdown of fats, proteins, and carbohydrates into units small enough to be absorbed.

The ileum has an especially thick lining of villi that complete this stage of food absorption.

The large intestine

Shorter and less convoluted than the small intestine, but much broader, the large intestine, or colon, starts in the right lower abdomen with the cecum, a short blind passage leading downward. The human cecum is the vestigial equivalent of a relatively much larger structure found in such herbivorous mammals as rabbits, where it is important for cellulose digestion.

Another vestigial structure, the vermiform (worm-shaped) appendix is a slim tubular cul-de-sac about 3.5 inches (9 centimeters) long, projecting from the otherwise blind end of the cecum. Lined with lymphatic cells, the appendix has little known value to the body and can even prove a liability. Bacterial infection may inflame it, producing the condition called appendicitis. Inflammation can even cut off blood flow to the appendix, killing tissue and causing gangrene. Or an infected appendix may burst, spreading infection to surrounding organs. Appendicitis can thus cause peritonitis or inflammation of the peritoneum, the thin membrane lining the abdominal cavity. Swift, simple removal of an inflamed appendix usually prevents such complications and leaves the work of the intestines unimpaired.

By the time swallowed substances reach the large intestine, the work of digestion and absorption is almost complete. What remains is mainly indigestible roughage, salts, dead cells from the lining of the gut, bile pigments, and water. All these enter the large intestine where the ileum joins it just above the cecum.

Peristalsis pushes undigested debris upward through the ascending colon, then horizontally through the transverse colon, which lies across the upper abdomen. Then comes a sharp change of direction, with the descending colon, which plunges down in the left side of the abdomen. Lastly, the load of waste material travels through a sharp bend, the sigmoid flexure, down through the rectum, a straight, short length of tube, and out through the anus—a hole closed and opened by a ring of muscle, the anal sphincter.

Considerable changes happen to the wastes during their passage through the colon. Bacteria feed on these wastes and help convert them into feces. The bacteria also produce valuable vitamins and enzymes that help digest some fibrous vegetable matter. These useful products pass through the colon wall into the body, together with much water—the colon is the principal site of water reabsorption—and some salts.

The colon, like the ileum, has—beneath its outer covering—a layer of longitudinal smooth muscle and, inside this, a layer of circular smooth muscle. These act together to move digested food from the cecum, into which food comes from the ileum, to the rectum, from which it is expelled as feces through the anus. Between the layer of circular muscle and the lumen is the mucous membrane. In contrast to the small intestine, the colon has no villi. The epithelium contains mucus-secreting cells and numerous absorptive cells, through which salts, other materials, and water are reabsorbed.

Food Categories and common sources	Vitamins and daily requirements	Needed for	Minerals and trace elements	Needed for
Proteins Eggs, fish, meat, milk products, nuts, potatoes, pulses, whole cereals	Vitamin A 0.75mg	Skin; mucous membranes; night vision	Calcium	Bones; teeth; muscles; nerves; blood clotting
	Vitamin B₁ 1.5mg	Nerves; heart muscle; general metabolism	Chlorine (as chloride)	Body fluids
Carbohydrates Cereals, fruit, potatoes, sugar	Vitamin B₂ 1.5mg	Skin; mucous membranes; general metabolism	Iodine (as iodide)	Thyroid hormones
	Vitamin B₆ 2mg	General body functions; amino acid metabolism	Iron	Hemoglobin and myoglobin formation
Fats Animal fat, milk products, nuts, oil	Vitamin B₁₂ 0.01mg	Nerve cells; red blood cells	Phosphorus (as phosphate)	Bones; teeth; cell membranes; metabolism
	Nicotinic acid 20mg	Skin; cell metabolism	Potassium	Body fluids; nerve and muscle action
Vitamins Eggs, fish, fresh fruit and vegetables, meat, milk products, nuts, whole cereals, yeast	Folic acid 0.2 mg	Nerve cell metabolism; red blood cells	Sodium	Body fluids; nerve and muscle action
	Vitamin C 40mg	Growth and repair of tissues	Cobalt	Vitamin B₁₂ (cyanocobalamin) action
Minerals Cereals, eggs, fish, fruit, meat, milk products, nuts, salt, vegetables, yeast	Vitamin D 0.01mg	Bone formation; calcium and phosphorus absorption	Copper	Blood formation; enzyme function
	Vitamin E 30mg	Cell membranes and general metabolism	Magnesium	Nerve and muscle action; enzyme function
Liquids Water, milk, other drinks, fruit, vegetables	Vitamin K not known	Blood clotting	Manganese	Cell metabolism; fat production
	Pantothenic acid 2mg	Fat metabolism; cell enzyme functions	Zinc	Enzyme function

Food consists principally of proteins, carbohydrates, fats, and liquids, which in turn provide the essential vitamins and minerals that the body requires. The digestive tract also needs a proportion of indigestible matter, called roughage, which is usually provided in adequate quantities by a varied diet. This table lists the most common sources of the different kinds of food, indicates the importance of the major vitamins, and the average adult daily requirements of them (expressed in milligrams—1 ounce equals 28,350 milligrams), and lists the main minerals and trace elements.

The urinary system

The urinary system consists of the kidneys, the ureters, the bladder, and the urethra.

Without an efficient disposal system, poisonous wastes would collect in body tissues. In fact, several body systems provide exits for unwanted by-products of the processes of living. Lungs remove carbon dioxide and some water and heat. The skin gives off heat and water with some salts and urea, a product of protein breakdown. The digestive tract expels feces containing indigestible food, some salts, bile pigments, and water. But most excretion—removal of the products of metabolism—involves the kidneys, ureters, bladder, and urethra, which combine to form the urinary system.

The kidneys

The kidneys filter blood brought by the renal arteries and removed by the renal veins. Filtration occurs in the renal cortex. Waste products collect in the renal pelvis and drain through the ureters to the bladder.

Kidneys ceaselessly filter substances from blood. They reabsorb some of these, with reabsorbed fluids, but principally, the kidneys act to concentrate chemical wastes and dispose of these as urine. Moreover, kidneys vary the amounts of salts and water they excrete, helping to maintain a healthy salt and water balance.

Kidneys work astonishingly hard. Each minute they process about 2.75 pints (1.3 liters) of blood—one-quarter of the amount pumped out by the heart in this time. All blood travels through the kidneys nearly 20 times every hour. Fifteen times a day they purify the body's entire fluid contents—handling a total of about 50 gallons (190 liters). Most of the fluid is reabsorbed, but approximately one-thousandth of the total volume passes out of the body as urine.

Remarkably enough, if one kidney is diseased or damaged, the other usually copes adequately.

From the outside, kidneys resemble a pair of purplish-brown beans the size of a man's fist. Each weighs about 5 ounces (140 grams). They lie on either side of the backbone, their concave sides facing inward. Cut open, a kidney reveals two major areas: a pale outer layer called the cortex, and a dark inner mass, the medulla. The cortex is made mostly of blood filtration units—venal corpuscles and tubules. The medulla contains tubules (loops of Henle) that collect the dilute filtrate and reabsorb most of the water, and the collecting ducts for the final concentrated filtrate that becomes urine. Blood for filtration flows into a kidney from the renal artery, which divides and subdivides into tiny branches. Treated blood leaves the kidney through a network of small veins that feed into the large renal vein.

How the blood is filtered

About a million blood filtration units, or nephrons, are packed into each kidney. Each nephron is a coiled tubule with a loop, and measures 1—2.5 inches (2.5—6 centimeters). The head of the nephron is in the cortex; it leads ultimately to a collecting duct that passes down through the medulla before opening into a large collecting area in the renal pelvis at the kidney's core. Each nephron's outer end (in the cortex) forms a double-walled cup known as a Bowman's capsule. This envelops a bulging knot of capillaries called a glomerulus. Blood driven through the glomerulus forces small molecules out through the capillary walls into the Bowman's capsule. Blood cells and protein molecules too large to pass through the filter remain in the capillaries. Filtration can occur at great speed because each kidney's glomeruli have an overall area of approximately a quarter of the total surface area of the body. The resulting filtrate includes water and dissolved sugar, salts, and urea.

In this way, the nephron removes impurities from blood, but leaves the latter too concentrated. So water and other valuable substances are returned to the blood as the filtrate trickles through the nephron's convoluted tubule, around a hairpin turn (the loop of Henle), and up again toward the cortex. Throughout this journey, salts, sugars, and even some urea filter out of the tubule and back into nearby capillaries.

By the time the fluid has passed through all

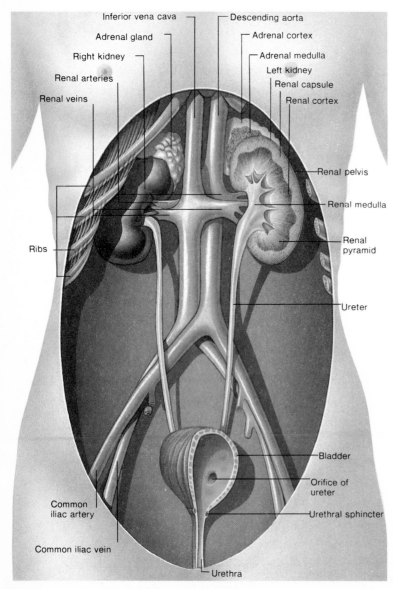

Inferior vena cava
Adrenal gland
Right kidney
Renal arteries
Renal veins
Ribs
Common iliac artery
Common iliac vein

Descending aorta
Adrenal cortex
Adrenal medulla
Left kidney
Renal capsule
Renal cortex
Renal pelvis
Renal medulla
Renal pyramid
Ureter
Bladder
Orifice of ureter
Urethral sphincter
Urethra

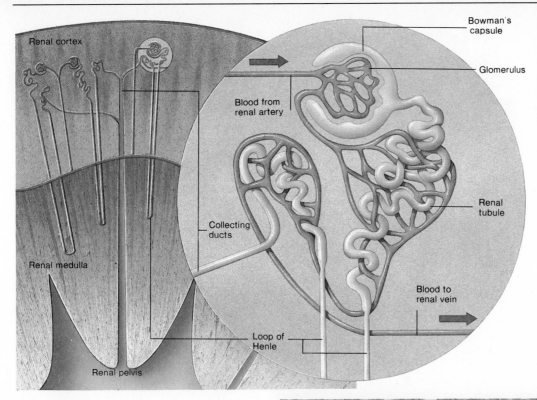

Renal cortex

Blood from
renal artery

Collecting
ducts

Renal medulla

Renal pelvis

Bowman's
capsule

Glomerulus

Renal
tubule

Blood to
renal vein

Loop of
Henle

Filtration occurs as blood from the renal artery enters the knot of capillaries called the glomerulus. Salts, glucose, and nitrogenous waste filter into the surrounding Bowman's capsule. As this filtrate passes through the renal tubule and the loop of Henle, which extends into the renal medulla before returning to the renal cortex, many of the dissolved substances are reabsorbed. The concentrated filtrate passes from the renal tubule to collecting ducts that drain into the renal pelvis. The filtrate passes from there through the ureters to the bladder.

the nephron tubule and on to a collecting tube and then into the hilum, the kidney's main collecting area in the renal pelvis, it has been converted into urine, a concentrated urea solution with some salts and other wastes, which must be removed from the body.

Ureters, bladder, and urethra

From the kidneys, drops of urine continuously run down through two narrow, muscular tubes called ureters, each about 10 inches (25 centimeters) long. The urine collects in a muscular storage bag, the bladder. The rate at which urine leaves the kidneys depends on the amount of water in the body. If the body is dehydrated, the kidneys release no more than a cupful of concentrated urine daily. If the body is abundantly supplied with water, daily output can rise to more than 5.25 gallons (20 liters) of very dilute urine. Urine normally leaves each kidney at a rate of about one drop a minute. Contracting smooth muscles in the ureter's wall squeeze the urine down into the bladder, which is walled by thick layers of smooth muscle, with a ring of skeletal muscle—the external urethral sphincter—around the narrow outlet at its base.

Emptying the bladder involves a spinal reflex action that makes the bladder contract, and a consciously directed order from the brain relaxing the external sphincter. Children gain bladder control only when they are old enough to learn to master both muscular actions. However, even adults cannot retain urine when the bladder is overly full.

During urination, also known as micturition, urine from the bladder leaves the body through a duct called a urethra. This is longer in men than in women because it passes through the prostate gland and the penis.

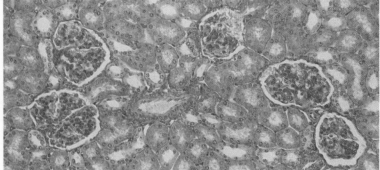

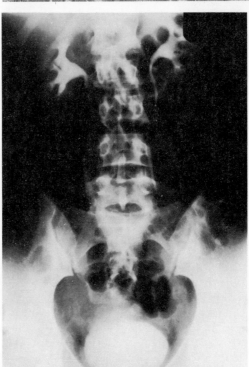

Renal corpuscles, comprising a glomerulus enveloped by a Bowman's capsule, lie in the renal cortex, surrounded by other corpuscles, renal tubules, collecting ducts, and some connective tissue containing blood, lymph vessels, and nerves.

An X ray of the abdomen taken when a radiopaque substance is introduced into the urinary tract shows each renal pelvis, at the top of the photograph, on either side of the spinal column; the two ureters; and the bladder, at the bottom, situated within the bones of the pelvic girdle.

Metabolism

Every year each person eats many times the body's weight in food, yet his or her own weight is little changed. The explanation for this apparent miracle lies largely in metabolism, a complex of chemical life processes whose name comes from the Greek *metabole,* meaning "conversion."

Catabolism and anabolism

Metabolism describes all chemical and physical changes that occur within a living organism, but more specifically refers to the changes that occur to food after it has been digested. Three principal products of digestion—amino acids, glucose, and fatty acids—take part in both anabolic reactions, when they are converted into body proteins, glycogen, or body fat, and catabolic reactions, when they are broken down through complex biochemical pathways to carbon dioxide, water, waste products, and energy.

Metabolic processes bring about two major kinds of change: catabolism (the breaking down of organic compounds derived from food) and anabolism (the synthesis or building up of complex compounds from simple ones, also derived from food).

Catabolism releases energy by breaking down digested fats and carbohydrates. The breakdown products serve as fuels combining with oxygen from air for oxidation, a gradual "burning" process, which releases energy for cell-building and the activities of cells and muscles. Anabolism uses energy to manufacture proteins, fats, and certain carbohydrates. Meanwhile, old and damaged cells are being broken down and removed. The whole metabolic process is carefully controlled by subtle feedback systems.

Metabolism maintains life by processes that largely balance the body's food input with its output of heat, mechanical energy, and processed body waste, to which is added waste from undigested roughage.

Enzymes in action

Metabolism involves complex chains of chemical reactions that would be impossible at body temperatures without help from the giant protein molecules called enzymes—biological catalysts that speed up chemical reactions between other substances without themselves undergoing metabolic change.

Specific enzymes operate on specific types of molecule (called the substrate), inducing chemical changes in the substrate molecules, which then break free from the enzymes and so allow these to tackle further substrate molecules. This happens astonishingly fast. Even at freezing point, one molecule of the enzyme catalase can break down 40,000 molecules of hydrogen peroxide in just one second. Accordingly, most enzymes are needed, and occur, in only tiny quantities.

Metabolism involves many kinds of enzyme—most acting on only one kind of substrate, in special conditions of acidity or alkalinity, in the presence of auxiliary activators called coenzymes.

Different enzymes cooperate in systems geared to the step-by-step breakdown or building-up of compounds. The major carbohydrate breakdown mechanism, glycolysis, occurs mainly in muscle, where the sugar glucose or the animal starch glycogen break down via intermediate compounds to pyruvic acid. This then enters the Krebs, or citric acid cycle—a complicated series of enzyme-controlled reactions that break down pyruvic acid in the presence of oxygen to yield carbon dioxide and ATP (adenosine triphosphate)—a source of energy that can be used for internal cell activity or for the external work of muscular contraction. Step-by-step release of energy involving oxidation may yield 673 kilocalories from just one gram molecule of glucose.

Oxygen required for energy release comes usually from air breathed in by the lungs. But the heart cannot always deliver enough oxygen to muscles. If energy demand exceeds oxygen supply, muscles can go on working for a time by anaerobic (oxygenless) metabolism. But this soon uses up all high-energy phosphate stores, and the resulting oxygen debt produces much lactic acid waste that prevents cells from working properly and causes muscular fatigue.

Catabolism breaks down most compounds to acetyl coenzyme A, a product that can be oxidized, or used as building blocks for making many complicated compounds. Almost all the fats and carbohydrates that the body needs can be built up like this, with help from different enzymes cooperating to form special metabolic pathways. In fact, most of the amino acid ingredients of proteins can be synthesized inside the body. Minerals and vitamins (except vitamin D) cannot be synthesized.

Metabolic facts and figures

The body releases about four kilocalories of

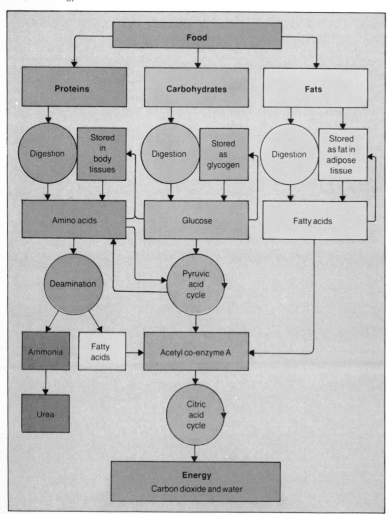

energy per gram of carbohydrates or protein catabolized, and nine kilocalories of energy per gram of fat.

The amount of energy released by the body in a given time is called its metabolic rate. This can be measured from the amount of oxygen consumed or carbon dioxide given off. A man's basal metabolic rate—energy output at rest per hour per unit surface area—is about 40 kilocalories per square yard of skin, compared with 32 for a woman. Sedentary male office workers expend about 2,520 kilocalories, about 400 more than women. A man performing heavy manual work may use as many as 3,600 kilocalories a day.

While the kilocalories content of food eaten matches the kilocalories of energy expended, body weight remains unchanged. If energy input exceeds output, the body may store the surplus energy as fat and put on weight. But if energy output exceeds input, the body first burns up its reservoir of fat and then starts to break down proteins as a source of energy, in time producing the muscle wastage and weight loss seen in malnutrition.

The liver's role

Besides producing the digestive fluid bile, the liver helps to process the carbohydrate and amino acid products of digestion brought by the hepatic portal vein from the digestive tract. It converts surplus glucose into the animal starch glycogen, storing it for reconversion and releasing it as glucose in later time of need. If the liver's glycogen stores are already full, liver cells begin transforming any extra glucose into fat, which travels around the body and collects just below the skin in adipose tissue cells in the abdomen and other places.

The liver also converts potentially poisonous nitrogenous wastes derived from protein into toxic urea, which is released into the

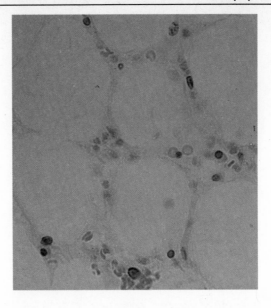

Fat cells store fat in adipose tissue. They have a nucleus and cytoplasm in which fat globules form. Large fat globules occupy a very much greater volume than the cytoplasm that surrounds them.

bloodstream and excreted harmlessly by the kidneys.

Other valuable liver functions include storing vitamins, notably B_{12} which is needed in manufacturing red blood cells, and minerals, including iron, which is required for hemoglobin. Lastly, the liver makes a range of blood proteins.

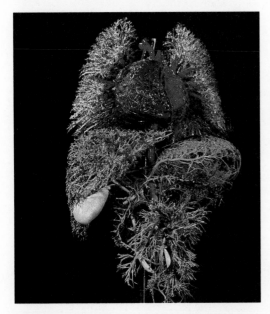

The blood supply to the thorax and abdomen is shown in a resin cast of the blood vessels. The liver is the triangular organ below the heart and lungs and above and left of the digestive system.

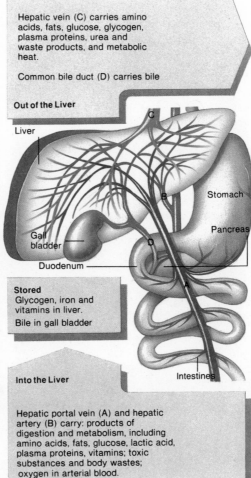

Hepatic vein (C) carries amino acids, fats, glucose, glycogen, plasma proteins, urea and waste products, and metabolic heat.

Common bile duct (D) carries bile

Out of the Liver

Liver

Gall bladder

Duodenum

Stomach

Pancreas

Stored
Glycogen, iron and vitamins in liver.
Bile in gall bladder

Into the Liver

Intestines

Hepatic portal vein (A) and hepatic artery (B) carry: products of digestion and metabolism, including amino acids, fats, glucose, lactic acid, plasma proteins, vitamins; toxic substances and body wastes; oxygen in arterial blood.

The hepatic portal system carries the products of digestion from the stomach and intestines through the hepatic portal vein (A). Oxygen arrives in arterial blood, supplied by the hepatic artery (B). The products of hepatic metabolism leave through the hepatic vein (C). Bile, containing pigment from the breakdown of blood cells, as well as bile salts, cholesterol, and urea, is produced in the liver and is stored in the gall bladder. From there, it reaches the duodenum through the common bile duct (D).

The nervous system

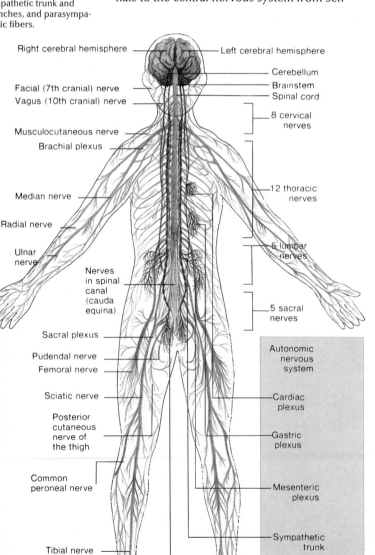

The nervous system centers on the brain and spinal cord.

The nervous system has three main parts. Central: the brain, cranial nerves, and spinal cord. Peripheral: sensory and motor nerves leading to and from the spinal cord. Autonomic: the sympathetic trunk and branches, and parasympathetic fibers.

All body systems would be immobilized without the nervous system, which receives and correlates information from inside and outside the body and reacts by sending signals to appropriate muscles and glands so that these produce coordinated responses. The body's nerve network has been likened to a telephone system, with the billions of elongated, interconnected cells called neurons serving as its wires.

Neurons form two great associated groups: the central and peripheral nervous systems.

Neurons and nerves

Neurons, or nerve cells, form the active units of the nervous system, although they are heavily outnumbered by glial ("glue") cells that help to supply the neurons with nourishment, support, and insulation. Neurons may be grouped broadly in three ways according to the jobs they do: sensory neurons (afferents) bring signals to the central nervous system from sensory receptors; motor neurons (effectors, or efferents) send signals out to muscles and glands; and interneurons (also called association neurons) serve as intermediaries.

Nerve cells are uniquely structured to communicate with one another. A typical neuron has three structural elements: a compact body, many short, branching "threads" called dendrites, and one very long "thread" called an axon. Dendrites receive signals from nearby neurons, and the axon hands them to another neuron muscle or gland. Naked dendrites and cell bodies color the gray matter of the brain and spinal cord; white matter consists of axons sheathed by a white, fatty, insulating substance known as myelin. Bundles of myelin-coated axons make up nerve fibers.

Unlike the electrical signals passed along a telephone wire, nervous signals travel by an electrochemical relay system. Inactive neurons tend to contain more potassium than sodium ions, while outside their cell membranes are more sodium than potassium ions. When a nearby neuron is stimulated, chemicals called neurotransmitters burst from sacs in knobs at its axon ends, leap the gap—or synapse—to the inactive neuron, and fill receptor sites in its cell membranes. This makes the cell lose some potassium ions and take in some sodium ions so that the cell's electrical charge is changed at the affected site. That charge flows through the cell at up to 220 miles (354 kilometers) per hour, which is very fast (but slower than an electrical impulse).

While excitatory neurotransmitters make neurons fire off signals, inhibitory ones tend to block them. A single brain cell may receive thousands of simultaneous signals. How it reacts depends largely on how many "fire" and "don't fire" signals it receives. Individual spinal and peripheral neurons act like brain cells, processing and responding to the information reaching them.

Central nervous system

The command center of the body consists of the spinal cord and a swollen and highly differentiated outgrowth of it, the brain.

The spinal cord forms a cylinder of nervous tissue some 16-20 inches (40-50 centimeters) long in an adult, extending from the brain stem down through the bony arches of the vertebrae. The cord bulges at the points where nerves branch off to the arms and legs. It is buffered by three membranes called meninges that continue upward to enclose the brain. Beneath the meninges, both brain and spinal cord are bathed by cerebrospinal fluid, which acts partly as a shock absorber, as well as serving to bring nourishment to the nervous tissue and protect it from infection.

If you slice through the column of the cord you notice an outer layer of white matter—myelinated afferent and efferent nerve fibers, respectively, which transmit signals up and down the cord. Inside this layer is gray matter, the arrangement of which resembles butterfly's wings in cross section. The "upper" wings, pointing toward the back of the body, contain

Right cerebral hemisphere

Facial (7th cranial) nerve
Vagus (10th cranial) nerve

Musculocutaneous nerve
Brachial plexus

Median nerve

Radial nerve

Ulnar nerve

Nerves in spinal canal (cauda equina)

Sacral plexus

Pudendal nerve
Femoral nerve

Sciatic nerve

Posterior cutaneous nerve of the thigh

Common peroneal nerve

Tibial nerve

Left cerebral hemisphere

Cerebellum
Brainstem
Spinal cord

8 cervical nerves

12 thoracic nerves

5 lumbar nerves

5 sacral nerves

Autonomic nervous system

Cardiac plexus

Gastric plexus

Mesenteric plexus

Sympathetic trunk

Pelvic plexus

afferent neurons that receive signals from outside the cord. The "lower" wings, pointing toward the front of the body, contain efferents, controlling muscles and glands.

Peripheral nervous system

Nerves originating in or linked with the central nervous system branch out through the body. This outer, or peripheral nervous system, has two overlapping components: the somatic ("of the body") and autonomic ("self-regulating") systems.

Somatic motor nerves supply striated (skeletal) muscle. Somatic sensory nerves supply sensory receptors in skin, tongue, nostrils, eyes, joints, and muscles.

Twelve pairs of cranial nerves arising from the brain supply ears, eyes, nose, facial skin and muscles, the tongue, jaw and neck muscles, and various internal organs. Thirty-one pairs of spinal nerves sprout from the spinal cord, supplying limbs and trunk. Sensory nerve fibers enter from the back, motor nerve fibers leave from the front, both passing in or out through gaps between vertebrae. Although there are approximately as many gaps as spinal nerves, the spinal cord ends high above the bottom of the spine, so the nerves of the lowest nerve roots must travel some distance inside the spine before they reach their exit holes.

Autonomic nervous system

Part of the peripheral nervous system works automatically, controlling the smooth muscle of internal organs and some glandular secretions. It normally functions outside conscious, willed control.

The autonomic nervous system has sympathetic and parasympathetic divisions, which operate to counteract each other—the sympathetic system generally having an excitatory effect, the parasympathetic system the reverse.

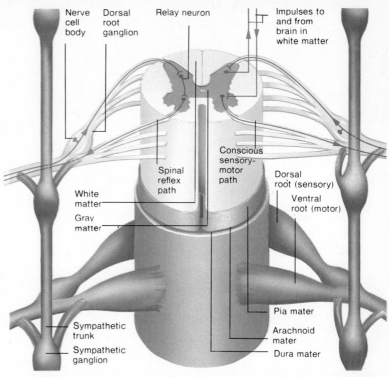

The sympathetic system releases chemical neurotransmitters to stimulate heart, lungs, and other organs. Nerves of the sympathetic system form two cords parallel with the spinal cord and linked to it along its length, but not at its ends. Pealike swellings in both of these cords, called ganglia, contain nerve-cell bodies.

The parasympathetic system, arising from both ends of the spinal cord, releases neurotransmitters that act mostly on the same organs as those affected by the sympathetic system, but in ways that slow them down. Under stress, the sympathetic system dominates; at rest, the parasympathetic system takes control.

Spinal sensory and motor pathways may or may not pass through the brain. In a spinal reflex *(left)*, a sensory signal enters by the dorsal root and synapses with motor fibers within the spinal cord. These then stimulate muscular action through the ventral motor root. In a conscious action *(right)*, the signal travels to and from the brain.

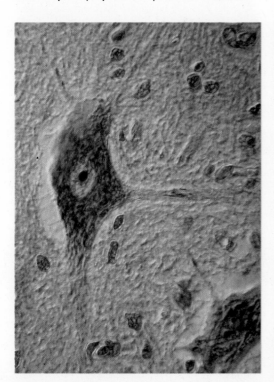

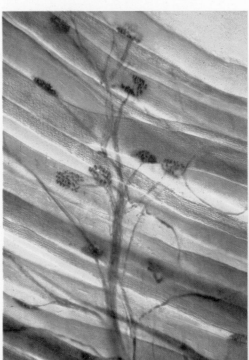

A spinal neuron *(far left)* consists of a cell body, with a nucleus, several threadlike dendrites linking with other neurons, and a longer fiber that carries the nervous impulse. In a motor neuron, this long fiber is covered by a fatty sheath and ends in a motor end plate.

Motor end plates *(left)*, shown here at the same magnification as the spinal neuron *(far left)*, attach to and stimulate individual muscle fibers.

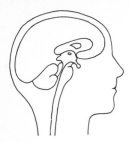

The brain is an outgrowth of the top of the spinal cord, enclosed and protected by the bony cranium of the skull.

The brain

The brain is shaped like a wrinkled walnut kernel, is about the size of a large grapefruit and appears as insubstantial as a moist, soft cheese. Two-fifths of it consist of no more than supporting glial cells. Yet it contains from 10 to 100 billion neurons with complex interlinking sensory, motor, and association pathways. Signals selectively transmitted through these routes enable us to eat, walk, lift loads, thread a needle, speak, love, hate, dream, think, remember, and make decisions. Computers may calculate faster than the human brain, but cannot match the versatility of this most amazing of all the body's mechanisms.

The brain has several major parts; each has its own shape and function, and all contribute to the amazing total of human mental capabilities. The principal areas of the brain are the brain stem, the cerebellum, and the inner and outer forebrain, which form the cerebral hemispheres or cerebrum.

Brain stem

This 3-inch (7.5-centimeter) long mass of nervous tissue forms the upper, clublike end of the spinal cord. The brain's evolutionary core, or root—the brain stem—carries sensory and motor nerve tracts and houses neurons controlling basic body processes. The brain stem has three sections: from the bottom up, the medulla, pons, and midbrain.

Neurons in the medulla control the automatic actions of the heart and lungs, serve as relay stations for five cranial nerves, and as the grand pathway for hundreds of millions of sensory and motor nerves connecting brain and spinal cord. Most of these cross over in the medulla, so that the brain's left side controls the right side of the body and vice versa.

Above the medulla, the pons and midbrain serve as further relay stations. Running through all three is a thicket of neurons called the reticular formation, which receives signals from sense receptors and controls consciousness.

Cerebellum

The cerebellum, or "little brain," accounts for 11 per cent of the brain's total weight. Bulging from the back of the pons, it lies tucked beneath the rear of the much larger cerebral hemispheres. The cerebellum monitors information from muscles, tendons, joints, and the inner ear and acts to adjust and coordinate muscle movements on instructions from the cerebrum. Every action, from drinking a glass of water to walking or playing the piano, proceeds smoothly primarily because of the unobtrusive work done by the cerebellum, which acts like an automatic pilot.

The inner forebrain

Distinctive groups of clustered cells form special structures deep inside the brain above the brain stem and around the ventricles—cavities filled with cerebrospinal fluid. Innermost of these structures are the thalamus and hypothalamus. The thalamus, a large double structure, is a major sensory coordinator, processing information from ears, eyes, mouth, and skin as it passes to the higher centers of the brain. Below the thalamus, the tiny hypothalamus controls thirst, hunger, sweating, shivering, and other processes essential to life.

Four neuron clusters, collectively called

The brain is composed of nerve tissue differentiated into a number of areas and structures, many of which have specialized functions. The cerebrum is divided into the left and right cerebral hemispheres, which appear to have separate but related areas of responsibility—the left being primarily concerned with speech and logical thought, the right with three-dimensional shapes and subjective judgment. Conscious movement is controlled by the frontal lobes; the parietal lobe monitors position and sensation; the occipital and temporal lobes are associated with sight and hearing, respectively. The cerebellum exerts fine control over muscular movements; the pons and medulla of the brain stem are centers for the regulation of essential body mechanisms, such as blood pressure, heart rate, and respiration.

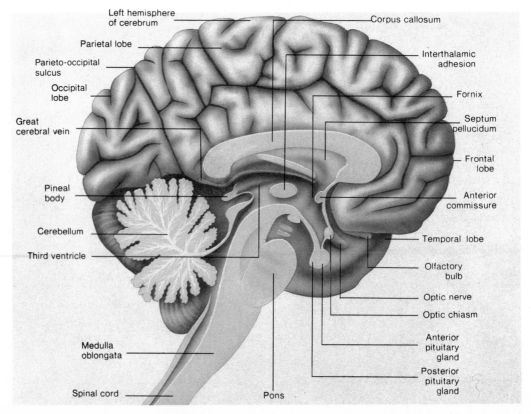

basal ganglia, crown the thalamus. Relaying information from cerebral hemispheres to brain stem and cerebellum, they help to regulate the body's movements. They also share a structure, the amygdaloid ("almondlike") body, with the so-called limbic system, a wishbonelike "mini-brain" encircling the brain stem and concerned with emotions and memory. The human limbic system resembles that of a primitive mammal, and, for this reason, it is sometimes called the "old" mammalian brain in contrast to the "new" brain, the cerebrum.

The outer forebrain

Seven-tenths of the cells of the entire nervous system lie in the cerebral hemispheres, the two large connected swellings at the front end of the forebrain. Deep wrinkles enormously enlarge the surface area of the cerebral cortex—the thin outer layer of gray matter that is, apparently, the seat of human intelligence. No other animal species has so much brain space allocated to this fragile layer. The human cerebral cortex contains about half a billion nerve cells with 620 miles (1,000 kilometers) of connecting fibers for every cubic half-inch.

Deep fissures in each convoluted hemisphere help to divide it into lobes, and special areas of cortex in different lobes deal with specific kinds of mental activity. Those areas receiving sensory input and dispatching motor signals are known as the sensory cortex and the motor cortex, also sometimes referred to collectively as the primary cortex. Primary cortex in the occipital lobes at the back of the brain receives signals from the eyes. Sensory strips of cortex down each side of the brain—where frontal and parietal lobes meet—receive input from the tongue, lips, face, head, hands, trunk, arms, legs, feet, and other areas. A strip of motor cortex running down the frontal lobe near the sensory strip triggers movement in specific muscles.

From primary cortex, signals flow to association cortex in the frontal, parietal, and temporal lobes. Here, received sensations may be associated with conceptual thought.

Prefrontal areas at the very front of the brain help to control personality and intellect. Speaking and understanding speech depend heavily on areas in three lobes of the left cerebral hemisphere. Visual recognition seems to reside in the right side of the brain.

Brain and mind

Most scientists believe that "mind" is just the product of the brain, not an independent entity, as some philosophers have held. Consciousness, perception, attention, memory, thought, judgment, emotion, personality, dreams, and hallucinations have all been shown to depend, at least partly, upon the function of some specific region of the brain. Yet much about the working of the brain remains mysterious. For instance, how do some mystics manage to achieve apparently voluntary control of automatic body mechanisms—for example, reducing their oxygen needs at times below the level normally needed for survival? How do techniques like hypnosis and autogenic training help certain people to cope

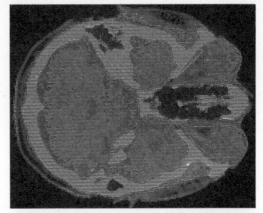

A cross section through the skull, made with a CAT (computerized axial tomography) scan, shows the horizontal relationship between the eyes, the nasal tissues, and the lower parts of the brain—the two temporal lobes and the cerebellum.

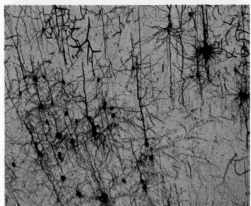

The cerebral cortex, the outer layer of the cerebrum, contains closely packed neurons with many interconnecting dendrites.

The limbic system forms two symmetrical loops, only one of which is illustrated, between the brain stem and the cerebral hemisphere. It is concerned principally with memory and emotion. The septum pellucidum is associated with pleasure, the amygdaloid body with aggression, the cingulate gyrus and hippocampus with memory. The thalamus and mamillary body appear to act as organizers. The fornix and anterior commissure link parts of the limbic system with each other and with other parts of the brain.

with chronic pain? Study of mind and the brain remains one of the most challenging and—from a mechanistic point of view—most mysterious areas of investigation into the nature of the human animal.

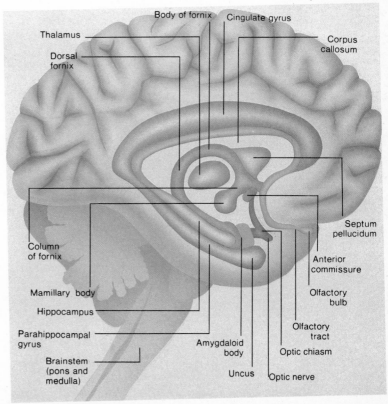

Body of fornix — Cingulate gyrus — Thalamus — Dorsal fornix — Corpus callosum — Column of fornix — Mamillary body — Hippocampus — Parahippocampal gyrus — Brainstem (pons and medulla) — Uncus — Amygdaloid body — Optic chiasm — Optic nerve — Olfactory tract — Olfactory bulb — Anterior commissure — Septum pellucidum

The eye

Eyes tell us more about the world around us than any other of our senses. They inform us of the size, shape, position, and color of objects from pinpoints a few inches from our nose to stars billions of miles away in space. This is possible because each eyeball contains a nerve net (the retina) that is sensitive to light waves, which it converts electrochemically to signals that can be interpreted by the brain. These nerve nets are enclosed by two roughly spherical organs, the eyes, which can focus light, control the amount of light entering the eye, and move to follow a light source.

Eyelid and eyeballs

The delicate eyeballs are protected by the bones of the skull and by the two eyelids. Each eyelid has three main layers: skin; muscles that make it shut and open; and the tarsi, made of tough fibrous tissue. Blinking protects eyes from injury and allows tears to bathe the eyes. Tears, composed of a saline bactericidal fluid, come from each upper eyelid's lacrimal gland. The fluid drains away through a tear duct opening at each eyelid's inner corner into the nasal cavity.

Eyeballs are jelly-filled spheres set in fat, supplied with muscles, and shielded by the bony orbits of the skull. Six ocular muscles coordinate each eye's movements so that both eyes can follow moving objects together. The eyes' overlapping fields of view produce the binocular vision that enables us to judge depth and distance.

Light falling on the eye passes through the transparent cornea—the bulging, transparent front of the outer layer of the eyeball. The rest of the outer layer (the sclera, or "white" of the eye) is opaque to light and is covered with a layer of conjunctiva. Light rays then continue through a so-called anterior chamber filled with the watery fluid known as the aqueous humor. This fluid and the cornea refract incoming light and serve as the front lens of the eye.

Light refracted by this outer lens then enters the pupil—a hole surrounded by a muscular diaphragm, the iris. The pupil appears black because light is not reflected out from the interior of the eye. Pigmentation of the iris gives the eye its color. It contracts or dilates in response to the intensity of light, contracting in bright light to prevent too much light from entering the eye and dilating in dim light to allow as much light as possible to enter the eye. Light next passes through a flexible, transparent crystalline lens. Ligaments connect this lens to ciliary muscles that can make it shorten and bulge, or lengthen and grow slimmer, thereby altering its focal length to bring near or distant objects into finer focus.

Refracted further by this lens, light rays reach the eye's posterior chamber. This is filled with the jellylike vitreous humor. After passing through this fluid, light rays reach the retina—a layered network of nerve cells lining the inside of the back of the eyeball and separated from its outer, scleral layer by the chorion, or choroid, a layer of blood vessels that brings nourishment and removes waste products.

The retina

The retina, or "net," covering the rear four-fifths of the eyeball's inner surface is a cup-shaped extension of the brain—linked to it by the second cranial, or optic, nerve. It seems to be back-to-front, for light rays must pass through the layers of nerve cells communicating with the optic nerve before they reach the retinal cells sensitive to light. Each retina has about 120 million rods and about 6 million cones. The long, thin structures known as rods are concentrated toward the rim of the retina. Rods are highly sensitive to low intensities of light but register only shades of gray. The six million cone photoreceptors are relatively short, thick cells that are most plentiful toward the back of the eye and concentrated especially at the fovea, a shallow retinal pit opposite the pupil. Cones work well only in good light but, between them, register green, red, and blue light, and so perceive the range of colors of the visible spectrum.

As light falls on both rods and cones, their light-sensitive pigments instantly decay and then re-form. This change sends electrochemical signals along the optic nerves to the brain, where the signals are interpreted as sight.

Inside the brain

We analyze and understand the images registered inside our eyes because each bit of the image travels in coded fashion from retina to visual cortex at the back of the brain. The journey through the fibers of the optic nerves is complicated. Nerves from each eye meet in the front of the brain at the optic chiasm. This is a partial crossing point where fibers from

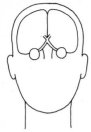

The eyes connect with the brain through the optic (2nd cranial) nerve. The visual pathways "cross over" at the optic chiasm.

The eye lies in the orbit of the skull, held in place by the muscles that move it and cushioned by fat. The eyelids cover the conjunctiva and cornea, which together protect the interior. Light enters through the cornea, is refracted by this and the aqueous humor before passing through the iris to the lens, which focuses it on to the fovea. Rods and cones in the retina transmit impulses through the optic nerve to the brain.

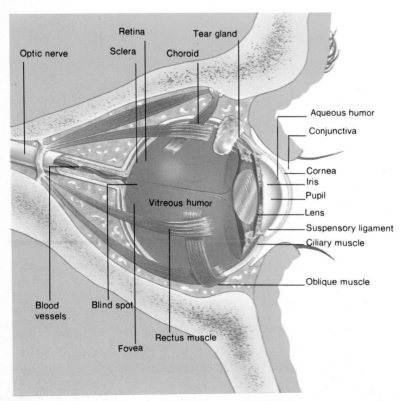

Retina
Optic nerve
Sclera
Choroid
Tear gland
Aqueous humor
Conjunctiva
Cornea
Iris
Pupil
Lens
Suspensory ligament
Ciliary muscle
Vitreous humor
Oblique muscle
Blood vessels
Blind spot
Rectus muscle
Fovea

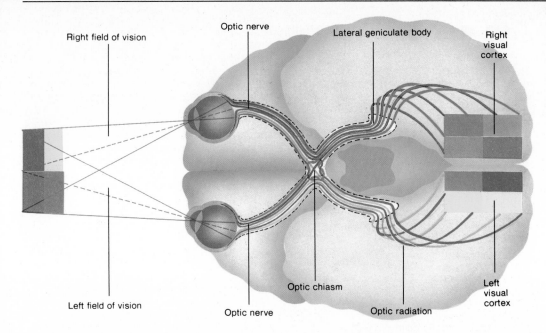

Right field of vision

Optic nerve

Lateral geniculate body

Right visual cortex

Left field of vision

Optic nerve

Optic chiasm

Optic radiation

Left visual cortex

The visual pathways from each retina cross over at the optic chiasm. Nerve impulses from the left of each retina—the right of the visual field—travel in the optic tract to the left of the brain; impulses from the right travel to the right. The optic tracts continue to the lateral geniculate bodies, which coordinate visual information with information from other parts of the brain. Impulses continue to the visual cortex at the back of the cerebrum, where they are interpreted.

each eye's inner (nasal) side switch over to join the nerve-carrying fibers from the outer (temporal) side of the other eye. From the chiasm, both sets of nerve fibers—now known as optic tracts—continue through the brain. After passing the lateral geniculate bodies (relay stations in the thalamus), these nerve fibers fan out in the so-called optic radiation, ending at the primary visual cortex at the back inner edge of each cerebral hemisphere.

The partial crossing of fibers at the optic chiasm ensures that signals from the right side of each retina reach the right visual cortex while signals from the left side of each retina reach the left visual cortex.

Research suggests that, in addition to coor-

dinating countless individual signals almost instantly, some specialization of visual perception may also occur. For example, different cell columns in the cortex may deal with signals from different regions in each retina. And three neighboring areas of cortex of some mammals (designated visual areas I, II, and III) have cells that are sensitive to different stimuli. The "simple" cells of visual area I react to bright lines and dark bars at special angles. Areas II and III have so-called complex and hypercomplex cells: the first register edges and movement; the second detect corners.

The retina appears red when viewed through an ophthalmoscope. Blood vessels enter through the paler optic disk (blind spot).

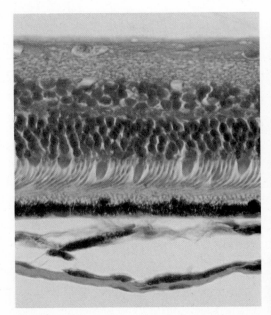

The retina (shown here in cross section) consists of several strata: from the top, there are nerve fibers to the optic nerve; several layers of ganglia and nuclei; rods and cones—the latter being the larger ovoid shapes among thin rods; and the pigmented layer.

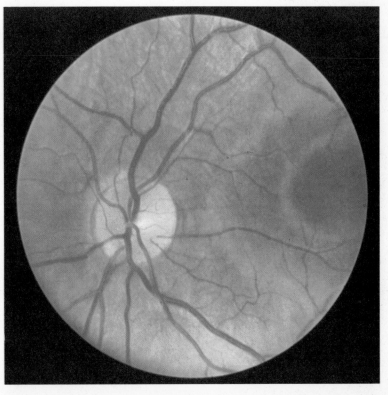

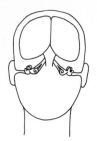

The ear

Ears convert pressure waves passing through the air into electrochemical signals that the brain registers as sounds. The ear itself has three main parts called the outer, middle, and inner ear.

The ears are located at the sides of the head and are concerned with the senses of hearing and balance.

Outer ear

The outer ear, also called the pinna, incorporates a flap of skin and cartilage connected to an opening in the head leading to a short cul-de-sac, the external auditory meatus, or canal. The auditory canal is a tunnel about 1 inch (2.5 centimeters) long. It contains a lining of wax and hairs that block invasive insects and bacteria, but let sound waves through to the middle ear.

Middle ear

The air-filled chamber contains structures that transmit sound vibrations from the outer to the inner ear. The middle ear roughly resembles a six-sided chamber joined to the nasal cavity and throat by the Eustachian tube, which opens during yawning or swallowing to equalize air pressure.

The eardrum, or tympanic membrane, which stretches across the outer entrance of the chamber, is a thin, delicate sheet of tissue that vibrates at the frequencies of the sound waves arriving from the outer ear. As it vibrates, it transmits vibrations to three tiny, connected bones (ossicles) that span the chamber. Among the body's smallest bones, these ossicles comprise the malleus (hammer), incus (anvil), and stapes (stirrup). The malleus and incus hang from the roof of the inner ear and are linked by synovial joints to each other and to the stapes. Ossicles pass on vibrations with diminished range of movement yet greatly increased pressure.

Inner ear: the cochlea

Different regions of the inner ear deal with sound and balance. Hearing depends upon the cochlea—a spiral tube resembling a snail's shell, filled with fluid and divided lengthwise by the basilar membrane into upper and lower chambers, separated from the middle ear by the oval and round windows, respectively.

It is in the cochlea that vibrations transmitted through the ossicles trigger signals in a nerve communicating with the brain. The stapes vibrates against the oval window, which in turn transmits pressure waves through the fluid of the upper chamber of the cochlea. The round window vibrates freely to equalize pressure between the cochlea and middle ear. Meanwhile, waves set up resonance in the basilar membrane and the attached organ of Corti—a tunnel flanked by hair cells that serve as auditory receptors. Disturbance of these

Each ear has three main parts: the external ear, the middle ear, and the inner ear. The external ear consists of the pinna and the external auditory meatus. The tympanic membrane forms the outer boundary of the middle ear. Sound waves cause it to vibrate, and these vibrations are transmitted by the three small ossicle bones—malleus, incus, and stapes—to the oval window of the inner ear. Vibrations are further transmitted from the oval window to the cochlea, which contains sensory cells that convert these vibrations into nervous impulses. These travel along the cochlear branch of the vestibulocochlear, or auditory, (8th cranial) nerve to the brain. The inner ear also contains the semicircular canals, or vestibular apparatus, which detect movement and posture and communicate with the brain through the vestibular branch of the auditory nerve.

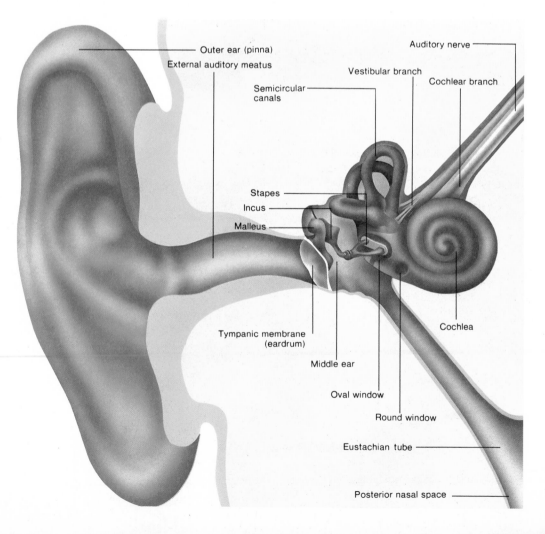

Outer ear (pinna)
External auditory meatus
Auditory nerve
Vestibular branch
Cochlear branch
Semicircular canals
Stapes
Incus
Malleus
Tympanic membrane (eardrum)
Cochlea
Middle ear
Oval window
Round window
Eustachian tube
Posterior nasal space

cells stimulates fibers of the cochlear nerve. This forms part of the auditory nerve, which transmits signals to the "hearing centers" in the temporal lobes of the brain.

Whether we hear a sound as high or low in pitch depends on the part of the basilar membrane that resonates most strongly. Low-frequency pressure waves are detected where the membrane is broadest, and high-frequency waves have their effect near its narrow end.

Much as both eyes work together to help us judge depth and distance, so both ears help us to determine where a sound comes from. This auditory sense is much less well developed than the corresponding visual sense, however, and the ears themselves are less suited than the eyes to distance judgment and direction finding.

Age, internal injury, or disease may result in hearing loss in one ear or both ears, but there are also a number of ways that deafness can be overcome. Disease that prevents sound vibrations from passing through the middle ear is not sufficient alone to prevent hearing completely because some vibrations find their way to the cochlea by way of the skull bones. Hearing aids set in these bones make use of this. Aids fitted in the outer ear can often help to compensate for damage to the inner ear. And because some acoustic nerve fibers cross from one side of the brain to the other on their way to the tops of the temporal lobes, damage to one temporal lobe need not necessarily cause deafness in the ear on that side.

Inner ear: vestibular system

The inner ear's vestibular system helps us to keep our balance, even with closed eyes. The system consists of three semicircular tubes, called canals, at right angles to one another, and two sacs (the saccule and utricle), all filled with fluid and located near the cochlea. The canals broaden at one end into flask-shaped chambers (ampullae). Each chamber has a gelatinous capsule containing the hair cells of a receptor organ. The saccule and utricle contain gelatinous masses called static receptors, weighted with crystals called otoliths. When the head moves, fluid flows through the canals and sacs, disturbing the gelatinous masses and hairs, and generating signals in nerve endings near the hairs' roots.

Different head movements and positions stimulate different groups of nerve endings in the vestibular system. The superior semicircular canal registers nodding, the posterior canal detects tilting, and the lateral (or horizontal) canal responds to turning. Different positions of the head are registered by the saccule and utricle, because these cause different weight distributions of the otoliths, which affect nerve endings in these parts of the vestibular system.

From the vestibular system, signals pass through the vestibular nerve, which merges with the cochlear nerve to form the auditory nerve. From the vestibular nerve, many fibers pass directly to the cerebellum, where they assist limb, eye, and trunk coordination.

Balance is coordinated by signals from the vestibular apparatus.

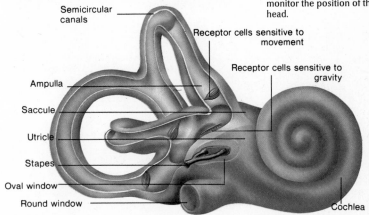

The semicircular canals, or vestibular apparatus, are oriented at right angles to each other. When the head moves, fluid flows and stimulates receptor cells in the ampullae. Other receptor cells sensitive to gravity monitor the position of the head.

Semicircular canals
Receptor cells sensitive to movement
Receptor cells sensitive to gravity
Ampulla
Saccule
Utricle
Stapes
Oval window
Round window
Cochlea

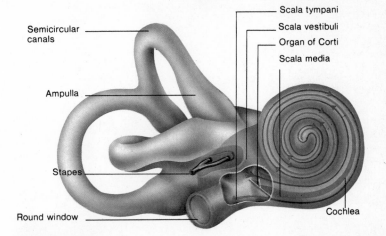

Semicircular canals
Scala tympani
Scala vestibuli
Organ of Corti
Scala media
Ampulla
Stapes
Round window
Cochlea

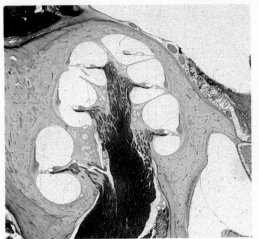

The cochlea carries vibrations from the oval window through the upper scala tympani, then the lower scala vestibuli to the round window. On the way, hair cells of the organ of Corti are stimulated and send signals to the brain, where they are interpreted as sound.

A cross section of the cochlea shows its three sections and the central cochlear nerve.

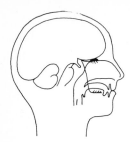

Smell and taste are the senses of the nose and tongue. Both are relayed by nerves from sensory cells in these organs to the brain.

Smell and taste

Smell helps us to distinguish pleasant from unpleasant or dangerous substances at a distance; taste involves direct contact. But both are chemical senses that depend on foreign molecules touching sensory structures called receptor cells. In some ways, smell and taste may be the most primitive senses. Sometimes —for example in the discernment of some of the more subtle flavors—both work together more closely than most of us realize.

Smell

Smell is detected by sensory cells in two patches of olfactory epithelium, one in the roof of each nasal cavity, just below the cranium. Between them, the two patches occupy approximately one square inch (5 square centimeters), yet scientists calculate that they include millions of rodlike bodies projecting from the buried sensory cells. Each rod ends in filaments, or "hairs," the total area of which may exceed that of the skin surface.

These sensitive hairs, in common with the entire surface of each nasal cavity, are moistened by the mucous membrane that lines the nose. This membrane is kept warm by a rich supply of blood vessels and so warms and moistens air breathed in through the nostrils. Moisture plays a key role in the sense of smell, for chemical receptors can only detect substances that can be dissolved.

Probably only two per cent of breathed-in air passes close to the cell receptors. Yet these are so sensitive that a single molecule of some substances is enough to excite one receptor ending—for instance, the human olfactory system can sense less than one hundred millionth of a gram of musk. Furthermore, some people can distinguish as many as 10,000 different odors.

Exactly how smell works remains debatable. But the stereochemical theory of olfaction suggests that most odors are combinations of a few primary odors produced by distinctively shaped chemical molecules that fit into matching olfactory sites, like keys into locks. This suggests there may be different basic odors, in rather the same way as there are different basic tastes.

Smell and taste are detected by specialized sensory cells in the nose and tongue, respectively. In the nose, olfactory nerve fibers extend from the olfactory bulb beneath the forebrain into membranes lining the nasal cavity. Airborne chemicals dissolve in these membranes' mucous covering and stimulate nerve fibers that convey signals to the olfactory bulb and then along the olfactory (1st cranial) nerve to the brain. Taste buds in the tongue also respond to chemical stimuli. Those at the front of the tongue stimulate the lingual nerve, a branch of the maxillary nerve, which in turn is part of the trigeminal (5th cranial) nerve. Receptors at the back of the tongue stimulate the glossopharyngeal (9th cranial) nerve. The mouth and nose are sensitive to other stimuli apart from taste and smell and are correspondingly well-supplied by other sensory nerves.

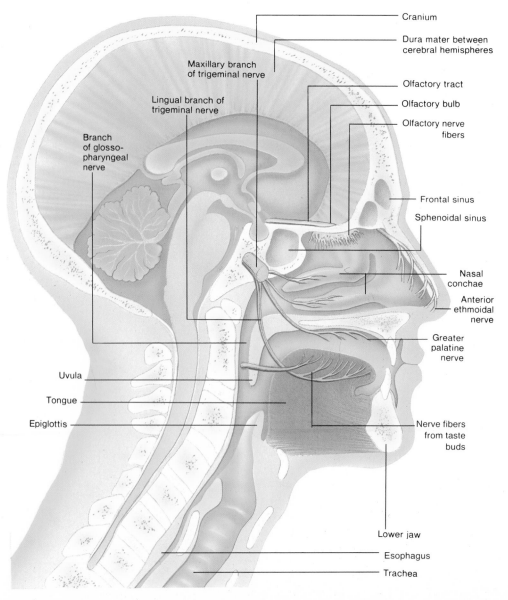

Cranium

Dura mater between cerebral hemispheres

Maxillary branch of trigeminal nerve

Lingual branch of trigeminal nerve

Olfactory tract

Olfactory bulb

Olfactory nerve fibers

Branch of glosso-pharyngeal nerve

Frontal sinus

Sphenoidal sinus

Nasal conchae

Anterior ethmoidal nerve

Greater palatine nerve

Uvula

Tongue

Epiglottis

Nerve fibers from taste buds

Lower jaw

Esophagus

Trachea

From the olfactory receptors, nerve signals travel to the two olfactory bulbs projecting from the brain, then on by complex routes to a diffuse olfactory region associated with the limbic system in the brain.

Taste

Compared with our sense of smell, our sense of taste seems poorly developed. Most taste-sensitive cells occur on the upper part of the tongue. A very few are found on the palate, lingual tonsils, and epiglottis. Groups of these receptors form each taste bud, and there can be many such buds on one papilla, or small projection on the tongue's upper surface, which feels rough because of the scores of papillae found there. Babies possess tens of thousands of taste buds, but numbers decrease with age: an adult normally has about 9,000.

Four types of taste buds, found in the papillae, enable us to distinguish between sweet, sour, salty, and bitter tastes. But the receptor cells that make up our taste buds do not have structural or functional differences that correspond to these tastes. The idea of the four categories of taste seems to be something that is learned. Taste categories may be only characteristics of taste; they tell us little about how the taste sense functions.

While olfactory signals pass through the olfactory lobes, taste signals travel through cranial nerves straight to the brain stem, then on to the brain's higher centers.

The taste of food

Taste and smell combine to help give many foods their flavors. This is apparent in the fact that flavors are difficult or impossible to distinguish when the mucous membranes are inflamed during an infection, such as a cold. The taste of food also depends upon its temperature: taste receptors are most highly sensitive to foods at temperatures of 85—105° F. (30—40° C).

In time, nerve cells adapt to prolonged exposure to certain tastes or odors so that these stimuli are no longer noticed. Furthermore, adaptation to one taste may also alter sensitivity to others. Thus, coffee tastes unusually bitter if you drink it after eating ice cream, while salt-adaption heightens sensitivity to bitter, sweet, and sour substances.

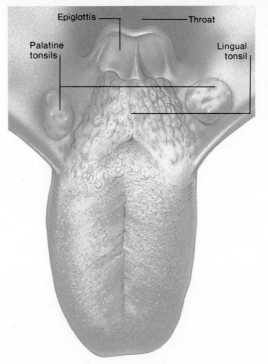

Epiglottis — Throat
Palatine tonsils — Lingual tonsil

The tongue is a muscular organ projecting from the floor of the mouth. Its surface is covered with three types of papillae—rounded fungiform, pointed filiform, and columnar vallate papillae—and taste buds are found on many of these. Four types of taste buds, found in the papillae, enable us to distinguish between sweet, sour, salty, and bitter.

Taste buds on the sides of papillae respond to chemicals dissolved in saliva or other liquids in the mouth.

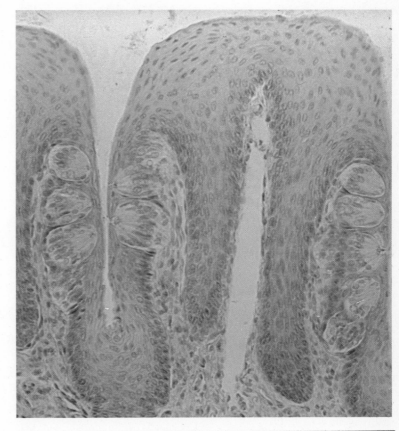

Fact entries

Tastes in man are of four types. Salty tastes are caused by the anions of inorganic salts such as the halogens chlorine and bromine, although a pure sensation of saltiness comes only from sodium chloride. Sour tastes come from the hydrogen ions in acids.

Sweet and bitter tastes tend to have organic origins. For instance, caffeine tastes bitter, sucrose tastes sweet. But sweet-tasting substances also include beryllium, a metal, and bitter-tasting substances include copper.

Taste in animals is similar, in that most vertebrates seem to share man's discrimination and sensitivity to tastes. Dogs, however, can taste sugars although not saccharin; and pigeons seem able to taste saccharin but not sugars. Chickens appear unable to detect either.

Even individual humans differ in their sensitivity. For example, 70 per cent of Caucasians can taste phenylthiocarbamide, a bitter-tasting chemical, but the other 30 per cent have not inherited the ability to do so.

The skin

Skin forms the body's largest organ. An adult's skin has a surface area of approximately 19 square feet (1.75 square meters) and weighs about 6 pounds (2.7 kilograms).

Skin provides the body with a tough, flexible barrier that protects against disease, injury, and loss of water from the moist internal tissues. It also helps control the body's temperature, excretes some wastes, and serves as a major sensory organ, registering pressure, pain, and temperature. An area of skin about the size of an adult thumbnail may contain about three million cells, 3 feet (90 centimeters) of blood vessels, 12 feet (3.7 meters) of nerves, and 100 sweat glands.

Skin has three layers of tissue: epidermis, dermis, and subcutaneous tissue.

Epidermis

A slice cut through the epidermis would reveal subsidiary layers of cells, the lowest alive and multiplying, the topmost cells dead and flaking off.

Cells of the stratum basale, or Malpighian layer, resemble close-packed posts or columns. As they multiply they give rise to the "prickle" cells of the stratum spinosum, the layer just above, some five to ten cells deep. Next comes the stratum granulosum. There are no blood vessels here to bring nutrients or carry away wastes, so this layer's cells die off and accumulate granules of protein waste. Above these is a clear layer called the stratum lucidum, where granules have changed into the tough fibrous protein keratin—the substance nails and hair are made. The stratum corneum, or cornified layer, the topmost layer of the epidermis, consists of flat, dead, keratinized cells that are continuously flaking off.

The epidermis lacks blood vessels and has few nerves, but contains granules of the pigment melanin. This dark brown substance helps to determine the color of the skin. The skins of dark-skinned people contain much melanin. The freckles and suntans of pale-skinned people are also caused by melanin. Strong sunlight stimulates production of this pigment, which helps protect the skin from damage caused by overexposure to the sun's ultraviolet radiation. Ultraviolet light also has a beneficial effect, however, by acting on the skin to help the body synthesize vitamin D—an important factor in the healthy growth of bones.

Freckles are small patches of melanin pigment in the Malpighian layer of the epidermis. The same pigmentation causes the skin to darken in response to sunlight and is responsible for the dark skin of some people.

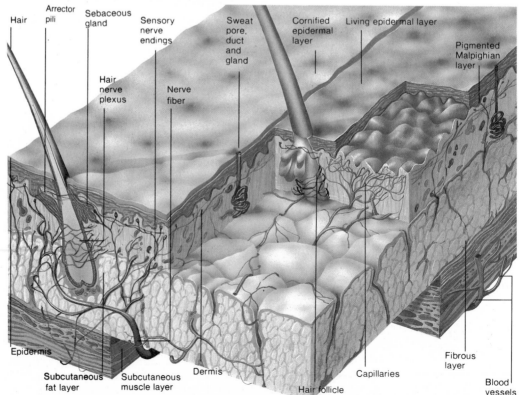

The skin has three principal layers—the epidermis, dermis, and a layer of subcutaneous tissue, composed of fat, a fibrous layer, and a layer of subcutaneous blood vessels and muscle. The epidermis itself has three main layers—the Malpighian generative layer, a layer of living cells, and an outer layer of dead "cornified" cells. The dermis contains numerous tiny blood capillaries, nerve endings, sweat and sebaceous glands, and lymph vessels. Hair follicles run through this layer. Associated with hair follicles are a blood supply, a sensory nerve supply, a muscle which can cause the hair to rise, and a sebaceous gland.

Hair

Arrector pili

Sebaceous gland

Sensory nerve endings

Hair nerve plexus

Nerve fiber

Sweat pore, duct and gland

Cornified epidermal layer

Living epidermal layer

Pigmented Malpighian layer

Epidermis

Subcutaneous fat layer

Subcutaneous muscle layer

Dermis

Hair follicle

Capillaries

Fibrous layer

Blood vessels

Dermis

This is a closely woven network of connective tissue, thinnest in the eyelids, thickest in the back, and everywhere far thicker than the epidermis. Tough protein fibers in the dermis give skin its tensile strength and bulk. The dermis also contains scattered blood vessels, lymph vessels, nerve endings, hair follicles, and glands connected with the epidermis.

Thousands of tiny projections called papillae jut up from the dermis and fit into tiny pits in the bottom of the epidermis. Papillae grouped in rows form the ridges on fingers, giving each individual a distinctive set of fingerprints. Each of these papillae has a rich supply of tiny capillaries—blood vessels bringing nourishment to growing skin, and regulating heat loss from the body. Little heat escapes from the skin when its capillaries constrict to block the flow of blood, but heat loss is substantial when capillaries expand and let blood pass through freely. Papillae also contain nerve endings sensitive to touch.

Subcutaneous tissue

This consists mainly of blood vessels, connective tissue, and cells that store fat. This tissue helps protect the body from blows and other injuries and also helps retain body heat.

Sensors in the skin

Hundreds of thousands of sensitive nerve endings are embedded in the skin, especially in such regions as the lips and finger pads. Between them, different kinds of sensor detect touch, pressure, heat, cold, and pain. Touch receptors are shaped like bulbs. Other nerve endings form a mesh embracing the roots of hairs: these sensors are activated when a hair bends. Free nerve endings, resembling branching twigs, may register pain as well as touch and pressure. But pain is felt by several kinds of nerve if these are subjected to intense pressure. All these sensors are mechanoreceptors: receptors that fire off signals to the central nervous system when deformed by touch or pressure. Besides these, the skin has two types of thermoreceptor, in the form of nerve endings sensitive to temperature change. One type senses cold, the other heat.

Glands in the skin

There are two important kinds of gland in skin: sebaceous glands and sweat glands.

Sebaceous glands open into hair follicles in the dermal layer of the skin. These glands secrete sebum, a fatty substance that lubricates the hairs and their surrounding skin. Sebum accumulating in a blocked gland may produce a soft, sebaceous cyst, which may appear alarming, but is benign.

Some 2.4 million sweat glands activated by the autonomic nervous system excrete water, salt, and the body wastes, lactic acid and urea. These escape through narrow ducts with openings forming the tiny holes called sweat pores. Certain sweat glands (called apocrine sweat glands), located in the temples, armpits, and the genital area, produce a thick secretion under emotional stress. Others (called eccrine

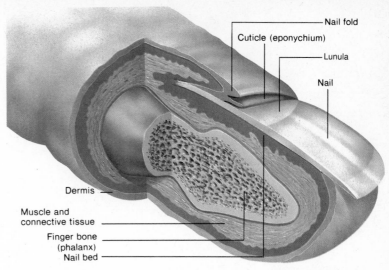

Nail fold
Cuticle (eponychium)
Lunula
Nail

Dermis
Muscle and connective tissue
Finger bone (phalanx)
Nail bed

Nail is a specialized horny tissue that grows at the ends of the fingers and toes. The nail root is buried in a fold of skin. The body of the nail grows continually from this until it extends beyond the end of the finger or toe.

sweat glands) are widespread in the skin and produce a dilute salt solution when the body temperature becomes uncomfortably high, either in response to external heat or to physical activity. This solution helps to cool the body as it evaporates.

A man marching through a hot desert may sweat 2.5 gallons (10 liters) of water in a day—half from his trunk, a quarter from the legs and thighs, and a quarter from the arms and head. Copious sweating causes salt loss and this may produce cramping in people who replace the water by drinking without also taking salt to restore its concentration in the blood.

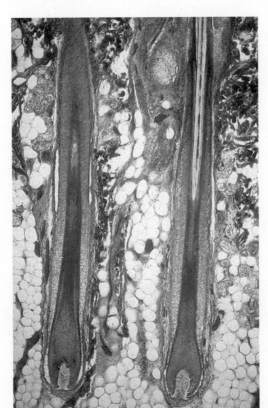

A cross section through skin shows two hairs in their follicles in the layer of subcutaneous fat just below the dermis.

The endocrine system

Endocrine glands are located in the head, neck, and abdomen.

The body's two main control mechanisms, which regulate all aspects of physical life, are the nervous system and the endocrine system. The endocrine system consists of eight principal ductless glands that release chemicals called hormones directly into the blood. These glands are the anterior pituitary; the posterior pituitary; the thyroid; the parathyroid; the islets of Langerhans in the pancreas; the adrenal cortex; the adrenal medulla; and the gonads—ovaries in a female, testes in a male.

Hormones at work

Endocrine glands and their hormones are shown below. The anterior pituitary influences the thyroid, adrenal medulla, and sex glands through thyroid-stimulating hormone (TSH), adrenocorticotropic hormone (ACTH), follicle-stimulating hormone (FSH), and luteinizing hormone (LH).

Hormones comprising several dozen different chemicals travel through the bloodstream and influence different kinds of "target" cells, modifying their activity in a variety of ways.

Each target cell has at least one type of receptor in its membrane, and each kind of receptor receives one type of hormone, which fits it rather as a key fits into a lock. For example, a hormone may cause the target cell to produce the messenger compound cyclic adenosine monophosphate, which affects such things as protein manufacture, energy storage, and even other hormone manufacture.

The action of endocrine glands

Endocrine glands are specialized chemical factories that produce hormones that perform a special task or group of tasks.

The thyroid and parathyroid glands lie in the front of the neck. The thyroid's main task is the control of energy metabolism by means of the hormones thyroxine and triiodothyronine. The thyroid uses almost all the iodine inside the body, principally to manufacture iodine-rich thyroxine, a hormone essential for growth and for regulating the body's basal metabolic rate. The thyroid gland also produces calcitonin, which encourages the deposition of calcium in bone, and so helps control blood calcium levels. The four parathyroid glands produce parathormone, which raises the calcium level in the blood, and helps control calcium metabolism.

The pancreas—a large gland opening into the small intestine—principally produces digestive enzymes, although its cell clumps called the islets of Langerhans produce the hormones insulin and glucagon, which regulate carbohydrate metabolism. Insulin stops the liver producing unwanted glucose, and prevents adipose tissue releasing glycerol and fatty acids. Glucagon counters the effects of insulin by boosting the release of glucose as this is required.

The adrenal glands, which lie one above each kidney, in fact each contain two glands. The outer part, the adrenal cortex, produces steroid hormones, including aldosterone and hydrocortisone. Aldosterone plays a major role in regulating salt balance in the body. Hydrocortisone is involved in metabolizing amino acids, fat, and glucose, and it helps to provide the raw materials and energy required for building and repairing tissues. As well as the testes and ovaries, the adrenal cortex synthesizes the male sex hormones (androgens) and the female sex hormones (estrogens), the balance of which in individuals of either sex determines secondary sexual characteristics.

The inner part of each adrenal gland, the adrenal medulla, produces epinephrine and norepinephrine—hormones that prepare the body for "fight or flight" in situations of stress—which between them increase heart rate, channel blood to muscles, and release glucose. These activities prepare the body for sudden action in an emergency, but also have an important role in active play.

The male testes and female ovaries yield testosterone and estrogen, respectively, which have fundamental effects on sexual development and reproductive activity.

The pituitary gland is the most important endocrine gland; among its functions is the control of other endocrine glands.

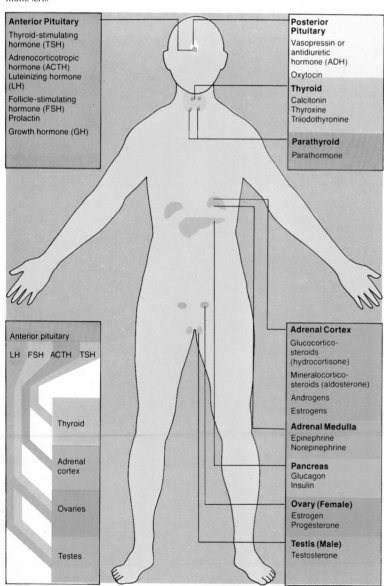

Anterior Pituitary
Thyroid-stimulating hormone (TSH)
Adrenocorticotropic hormone (ACTH)
Luteinizing hormone (LH)
Follicle-stimulating hormone (FSH)
Prolactin
Growth hormone (GH)

Posterior Pituitary
Vasopressin or antidiuretic hormone (ADH)
Oxytocin

Thyroid
Calcitonin
Thyroxine
Triiodothyronine

Parathyroid
Parathormone

Anterior pituitary

LH FSH ACTH TSH

Thyroid

Adrenal cortex

Ovaries

Testes

Adrenal Cortex
Glucocortico-steroids (hydrocortisone)
Mineralocortico-steroids (aldosterone)
Androgens
Estrogens

Adrenal Medulla
Epinephrine
Norepinephrine

Pancreas
Glucagon
Insulin

Ovary (Female)
Estrogen
Progesterone

Testis (Male)
Testosterone

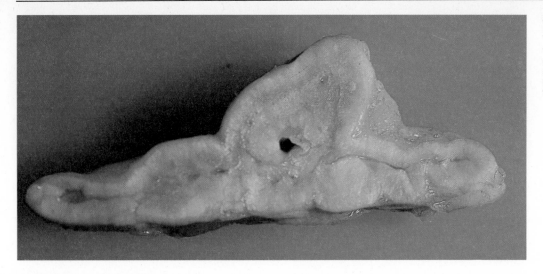

An **adrenal gland** is located on top of each kidney. The outer adrenal cortex, which produces one group of hormones, completely encloses the adrenal medulla, which produces different hormones.

Controlling the endocrine system

Too much or too little of any hormone may cause deformity, disease, or death. The pituitary gland and the hypothalamus of the brain control which hormones are released, in what quantity, and when.

The pituitary is a gland about the size of a pea, suspended in a bone cavity below the brain and above the nasal cavity. This tiny unit releases more than two dozen hormones that regulate the activity and hormone output of almost all the other endocrine glands.

The pituitary's anterior and posterior parts work separately. The anterior lobe (front part) releases trophic (nourishing) hormones, each of which triggers the production and release of a special hormone in a "target" gland. Thyrotropic, or thyroid-stimulating, hormone (TSH) stimulates the thyroid gland to produce thyroxine. Adrenocorticotropic hormone (ACTH) encourages hormone output from the cortex of each adrenal gland. Follicle stimulating hormone (FSH) and luteinizing hormone (LH) act upon the ovaries and testes. The anterior pituitary also produces growth hormone (GH), which indirectly affects cartilage in ways that are essential to growth and broadly influences metabolism. Changes in the anterior pituitary's output of gonadotropic hormones initiate sexual maturity.

The posterior lobe (rear part) of the pituitary stores and releases two hormones manufactured in the adjacent hypothalamus, a complex region of the brain located immediately above the pituitary and beneath the thalamus. Vasopressin, or antidiuretic hormone (ADH), controls urine output and so helps to maintain the water balance of the body. Oxytocin causes the uterus to contract during childbirth and stimulates the release of milk during nursing.

The pituitary gland knows when to liberate hormones stimulating target glands or muscles by a process called "feedback"—by means of which the controller is itself controlled. For example, when the thyroid gland releases thyroxine into the bloodstream, its presence inhibits the pituitary's production of TSH. This reduction in TSH results in a reduction in the thyroid's output of thyroxine. As this reduces, the pituitary responds by producing more

TSH, so that overall, a balanced output of thyroxine is maintained.

This example illustrates the principle, but oversimplifies the mechanism of endocrine feedback. Endocrine feedback mechanisms depend to a great extent on the hypothalamus, chief coordinator of the endocrine and nervous systems. This part of the brain combines hormonal feedback information from the blood with nerve impulses received from brain centers, including those controlling body rhythms. The hypothalamus responds by sending amino acid chains—called peptides—to the pituitary, and it is primarily these that stimulate or inhibit pituitary hormone output. Thus, the peptide called thyrotropin-releasing hormone (TRH) stimulates manufacture of thyrotropin (thyrotropic hormone, or TSH) in the pituitary, and so indirectly affects the release of thyroxine from the thyroid gland; in this way, the central nervous system exerts control over the simplified feedback system described above.

Endocrine feedback between the thyroid and parathyroid glands controls calcium metabolism. Low blood calcium levels stimulate the parathyroid glands, causing them to release parathormone, which decreases the deposition of calcium in bone, decreases calcium excretion by the kidneys, and increases intestinal calcium absorption, thus raising blood calcium levels. This stimulates the thyroid to produce calcitonin, which has the reverse effect.

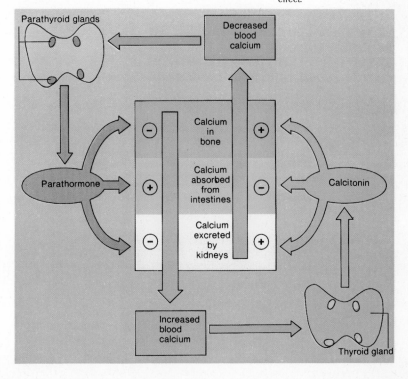

Sex and reproduction

Sex is probably surrounded by more interest and perhaps confusion than any other area of human activity. On a purely biological level, sex is the mechanism by which humans reproduce their young—a process that involves transferring a male reproductive cell (sperm) into the female reproductive tract, where it must join with a female reproductive cell (ovum) to produce a single fertilized egg (zygote). Over a period of nine months, this fertilized cell then develops within the female into a new individual.

Among humans, however, sex has also become a way of expressing profound emotions such as love and passion, a form of emotional expression unique to humans and which, in every age and culture, has been an integral part of human behavior.

Male and female reproductive systems

The male and female reproductive systems are perfectly designed for the job they have to do. The female system produces the ova and con-

tains an organ, the uterus, or womb, in which the developing offspring is accommodated. The male system produces sperm and includes an organ, the penis, which deposits sperm within the female. Although both systems differ in structure, housing, and function, both develop from the same embryonic tissue and, in their adult forms, contain many counterpart or corresponding organs.

The female reproductive organs are housed inside the body within the pelvis. From the outside, all that can be seen are the external genitals, known collectively as the vulva. At the front, as if looking through a woman's open legs, is the mons veneris or mons pubis, a pad of fatty tissue that lies over the pubic bone and which from puberty onward is covered by pubic hair. Running down and back are two folds of skin, the labia majora, which surround two smaller folds, the labia minora. At their front, the labia minora form a hood under which lies the clitoris, a small, highly sensitive organ corresponding to the man's penis and similarly formed of erectile tissue. Below the clitoris lies the urethra, then below this, the vaginal opening. In women who have not had sexual intercourse, this opening is partly closed by the hymen, a thin membrane that is usually torn or ruptured the first time that a woman has coitus, although it may be stretched or torn earlier.

The vagina itself is a muscular passage about 4 inches (10 centimeters) long, which leads up from the vulva to the uterus. It is capable of great distention; during childbirth it distends greatly to allow a child to be born. A minute opening, the os uteri, forms the entrance to the cervix, or neck, of the uterus. Lined by a mucous membrane called the endometrium, the uterus is a small pear-shaped organ within which the growing fetus is sheltered.

From either side of the uterus, the Fallopian tubes reach back to the ovaries. These oval-shaped organs are the female gonads, or reproductive glands, equivalent to the male testes. The ovaries release a ripe ovum every month and also produce the female sex hormones progesterone and estrogen. These play a vital role in the female reproductive cycle and are also responsible for the development of such secondary sexual characteristics as breasts, fat, and body hair.

The male reproductive system lies both inside and outside the body and, unlike the female system, is linked to the urinary system. Visible organs are the penis and testes. The penis, whose size and shape may vary considerably, is normally flaccid. Behind and below the penis are the two testicles, or testes, the male gonads. These produce the sperm cells and the male sex hormone testosterone, responsible for such secondary sexual characteristics as facial hair and deep voice. The testes are flattened oval-shaped organs that lie inside the baglike scrotum. Within them, sperm cells are continually produced inside coiled seminiferous tubules. Once formed, the sperm cells are stored inside epididymides, two tubular organs adjacent to the testes.

Seminal vesicles
Prostate gland
Bladder
Pubic bone
Vas deferens
Urethra
Penis
Testis
Epididymis
Scrotum

Male sex organs are shown in cross section, *above*. The male gametes—the sperm—are produced in the testes, which lie in the scrotum. They travel from the epididymis of the testis along the vas deferens to the seminal vesicles, which are located at the rear of the prostate gland. The sper-

matic ducts join with the urethra, the tube through which urine passes out from the bladder. The testes also produce the male sex hormone testosterone, which is secreted into the bloodstream and is responsible for initiating and maintaining male sexual characteristics.

Birth control

When reproduction is not the desired result of sex, some form of conscious regulation is required. This is commonly referred to as birth control. Although conception—the fertilization of an ovum by a sperm—is the natural result of sex, it does not necessarily happen every time two people have sexual intercourse. Because of her monthly reproductive, or menstrual, cycle, a woman is only able to conceive during a limited number of days each month, after ovulation and before the menstrual period. These days can be identified, although not always with certainty, by counting the days between menstrual periods and also by observing certain associated physical changes, such as small alterations in body temperature. The time before ovulation, when sexual intercourse will probably not lead to pregnancy, is called the "safe" period, and restricting sexual activity to these days is regarded by many as the most natural—and by some, as the only acceptable—form of birth control. The technique is sometimes referred to as the rhythm method of birth control.

Other methods of birth control range from using hormonal contraceptives, through physical or chemical barriers, to surgical sterilization. Hormonal methods, such as the oral contraceptive pill, work by preventing ovulation. Physical barriers, such as the condom or diaphragm, prevent sperm from reaching an ovum in the uterus. Chemical barriers—usually in the form of foam or gel—kill sperm before they reach the uterus. Another technique, involving an intrauterine device (IUD), seems to prevent the ovum from implanting in the lining of the uterus. Surgical sterilization involves cutting or tying off the tubes through which the sperm or the ovum must pass—the vas deferens in a man, the Fallopian tubes in a woman. In both cases, pregnancy is prevented because the partner operated on is made sterile.

Sexual activity

It is still not known exactly what determines sexual activity in humans. It would seem there are physiological rules that may be linked to changes within the body, such as changes in hormonal level that possibly interact with the central nervous system. But age, social, cultural, and psychological factors all play a part in determining human sexual behavior.

From various investigations into human sexual activity, such as the Kinsey Reports of the late 1940's and 1950's, the studies conducted over the last four decades by Masters and Johnson, and, more recently, surveys by Shere Hite, it is clear that individual requirements and practices vary enormously, ranging from those who live active sexual lives, whether with many partners or in a pair-bonding, to those who seem content to live with little or no sexual involvement.

Reproduction

Reproduction is a complex process, and for conception to occur a number of varying conditions must first be met. Some of the most

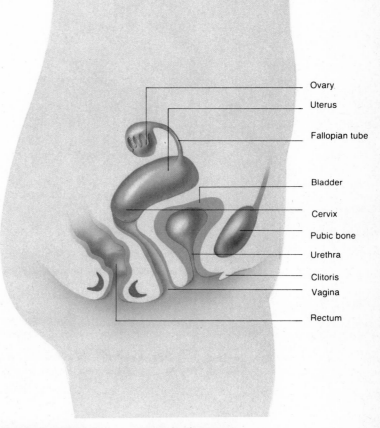

Ovary

Uterus

Fallopian tube

Bladder

Cervix

Pubic bone

Urethra

Clitoris

Vagina

Rectum

Female sex organs are shown in cross section. The vagina leads to the cervix of the uterus (the neck of the womb), and the uterus itself connects, by means of the Fallopian tubes, with the ovaries. These structures lie above and behind the uterus. During ovulation, at about the middle of the menstrual cycle, an egg is released from an ovary and travels down a Fallopian tube to the uterus. The ovaries also produce the female sex hormones progesterone and estrogen, which initiate and maintain female sexual characteristics.

The female reproductive cycle depends on the menstrual cycle, which is based on monthly ovulation. During the menstrual cycle, the lining of the uterus thickens in preparation for the implantation of a fertilized ovum. If no ovum implants, the lining breaks down and is expelled as menstrual bleeding. An ovum, grown in a follicle of the ovary, is then released and is guided into the Fallopian tube by the tube's fingerlike fimbria. As it moves toward the uterus, it may encounter sperm (A), one of which may penetrate and fertilize it (B), causing cell division (C, D) to begin. After a few days, a fertilized ovum—now developed to the blastocyst stage (E)—reaches the uterus lining and implants there.

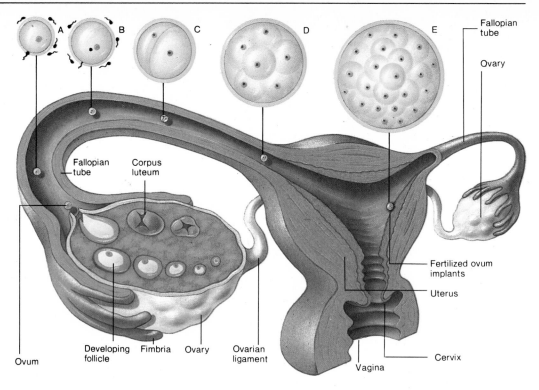

significant relate to the different sexual cycles of men and women.

Normally from puberty, a man is physically ready to reproduce at any time. From puberty, the male body continually manufactures sperm at a rate of some 200 million a day; at any one time there may be millions of mature sperm available in the seminal vesicles that can be released when a man ejaculates. By contrast, however, the ovaries produce a few thousand eggs, or ova, but only a few hundred of them are released during the female's lifetime. Normally, only one egg at a time is released during ovulation.

Female reproductive cycle

A woman is born with a full complement of immature ova contained within ovarian follicles. Some 2 million are present at birth, declining to about 300,000 by puberty. Every month, a woman's body undergoes a routine cycle of physical changes during which an ovum is released and the body prepares for gestation.

This cycle is known as the female sexual, reproductive, or menstrual cycle. It begins at puberty sometime between the ages of 10 and 16 when its onset is known as the menarche; the menstrual cycle repeats itself every 24 to 32 days in most women, unless an egg is fertilized. This cycle continues until the menopause, which usually occurs between the ages of 45 and 55 in most women.

The monthly cycle is affected by various hormones controlled by the hypothalamus. During the first phase—the follicular phase—the follicle-stimulating hormone (FSH) produced by the pituitary causes ovaries and ovarian follicles to enlarge; it also causes the ovaries to produce estrogen. One ovarian follicle outstrips the others in growth, ruptures and then, due to the action of luteinizing hormone (LH), releases the single egg. This is

called ovulation and occurs midway through the cycle.

The mature ovum then enters the Fallopian tube and is propelled into the uterus. There, due to the action of estrogen and progesterone, the endometrium has become thickened and vascular in preparation for the arrival of a fertilized egg. If the egg is not fertilized by a sperm within about 12 hours, it dies.

During the second half of the cycle—the luteal phase—LH causes the follicular remains to form a bright yellow structure, the corpus luteum, and the endometrium continues to thicken. If a fertilized egg fails to arrive, the corpus luteum degenerates and the endometrial lining is shed together with blood, passing out of the body as menstrual flow. Menstruation lasts 3 to 7 days, then the entire cycle begins again.

Fertilization and implantation

Fertilization occurs high up in the Fallopian tube and as it can only happen if both male and female cells are present, intercourse and ovulation must occur within about 12 hours of each other.

When the man ejaculates, some 400 million sperm are deposited into the woman's vagina. Propelled by tail-like structures, the sperm make their way fairly rapidly up the vagina, through the cervix, and into the uterus. This takes less than an hour, but at least half the number die in the acidic conditions of the vagina; others die as the sperm continue to travel to the top of the uterus and into the Fallopian tube. Here, conditions are favorable for the few hundred sperm that remain and they can survive for up to 72 hours.

Fertilization occurs immediately if an ovum is already present. It is accomplished when one male sperm penetrates the surface of the ovum. The cell wall then becomes impenetrable to other sperm, and the nuclei of the two cells fuse together. Cell division begins almost at once, the ovum subdividing or segmenting, first into two and then doubling with each division until it becomes a rounded mass of cells—the morula. As the cells increase in number, they also differentiate to form the different cells that make up the human body. As the process continues, a fluid-filled cavity develops in the morula, now called the blastocyst; the outer layer forms a cellular wall—the trophoblast, which will form the placenta—while the remaining cells form a mass from which the fetus and amniotic sac will develop.

During this process, the fertilized ovum has been making its way toward the uterine cavity, and about seven days after fertilization, the blastocyst implants in the endometrium. Small projections on the trophoblast, called chorionic villi, burrow into the uterine wall so that the blastocyst becomes completely embedded, obtaining its nourishment by diffusion from the uterus. Once implantation has occurred, conception is complete, the normal menstrual cycle is suspended, and pregnancy is established. Occasionally, the fertilized ovum fails to reach the uterus and instead implants elsewhere in the reproductive tract. This is known as ectopic pregnancy and almost invariably requires surgery.

Boy or girl?

The sex of the new infant is determined at the very instant of fertilization and depends entirely on the pattern of sex chromosomes present in the nucleus of the sperm. The nucleus of every cell in the body, except the germ cells (sperm or ovum), contains a "blueprint" of information determining how that cell functions. Forty-four of these chromosomes are somatic—not concerned with reproduction—while two are sex chromosomes. These are of two types, X and Y; females have two X chromosomes (XX), and males have one X and one Y chromosome (XY). Germ cells, however, only contain 23 chromosomes, half the normal number. Each female ovum therefore contains 22 somatic chromosomes and one X chromosome; each male sperm contains 22 somatic chromosomes and either an X or a Y chromosome.

At fertilization, the fusion of the cells ensures that the newly fertilized ovum contains its full complement of chromosomes but its sex depends on the sperm. An ovum fertilized by an X-carrying sperm will develop into a female embryo; one fertilized by a Y-carrying sperm will develop into a male.

Infertility

Infertility—the inability to produce children—affects about one in ten couples. There are many causes. In about 40 per cent of cases, infertility is due to male sterility—low sperm count, abnormal sperm, or impotence. In women, the most common cause is blockage of the Fallopian tubes. Other causes are failure to ovulate and cervical disorders. In one case in ten, no cause will be found, but in other cases, medical investigation will reveal a cause that can be treated successfully.

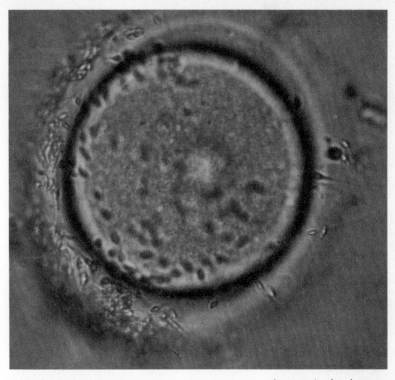

An ovum is a female reproductive, or germ, cell. This photograph shows its nucleus, approximately central, surrounded by cytoplasm, which in turn is surrounded by the zona pellucida, in which a number of sperm can be seen.

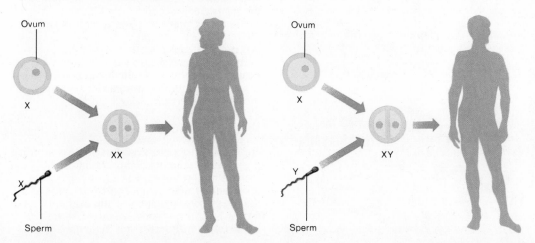

Sex chromosomes in the nuclei of body cells are of two types, called X and Y. All cells in a female have two X chromosomes; all in a male, one X and one Y. Germ cells have only one sex chromosome, however an ovum has an X, but a sperm can have either an X or a Y. When a sperm fertilizes an ovum, the resulting cells will therefore have either two X chromosomes and be female or one X and one Y and be male.

Pregnancy and childbirth

Pregnancy, or gestation, is the period during which one single cell develops into a fully formed human being within the mother's body. It begins at the moment of conception and normally continues for approximately 266 days, or nine calendar months, until the child is born.

Stages of development

The embryo starts life as a single fertilized egg no larger than a pinpoint. Contained within its nucleus, however, are the hereditary or genetic units that determine the infant's ultimate development. These are carried on twisted ribbonlike strands of DNA within the chromosomes, which provide the "instructions" for and control the manufacture of the proteins that will build up the new body.

Development begins with cleavage, or cell division. The initial single cell undergoes repeated mitotic division to form firstly a solid, many-celled morula, and subsequently a hollow sphere, the blastocyst, which on about day seven implants in the endometrium. Clustered to one side of the blastocyst is a mass of cells—the embryo—which continue to divide but also undergo gastrulation. This is a complex process of rearrangement whereby cells migrate into layers and take up approximately definitive positions inside the embryo. The embryo invaginates, or pushes in on itself, so that it at first resembles a diminutive cuplike structure and subsequently an elongated pouch. By about the 12th day after conception, two distinct layers of precursor cells—an inner endoderm and outer ectoderm—have formed. And during the following week a third middle, or mesoderm layer, is produced between them.

As the cells migrate they also differentiate, changing structure and function to be transformed into the specialized cells, tissues, or organ types of the mature body. As individual cells differentiate, so too the entire mass begins to develop a rudimentary human shape.

All body systems and vital organs are formed within the first three months, though nearly all the body systems still have much developing to do. From the endoderm develops first a primitive gut, then the respiratory tubes, lungs, liver, and digestive organs; from the ectoderm develop the skin, sense organs, and nervous system; the mesoderm is the source of all the body's connective tissues, bone, cartilage, muscles, heart, blood vessels, and urogenital system.

Nourishment is obtained from the mother's body via a complex life-support system. First to develop is the amniotic sac, a fluid-filled bag of membranes in which the developing embryo is cushioned and protected at constant temperature. A cap-shaped pad of tissue—the placenta—forms at the point of implantation and to this the embryo is attached by the umbilical cord. Maternal and embryonic bloodstreams remain separate but nutrients and waste are exchanged from one to the other via the placenta.

By the end of the third month, although the fetus is only about 3.5 inches (9 centimeters) long, it is easily recognizable as human. Most of the major internal organs are fully formed, the circulatory system functions, and rudimentary genitals have appeared. From this point (or in some cases from as early as eight weeks), the embryo is called a fetus, which grows and matures during the remaining six months until birth.

The course of pregnancy

For most women the first sign of pregnancy is the absence of menstruation. Other early signs include feelings of nausea (morning sickness), increased urination, and some heaviness in the breasts. Pregnancy can, however, be confirmed by a urine test six weeks after the last period. This will detect chorionic gonadotro-

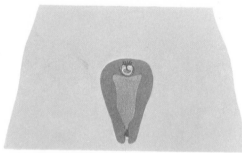

At 4 weeks, the embryo's spinal column, nerves, some blood vessels, and the heart have started to form. Length is about .25 inch (0.5 centimeter).

At 9 weeks, most basic development is complete. All major body systems have formed. Length is about 1.25 inches (4 centimeters).

At 14 weeks, facial features—eyes, nose, mouth, ears—are recognizable. Sex organs start to develop. Length is about 4.75 inches (12 centimeters).

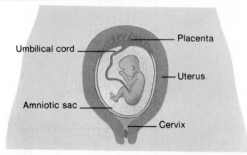

At 20 weeks, the baby has formed hair and nails. A fine fur—lanugo—covers the body. Length is about 8 inches (20 centimeters).

Placenta

Umbilical cord

Uterus

Amniotic sac

Cervix

pin, a hormone produced by the placenta.

Most symptoms of pregnancy are caused by changed hormonal levels in the body and, from the third month, by the increased pressure and size of the fetus. High levels of estrogen and progesterone are responsible for feelings of nausea and possibly for the emotional swings of the first months. After about six weeks, hormonal activity also prepares the breasts for nursing. Breasts may feel itchy or heavy as they begin to enlarge; veins become prominent and, from about the 12th week, a thin fluid—colostrum—is secreted. The areolae become mottled as pigmentation increases, and increased pigmentation may also appear on the face, lower abdomen, and genitals.

As the fetus increases in size, the abdomen swells and the mother's weight gradually increases—an average gain of 20 to 25 pounds (9 to 11 kilograms). Posture may alter to compensate, and many women experience backache and lethargy. Other uncomfortable side effects may include constipation, hemorrhoids, indigestion, and varicose veins.

The movements of the developing infant can usually be felt by about 20 weeks; by about the 32nd week, pressure may lessen as the baby engages, when the fetal head passes the pelvic inlet, having turned head down in the pelvis.

Ensuring health

Pregnancy is a natural condition, not an illness. Nevertheless, a good diet, exercise, regular prenatal care, and medical supervision are the best way to ensure a good pregnancy and healthy baby. A woman should visit her physician as early as possible for a thorough medical examination during which weight, blood pressure, blood group, and medical history can be checked. Thereafter, regular visits to a clinic or physician are essential to monitor progress. Prenatal medical care can help prevent or arrest complications, such as threatened miscarriage or toxemia—a serious condition in which there are any two of the following: excessively raised blood pressure; swelling of hands, face, and feet; and the appearance of protein in the urine.

A woman can do a great deal herself to ensure health. The baby obtains all its nourishment from the mother, so a balanced diet with adequate iron and calcium is essential. Smoking, excessive alcohol, and certain drugs cause damage and must be avoided. Drugs should only be taken under strict medical supervision.

Contact with infectious diseases, particularly rubella, during the first three months can also cause damage to the fetus. Some factors are uncontrollable, however, notably chromosomal abnormalities resulting in such genetic disorders as Down's syndrome. These may well cause early, spontaneous miscarriage but if not, some can be detected by amniocentesis—the testing of the amniotic fluid—at a relatively early stage (between the 12th and 16th weeks).

Birth

Birth, or parturition, marks the culmination of nine months of pregnancy. For the expectant mother it can be exciting and alarming, but

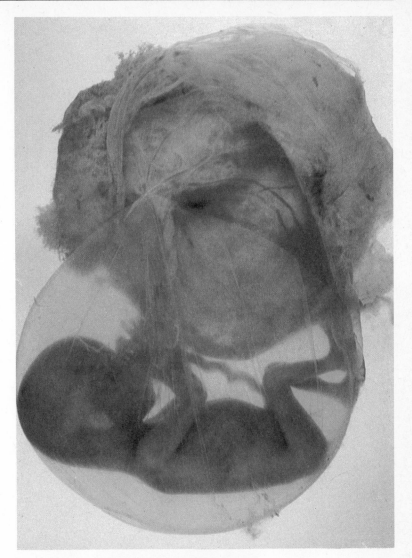

A **fetus** at 16 weeks is only about 6.25 inches (16 centimeters) long but already has recognizable features and shape. The fetus lies within the amniotic sac and is attached to the relatively large placenta by the umbilical cord.

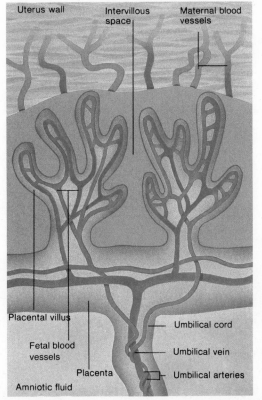

Uterus wall   Intervillous space   Maternal blood vessels

Placental villus

Fetal blood vessels

Placenta

Amniotic fluid

Umbilical cord

Umbilical vein

Umbilical arteries

The **placenta** is the physical link between mother and child. Through it the maternal and fetal blood circulations provide a fetus with everything it needs to develop and grow. The transfer between maternal and fetal circulations occurs in the intervillous space, which is filled with maternal blood. Microscopic projections from the placenta, called villi, allow the fetal circulation to exchange dissolved oxygen and carbon dioxide as well as nutrients and wastes.

anxiety can be lessened by an understanding of the processes involved.

During the final weeks of pregnancy, the woman's body prepares itself for labor. The cervix softens and uterine contractions that have been occurring throughout pregnancy become more noticeable. Finally, the ligaments of the pelvis soften and become more flexible, the cervix begins to be "effaced" and the baby's head "engages" low in the pelvis.

Stages of labor

Labor is divided into three stages. First, the cervix dilates so that the baby can pass through; second, the baby is delivered; and third, the placenta and membranes are expelled. These stages are not clear-cut but tend to merge into each other. No one knows for sure what actually initiates labor, although it is thought that hormones produced by the mature fetus may stimulate the production of prostaglandins, which in turn act on the uterus. Various signs indicate that labor is imminent. Regular contractions occurring every 15 or 30 minutes are the most common sign; others include the expulsion of a mucous plug from the cervix—called the "show"—and a gush of fluid as the amniotic sac ruptures.

The first stage is characterized by increasingly intense muscular contractions as muscle fibers pull the lower uterus and cervix up and around the head of the fetus. This stretching and pulling in turn dilates the cervix to allow the baby to pass through. The process may take anything up to 20 hours; usually, however, it lasts about 8 to 14 hours for a woman having her first child, and about half this for subsequent children.

As dilation proceeds, contractions become more frequent and intense until toward the end of the first stage—the transition period—when they occur every two to three minutes, each contraction lasting about 60 seconds. This period is particularly painful and a woman may also experience nausea, backache, and leg cramps. Increasing too may be an uncontrollable desire to push or bear down as the pressure from the baby's head against the cervix intensifies.

Once the cervix is fully dilated, the second stage is entered and the powerful "bearing down" reflex is accentuated. From this point, the woman can participate actively, bearing down with each contraction to push the baby out of her body. In a normal delivery the baby is born head first. The head rotates beneath the pubic arch and, as it emerges, rotates back to its original position. Shoulders and trunk follow in the same way and the baby is born. The baby breathes in and makes a first cry. The umbilical cord is usually cut at this stage.

The third and final stage occurs within the next 15 minutes as the placenta and umbilical cord are expelled. This is a painless process that may be aided by light pulling on the cord. Once delivered, the placenta is checked to ensure that nothing has been left in the uterus that might cause hemorrhage. Subsequent contraction of the uterine wall usually stops further bleeding.

Relief of pain

Childbirth is painful and the damaging effects on both mother and child of a prolonged and distressing birth are now well known. Today the emphasis is on "natural" drug-free labor, and the woman who understands what is happening and who is adequately prepared with breathing and other exercises can frequently give birth unaided and with a minimum of pain and discomfort. It is also essential that a woman in labor is not left alone; the sympathetic presence of her partner or another relative is actively encouraged. Most women do, however, choose some form of pain relief. Among drugs available are: the epidural anesthetics, which are administered in the spine and block out all sensation in the lower part of the body; analgesics such as pethidine; and inhaled anesthetics. These drugs can affect the baby, however, and today they are used with considerable caution.

At 28 weeks, the baby is lively and is about to turn head downward in the uterus. A greasy material—vernix—covers the body.

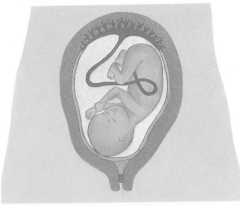

At 34 weeks, the baby has turned head down and can no longer move easily in the uterus. The uterus lies at about the maximum height in the abdomen.

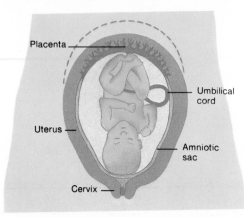

At 38 weeks, the baby is ready to be born. The uterus has "lightened," settling lower in the abdomen. The cervix of the uterus begins to be "effaced," and the baby's head "engages" in the pelvis.

Placenta

Umbilical cord

Uterus

Amniotic sac

Cervix

Birth is a profound experience for both mother and baby. Close physical contact between them immediately after birth may help to lessen the shock and strengthen the natural bond between mother and baby.

Problem births

Most births are perfectly normal but problems can and do occur. Breech presentation, where the baby is born feet or buttocks first, is one example. In this case, duration of labor is critical: too fast a labor may result in damage; too long a delivery may cause oxygen starvation. In a breech presentation, delivery is usually in three stages: breech and legs, shoulders, and then head, forceps (large surgical tongs) being used to ease the head out. Where a normal vaginal delivery is impossible, a baby may be delivered by Caesarean section. This involves making an incision in the mother's lower abdomen and delivering the baby through it.

Labor may sometimes be induced artificially—a controversial practice but one usually carried out where the health of mother or baby is at risk. Reasons for induction include preeclampsia, postmaturity of the fetus, Rh factor incompatibility, or diabetes. Induction may involve artificially rupturing the amniotic sac or the intravenous infusion of oxytocin to stimulate contractions. Finally, where there is a danger of the baby's head tearing the perineum, an incision in the vagina—an episiotomy—may be made.

After the birth

The body returns to normal remarkably quickly. Initially there is a steady loss of a bloody substance—lochia—from the vagina as the placental site and uterine lining break down. This should end after 10 days, and within six weeks uterus, cervix, and vagina should have returned to normal. Postnatal exercise helps to tone up stretched muscles. Breasts secrete colostrum for the first two or three days after birth, before the milk flow begins.

One common feature of the postbirth period is depression, which may be caused by hormonal imbalance or emotional and social factors. Whatever the cause, however, postnatal depression is distressing, and sympathetic treatment and support from family and friends

are essential for a speedy recovery. It should not be confused with the much rarer postpartum depression, which is a far more severe form of mental disturbance.

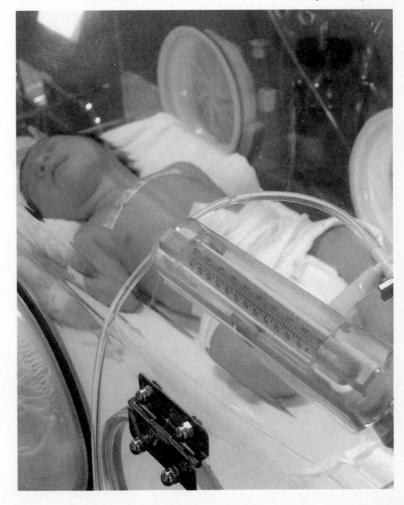

Premature babies, born before the 36th week, and very small babies—for instance of less than 5.5 pounds (2.5 kilograms) in weight—may not be fully developed and may need to spend their first few days in an incubator. This controls the baby's environment, keeping it sterile and at a constant temperature and humidity. Premature babies usually grow fast and can soon catch up with those not born prematurely.

Human development

The development of an individual is a process of physical, intellectual, and emotional growth and change. Two main factors—heredity and environment—determine a child's development from birth onward.

Physical development

The most rapid period of physical growth occurs during the first two years. Intellectual development is equally rapid during this time. In the first 12 months, the average infant's weight triples and its body size increases by about half. As a general rule, by the age of two a baby's height is already about half what it will be as an adult. The brain also develops rapidly and brain growth is largely complete by the age of two years. Motor skills and learning abilities improve as nerve tracts acquire their outer coating of myelin and develop new pathways between cells. These two processes continue up to about the age of five. The cartilaginous elements of the fetal skeleton also gradually harden into bone. Between the ages of five and seven, the first permanent teeth appear, and the bones of trunk and limbs con-

tinue to lengthen. The growth rate becomes less perceptible after about the age of six but speeds up again just before puberty.

During adolescence a person develops from a child to an adult—a process that involves profound physical and emotional changes. Puberty—the onset of sexual maturation—occurs when, under the stimulation of the pituitary gland, the sex glands begin to release their hormones into the bloodstream. As a result, the reproductive organs mature and secondary sexual characteristics develop. Long bones undergo a burst of growth before attaining their final adult size. Muscles, brain, and central nervous system also complete their physical development at around this time, although some of the bones of the skull do not fuse permanently until the late thirties.

The early twenties mark the peak of physical development as muscles, heart, blood, and lungs all operate at maximum efficiency. Emphasis switches then from growth to maintenance and repair of the body. In the late twenties, however, the body begins its gradual physical decline. This process is hardly notice-

The elderly and the very young often have a special affinity. Both are at extremes of human development, need more than average care from others, and tend to be kept slightly apart from normal everyday adult life. For these reasons they are often left to look after each other. Commonly, both also have a special affinity with animals. In many rural communities the care of farm animals is the responsibility of the older and younger members of society.

able at first and—in active people—may not become apparent for many years. In most people, however, it becomes increasingly evident in their thirties and forties.

Exactly what causes aging is still uncertain, although genetic factors and wear and tear all play a part. The symptoms of old age are essentially an accumulation of defects: the nervous system, muscles, and skin deteriorate, major organs become less efficient, and disorders such as arteriosclerosis become more common.

Mental and social development

Mental and social development depend both on physical factors and on learning. According to the Swiss psychologist, Jean Piaget, intellectual development also moves through regular and recognizable stages. Until about the age of two, sensation and reflexes are closely linked. Gradually, the use of language develops and, as hand-eye and eye-ear coordination increase, mental processes develop from intuition based on incomplete perception to reasoned thought. By about the age of 12, a child has usually developed an adult ability to conceptualize and reason.

Less measurable, perhaps, is the process of social development, or socialization—the acquisition of a "social self" with values and beliefs that influence an individual's personal behavior and aspirations. This process begins in childhood, with the family being the chief socializing agent in most cultures. The family, and subsequently, school and peer groups, interpret the prevailing culture and present the child with a social pattern of desirable actions and probable results.

One of the most crucial aspects of the socializing process is "sex typing," by which a child adopts behavior patterns considered appropriate to his or her sex in a process of copying and encouragement reinforced by reward.

Heredity versus environment

One of the most controversial questions surrounding human development is the extent to

which an individual is the product of his or her environment and upbringing on the one hand, or of genetic inheritance on the other. The question of "sex typing" can be seen as a specific example of this. The controversy affects such aspects of development as personality, aptitude, and intelligence particularly. Although various tests have been carried out, for example, on identical twins raised in the same or different environments, findings remain inconclusive. All that can be said with certainty is that heredity, culture, socialization, economic factors, and experience all play important roles in transforming the newborn infant into an adult individual.

Women, traditionally, have the chief responsibility for rearing children, either in the home or in play groups and nurseries, as illustrated here. With more women returning to full-time employment after having had babies, however, these traditional roles are changing. Some are even being taken over by men, for whom the role of "househusband" is becoming increasingly common.

The change into manhood coincides with the peak of physical development and fitness, which many men maintain by taking part in sports and games.

The first 12 months

For a newborn baby, the outside world is a frightening but exciting place. The first year is a foundation year, during which a normal baby acquires basic skills that will be built upon through the rest of its life. For instance, in these months the baby's eyes, ears, and tongue develop abilities that will be necessary for learning to read and speak. The baby be-

gins to learn how to control its muscles; it also experiences emotion, and begins to understand language. It grows its first teeth and learns to smile, laugh, and eat solid food.

Physical changes

An average newborn baby weighs 6-9 pounds (3-4 kilograms) and is approximately 20 inches (50 centimeters) long. By 12 months, it weighs roughly 19-26 pounds (9-12 kilograms) and has increased its height by approximately 28-33 inches (70-80 centimeters). A newborn baby's brain is around 25 per cent of its final adult brain weight, although the baby's body is only 5 per cent of its adult weight. During the first year, the brain grows very fast, allowing the baby to learn an enormous amount.

A newborn baby's skeleton is soft and incompletely formed, and its skull has gaps (fontanels) between the main bony plates. This softness and flexibility allows the baby to pass through the mother's birth canal without damage. The fontanels close during the first 18 months, and the bones harden as the child grows. In fact, the whole process of ossification, which changes soft cartilage into hard bone, begins before birth and continues until about age 20.

In the first 12 months, the skeleton strengthens until the legs are able to support the baby's weight. The first tooth usually appears about the sixth or seventh month, and the baby usually begins to take solid food, rather than just milk, at around two months.

Reflexes and senses

Newborn babies show a number of instinctive actions and responses known as reflexes. They include the rooting reflex, where the baby turns the head if the cheek is gently touched; the grasp reflex, in which the hands tightly clutch anything placed against the palm; and the step reflex, in which the baby steps when a foot is placed on a horizontal surface. These reflexes are later superseded by more complicated reactions, such as turning toward a familiar sound, and reaching out to grasp an object the baby can see. By 12 months, a baby has developed the full width of vision he or she will have as an adult, and can focus on small objects at a distance.

From the earliest months, babies gaze longer at patterned and colored shapes than at plain white or gray ones. A normal baby's hearing develops rapidly, and improved coordination helps it to turn toward sounds it has located. By eight weeks, a baby utters the first recognized phonemes—sounds that later join to form speech. By one year old, he or she has mastered some of the more difficult sounds, such as "b," "g," "p," and "t"; many babies say their first recognizable words just before the first birthday.

Physical abilities

A baby's motor (movement) development is very rapid; through the first 12 months, it

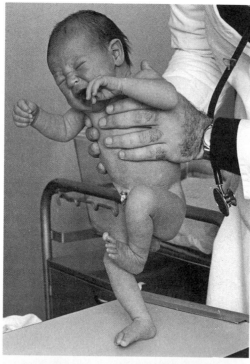

A newborn baby shows primitive reflexes in the first few weeks of life. An example is the step reflex: when one foot is placed on a horizontal surface the baby raises the other leg, as if in an attempt to walk.

A baby's curiosity increases rapidly after the first few weeks. Objects are observed dimly at about two weeks. Familiar shapes such as a parent's face may be recognized at about three or four weeks. The eyes begin to focus at about eight weeks, though rapidly moving objects cannot be followed with the eyes until a baby is about one year old.

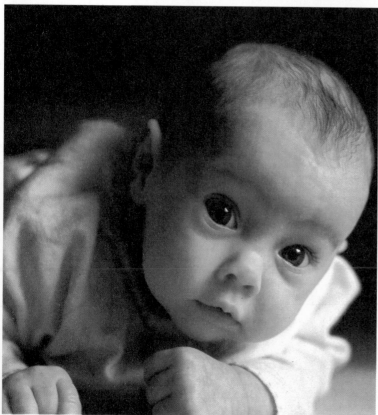

develops from a helpless infant into a mobile, inquisitive individual. Noticeable muscle control begins at about three months, when the baby can hold up the head. As the limbs and muscles strengthen, coordination improves and, by about six months, a baby is able to roll over and sit up without support; by about nine months, he or she can reach a standing position; and by about 12 months, the baby walks when one hand is held. The baby learns first to clutch objects in a closed fist, then to grasp them with the thumb on one side and fingers on the other, and then to pick up fairly small objects with finger and thumb.

Personality and emotions

In the mother's womb, a baby is comfortable, warm, dark, and soothed by the mother's heartbeat, so for the first few weeks after birth, bright lights, loud noises, and sudden movements can be very distressing. Babies gain tremendous pleasure and security from warmth and physical closeness, and benefit from as much as they can get.

By about six weeks, the baby has learned to smile, and at four months he or she laughs and giggles. Through the first year the baby gradually comes to feel more complicated emotions such as jealousy, petulance and affection.

By its first birthday, a baby is able to respond to simple commands, such as "come here," and to understand the meaning of "yes" and "no"; babies love imitating adult behavior, and will "burble" contentedly, although incomprehensibly, while playing. In these vitally important, formative 12 months, the foundations are laid for all types of adult behavior, emotions, and skills.

Immunization

Babies receive some immunity from the mother before birth, and some from antibodies in breast milk. Nevertheless, they are vulnerable to infection and so are usually immunized against certain infectious diseases between the ages of 3 and 12 months, with a booster dose at about age 5. Inoculations against diphtheria, tetanus, and poliomyelitis are the most common. In Europe, vaccination against pertussis (whooping cough) is fairly common, but reactions causing brain damage have occurred in a tiny percentage of cases. Vaccination against measles and mumps is also available. Vaccination against tuberculosis is only given to babies who are at risk; otherwise, children are usually vaccinated at about age 10 to age 12.

Walking, with clumsy, staggering steps, starts at about ten months, but a child needs to hold something for balance at first. The first unaided steps usually occur at about age one, although even then a child may still move faster on hands and knees.

Teething is painful and babies do not suffer in silence. The upper and lower incisors appear first, at about six to twelve months, and it is these that are hurting the child in the photograph *(left)*. Other childhood, or "milk," teeth emerge in the approximate sequence shown diagrammatically below.

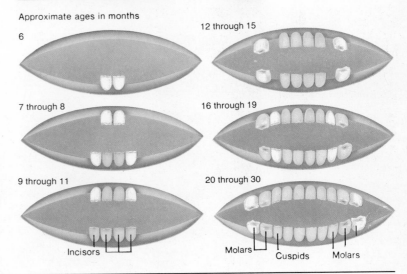

Approximate ages in months

6

7 through 8

9 through 11

12 through 15

16 through 19

20 through 30

Incisors

Molars   Cuspids   Molars

Fact entries

Freud, Sigmund (1856-1939), Austrian psychoanalyst, whose research into neuroses led him to postulate a theory of childhood sexuality, which in turn showed him the significance of sexuality in many aspects of human behavior.

Montessori, Maria (1870-1952), Italian child psychologist and educator, whose work with preschool and retarded children stressed the importance of a stimulating environment, in particular one full of things children can handle and touch, in the education of young chil-dren. The first woman ever to graduate in medicine at the University of Rome, she then lectured there, and was appointed government inspector of schools in 1922. She traveled the world supervising training courses.

Piaget, Jean (1896-1980), Swiss psychologist whose study of the thought processes of children and of the growth of their intelligence helped to establish child psychology as a science and also has had considerable influence on educators.

Spock, Dr. Benjamin (1903-   ), American pediatrician whose book on *Baby and Child Care* (1946) became a standard reference for many parents in the 1950's to 1970's. Although he retracted some of his teachings, his methods remain popular.

Age 1 through 5 years

A child never learns faster and grows more quickly than in its first 12 months, but the next four years are also times of astonishing development, particularly of the mind.

By the age of five, most children have grown to over 3 feet (1 meter) tall—more than half their adult height—but a five-year-old's brain is 90 per cent of final adult brain weight. At about 18 months, a normal child can walk reasonably well on its own; at two years, it can run steadily; and by five, it can jump, skip, and hop and walk along a bench without falling off.

Conceptual development

Conceptual development begins from the time that a child first begins to understand actions and spoken words. It continues throughout life, as there is a need to deal with all sorts of abstract ideas, from the simple to the complicated. Nutrition in infancy plays a very important part in this development, and inadequate feeding up to the age of 18 months may permanently impair a child's conceptual abilities.

At age two, children's abstract concepts are limited; they know their first name, and can point to common objects such as eyes, hair, or shoes. At this stage, a child cannot match pairs of three-dimensional shapes, but can use pencil and paper to copy simple lines.

By age three, a child knows its age in years, and is beginning to be able to match shapes by trial and error. The child can copy circles, name some colors, and count up to ten. There is also considerable understanding of the concept "where," "what," "who," and "whose."

At four, a child can speak well and can understand simple comparisons such as "bigger" and "colder," and constantly asks questions beginning "Why . . .?", "When . . .?" and "How . . .?"

At age five, a normal child has a vocabulary of 1,500-2,000 words and can repeat its full name, age, birthday, and address. A child of this age can copy a square and eight or nine simple capital letters and, when matching three-dimensional shapes, has learned to compare objects by eye before moving them to their correct positions.

Achievements

Coordination improves rapidly through the first five years. At 18 months, a child can build a small tower of bricks and shows the first signs of being right- or left-handed. At two years, he or she can throw a ball and turn the pages of a book. At three years, a child can stand briefly on one leg and use a spoon and fork.

Preschool children paint using colors freely, but showing little control of line and form.

Two- and three-year-olds are often happiest playing alone and tend to be preoccupied with their own games even in the company of other children. Nevertheless, most welcome the security of an adult's presence nearby and will complain loudly if they feel neglected.

Health

Toilet training occurs between the ages of one and four, beginning (usually at 15-18 months) when the child is able to signal that a diaper is wet or soiled. Most children have stopped wetting the bed at night by age three, with maybe a few accidents up to the age of four.

Children aged one through two require approximately 1,200 calories per day; by age five, this need increases to around 1,600 calories. At age five, most children sleep for about ten hours a night. Nightmares, however, can send a child screaming to the parents for reassurance and the warmth and comfort of the parents' bed. A child may also need reassurance before bed, particularly about fears of the dark. By the age of six, most children have given up daytime naps.

As children become more active, so the risk of illness increases—in this age group, however, major infectious illness is less common than minor injuries from accidents. Exploration can also lead to serious accidents, particularly from poisoning, but also from burns or scalds. General health care includes sensible safety precautions, particularly in the home and garden; choice of clothing and footwear that inhibits neither movement nor growth; personal hygiene, including care of the teeth; nutritious diet; and a friendly acquaintance with both doctor and dentist to ensure that the natural anxieties about such encounters are minimized.

Emotions

Through these years, emotions can change drastically as children discover their individuality. The two- to three-year-old stage can be particularly trying for the parents, as a child tries rebellion, demands constant attention, shows jealousy and possessiveness, and throws temper tantrums. Not all children show all these characteristics and some show them more vigorously than others. Nevertheless, these problems are familiar enough to most parents, and few families avoid the experience completely.

Emotions generally fluctuate a bit less in a four-year-old, and at this age, children start to play and share happily with other children. By the age of five, a child can show considerable concern and responsibility in protecting the interests of younger children.

Emotional upsets through these years are common particularly when new babies are born in the family. These can trigger rebellion or nervous habits, and a child may develop irrational fears. If at this age the child must be separated from its parents—for instance, to enter the hospital—great reassurance can be needed to quell fears of permanent separation. Starting school may also be difficult, but is often more traumatic for the parents than the child! Generally, if parents have encouraged their child's independence and have tried to understand and relieve any fears, the child should be able to make the transition to the next stage of life easily.

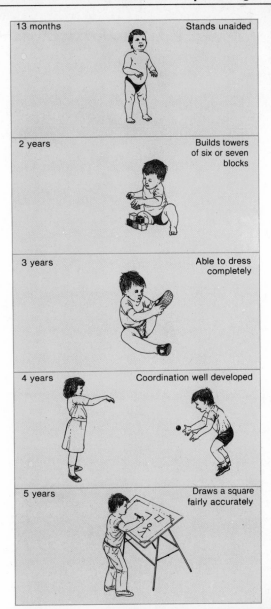

13 months	Stands unaided
2 years	Builds towers of six or seven blocks
3 years	Able to dress completely
4 years	Coordination well developed
5 years	Draws a square fairly accurately

Physical skills develop at different ages. The illustration shows certain "landmarks" in the development of an average child—but of course, individual children's development may vary considerably from these stages.

Playing with other children reveals a child's emotional development and usually begins during the fourth year. Playing together encourages imagination but also leads to quarreling—particularly if toys have to be shared or desires conflict in other ways, for instance, where two children both want to be the center of attention. At this age, children can be generous, even altruistic, to those they regard as friends, but they also can bully smaller or less confident playmates ruthlessly.

Mental and physical development are extremely rapid between the ages of five and ten. The illustration identifies some representative stages. Children have almost unlimited energy and curiosity—often to their parents' exasperation, but to their pleasure and entertainment too, because the first clear indications of a child's individuality and character start to appear at this age.

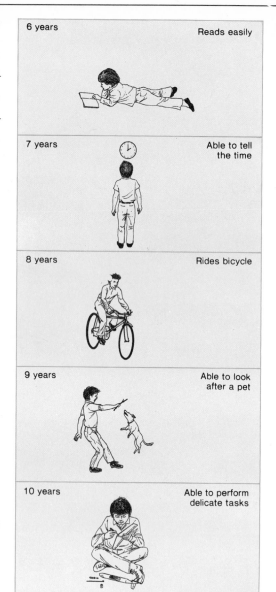

6 years — Reads easily

7 years — Able to tell the time

8 years — Rides bicycle

9 years — Able to look after a pet

10 years — Able to perform delicate tasks

Abundant energy, channeled into physical activity, typifies children in the five-through ten-year-old age group. They develop their physical prowess and coordination through all kinds of play. This gives them ample opportunity to interact with other children—with friendship and with aggression—and helps them develop their individual and social characters.

Age 5 through 10 years

The years from ages five through ten take a child from the first experience of formal education to the months preceding puberty. At five, a child is still very dependent, physically and emotionally, on the parents. By age ten, the child is much more an individual, exhibiting personal talents and tastes, and is independent in many everyday activities. The skills and coordination learned in early childhood are used at this age to develop new interests and hobbies, and carry the child further along the way to full independence.

Through these years, a child can learn to cook simple meals, be totally responsible for a pet, use books for self-directed studies, and carry out many other activities that serve as landmarks of independence.

Achievements

During the years five through seven, the normal child finally masters the more difficult sounds of speech and becomes confident about using them. The soft consonant sounds, such as "r," "th," and "ch," are the last to be learned—up to this age the child may still be confusing or mispronouncing them. By age six or so, the language center in the brain has developed an intricate network of interlocking nerve pathways, which through the rest of life allow the person to construct complex sentences in speech, thought, and writing.

Coordination continues to improve, helped by practice, and a child can learn to draw and to write neatly. By age six, simple words are usually written confidently; cursive writing is learned soon after. The child becomes increasingly adept at skills such as model building and sewing, which require very fine and well-controlled hand movements. By age ten, most children can draw objects realistically. Children at this age have a great deal of energy and often occupy themselves with activities such as bicycle riding, playing games with other children, exploring, and pursuing their favorite hobbies.

Conceptual development

At the age of five or six, a child's grasp of abstract ideas is based on simple comparisons such as "hotter," "younger," "more," and so on. From about age seven, the child slowly learns to make decisions and solve problems based on logic rather than intuition or guesswork. This skill improves rapidly through the next years—by the age of about 12 a child can reason, on a simple level, in the same way as an adult. From the age of eight, the child begins to use many adjectives as he or she learns more about the quality of objects and actions.

It is not until about the age of ten, however, that a child begins to have a thorough grasp of ideas involving time. Simple time descriptions such as "today," "tomorrow," "at four o'clock," or "on Saturday" are understood first, then more abstract concepts, such as "when you were a baby" and "next November," follow later.

Mental problem-solving also begins at about this age, and a child no longer needs to see every stage of a simple problem either physically or on paper to be able to work out the answer.

Health

As soon as they start school children are exposed to many common infections—from colds to measles, mumps, and chicken pox. Normally, they are very resilient and recover from these illnesses quickly if they contract them. Generally, however, vaccination against most of these disorders is carried out before the child starts school. This form of conferred immunity not only protects the children and their contacts at school, but also protects any parent who has not been immunized and who would suffer more seriously from the illness as an adult if the infection were contracted.

School is also the place where learning difficulties first become evident, though not always in obvious ways. An apparent reluctance to attend classes may mask dyslexia, for instance. Because everyone goes to school, and most enjoy (or at least accept) it, children who do not—for whatever reason—tend to hide their fears. These are likely to show nevertheless, but not directly. Abdominal pains, bedwetting, fatigue, and even an obvious "unusual" change in behavior may all reflect a child's unhappy mind.

Children are notoriously picky about food, but it is essential that they have a balanced and nutritious diet, with adequate quantities of fresh fruit and vegetables, protein, bread, and milk. Up to the age of ten, boys and girls have similar calorie requirements: about 2,400 calories per day. After this age, boys and men need around 500 calories per day more than girls or women of the same age.

By nine, children of both sexes are about 4 feet 8 inches (120-140 centimeters) tall, although during adolescence, boys begin to grow faster than girls. During these years, the milk teeth are gradually lost and replaced.

Finding out about the world and practicing independence are among the dominant concerns of this age group, but this process can have its dangers, and supervision and adequate precautions are still needed. About half the deaths that occur between the ages of five and fifteen are caused by accidents.

Emotions

Young children react badly to anything that upsets them deeply. Such upsets are caused by many things, including parental discord, or losing physical or emotional security (for instance, by moving or starting a new school).

Children are also strongly influenced by their peers, and often goad one another into behavior that they know is generally unacceptable. Many children at this age go through phases in which they do precisely what they have been told they should not: lying, cheating, stealing, fighting, swearing, smoking, and going where they have been forbidden to go are all common. Views differ on the best parental reaction to such behavior on the as-

sumption that it is a temporary aberration rather than a permanent character defect or psychological fault. Overall, however, it seems that a natural reaction (disapproval, annoyance, or anger) is most appropriate and can do little harm, so long as the child recognizes that this reaction is a direct response and does not imply any genuine or permanent rejection.

Team sports help children learn how to direct their energy and competitiveness toward common rather than individual ends.

Books stimulate the imagination and so appeal to many children in this age group, if they have not yet associated books with discipline and schooling.

Puberty and adolescence

Through puberty and adolescence, girls become women and boys become men. Puberty sees the start of the physical aspects of this transformation and occupies roughly the first half of the teenage years. Adolescence covers the second half of the teenage period up to the usually undefined point at which a person is seen to be "adult." It is a time of learning independence and emotional maturity and of coming to terms with adulthood.

It can be a difficult time for the teenager because of mood changes, the strength of sexual feelings, and the desire or even the need for ever-increasing independence.

Physical changes in girls

The physical changes of puberty usually occur in girls between the ages of 10 and 14, although there is considerable individual variation. Nutrition, heredity, body weight, and so-

cial factors all influence the age at which any particular girl begins puberty. The changes are started by hormones released from the pituitary gland at the base of the brain; these hormones cause the ovaries to mature and to release estrogen into the bloodstream. Estrogen causes the nipples to darken and the breasts to grow, slowly at first, as the milk ducts enlarge and increase in number. Pubic hair, followed by axillary (armpit) hair, begins to appear, then gradually grows coarser, darker, and more prolific.

About a year after these changes begin, the menstrual periods start, when the uterus sheds its lining each month. The menarche (first period) is usually preceded by a monthly clear discharge for one or two months. The first periods may be very light, not much more than a slight, bloodstained discharge, or may start immediately with a normal adult level of menstrual flow.

The estrogen causing the external changes of puberty also induces growth of the uterus, vagina, ovaries, and labia (the folds of skin around the entrance to the vagina), and changes the vaginal secretions from alkaline to acid. The pelvis grows wider to allow for childbearing, and other hormones (androgens) in the bloodstream cause a slight hair growth on the upper lip.

Ovulation (production of an egg for possible fertilization) usually starts a few months after the first menstrual period.

Physical changes in boys

Changes in boys at puberty are also started by pituitary hormones, which cause the testes to grow and the scrotum to enlarge and become ridged and darker in color. Spermatozoa

Adolescents are particularly adept at learning new skills and benefit enormously from careful teaching and encouragement—probably more than any other age group. Skills acquired at this age often serve as the basis for future employment, or at least serve as interesting hobbies in adult life.

Physical development in boys and girls is controlled by hormones released from the anterior pituitary, which is stimulated by a releasing factor (black arrow) from the hypothalamus in the brain. In boys, pituitary hormones make the testes produce testosterone, which causes the body to develop such male characteristics as facial and body hair, male sexual organs, a deeper voice, and heavier musculature. In girls, pituitary hormones stimulate the production of progesterone and estrogen by the ovaries. Progesterone initiates the development of the breasts and affects the menstrual cycle; estrogen causes the body to develop female sexual characteristics. In both boys and girls, the levels of sex hormones in the blood are monitored by the hypothalamus: this feedback mechanism controls the hormone output of the pituitary.

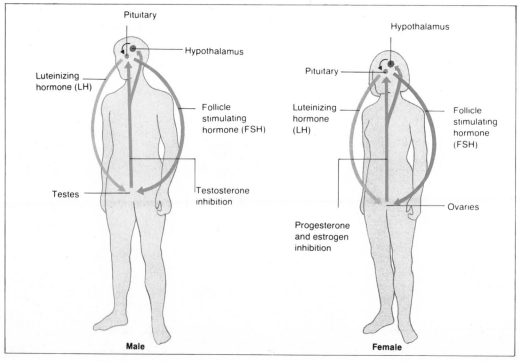

Male

Female

begin to be formed, although many of these do not reach maturity in the early years. Testosterone released into the bloodstream causes a sudden increase in height and weight. The penis increases in size, and hair begins to appear in the armpits and in the pubic region. In early puberty, boys may also experience uncomfortable swelling in one or both breasts. This is caused by sensitivity to hormones in the blood, and soon disappears.

The hormones that bring about a boy's gradual physical and emotional development into a man have various direct and indirect effects on the body. The vocal cords enlarge as changes occur in the larynx, and the voice slowly deepens. The prostate gland starts to secrete substances that form part of the seminal fluid. Hair begins to grow in the pubic region and on the face. The muscles grow, the shoulders broaden, and the body thickens generally. Boys usually complete these physical changes by about age 18.

Changes in both sexes

At puberty, both boys and girls tend to accumulate extra fat. It disappears later in most boys, but girls tend to retain it around the hips, thighs, and breasts. Because of increased hormonal action, the sebaceous glands increase their activity, causing the skin to become oilier and coarser. Blood pressure and lung capacity increase, but average heart rate, respiration (breathing) rate, and body temperature all tend to fall as the child gets older. The muscles become stronger and, particularly in boys, more noticeable. Sexual urges grow stronger as hormonal action increases and the sex organs develop.

Hygiene

When axillary (armpit) and pubic hair starts to grow, perspiration also increases in those

areas, and teenagers become conscious of the need to pay extra attention to personal hygiene. When their periods start, girls should be advised how sanitary napkins or tampons are used and how often they should be changed. The overactive sebaceous glands in the skin, which are frequently the cause of teenage skin problems (notably acne), can be controlled by careful washing and specially medicated soaps and creams.

Social and psychological development

The psychological changes involved in puberty and adolescence are immense, as teenagers face adulthood, gain independence, and

Social transitions as well as physical ones occur at puberty and in adolescence. Often this transition takes a symbolic form, even if the symbol is no more obvious than wearing "adult" clothes or makeup. Sometimes, however, the symbolism is formalized, as in the Jewish ceremony of *bar mitzvah,* shown here, which symbolizes a child's acceptance into the adult community.

Many adolescents enjoy group activities, particularly if they help channel exuberance and energy into physical activity. Intensely loyal to their team, these cheerleaders are trying to arouse enthusiasm within the crowd before the ball game.

Sports and outdoor activities are almost as important as study and social life to many teenagers. Those activities with marked social aspects—like surfing, for instance—understandably have the greatest appeal. Such activities also provide an opportunity to show great personal skill, which is important for the social competitiveness of teenagers.

come to terms with their maturing bodies and sexual feelings. Teenagers need great understanding from their parents, teachers, and other concerned adults during puberty but providing this can be difficult, because teenagers can be very unlovable when they are confused by mental, physical, and emotional changes beyond their control.

Most teenagers at around the age of 15 or 16 become involved in heterosexual relationships. These may be very casual, as emotional attachments move easily among several different boyfriends or girlfriends, or they may be far more profound. Romantic love is a common feature of the teenage years, and many relationships formed at this time are taken very seriously.

Mood changes

Adolescence can be a worrying time because hormonal activity often induces sudden and inexplicable mood changes, which may surprise the teenager as much as the family. The teenager does not really know whether he or she is a child or an adult. An adolescent is expected to obey parental and school discipline, and yet is also expected to be self-motivated about work, looking after money and other responsibilities. Most teenagers also worry that they are developing too fast or too slowly, or that they are not changing in the same way as everyone else. Any negative feelings about puberty that have been acquired in childhood come to the forefront during the teenage years.

Adolescent girls may suffer additional problems due to menstruation, specifically premenstrual tension and menstrual cramps. Premenstrual tension is a mixture of physical and psychological symptoms that may include fluid retention, temporary weight gain, skin disturbances, headaches, depression, fits of temper, breast tenderness, and a feeling of heaviness and lethargy. The syndrome occurs for several days before, and during the first

few days of, each period, and can be aggravated by stress. Menstrual cramps also may begin in adolescence and may be severe enough to cause temporary absence from school. These problems can upset a girl's life considerably and cause substantial distress.

Sexuality

Sexual feelings emerge slowly during puberty and become a dominating influence during adolescence. Curiosity about sexual matters and the physical characteristics of the opposite sex is intense for most adolescents. This curiosity may take the form of questions to parents or teachers, but is also pursued by reading as much as possible relating to sexuality and by sharing information with other children of the same age group. Sexuality has a social as well as a physical aspect, and many young teenagers feel happier meeting the opposite sex in groups, or at least with another couple, before they are confident enough to go out with their date alone.

Social and psychological problems

For most people the changes of adolescence are at worst merely temporary troubles. For some, however, they can cause serious problems. Compulsive eating, leading to excessive weight gain, or self-starvation, called anorexia nervosa, may occur. Periodic depression—as an aspect of mood changes—is common, but can become acute and, in extreme cases, result in attempted or actual suicide.

Social problems tend to be associated with an adolescent's desires for sexual discovery, novelty, excitement, independence, and rebellion. They are most likely to occur when circumstances or an individual's reaction to them get out of control. The main areas of teenage social problems in Westernized societies are concerned with sex (in particular with sexual diseases or unwanted pregnancies), drug abuse, and crime.

An awareness of the causes of sexual problems and the willingness of parents to advise helpfully about their avoidance or, if necessary, their treatment, is the easiest solution to the first of these problem areas. Professional advice and treatment centers such as Family Planning or contraception clinics, pregnancy advisory centers, and clinics for the diagnosis and treatment of sexually transmitted (venereal) diseases are alternatives or adjuncts to parental guidance.

Criminal activities, such as drug abuse or petty theft, are often tempting to teenagers because of the excitement of risk and the gesture of rebellion they embody. But minor "risk-taking" leads all too easily—usually through association with friends who take similar or greater risks—to deeper involvement. The penalties are also serious because they don't stop when the "debt to society," whether a fine or a prison sentence, has been paid. A criminal conviction can, and usually does, literally change a person's life.

Such difficulties affect only a minority of teenagers, however, and most families cope with the emotional upsets of adolescence with a minimum of antagonism. Even where conflict occurs it tends to pass quickly because it is

Study is a dominant feature of the teenage years for most adolescents. As they grow older, emphasis shifts gradually from organ-ized classes to more independent study. Examinations usually mark the various stages of formal education.

Discos appeal to all ages, but perhaps to adolescents most of all, because they provide a context in which young people can meet others away from the critical eyes of their elders. Loud, emotive music and the excitement of dancing also helps some adolescents to overcome shyness.

more likely to be an expression of reaction to change—by either parents or children—than a reflection of deeper hostility.

Conflict

As they begin to develop into adults and seek their own standards, teenagers naturally tend to become resentful of rules and restrictions imposed by others. School and family discipline is irksome, and rebellion against authority is a common reaction. Parental values are superseded by influences from school, the media and, in particular, the opinions of friends. Many adolescents become strongly concerned about moral questions, especially those relating to social issues such as justice,

politics, religion, war, and class. As a result, they frequently come into conflict with their families, especially over specific principles or details of ideology.

Most adolescents live at home during this transitional period, while they are finishing their schooling or while training for a job. Meanwhile, they become old enough to drink, smoke, vote, drive, and marry, and crave emotional and financial independence. This wrestling with two different roles—as an independent individual on the one hand and as part of a family on the other—has a maturing effect that probably does as much as anything else to equip the adolescent for adulthood.

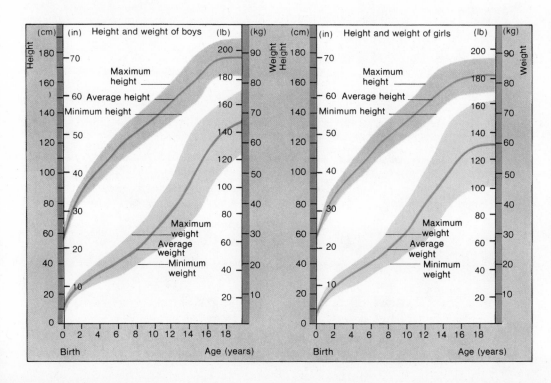

The growth of boys and girls follows similar but not identical patterns from birth to the late teens, when height and weight stabilize. The graphs show the increase in height and weight for each sex. The average height and weight of each sex (the dark mid-lines of each graph) remain almost identical until the mid- to late-teens, when young men continue to grow after young women stop. Differences occur chiefly in rates of growth—with girls growing faster in the early teens—and in variations between maximum and minimum heights and weights, with girls showing a greater variation in weight.

Adulthood

Adulthood begins when the genetic program of growth is complete—that is, when the body has grown to its full height and has also undergone the sexual changes that make adolescents physically mature. This stage is generally reached between the ages of 16 and 20. It occurs slightly earlier for females than males, who may still be growing in their early twenties. Today, a person legally becomes an adult at age 18 in most states of the U.S., in most Canadian provinces, and in most European countries.

Emotional maturity is not yet complete at the onset of adulthood, however, and is consolidated during the twenties. There is still great potential for learning and for improving society-related skills, such as independence, business acumen, and responsibility.

Physical concerns

The peak of physical health, for both males and females, occurs in the last few years of the teens and in the early twenties. Furthermore, opportunities for maintaining fitness are readily available at school and college and in leisure hours. Work responsibilities grow, people marry and have children, opportunities for physical exercise become fewer, and many people even in their mid-twenties take no physical exercise at all.

Few people cut down on their food consumption in adulthood—instead, it often increases as family life is established. At the same time, actual physical requirements decrease steadily, and as a result, many people eat far more than they need. This can rapidly cause overweight, which in turn contributes to numerous disorders, such as high blood pressure, heart disease, diabetes, and varicose veins. Smoking and drinking may also increase, contributing to unfitness and ill health. Regular exercise is therefore important, not only to maintain fitness and health, but also as a form of relaxation from stress. The need for a balanced and moderate diet is also essential.

Motivation

During early adulthood, personal motivation tends to be at its strongest. A young adult may be keen to establish a successful social role and career, to build up satisfactory emotional relationships, to earn money for necessities

In all societies, there is social pressure to conform, and most people bow to this pressure on reaching adulthood. Another dominating factor in Westernized societies is the work ethic, and nowhere are the two more obviously combined than in a crowd of similarly dressed commuters on their way to work.

The nuclear family, consisting of mother, father, and children, is the basic social unit in adulthood in most societies. Social scientists also recognize the concept of the extended family, which may include grandparents, and brothers or sisters of the adults (and their children, if any).

and luxuries, and to explore new ideas—in short, to define and fulfill ambitions, and to face the challenges that the adult world offers. So, providing the opportunities are available, many young adults tend to be ambitious, enthusiastic, zealous, and dedicated, whether in choosing a marriage partner, rearing children, or pursuing a career.

This motivation is likely to persist until at least the age of 35-40, but thereafter, there is a tendency for it to diminish. Although a few people find their 40s to be some of the most productive and energetic years of all, a typical 40-year-old has established a satisfactory way of life, which may include a home, a family, and a career, through a high level of output in the previous years. From this age onward, energy is more likely to be directed into consolidating these established positions, rather than breaking new ground. Consequently, if something goes wrong—perhaps resulting in divorce, illness, bereavement, or unemployment—people in mid-adulthood find it much harder than do young adults to start afresh.

Emotions

Emotional maturity lags behind physical maturity because it involves some social skills and experience that can be gained only in the adult world. A mature adult has to learn to handle emotional responses, and how and when to show feelings or conceal them. Some emotional responses are expressed principally in social reactions, which come into play, for example, when standing up for one's rights at work or coping with shyness in oneself or in others. Other aspects of emotional maturity are learned in interpersonal relationships, especially between marriage partners. The individual has to learn to deal with anger, fatigue, pleasure, frustration, professional or sexual jealousy, physical attraction, and many other emotions. Sexual maturity is reached physically in adolescence, but emotionally takes somewhat longer to develop as lasting sexual relationships are initiated and established.

Stress

Stress is a normal physiological condition that, to a certain degree, is both healthy and necessary for people to function at their best. Too much stress without relaxation, however, tenses the body chemically and physically, and, over a period of time, can cause significant harm.

Stress occurs particularly in people who work long or irregular hours and in those who are experiencing emotional difficulties. It can also be caused by poor working conditions, poor housing, poverty, and lack of satisfaction and can be aggravated by major incidents that are not unpleasant in themselves, such as moving home, getting married, or having a baby.

This condition contributes to many disorders, psychological problems, and emotional and sexual difficulties. A successful and relatively stress-free adulthood can often be achieved by balancing work, emotional life, relaxation, exercise, sleep, sexual activity, and leisure pursuits.

Sports keep people fit, and physical fitness helps minimize the effects of stress. Some sports, such as tennis, have a strong social aspect, too. If this generates too much social competitiveness, however, it can actually increase stress and counteract any benefits the physical activity itself may bring.

Stress, an important aspect of life in industrialized nations, has a number of different effects on the body. In themselves, these effects are harmless, and in certain circumstances are necessary and can even be beneficial. The illustration below shows the normal bodily reactions to stress and indicates the parts of the body that stress affects.

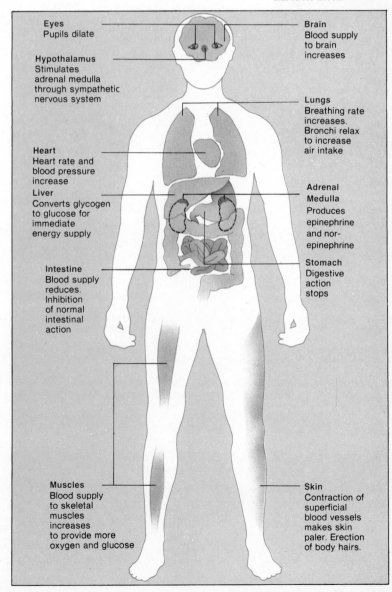

Eyes
Pupils dilate

Hypothalamus
Stimulates
adrenal medulla
through sympathetic
nervous system

Heart
Heart rate and
blood pressure
increase

Liver
Converts glycogen
to glucose for
immediate
energy supply

Intestine
Blood supply
reduces.
Inhibition
of normal
intestinal
action

Muscles
Blood supply
to skeletal
muscles
increases
to provide more
oxygen and glucose

Brain
Blood supply
to brain
increases

Lungs
Breathing rate
increases.
Bronchi relax
to increase
air intake

Adrenal
Medulla
Produces
epinephrine
and nor-
epinephrine

Stomach
Digestive
action
stops

Skin
Contraction of
superficial
blood vessels
makes skin
paler. Erection
of body hairs.

Aging

A healthy outdoor life can improve longevity, although it may also accelerate the visible effects of age. The wind and sun, in particular, age the skin, as the wrinkled face of this Portuguese fisherman shows.

Aging is accompanied by the gradual physical deterioration of the body. The diagram shows three factors—brain weight, heart output, and reaction time—that deteriorate steadily from age 20. By age 80, these have deteriorated to 85, 65, and 50 per cent, respectively, of what they were 60 years before.

Loneliness afflicts the elderly more than anyone. It is one of the main social problems of aging, and particularly affects those whose family does not live nearby, whose husband or wife has died, or who have outlived their friends. The problem is especially acute in towns and cities where people tend to be unconcerned with the welfare of others, but it also occurs wherever family and community ties have broken down.

The average life span of people in the Western world today is approximately 70 years—a little less for men, a little more for women. It has increased enormously since the middle of the last century, when the average life expectancy at birth for either sex was only about 40 years. During this century, better medical care and improved working and living conditions have also helped to prolong life significantly.

The human body begins to deteriorate in the 20's and 30's, and as age advances, all of the body's systems become less efficient. One of the major concerns of middle and old age, therefore, is the need to come to terms with the physical, psychological, and social changes this deterioration involves.

Coming to terms with old age is usually made easier by the fact that the mind normally deteriorates less rapidly than the rest of the body. A person who is mentally alert can often find great pleasure in a life that allows time for peace and reflection, particularly if these are balanced by stimulating interests and adequate physical activity.

External changes

Many physical changes are immediately obvious. White hairs appear as hair follicles lose their sources of pigmentation. Wrinkles increase as the skin loses its elasticity. Middle age is often associated with an increase in weight, followed by a significant decrease as old age advances. Muscle tissue is often replaced by fat, particularly around the trunk, while the arms and legs generally become thinner. Older people tend to lose height because of the compression of the vertebrae in the spine that results from the gradual loss of calcium from bone (osteoporosis)—which affects post-menopausal women particularly—and because of the tendency to stoop as muscle tone is lost.

Internal changes

Changes associated with aging also take place within the body's systems. Many internal organs, such as the kidneys, spleen, pancreas, lungs, and liver, become smaller in normal elderly people and less efficient at performing their tasks. The circulation of the blood is also affected by aging. The heart's pumping action is less efficient, and its response to exercise or stress, by increasing the heart rate, is more extreme. The blood vessels (veins, arteries, and capillaries) throughout the body lose some elasticity and tend to become convoluted. The bones become more brittle—also a result of osteoporosis—which makes older people more liable to fractures from falls or other accidents. The body becomes more sensitive to extremes of temperature and may take longer to recover from illness. Susceptibility to infection is increased, and the risk of cancer and some other disorders is greater.

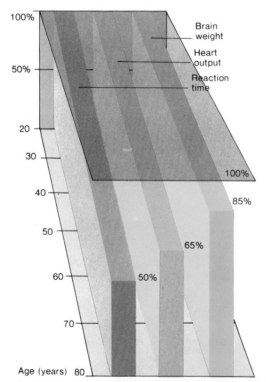

Brain weight
Heart output
Reaction time

100%
50%
20
30
40
50
60
70
80

100%
85%
65%
50%

Age (years)

The nervous system

Other changes associated with aging affect the nerves and their related functions. Nerve cells degenerate in old age and are not replaced, and the blood supply to the brain and other parts of the nervous system is affected by any general deterioration—for instance, caused by arteriosclerosis—that involves the circulation. This tends to reduce the brain's efficiency, and a decline in intellectual performance may follow the brain's gradual physical decline. Aspects of intelligence most likely to be affected by aging include logic, understanding three-dimensional images, problems involving numbers, and the ability to grasp new ideas. Other functions related to the brain also lose their efficiency: reflexes and physical movements become slower, and the memory—especially for recent events—may deteriorate. In severe cases, this can lead to senile dementia, which is characterized by loss of memory, unreasonable or childlike behavior, disconnected or incoherent speech, and a lack of awareness. The senses, too, are affected. Smell, taste, sight, touch, and hearing all deteriorate, causing increasing isolation of elderly people as everyday tasks and conversations become more difficult.

Menopause

Menopause literally means "stopping menstruation," although much more is involved than simply the end of the monthly periods. The menopause usually begins any time between the ages of 45 and 50, and has various physical and psychological effects. The cause of this "change of life" is an alteration in the usual monthly female hormone cycle, particularly affecting the production of progesterone, estrogen, and FSH (follicle-stimulating hormone). The woman stops ovulating and menstruating, although this rarely happens suddenly. She may also experience insomnia, headaches, severe mood swings, "hot flashes," and emotional disturbances, all related to hormonal changes. After the menopause, women become more susceptible to heart disease and bone deterioration.

Prospects for the elderly

Although aging does undoubtedly bring problems, in most cases these are no more than limitations; only rarely are they incapacitating. Furthermore, these limitations tend to be reduced by improvements in communal and personal health care—important aspects of which are health screening, improved diet, and an appreciation of the benefit of exercise to both body and mind—and also by medical advances, particularly in combating killers such as cancer and heart disease. Consequently, it is also likely that with life expectancy increasing, people are seeking to ensure that the quality of their lives improves too. To this end, some elderly people engage in social and political activities to improve their circumstances, while others tend to concentrate on developing satisfying leisure pursuits or even starting new careers.

Persons over the age of 60, most of whom have retired, form a substantial segment of the voting population. Pensioners demonstrating in England show the political significance of this group, which will grow larger as health care improves and life expectancy is extended. As a group, it is likely to be more eager than most to see results quickly. It is also likely to be more skeptical than most of promises that can be deferred.

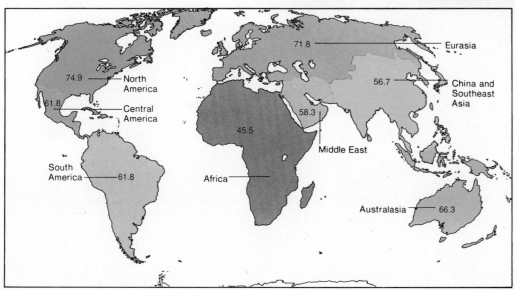

Life expectancy, calculated as the average age to which people live, varies from country to country and continent to continent. The map shows the average life expectancies of populations in eight broad geographical areas.

Illness and health

All of the body's organs and systems have specific functions to perform; illness basically results from the failure of any of them to function normally. Illnesses may be acute, producing severe short-lived symptoms, as in influenza; chronic, with symptoms that are prolonged, as in arthritis; or recurrent, as in malaria or various allergies. Good health is ensured not only by avoiding disease, but also by preventing illness through general health care, hygiene, or such specific methods as vaccination, and by strengthening the body's natural defenses through diet, exercise, and avoidance of stress.

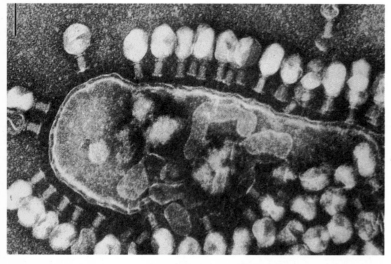

Causes of illness

Illness usually results from a combination of factors, such as the coincidence of an infection and low natural resistance. This is not always the case, however—for example, hereditary and congenital disorders originate before birth.

Congenital disorders affect the developing embryo and may be caused by chromosomal abnormalities or cellular damage. The best known examples include cleft palate and Down's syndrome (commonly called mongolism). Embryonic development may be seriously affected by diseases such as rubella. If contracted by the mother in the early stages of pregnancy, rubella can cause abnormalities in the child's heart, eyes, and ears. Certain drugs taken by the mother during pregnancy may also result in congenital disorders, and a pregnant woman should take no drugs without medical supervision.

After birth, a person's health is at the mercy of various external factors. Good health depends, to a great extent, on adequate nutrition and maintenance. Vitamins and minerals are essential for the proper working of the body and their lack may give rise to various deficiency disorders. For example, insufficient iron, needed to make hemoglobin, may result in anemia. And lack of vitamin D is the cause of rickets, an uncommon disorder in developed nations but only too common in the Third World.

The best-known causes of illness are living organisms, which range from microscopic viruses and bacteria to larger parasites such as tapeworms; they affect the body in many different ways. Viruses attack the cell structure of the body. The poliomyelitis virus, for instance, causes paralysis by growing in and destroying certain types of nerve cells in the spinal cord. Other viral diseases include influenza, mumps, smallpox, rabies, and herpes. Bacteria cause disease by producing poisons (toxins), or enzymes, which harm living cells. Bacterial infections include pneumonia, tetanus, and pertussis (whooping cough). Other pathogenic organisms that affect the body include various protozoa, such as amebas, which cause a form of dysentery, and fungi, which cause disorders such as athlete's foot.

Normal body tissue has the ability to repair itself, but with aging, this mechanism becomes less efficient and may gradually give way to degenerative disorders. Arteriosclerosis, or hardening of the arteries, is one of the most significant of these. Causing reduced blood flow, it can lead to vascular thrombosis (clot in a blood vessel) and coronary heart disease.

Tumors and cancers stand in their own category and are the result of abnormal cellular growth. Many tumors are benign—they develop slowly and do not spread—but, if sited in delicate areas, such as the brain or spinal column, may cause damage by pressing against sensitive tissues. Cancers, in contrast, are malignant tumors caused by cell mutation. They can spread rapidly and cause death by destroying healthy tissue.

Changing patterns

As little as 100 years ago, four out of ten babies failed to reach adulthood. Today, life expectancy in the Western world is approximately 70 years for a man and a little more for a woman. There are many reasons for this dramatic improvement, among them rising living standards in housing, nutrition, working environment, and sanitation, which have removed many of the conditions in which disease once thrived. Medical advances also have played a large part. Some of the most significant contributions to present-day health include a greater understanding of the causes of illness, the use of preventive measures such as vaccination programs, major advances in surgery, and the development of antibiotics and other drugs. As a result of these advances, infectious diseases, such as smallpox and poliomyelitis, have been eradicated in many parts of the world, and a person's chance of a long and healthy life is better than ever before.

Health and society

Illness may not just be a question of the failure of one of the body systems. Often it is also closely tied to climatic, social, and environmental factors. Although many infectious diseases have been eradicated in the Western world, most are still common in the Third World, that is, in developing countries, where malnutrition and poverty combine to perpetuate high levels of infant mortality and low life expectancy.

Ironically, the material benefits of improved

social living in the Western world have themselves created new health problems. As traditional killers have disappeared, new ones have taken their place. Heart disease and cancers, once little known, are now common and account for a large proportion of all deaths.

Today it is known that such diseases of affluence are directly related to diet, sedentary occupations, smoking, and the stresses of twentieth-century living. Medical cures for these illnesses remain elusive, but some of them can be prevented, and current medical views emphasize the importance of healthy diet and regular exercise, and the dangers of stress, smoking, and alcohol. Good health may, ultimately, depend as much on changes in the way we live as on current or future developments in medical science.

Vaccination gives immunity to specific diseases. Children are usually vaccinated against diphtheria, tetanus, pertussis (whooping cough), and poliomyelitis.

The main causes of death reflect factors such as climate, diet, and standards of medical care. In the U.S., for instance, diet and life style can be linked with the high proportion of deaths from cardiovascular disorders.

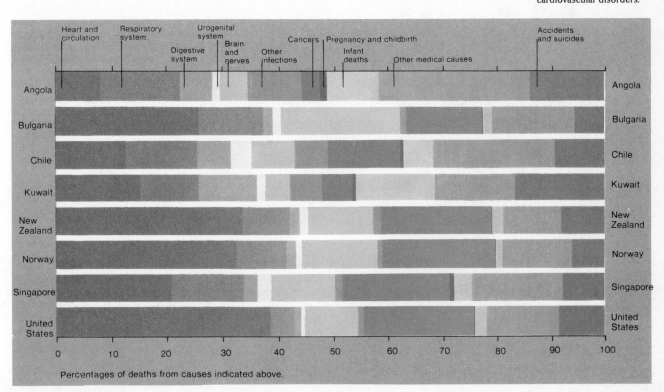

Percentages of deaths from causes indicated above.

Disorders and deficiencies

Most people go through life in general good health, suffering occasionally from temporary disorders, which are more inconvenient than threatening. The common cold is a typical example of an infectious illness that is a great nuisance, but not permanently debilitating.

The human body is, however, susceptible to a wide variety of more serious disorders and diseases, which include hereditary conditions; defects present at birth; disorders caused by dietary defects or deficiencies; disorders that affect one or other of the body systems; neoplasms, whether benign tumors or malignant cancers; conditions that affect the brain or nervous system (or both); psychosomatic disorders—mental disturbances that produce the physical symptoms of illness; and many complaints associated with occupation, environment, and the body's natural degeneration.

Hereditary disorders

Some disorders may be inherited from one or both parents and may affect a child directly. In other cases, an inherited disorder may not be apparent for one or more generations. Severe hereditary disorders include hemophilia (in which a person's blood fails to clot, resulting in excessive bleeding from even minor injuries), some types of dwarfism, sickle-cell anemia (in which a person is anemic because of abnormally-shaped red blood cells), and the rare Friedrich's ataxia (which causes problems with muscular coordination). Color blindness is an example of a less serious inherited disorder. Certain hereditary disorders such as hemophilia, like some birth defects (for example, the condition known as Down's syndrome), can be detected during pregnancy by the technique of amniocentesis.

Each part of the body is susceptible to its own set of characteristic disorders, and there are other conditions that affect the body as a whole. The chief categories are infections (which often cause inflammation of a tissue or organ); traumas, which usually result from injury; tumors and other abnormal growths; deficiency diseases; and degenerative disorders, generally resulting from the process of aging. Disorders that affect the whole body include, as well as generalized infections, those involving the skin, the skeleton, the circulation, the lymphatic system, and the peripheral nervous system. Certain glandular disorders, particularly those involving hormones, may also have a profound effect on the whole of the body. The illustration indicates some of the disorders that can affect the various parts of the body.

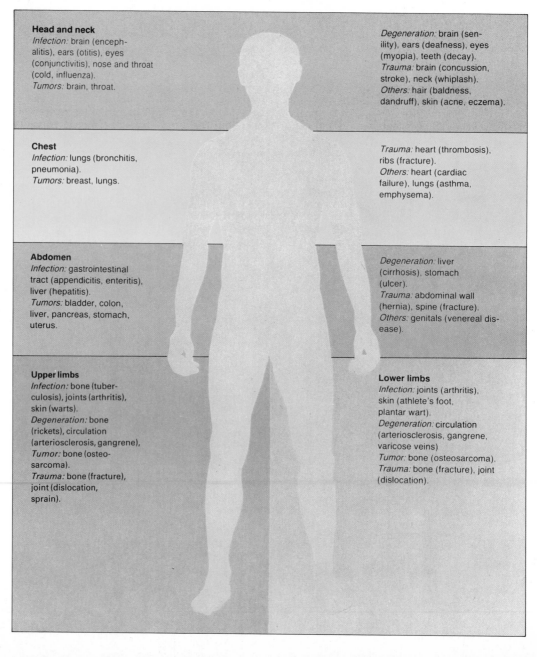

Head and neck
Infection: brain (encephalitis), ears (otitis), eyes (conjunctivitis), nose and throat (cold, influenza).
Tumors: brain, throat.

Degeneration: brain (senility), ears (deafness), eyes (myopia), teeth (decay).
Trauma: brain (concussion, stroke), neck (whiplash).
Others: hair (baldness, dandruff), skin (acne, eczema).

Chest
Infection: lungs (bronchitis, pneumonia).
Tumors: breast, lungs.

Trauma: heart (thrombosis), ribs (fracture).
Others: heart (cardiac failure), lungs (asthma, emphysema).

Abdomen
Infection: gastrointestinal tract (appendicitis, enteritis), liver (hepatitis).
Tumors: bladder, colon, liver, pancreas, stomach, uterus.

Degeneration: liver (cirrhosis), stomach (ulcer).
Trauma: abdominal wall (hernia), spine (fracture).
Others: genitals (venereal disease).

Upper limbs
Infection: bone (tuberculosis), joints (arthritis), skin (warts).
Degeneration: bone (rickets), circulation (arteriosclerosis, gangrene).
Tumor: bone (osteosarcoma).
Trauma: bone (fracture), joint (dislocation, sprain).

Lower limbs
Infection: joints (arthritis), skin (athlete's foot, plantar wart).
Degeneration: circulation (arteriosclerosis, gangrene, varicose veins).
Tumor: bone (osteosarcoma).
Trauma: bone (fracture), joint (dislocation).

Other birth defects

Some defects are not inherited but acquired while the fetus is in the uterus. Faults in normal physical development may cause such disorders as cleft palate, harelip, spina bifida, hydrocephalus (water on the brain), and congenital heart abnormalities. Faults in the chromosome distribution can lead to Down's syndrome, in which the child has an abnormal number of chromosomes.

Other disorders appear as a result of abnormal circumstances during pregnancy. For instance, a baby may be born deaf, or with cataracts in the eyes, or even with heart disease, if its mother contracted rubella (German measles) during the first three months of pregnancy. And certain drugs taken by a pregnant woman may cause abnormalities in her child. Damage to the baby may also be caused during complicated births. For example, if the fetus does not receive sufficient oxygen during the birthing process, brain damage (cerebral palsy) or even death might result.

Dietary defects and deficiencies

The necessity for a normal, well-balanced diet is well known, and generally the body compensates for variations, losses, and temporary excesses in diet. At its simplest, this is illustrated by the body's desire for liquids (thirst) after an insufficient intake of fluids or after eating salty food. But certain disorders are actually aggravated by a normal diet. Celiac disease makes the intestines react to the protein called gluten (an ingredient of wheat flour) in such a way that normal absorption of other nutrients is prevented. A gluten-free diet is usually prescribed in order to relieve the symptoms and prevent further deficiency disorders from developing. Phenylketonuria (PKU) is a hereditary deficiency disorder in which enzymes that normally break down the amino acid phenylalanine are absent, so that this substance (which occurs in many foods) accumulates in the blood and damages the brain, causing symptoms that range from irritability to convulsions. In most countries, babies are tested at birth for this deficiency, which can be corrected by adjusting the baby's diet.

Malnutrition, resulting from a diet that lacks essential vitamins, is responsible for diseases such as rickets, scurvy, and beriberi. Severe malnutrition in children up to the age of eighteen months causes an irreversible reduction in intellectual ability. Overindulgence can also lead to problems. For instance, a diet rich in sugar may lead to obesity and aggravate diabetes, and diets rich in animal fats contribute to heart disease and disorders of the circulatory system.

Some foods that have no ill effect on most people cause abnormal, allergic reactions in others. The reaction can vary from a temporary rash or digestive disturbance to water-filled blisters over most of the body.

System failure

Occasionally, one of the body's systems fails completely. Disease or damage to the kidneys may lead to kidney failure, which can be fatal if both kidneys are affected and the condition is

untreated. Cardiac failure may cause the heart to stop pumping blood around the body, and unless the heart is restarted quickly this will result in death. The term cardiac failure also describes partial failure of the heart, which results in an accumulation of blood in various organs because circulation is impaired. Liver and lungs may be damaged by disease or toxic substances, and this damage may also be fatal.

The body's systems are finely balanced, and although some effect usually occurs if a system is only partly faulty, nevertheless the body has a remarkable capacity to cope with—and

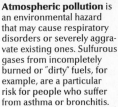

Atmospheric pollution is an environmental hazard that may cause respiratory disorders or severely aggravate existing ones. Sulfurous gases from incompletely burned or "dirty" fuels, for example, are a particular risk for people who suffer from asthma or bronchitis.

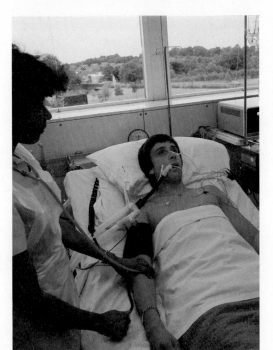

A chronically ill person usually needs a prolonged course of treatment, sometimes involving a long stay in a hospital. The aim is to support the patient so that he or she can live at home and lead as normal a life as possible.

Rickets is a deficiency disease caused by a lack or insufficiency of vitamin D. The vitamin is supplied in sufficient quantities in a balanced diet containing such foods as eggs and fish; it is also formed in the skin on exposure to sunlight. Its deficiency affects calcium metabolism and results in deformed bones in children. In adults, vitamin D deficiency causes osteomalacia, which is also characterized by a softening of the bones.

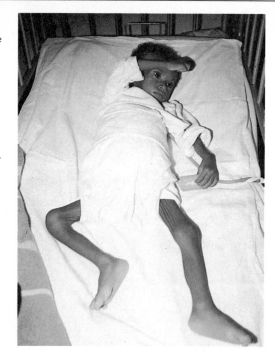

Hemophilia is a comparatively rare but serious inherited disorder. People with the condition lack an essential clotting factor in their blood, and, as a result, bleed excessively from even a minor cut or bruise. Most hemophiliacs are males; they inherit the disorder from their mothers, who are carriers but do not themselves suffer from the disease. However, as the diagram shows, it is possible for a girl to be a hemophiliac if her father has the disease and her mother is a carrier.

even compensate for—partial failure of its systems.

Old age is associated with general slow degeneration and gradually decreasing efficiency of all the body's systems. The lungs, heart, liver, kidneys, and brain all work less well, and the senses tend to deteriorate. Sight and hearing in particular are liable to suffer quite rapid decline in older people; this probably contributes more than anything else to the problems of aging.

Causes of disease

Some diseases and disorders seem to occur without obvious cause, as with some cancers and other growths and with many of the disorders that affect the nervous system. Many conditions, however, are brought about by specific identifiable circumstances.

Certain lifestyles give rise to particular hazards, and some occupations are associated with specific diseases. For example, cardiovascular disorders are particularly prevalent in sedentary workers who are also subject to stress; and respiratory diseases such as asbestosis, bagassosis, or silicosis, are likely to affect the lungs of those who work in conditions in which large quantities of certain types of dust are inhaled.

There are some disorders that may occur at particular stages of life; for instance, one type of leukemia is more common in children and young adults than in older people, and gallstones are particularly likely to affect middle-aged people. Other conditions, such as allergies and chilblains, can occur at any age.

External factors

Excessive use of alcohol or tobacco, abuse of drugs, stress, obesity, and poor diet can all cause or aggravate certain disorders. For instance, smoking is associated with bronchitis and with several other conditions, best known of which is lung cancer. Women who smoke or drink during pregnancy also risk causing significant harm to the child in their womb. Stress is a significant cause of ulcers of the duodenum, and is strongly associated with cardiovascular disease. Lack of exercise, especially in combination with a sedentary occupation, has been associated with obesity and circulatory disorders, and especially with cardiovascular disease.

Neoplasms

New growths of normal or abnormal body tissue are known medically as neoplasms. They can take many forms—some are harmless; some cause discomfort, irritation, or pain; and some are potentially fatal. Examples of harmless (benign) growths are common warts, moles, and fatty growths known as lipomas. Growths capable of causing pain or difficulty include fibroids (fibrous lumps in the uterus), and polyps in the nose, rectum, or vagina.

Malignant growths of excess tissue are called cancers. Such growths can be found in almost any part of the body, including the brain, lungs, breasts, uterus, bones, kidneys,

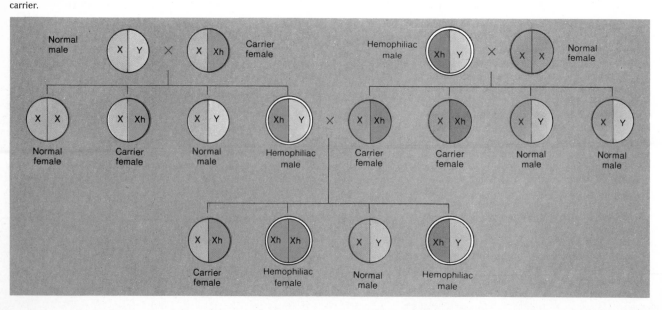

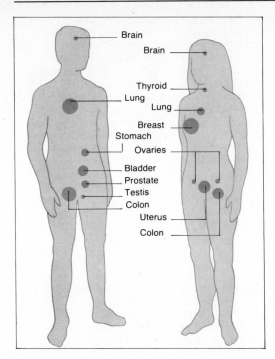

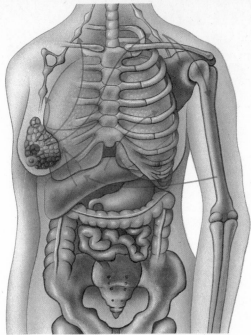

Cancer takes various forms and can affect almost any body tissue or organ. The diagram *(far left)* shows the most common sites in men and women, with the size of the colored spot indicating the relative incidence. Untreated cancer can spread from the primary site by the process of metastasis. The diagram *(left)* indicates how breast cancer can progress first to the lymph nodes and then to the bones, from which it moves to the liver and finally the lungs.

mouth, stomach, liver, and colon. Cancerous cells multiply abnormally fast and so starve surrounding tissue of nutrients. If the malignant growth is confined to only one accessible area, it can often be removed by surgery or destroyed by radiation or chemotherapy. Once cancerous cells have entered the bloodstream or lymphatic system, however, they may spread to almost any part of the body. If this happens, it is very difficult to halt the disease. Some cancers are caused by known cancer-producing agents (carcinogens) such as tobacco smoke, ultraviolet rays, and X rays.

Neurological conditions

The brain and nervous system are also subject to various disorders. The brain is the most complex organ of the body and is—directly or indirectly—involved in all bodily functions. If something goes wrong with the brain's functioning, for example as a result of epilepsy, injury to its tissues, a brain tumor, a stroke, or encephalitis (inflammation of the brain), the results can be far-reaching and sometimes unpredictable.

Diseases can also attack the nerve pathways. One of the best known, and most serious, examples is multiple sclerosis. In this disorder, the cause of which is unknown, the protective cells around the nerves of the brain and spinal cord are damaged, causing a variety of symptoms that may become progressively more severe and can eventually lead to invalidism. Infections of specific parts of the nervous system, such as poliomyelitis (an infection of the spinal cord), can also result in paralysis.

Psychological and similar disorders

The mind can affect the body, and many physical disorders are thought to be caused or aggravated by emotional disturbances. Stress is perhaps the most common of such causes, and can be a significant factor in disorders

such as indigestion, stomach ulcers, headaches, palpitations, high blood pressure, heart disease, and diabetes. It may aggravate disorders like asthma, eczema, psoriasis, excessive sweating, and migraine. Combined with emotional difficulties, stress can lead to such severe conditions as alcoholism, drug dependence, and anorexia nervosa.

Sexual difficulties may result from emotional problems, perhaps related to irrational guilt or fear or to feelings of inadequacy, or they may be a result of stress. The most common physical symptoms associated with sexual difficulties of this sort are inability to achieve an erection or experience orgasm.

Sympathetic advice and possibly psychotherapy may be needed to resolve psychologically based physical problems—the physical symptoms are unlikely to disappear unless the underlying emotional problem is dealt with.

Curvature of the spine in the elderly may result from osteoporosis, a degenerative disorder in which a gradual loss of calcium causes porosity of the bones. The vertebrae, in particular, may become deformed and compressed, leading to a stiff neck and a characteristic stoop, which in turn affects the way the person walks.

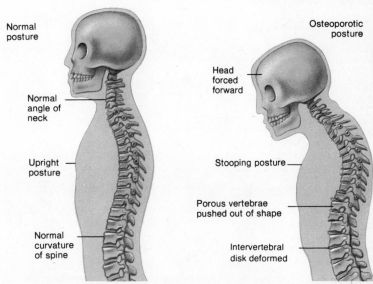

Infection

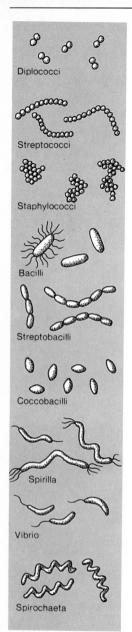

Diplococci

Streptococci

Staphylococci

Bacilli

Streptobacilli

Coccobacilli

Spirilla

Vibrio

Spirochaeta

Bacteria have a variety of forms, several of which are shown above. Among these there are three main types—cocci, which are roughly spherical or oval; bacilli, which are elongated, or rod-shaped; and spirilli, which have a spiral shape. Size varies considerably, but most bacteria are between 0.2×10^{-3} and 2.0×10^{-3} millimeters in length. The photo-micrograph is of a *Salmonella* bacterium, the type that causes various infections of the gastrointestinal tract, including typhoid.

Everyone—including healthy people—carries some microorganisms on the skin or in the body, but normally the body's natural defenses prevent these from causing harm.

Infections occur when the body is invaded by disease-causing organisms—bacteria, viruses, fungi, protozoa, or larger metazoa, such as tapeworms. They may enter the body by various means: through the nose or mouth; through a break in the skin; or through physical contact with an infected person or thing, as in sexual or skin infections.

Some infections, such as a common cold, are minor and short-lived; others, such as athlete's foot, are more persistent, but are still not life-threatening. Certain infections, however, for example those that cause meningitis, poliomyelitis, typhus, and rabies, are extremely dangerous. Infections by protozoa or larger organisms are more properly called infestations, and are caused by organisms that live on humans as parasites.

Agents of infection

The most common infective agents (pathogens) are bacteria. Many forms live harmlessly in the human body, particularly in the lower digestive tract, but others cause minor or severe infections such as boils, tonsillitis, and pneumonia.

Viruses are smaller than bacteria, and can be seen only with the aid of an electron microscope. Viral infections include the common cold, chickenpox (varicella), poliomyelitis, and herpes.

Rickettsias are unusual agents of infection found on fleas and lice; they have characteristics in common with both bacteria and viruses, and can transmit diseases such as typhus to humans.

Fungi are plantlike organisms that can cause various diseases, including ringworm

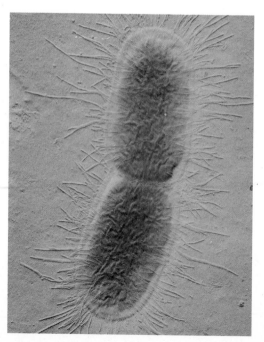

and thrush—the common name for moniliasis or candidiasis.

Protozoa are single-celled parasites that cause diseases such as malaria, amebic dysentery, and toxoplasmosis. Metazoa are many-celled parasites, such as tapeworms and lice.

The spread of disease

Diseases spread in various ways. Poliomyelitis and cholera are transmitted by contaminated water. Many viruses, such as those causing chickenpox, are spread by airborne droplets that are sneezed, coughed, or breathed out by someone with the disease. Diseases such as gonorrhea, syphilis, and AIDS (Acquired Immune Deficiency Syndrome), which are transmitted by sexual contact, are known as venereal diseases.

Infectious organisms can be contained in the saliva, sputum, vomit, blood, pus, or excreta (waste products) of an infected person. Food may be a carrier of disease, particularly if it is neither fresh nor freshly cooked, or if it is contaminated with animal- or insect-borne diseases such as tapeworm or salmonella.

Some diseases are caught directly from animals. For example, psittacosis can be caught from certain birds, and rabies is transmitted through the saliva of infected mammals.

Open wounds can become infected by any bacteria that come into contact with them. Most serious of such infections is tetanus, caused when tetanus bacilli—which are commonly found in soil—enter the body through a dirty wound. Tetanus can be prevented by vaccination. If the disease develops, however, it can be fatal.

Prevention of disease

Hygiene is the key to preventing the spread of many diseases. Important principles of hygiene include: washing the hands after going to the toilet and before handling food; covering any wounds before handling food; keeping a sickroom clean, and disinfecting or destroying any soiled handkerchiefs or dressings; and washing a sick person's dishes, eating utensils, and clothes separately from those of the rest of the family.

It is also important to take extra care of hygiene when traveling abroad because of the presence of infective agents to which the body is unaccustomed, and to have any recommended inoculations before starting a trip. Keeping pets and farm animals as clean as possible, and washing the hands after handling them—particularly before touching food or anything that might come into contact with it—is another good principle. In any case, it is sensible for each member of a household to have his or her own facecloth, toothbrush, and hairbrush.

The body has various systems for preventing and fighting infections. The skin prevents many organisms from entering the body, and blood clots and tissue repairs soon seal any minor wounds in the skin. The tonsils, adenoids, and mucous membranes of the nose and throat help to trap any inhaled germs. The lymph nodes together with the spleen manufacture antibodies against infections that penetrate the outer defenses, and the liver can destroy various disease-produced toxins. White blood cells attack invading germs, and blood also contains antibodies, produced by white cells in response to infection, which provide protection (immunity) against further attacks by the same infecting agents.

Immunity is mostly developed by the body's natural immune system, but some immunity can be conferred. Newborn babies inherit antibodies from their mothers and acquire others from mother's milk. Others again are developed in response to specific infections. Immunity can also be induced artificially by vaccination, which involves introducing dead or weakened disease agents into the body to stimulate the formation of antibodies.

Curing infections

Antibiotics are the most successful agents that mankind has created to combat infectious diseases. Most work only against bacterial infections, however, such as tonsillitis and pneumonia. Sulfonamides and other drugs can also be effective against bacteria.

Viruses are far more resistant to known drugs. The symptoms of viral diseases can be treated—for instance, decongestants relieve the symptoms of colds—but generally viral infections must be left to take their natural course.

Fungicidal drugs can ease such conditions as athlete's foot, and ultraviolet radiation from sunlight or from a sunlamp helps to kill the germs that are present in acne. Certain drugs are effective in eliminating parasites, such as threadworms and tapeworms. Drugs known as antitoxins counteract the effects of toxins produced in the body by infecting organisms. When drugs fail or are inappropriate, however, surgery is also a possible treatment—for instance, to remove an infected appendix.

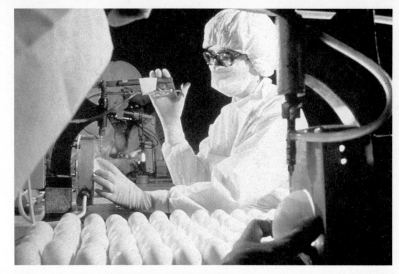

Fertilized hen's eggs are used as a living culture medium in which to grow viruses for making vaccines. Here eggs are being injected with a strain of influenza virus.

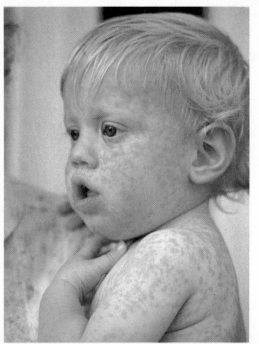

Measles, an infectious disease caused by a virus, causes a rash on the face and body. Contracting the disease usually confers immunity for life, but there is a vaccine available for immunizing babies.

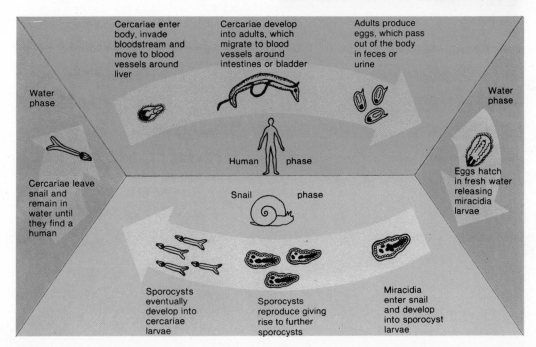

Water phase

Cercariae enter body, invade bloodstream and move to blood vessels around liver

Cercariae develop into adults, which migrate to blood vessels around intestines or bladder

Adults produce eggs, which pass out of the body in feces or urine

Water phase

Cercariae leave snail and remain in water until they find a human

Human phase

Snail phase

Eggs hatch in fresh water releasing miracidia larvae

Sporocysts eventually develop into cercariae larvae

Sporocysts reproduce giving rise to further sporocysts

Miracidia enter snail and develop into sporocyst larvae

Schistosomiasis, formerly known as bilharziasis, is a disease caused by *Schistosoma* parasites, which are common in tropical America, Asia, and Africa. The parasite also depends on some types of water snail, and people become infected from water in which these snails live. The parasite's life cycle has four phases: one in snails, one in humans, and two intermediate stages in water, from which both hosts acquire the infestation.

Allergies

Although medical controversy focuses on the causes and mechanisms of allergy—even on the definition of the term—to the lay person the chief mystery is, how can a person suddenly become allergic to things that hitherto have caused no harm? And why do certain things affect one person strongly and others not at all?

Much remains to be learned. But from the beginning, the word "allergy" has been used to describe a type of adverse reaction by the body's immune system to a foreign substance. Normally, the immune system develops antibodies only as a response to the presence of a potentially harmful substance (such as a virus). The antibodies produced are then specific to that substance, and will be produced again immediately if that substance is encountered later. In an allergy, this mechanism is brought into operation by a harmless substance (like pollen or some foodstuffs). Re-exposure to this substance—known as an allergen—results in the production of antibodies, and a subsequent allergic reaction.

Allergic reactions

Many allergic reactions involve a common mechanism—the over-production by the body of a type of antibody known as IgE. This antibody binds to the surface of a special cell called a mast cell. When the IgE antibody combines with the allergen, the mast cell releases its contents, called H-substances. These include histamine, prostaglandins, and leukotrienes, which are the most important mediators of allergic reactions. These mediators cause tissue swelling, because they increase local blood flow and also cause small blood vessels to leak fluid into the surrounding body tissues. Several common symptoms of allergy result, for example, in swollen, red, itching lumps in the skin (urticaria or hives), a stuffed-up, runny nose (rhinitis), or red, itching eyes (conjunctivitis).

Some allergic reactions are relatively minor, but mast cell allergic mediators also cause more severe reactions, such as anaphylaxis or asthmatic attacks. Anaphylaxis occurs when histamine is released into the bloodstream in large quantities. This produces a sudden fall in blood pressure, which causes physiological shock. There also may be intense swelling of tissues in the throat, which can cause asphyxiation. Anaphylaxis is rare, but can occur if a susceptible person is injected with a drug, such as penicillin, to which he or she is allergic, or suffers an allergic reaction to insect stings. In an asthmatic attack, the release of histamine and leukotrienes in the walls of bronchi in the respiratory tract causes the smooth muscle to contract, thus narrowing the bronchi and causing partial respiratory obstruction. The characteristic asthmatic wheezing and difficulty in exhaling results. Another common cause of allergic reaction is certain food, and recent studies suggest that migraine headaches may be associated with food allergies in some way.

Certain allergies, especially hay fever, asthma, and eczema, often run in families. This pattern is known as atopy, and those who are affected are described as atopic. Individual members of a family may be afflicted with one or all types of reaction, due to excess IgE production. The exact reason for this is not known, but it is probably due to a minor abnormality in the complex control systems that regulate immune responses to foreign substances. Because the immunoregulatory network changes during an individual's lifetime, new allergies may appear and old ones disappear in a totally unpredictable manner.

Allergy and the twentieth century

Current thinking suggests that the changes in diet, in the environment, and in the stresses of everyday life characteristic of modern times actually encourage the development of aller-

Food allergies in babies may be one cause of hyperactivity, in which the baby cries and moves incessantly. Among the chief culprits are food colorants added to some foods (such as orange juice), although even the staple food—milk—causes an allergic reaction in some babies.

Pollen grains, shown here greatly magnified, are the allergens that cause allergic seasonal rhinitis, better known as hay fever. Its symptoms may be relieved by antihistamine drugs, but the cause needs desensitization treatment.

gies, both by increasing the number of power-ful potential allergens and by increasing the overall susceptibility of people.

Chemical fertilization, allowing the land to be overexploited, reduces the amount of trace substances in the harvested products. Refining common ingredients such as flour and sugar also reduces the level of trace elements that once probably afforded some protection against the development of various sensitivi-ties. In addition, the use of chemical additives, especially colorants, in food has greatly in-creased.

A further dietary factor seems to be the contemporary fashion for early bottle-feeding and weaning of infants. A baby's own immune system is not fully developed until about nine months of age, and allergies—from which ma-ternal antibodies in milk may afford some protection—can develop easily before this time.

Our natural environment is now heavily polluted. Many of the pollutants either bring on allergic states or are themselves potential allergens. They include many chemicals, such as gasoline, cosmetics, and cleaning products.

Another possible reason for the increasing incidence of allergies is that, with growing public awareness, it is becoming fashionable to diagnose them as a cause of illness.

Allergy diagnosis

If inhalation, contact, or ingestion of a sub-stance results in an allergic reaction with obvi-ous symptoms, diagnosis of allergy is easy. An example is a rash that develops after eating strawberries. But allergic symptoms may also derive from a cause that is less easily distin-guished. The oldest method of tracking down the source of such "hidden" allergies is the ex-clusion (or elimination) diet, in which a simple, basic diet that produces no reaction is gradu-ally enlarged over several weeks by adding suspect foods one after another until the reac-tion occurs. A recent study involving children with severe migraine has shown that marked improvements can be achieved by excluding certain dietary elements.

More modern means of diagnosis are skin tests and blood tests. Skin tests are of two types. Prick or scratch tests are suitable for some types of allergy; patch tests are better for other sorts of allergies. Blood tests are more accurate; the most common are the radio-allergosorbent test (RAST) and the cyto-toxic tests.

Allergy treatment

Therapies range from the orthodox to the un-usual. Some relieve the symptoms rather than actually treating the underlying allergy. This is particularly true of the suppressive drugs commonly prescribed, such as sodium chro-moglycate, antihistamines, and steroid prepa-rations.

The method known as desensitization at-tempts to reduce the allergic response gradu-ally. This treatment starts with the administra-tion of a very dilute form of the allergen, then slowly increases the amount of allergen that can be tolerated without producing symp-toms.

There are thousands of potential allergens, and the chief types are shown in the diagram: animal fur and dander, feathers, mites in house dust, pollen, foods such as milk, eggs, straw-berries, and shellfish, alco-holic drinks, drugs, cosmet-ics, soaps and shampoos, atmospheric pollutants, and man-made fibers.

Another treatment is to avoid the allergen. Appropriate food can be excluded, or ionizers can be used to precipitate pollens out of the air, for example. And, given time, many aller-gies or sensitivities disappear of their own ac-cord.

Finally, some people are apparently allergic to everything in their environment—a condi-tion sometimes described as "total allergy syn-drome." It is possible that they have a break-down in their immune system that causes the easy development and endless accumulation of allergies. It is more probable, however, that their condition has been falsely blamed on al-lergies and is, in fact, something else that has yet to be properly understood.

Once an allergic reaction begins, the results can be rapid and dramatic—partic-ularly on the skin. The woman in this photograph is allergic to adhesive tape, and contact with only a small area caused an erup-tion of lesions over nearly all her body.

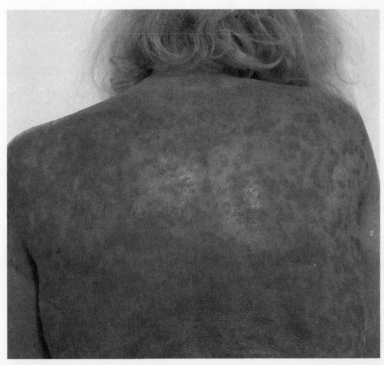

Accidents

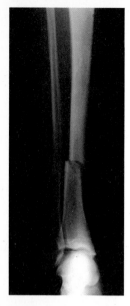

Broken bones are among the most common injuries that result from accidents. The limb bones—for example the tibia of the leg, shown in this X ray—are the most vulnerable, and need prompt specialized treatment if they are to heal properly.

About one-third of all accidental injuries occur in the home, the majority of them to the very young or the elderly. Accidents affecting adults tend to be on the roads or at work, though older children and young adults are most likely to be injured while playing some sport. Among the otherwise healthy 10-30 age group, they are one of the most common causes of death. To a far greater extent than most people believe, however, accidents can be avoided by taking simple safety precautions in the home, at work, and on the roads, by an awareness of the dangers, and by using common sense.

Cuts, abrasions, bites, and bruises

These injuries are often superficial, and if so, can be treated at home or in the nearest convenient place, where the damaged area can be cleaned thoroughly and the flow of blood can be brought under control. A deep or extensive cut that persists in bleeding may require stitches (sutures), in which case it is treated by a qualified physician. Stitches are usually inserted under a local anesthetic, and removed about seven days later.

More serious cuts, abrasions, and some bites involve a greater possibility of infection and need more comprehensive treatment. An antitetanus injection is often administered, especially if the victim has not had an immunization course during the previous three years. In the case of an animal bite, extra precautions are normally taken, and these may include a series of antirabies inoculations. Snakebites are treated with a serum injected into the bloodstream.

Bruising (contusion) is usually a superficial injury that occurs when a blow or fall ruptures the tiny capillaries in the skin. Blood seeps out of the capillaries into the surrounding tissues and is slowly fragmented and absorbed. The red hemoglobin in the lost blood turns purple as its oxygen is dissipated and later turns brown and yellow as it is broken down into bile pigments.

Bruising rarely requires treatment, although a large collection of blood (hematoma) may have to be reduced by being drawn off with a syringe and needle. Contamination must be avoided scrupulously, and antiseptics and sterile dressings are used because stagnant blood is an ideal growing medium for harmful bacteria.

Burns

Burns are caused by a wide variety of accidents that need not involve a naked flame—merely heat. The damage common to all types of burns is the alteration (denaturation) of tissue protein at the affected site, which is followed by tissue death. Apart from fire, this damage can be caused by boiling liquids (when it is called a scald), hot gases (which are particularly dangerous to the respiratory system), an electric current, corrosive chemicals, friction, radiation from the ultraviolet rays in sunlight or from radioactive materials, and even by contact with extremely cold surfaces, particularly if these are metal.

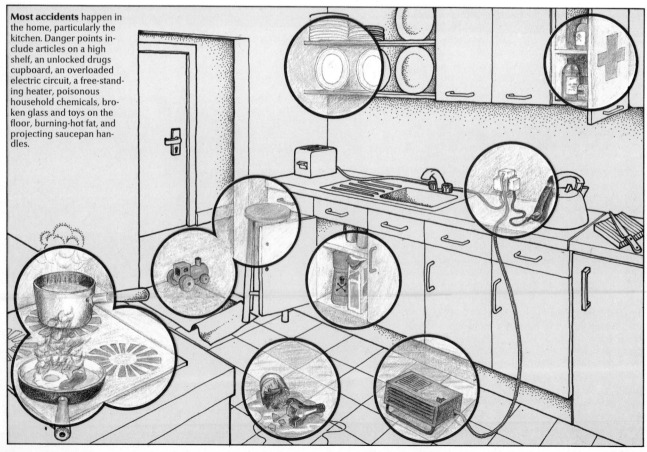

Most accidents happen in the home, particularly the kitchen. Danger points include articles on a high shelf, an unlocked drugs cupboard, an overloaded electric circuit, a free-standing heater, poisonous household chemicals, broken glass and toys on the floor, burning-hot fat, and projecting saucepan handles.

First-degree burns affect only the outer, inert skin layer. Second-degree burns destroy living tissue but leave sufficient growing layer for the surface to be restored. Third-degree burns involve the entire thickness of the skin and generally require skin to be replaced by grafting.

When tissue is burnt, plasma leaks out of the blood vessels and may form blisters under the skin. When the burning is extensive, the circulation may be adversely affected. This, and the severe pain, can lead to clinical shock.

Poisons

Poisoning can have the same effect on the circulation as shock, for instance, by interfering with the nervous system. A number of chemicals and vegetable poisons, such as strychnine and some of the fungal (mushroom and toadstool) poisons, affect the nervous and circulatory system in this way. Other poisons include corrosive substances, which affect the internal or external body surfaces, and metabolic poisons. The latter cause death by impairing cell function—cyanide, for instance, blocks oxygen transportation and causes chemical suffocation.

Fractures

Broken or cracked bones (fractures) are the commonest result of accidents. Shock may complicate fractures, especially when a large bone such as the femur is involved, because heavy bleeding may occur around the break. Pain and distress also contribute to the shock reaction.

Fractures are usually treated easily by orthopedic specialists, and heal more quickly in younger than older people. But a badly shattered bone may remain brittle for a long time and be in constant danger of breaking again.

Shock

This refers to a serious internal physical condition in which the blood pressure falls well below normal—in severe shock, the blood pressure can fall as low as 60/20 mm of mercury (the normal level is about 120/80 mm). In such circumstances, the blood circulation fails to maintain an adequate flow through the tissues and back to the heart. The brain cannot function because of lack of oxygen, and for this reason, shock is a common cause of death following a serious accident or acute illness.

Circumstances in which shock occurs include hemorrhage, which reduces the blood pressure directly by lowering the blood volume; reduced efficiency of the heart, for instance, after a heart attack (coronary thrombosis), when its pumping action is impaired; and the abnormal dilatation of certain blood vessels, which causes the pressure in the circulatory system to drop. To some extent, every accident—even a relatively minor physical injury—causes shock. Shock may also result from the body's reaction to surgical treatment, some drugs, emotional stress, and severe allergic reactions.

Sports and hobbies can also involve accidents. The protective clothing worn by this young skateboarder is about to be put to a severe test.

Highway traffic accidents are all too common. Relatively few are fatal, although almost all result in injury and considerable physiological and psychological shock.

Natural defenses

The human body is constantly bombarded by an incalculable number of microorganisms, of which bacteria and viruses are the most common. Most of them are harmless, but some are agents of infection (pathogens). The latter invade the body in various ways—through injuries, from infected people or animals, from contaminated food or drink, or in the air we breathe.

Pathogens have four main routes into the body: through the respiratory tract and the lungs; through breaks in the skin; through the digestive tract into the stomach and bowels; and through the reproductive and urinary tract. Once inside the body, infection may remain in the area where it arrived, or it may travel through the blood or lymphatic systems to other parts of the body.

In the face of such constant attack, the human body has a formidable array of natural defenses. It fights infections in two main ways: by preventing the entry of harmful microorganisms into the body; and by destroying or neutralizing those that do enter.

Barrier defenses

Skin provides the main physical barrier to infection. It has a slightly acid surface that is too cold and hostile for most germs and is further protected by bactericidal chemicals in sweat.

The natural openings into the body are protected too. The sensitive mucous membranes that line the body's orifices and internal passages are sticky so they can trap harmful invaders; they also contain bactericidal substances. The nose, for instance, filters air entering the respiratory tract. Mucus and hairs in the nostrils trap some unwanted particles; others are trapped farther along and removed by cilia of the trachea and bronchi, so that they can be expelled from the body by coughing or sneezing. Specialized dust cells in the lungs produce macrophages that engulf minute particles that pass the other defensive barriers. The acidic conditions of the stomach kill most invasive agents that are swallowed. The secretions of certain glands also serve as barriers: tears, nasal and vaginal secretions, saliva, and the digestive juices all contain antibacterial enzymes or other chemicals.

Internal defense systems

Where pathogenic organisms do manage to gain access to the body's tissues, complex internal defenses take over, responding directly to the physical presence of invading organisms and to the toxins produced by them.

Phagocytes are specialized cells that engulf and digest harmful bacteria. Some of these are highly mobile, such as the white blood cells called polymorphonuclear leukocytes or the single-nuclear monocytes that circulate in the

Respiratory System

Respiratory Defenses

- Nose
- Throat
- Trachea
- Bronchi
- Lungs

- Nasal cilia and mucus
- Nasal hairs
- Adenoids
- Tonsils
- Cough reflex
- Tracheal cilia and mucus
- Bronchial cilia and mucus
- Macrophages in dust cells of lungs
- Natural defenses in blood supply to lungs

The respiratory system *(above)*—from the nose through to the lungs—is continually exposed to harmful agents, but has a formidable array of defenses to combat them. Hair and mucus in the nasal passages filter out dust and dirt; lymphatic tissue of the tonsils and adenoids kill bacteria and viruses; hairlike cilia *(right)* sweep mucus up the bronchi and trachea to the throat; and cells called macrophages *(far right)* engulf dust particles in the lungs.

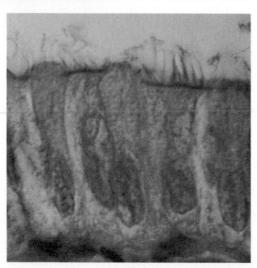

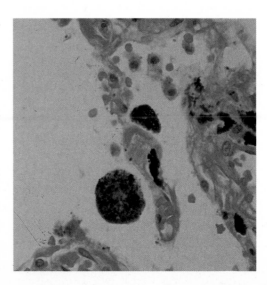

blood. When a cut or abrasion results in local bacterial invasion, increased numbers of phagocytes migrate to the invaded area, where they surround and ingest the bacteria to prevent them from spreading.

Other phagocytes, called macrophages, are more permanently located in specific parts of the body—particularly the lungs, spleen, liver, and lymph nodes—where they filter infective agents out of the blood and lymph circulation.

The lymphatic system plays a crucial role in the body's "immune response," the highly complex defense mechanism by which antibodies are formed in direct response to the presence of antigens—foreign substances, usually proteins, produced by invading organisms. Special white blood cells called lymphocytes, which are formed in the lymphoid tissue of the bone marrow, thymus, lymph nodes, spleen, tonsils, and adenoids, detect any alien protein that enters the bloodstream. Lymphocytes and plasma cells then produce a protein called an antibody. Released into the bloodstream, the antibodies attack the antigens. Some cause bacteria to clump together, and so prevent their spread; others affect the surface of bacteria and make them vulnerable to phagocytes; still others (antitoxins) neutralize poisonous toxins produced by antigens.

Antibodies are not general in their action. Those produced in response to the antigens of diphtheria bacteria are not able to react with those of tuberculosis bacteria, for instance. Nor does the body produce large numbers of antibodies on immediate exposure to an antigen. Large-scale production of antibodies occurs only a few days after exposure; it recurs much more rapidly during subsequent exposure. Once antibodies have been formed in response to a particular bacterium or virus, however, they never completely disappear from the bloodstream and so form the basis of lifelong immunity against that particular illness. The best-known example is the immunity acquired to childhood diseases such as measles. Following the same principle, vaccines—containing dead or weakened pathogens—confer artificial immunity by stimulating antibody production.

Pathogenic microorganisms are not the only foreign proteins that bring about antibody production. The body's tendency to reject skin grafts or transplanted organs is also due to its built-in ability to recognize foreign tissue.

Self-repair

Infection usually results in cellular damage. Where this occurs, special mobile cells called fibroblasts lay down strands of fiber to form a scaffolding onto which new cells can grow from healthy, neighboring tissue. In open wounds, the ability of blood to clot is important in preventing excessive loss of blood. The process consists of a complex series of chemical reactions but culminates in the conversion of a fluid substance, fibrinogen, into a mass of thin protein threads (fibrin), which forms the core of the clot.

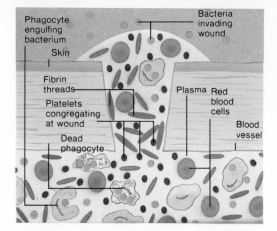

An injury to the skin results in invasion by bacteria, which are met by the body's second line of natural defenses, the blood. Phagocytes migrate to the injured area and engulf invading bacteria. Blood platelets, which have an important role in blood clotting, also concentrate at the site of bleeding.

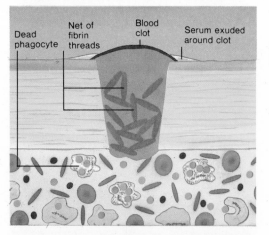

Blood clotting helps to seal the wound so that tissue repair can proceed. Phagocytes continue to destroy bacteria, while spent phagocytes and dead bacteria accumulate as pus.

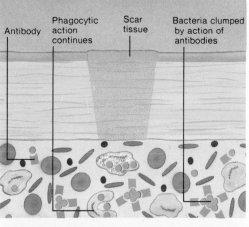

New tissue repairs the damage at the site of the wound. Antibodies formed in response to the invading antigens help to eliminate any remaining bacteria and confer a degree of lasting immunity.

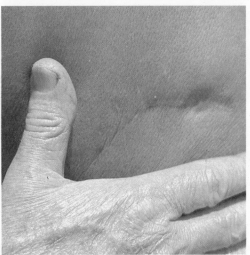

Scarring can be extensive at the site of a large and ragged wound. This photograph shows a spear wound that was stitched to close it and minimize scarring, but nevertheless the skin has been distorted by inelastic scar tissue.

Community health

Community medicine's prime concern is to prevent disease. Communal health responsibilities include: controlling housing standards and population density; the disposal of domestic and industrial waste; the maintainance of public hygiene; health screening; the elimination of sources of disease and infection, for instance, by vermin control or by neutralization (or drainage) of malarial swamps; and defining acceptable standards of burial. They can also extend to the provision of training and research facilities; the establishment and staffing of hospitals and clinics; the provision of medical emergency services; and the arrangement of financial support for sick people.

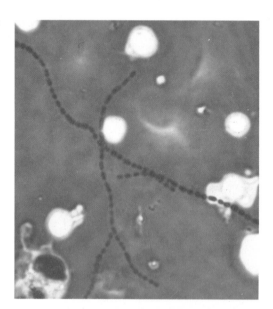

Milk is sterilized or pasteurized to kill bacteria such as these streptococci, which were photographed in a stained sample of untreated milk.

Baby clinics are a valuable aspect of community health because they allow pediatricians to regularly monitor the progress of growing infants. Any disorders are diagnosed and treated promptly. Parents are also given advice about vaccinations.

Water supply and sanitation

People everywhere need a constant supply of clean water for drinking, cooking, and washing, and also facilities for the removal of sewage waste. The latter must never contaminate the former, otherwise epidemics such as dysentery, typhoid, and cholera can result.

Water is collected from natural sources and stored in reservoirs. It is then purified and distributed for public usage. In some countries, one or two parts of fluoride per million are added to water, to help prevent tooth decay. Constant checks are carried out at all stages to see that no contamination occurs.

An adequate public and domestic water supply enables the sewage system to use waste water to transport the sewage from its source (washrooms) to sewage treatment works. This ensures that the transport is relatively swift and enables the system to be enclosed, which greatly reduces the spread of diseases, especially those such as food poisoning and dysentery, which are transmitted from feces to food by flies.

Vaccination programs

Children, adults, and animals are vaccinated against disease according to the principle established by a British doctor, Edward Jenner, in 1796. He discovered that people who had been given cowpox were protected against smallpox; this is because the cowpox virus, which causes a mild disease, stimulates production of antibodies that are effective against the smallpox virus. Babies are vaccinated against poliomyelitis, tetanus, and diphtheria and may also be vaccinated against measles and mumps. Susceptible children are vaccinated against tuberculosis. Girls who have not contracted rubella (German measles) naturally by about the age of 13 can be vaccinated against the disease at this age. Vaccination against typhoid, cholera, and yellow fever is also required for people of all ages who are traveling in areas where they may contract these diseases. Smallpox vaccination has effectively eradicated the disease.

Hygienic food processing

Hygienic controls are introduced at all stages of food production, from breeding and growing, to slaughtering and harvesting, to preparation and packing, to transporting and storing, and to selling, cooking, and serving. Such controls are obligatory in many countries, particularly where the food is being produced for storage and wholesale national or international marketing.

To prevent the spread of tuberculosis and brucellosis through dairy products, milk is pasteurized by being heated to 161° F. (72° C). This process kills most bacteria in the milk and improves its storage qualities without affecting its taste.

Cattle are vaccinated against brucellosis and tuberculosis, and meat is inspected for infections such as tapeworm after animals have

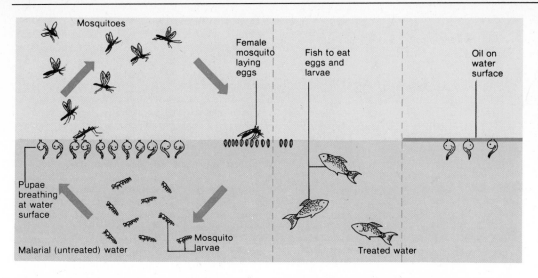

Malaria (untreated) water
Treated water

Malaria is spread by mosquitoes, so the disease can be prevented by destroying these carriers. The life cycle of a mosquito has three aquatic stages. Fish introduced to the breeding grounds reduce the population of mosquito eggs, larvae, and pupae. Alternatively, pupae can be killed by a thin layer of oil on the water surface, which prevents them from breathing.

been slaughtered in accredited slaughterhouses. Tuberculosis of the bone and brain tissue of cattle, which was common 50 years ago, is now rarely encountered in developed countries, as a result of scrupulous agricultural controls. Similar controls are applied to all other animals used as sources of food.

Food-processing factories, hotels, and restaurants are regularly inspected for the presence of vermin such as rats, mice, and cockroaches, and for evidence that adequate standards of hygiene are maintained in all parts of the operation where food might be contaminated. Stringent controls are also imposed to ensure that imported foods are fit for human consumption.

Food additives

During manufacture, processed foods may be enriched with substances that benefit health, particularly vitamins and minerals, which are sometimes destroyed in the commercial preparation of such foods. Iron and other minerals are added to bread and cereal foods, and glucose is sometimes added to drinks and candies. Some foods contain extra bran to provide roughage, which helps prevent bowel disease.

Health screening

In many countries, schoolchildren are tested for tuberculosis susceptibility. Chest radiography—which may be provided by companies, schools, or local health authorities—is

available if necessary to check for disorders such as tuberculosis, lung cancer, chronic chest infection, and other conditions. Regular health checks and education programs are also instituted wherever possible, often under the direction of international bodies such as the World Health Organization.

Women, particularly in developed countries, are advised to have regular cervical smear tests and to examine their breasts for lumps. Both these examinations increase the chances for cancer being detected at the earliest opportunity, when it can be treated without much difficulty.

Mothers are encouraged to take their babies and children to clinics at special centers or at their doctor's office, where their development, weight, and rate of growth are noted against a chart of normal development, in order to identify abnormally slow or fast developers. Their feeding programs are discussed and dietary advice is given where necessary. Nursing mothers are advised to continue breastfeeding as long as possible. In some countries, however, the need to return to work and the availability of artificial milks has encouraged many mothers to stop breastfeeding too soon. Consequently, their babies fail to acquire natural immunity to certain diseases and also suffer from illness caused by contamination of the artificial food. An important aspect of health education is the identification and correction of such harmful trends.

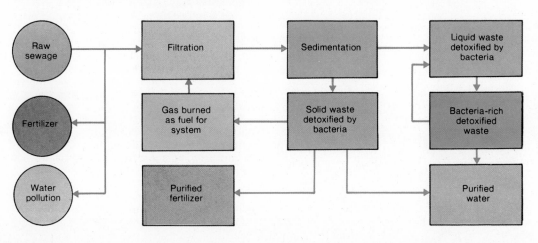

Safe sewage disposal is fundamental to community health. In primitive communities, sewage may be disposed of by using it as a fertilizer or by throwing it into a river. In an urban community, however, sewage can also be a serious source of disease if it is not properly treated.

The hands are a source of infection, even after washing. This photograph shows the growth of bacteria after a "clean" hand was pressed palm-down on a culture plate.

Personal health

In the second half of the twentieth century, good health is accepted as normal by most people who live in developed countries. This has resulted partly from improved standards of prenatal and child care, hygiene, nutrition, and preventive medicine; partly from better educational methods and communication; and partly from the astonishing advances that have been made in all areas of medical science. Unfortunately, many people take good health for granted and fail to treat their bodies with sufficient care and consideration.

Diet

A balanced diet containing the basic food types—proteins, fats, carbohydrates, vitamins, minerals, and fluids—is essential for satisfac-

tory growth, development, and health. Babies require these in an easily digestible form, and breast milk is the best possible nutrition for an infant.

In Western countries, a large percentage of the daily protein requirement is supplied by meat. This is a good source of essential amino acids (protein building blocks), but red meat from farm stock also contains substantial quantities of saturated fat, which contributes to the development of heart disease. Research shows that communities with a diet containing a large proportion of fish, for example the Japanese, suffer less from heart disease, high blood pressure, and strokes. In contrast, a diet lacking even eggs or dairy proteins—for example, the diets based on rice, millet, or root vegetables that are common in poor nations—is likely to lead to some degree of protein deficiency.

In the West, it is possible to eat a perfectly balanced diet, but most people forego this opportunity. They tend to eat too much fat, sugar, and starch, and, as a result, suffer ill health from digestive problems, cardiovascular disorders, and obesity. An example of a balanced diet is one consisting of a small amount of meat; fish, eggs, and dairy products; raw or lightly-cooked fruit and vegetables; whole grain flour products; whole grains, nuts, and seeds.

Exercise

People living in agricultural societies are often much healthier than those in technologically developed ones. Outdoor activity keeps people strong and supple, whereas a more sedentary life style is more likely to produce joint degeneration and muscular weakness at a relatively early age.

Hard manual labor and physical exercise are not necessarily the same thing, however, as can be deduced from the poor physiques of some manual laborers. To be lastingly beneficial, exercise should rhythmically contract and relax the various muscle groups and should exercise the heart and lungs moderately. The best forms of exercise to avoid excess weight and keep the heart and blood vessels healthy are swimming, skiing, racket games, dancing, cycling, vigorous walking, and jogging.

Relaxation

People in developing countries are often undernourished and overworked, but in many respects they are better at relaxing than people in developed countries. Many practice meditation, and take part in sports, dancing, singing, and games, all of which are more beneficial than the passive entertainment of television that occupies so much of the leisure time of their counterparts in developed nations.

Exercise is an excellent way of combating the ill effects of stress. The "fight or flight" mechanism, which is the physiological basis of stress, is given an outlet through physical activity and so is prevented from harming the person, physically or mentally. Meditation is also a good way of calming the mind and inducing a sense of mental and emotional well-being. Laughter, too, is an excellent antidote to

Constituent of tobacco smoke	Acts against	Likely result
Nicotine	Natural defenses	Respiratory illness
	Heart	Heart disease
	Circulation	Circulatory disease
	Digestion	Stomach ulcer
Irritants	Respiratory tract	Chronic bronchitis
Carbon monoxide	Blood oxygen (reduced)	Damage to fetus
Carcinogens	Mouth, throat and lungs	Cancer of these and other parts of the body

Tobacco smoke is a major cause of illness and disease. Four main constituents—nicotine, irritants, carbon monoxide, and cancer-producing agents (carcinogens)—affect the respiratory tract (mouth, throat, and lungs) directly, and the circulatory system, stomach, and, in pregnant women, the fetus indirectly.

Alcohol produces a sense of euphoria and a loss of mental and physical control. The chart shows the approximate effects of an increasing number of drinks and the corresponding level of alcohol in the blood (expressed as milligrams of alcohol per 100 milliliters of blood).

Pint of beer is equivalent to Glass of wine is equivalent to 2oz of spirits

Number of drinks	Effect	Blood alcohol (mg/100ml)
10	Unconsciousness	200
9	Memory loss	180
8	Double vision	160
7	Loss of coordination	140
6	Recklessness	120
5	Exhilaration	100
4	Bad judgment	80
3	Carelessness	60
2	Loss of inhibition	40
1	Relaxation	20

stress, and recreational pleasure is as important to health as is physical exercise.

Hygiene

Before the discovery of bacteria and viruses, and the identification of their role in causing disease, cleanliness was considered a luxury. Now, however, the importance of personal hygiene is accepted in nearly all countries of the world.

Personal hygiene includes washing the hands after visiting the washroom, as well as maintaining the washroom itself and the washing areas in a hygienic state. This involves regularly rinsing the sink and toilet with disinfectant and providing soap and either clean towels or hot-air hand driers. The hands should always be washed before preparing or eating food.

Preventive measures

There are certain preventive measures that most people can take against disease—and some which depend upon their availability. Principal aids to personal health are eating a balanced diet; taking regular exercise; learning to relax; and keeping oneself, family, and home as clean as possible. Others are to avoid smoking, drugs (except when medically essential) and excessive quantities of alcohol. Most peoples' environment is determined largely by their means of livelihood, but where an option exists, it makes sense to choose to live a life in which pollution and stress are minimal.

As additional aids to ensuring personal health, the following can also be beneficial: inoculation against infectious diseases, particularly for babies and young children; regular routine tests, such as breast examination and cervical smears; and regular tests of blood pressure and heart rate.

Regular exercise can help to maintain good health, and running—alone or in company—is popular because it allows people to keep fit relatively easily. Running in the countryside adds to the enjoyment and avoids damage to bones and joints that can be caused by running on roads.

Drinking and smoking are harmful but are great social pleasures nevertheless; many people tolerate or ignore the dangers for the sake of relaxation and conviviality.

Treatment of illness

The treatment of illness begins with the investigation of a patient's symptoms and the diagnosis of their cause. Treatment then aims to eradicate the cause, by means of drug treatment, surgery, modifications to lifestyle or, increasingly, where conventional methods seem inappropriate, by recourse to those alternative therapies that have been approved by scientists.

In all medicine, however, investigation and diagnosis must be the starting point. Laboratory tests, X-ray and exploratory techniques are now aided by computers, which speed up the rate at which diagnoses can be made and treatment started. Ten years ago, the fastest autoanalyzer could investigate the blood chemistry of several patients simultaneously and produce hundreds of results within an hour. Nowadays, medically computed analyzers are many times faster.

Physical examination

No machine, however advanced, is ever likely to replace the physical examination of the patient by the physician. An easy physician-patient relationship has an important effect on the patient's mental state, which in turn may influence the healing process. At a more complex level, the physician may be able to make judgments more subtle than any machine can. Ideally, physician and machine complement each other in diagnosis.

Complete physical examinations are usually carried out in a clinic or a physician's office. The patient's case history generally indicates which body system requires initial exploration.

When the heart and major blood vessels are examined, the pulse is felt, the heart is listened to with a stethoscope (auscultation), and the blood pressure is measured. Air entry into both lungs is checked, and the chest tapped (percussed) to define air-containing areas. The abdomen is felt (palpated) with the flat of the hand to test for swelling, tenderness, or other abnormality. Internal examination, rectal (per rectum or PR) or vaginal (per vaginum or PV), explores the contours of the rectum and vagina, respectively.

Eyes are examined with a small flashlight for pupil size and reaction; each retina is studied with an ophthalmoscope that focuses on the light-sensitive membranes at the back of the eye. The eardrum is examined with the otoscope, and the mouth and throat with a flashlight and tongue depressor.

Cranial and spinal nerves are tested by the muscular power and surface sensation of the parts they supply. Spinal reflexes are gauged with the patellar hammer, used to elicit a series of reflexes, best-known of which is the knee jerk.

Laboratory analysis

Requests by a doctor for "culture and sensitivity" tests to be made on a particular specimen usually refer to urine samples. A drop is studied microscopically, by the laboratory analyst or pathologist, then "plated out" onto the surface of a culture medium (jelly) in special disposable plates, before being incubated for 24 hours.

Growths (cultures) of bacteria appear as small white or colored "colonies." Their sensitivity to antibiotics is tested by their reactions to paper spots in the jelly, each spot being impregnated with a different antibiotic. Those to which the bacteria are sensitive inhibit the growth of the bacteria colonies in their vicinity.

Sputum (phlegm) is treated similarly, and for whooping cough special "cough plates" are

Antibiotic drugs are tested on a culture plate containing a jellylike medium *(right)* with a colony of bacteria. Different drugs or different concentrations of drugs inhibit bacterial growth to varying extents, leaving a clear area in the culture. Similar techniques *(below)* are used in pathology laboratories to analyze samples as part of medical investigation and diagnosis.

Antibiotic spots

Bacteria

Culture plate

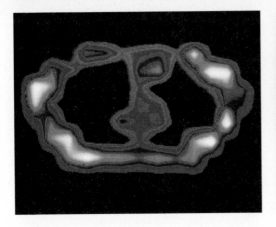

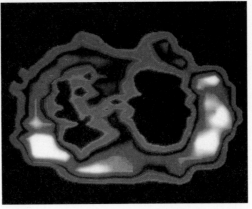

Nuclear magnetic resonance (NMR) techniques can be used instead of X rays to examine the interior of the body. NMR can reveal more detail than X rays and has no known side effects. One NMR image *(far left)* shows a cross section of a normal chest. The other *(left)* indicates the presence of a tumor in the patient's lung.

available to catch the droplets of infected sputum from suspected patients.

Urine and blood are also tested chemically for abnormal constituents, or abnormally high or low levels of substances that are usually present in known proportions. A raised level of urea in urine, for instance, suggests kidney disease, while a low level of thyroid hormone in the blood characterizes malfunction of the thyroid gland.

Blood samples are tested for clotting ability (erythrocyte sedimentation rate, or ESR). They may also be given a "blood count," in which the red cells per cubic millimeter are counted and examined for shape, size, and hemoglobin content. White cells are also counted and the various types identified.

Feces are examined for blood, which indicates bleeding in the gastrointestinal tract, and for evidence of infection or parasitic infestation.

Other techniques

The interior of the body can be examined visually by endoscopy, using a flexible fiberoptic tube that can be introduced either through natural openings or a small surgical incision.

Endoscopes are usually named for the part of the body they examine. A bronchoscope allows the physician to examine the windpipe (trachea) and the bronchi of both lungs. Cancerous growths can be detected in this way. A gastroscope shows the lining of the esophagus and the stomach. Similarly, a colonoscope, sigmoidoscope, and cystoscope view the interiors of the descending colon, sigmoid colon, and bladder, respectively.

Patients are given either a sedative or a general anesthetic before endoscopic procedures. During the examination, the physician can remove a tiny piece of tissue for a biopsy. Then the pathologist examines it for the presence of abnormal cells that might indicate an infection, cancer, or changes due to a disorder, such as ulcerative colitis (which affects the lower gastrointestinal tract).

As well as being used to diagnose skeletal problems, X rays can be used to investigate abnormalities of the soft tissues and internal organs. Tomography produces X rays of structures in a selected plane of the body, by computer-aided interpretation of a sequence of X-ray scans.

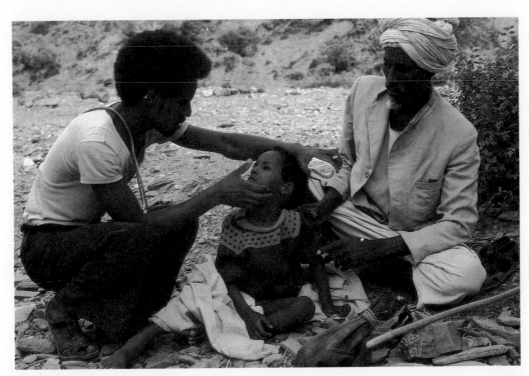

A physician, whether in a well-equipped office or, as here, without sophisticated technical aids in the open air of the bush, often remains the first (and most important) contact with the patient, making the first diagnosis and prescribing the preliminary treatment.

Ear, nose, throat, and respiratory disorders

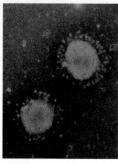

The common cold is the most common respiratory disorder in nontropical countries. Because it is caused by viruses (one type of which is shown above, much enlarged), it is difficult to treat, and most palliatives at best only relieve symptoms such as headache and sore throat.

Many of the disorders that affect the ears, nose, and throat result from infections, often producing symptoms of soreness and inflammation. The major sites for such infections are the sinuses; nasal passages and adenoids; throat and tonsils; larynx and trachea (windpipe); and the ears themselves. The ear canal may become blocked with wax, causing temporary deafness; inflammation of the middle ear results in earache; and disorders of the inner ear may cause dizziness or loss of hearing.

The respiratory system represents a compromise. On one hand, it must provide a large and effective area for exchanging oxygen with the environment; on the other, it must prevent harmful environmental agents from reaching deep into the body. Disorders of the system are generally characterized by ineffective gas exchange or failure of defenses. The whole system from the nose to the bronchioles (with an extension to the middle ear) is lined by specialized mucosa, and these structures are therefore considered together.

Ear disorders

Infections that spread from the nose or pharynx usually affect the middle ear. The Eustachian tube can be blocked by inflammation of nasal tissues, and this can cause acute ear infection (otitis media), or serous otitis, caused by accumulation of fluid in the ear (glue ear). The latter is usually treated with antihistamines, to reduce the inflammation and allow the fluid to drain, though surgery may be required to equalize pressure in the ear by inserting a small tube (grommet) in the eardrum. In some cases, the adenoids (lymphatic tissue at the back of the nose) need to be removed to cure persistent inflammation and blockage.

Untreated middle ear infections can spread to the mastoid bone behind the ear. The honeycomb structure of this bone allows infection to develop to such an extent that antibiotics may be ineffective, and if so, only surgery can eradicate the disease. Untreated mastoiditis can spread farther to destroy the inner ear, or to cause meningitis or an abscess in the brain.

Deafness can result from a scarred or ruptured eardrum—whether from infection or from an accident—but is more commonly caused by degeneration (ostosclerosis) of the small bones of the middle ear, which transmit sound. Persistent exposure to loud noise can also damage the ear and cause progressive hearing loss. Formerly untreatable, such damage can now be repaired by microsurgical techniques: a new eardrum can be fashioned from the lining of the ear canal and damaged bones can be removed or replaced by plastic components. Deafness can also be caused by obstructions of the ear canal (external auditory meatus), with wax, inflammatory tissue, or fibrosis after infection, or even a foreign body.

Sounds similar to those of bells, rushing water, rustling leaves, or even aircraft taking off, may all be generated within the ear, and afflict those who suffer from tinnitus. These symptoms may be due to aging or degeneration of the cochlea, but this is not known for certain. Until recently there was no treatment, but now many patients benefit from "masking therapy" which, paradoxically, produces actual noise in a device worn like a hearing aid.

Nose disorders

Most disorders affecting the nose are caused by pathogens—primarily viruses—or allergens, such as dust mites or pollen grains.

The common cold is caused by viruses. Treatment concentrates on relieving the symptoms; there is still no specific cure. A new drug, interferon, may help to prevent colds, but it is still undergoing clinical trials.

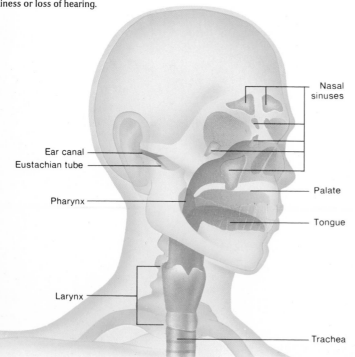

Nasal sinuses

Ear canal
Eustachian tube

Pharynx

Palate

Tongue

Larynx

Trachea

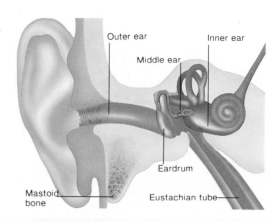

Outer ear

Inner ear

Middle ear

Eardrum

Mastoid bone

Eustachian tube

Throat disorders

Numerous bacterial or viral infections affect the throat. Medical names identify the main sites of infections—pharyngitis (pharynx), laryngitis (larynx), and tonsillitis (tonsils) are examples. Streptococcal throat infections are particularly dangerous because of the risk of complications such as rheumatic fever or glomerulonephritis. Throat swabs are taken to identify the infecting organism, which is then

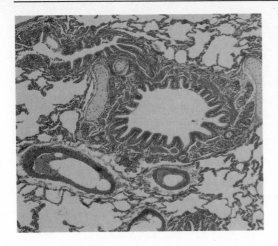

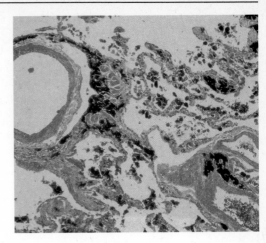

The lungs are susceptible to various infections that may cause inflammation that results in pneumonia or pleurisy. They are also vulnerable to the effects of inhaled chemicals and dust particles, whether from the atmosphere, working environment, or tobacco smoke. These photographs contrast tissue from a healthy lung *(left)* and from the lung of a smoker *(right)*.

treated with antibiotics such as penicillin. Apart from infection, irritants such as cigarette smoke or alcohol, or even overuse—for instance, shouting—can cause laryngitis. Cigarette smoke and alcohol also encourage the development of cancer in the throat.

Lung disorders

Cigarette smoke and atmospheric pollution are among the commonest—and are certainly the most preventable—causes of lung disease. Disorders due to smoking range from minor ones, such as laryngitis, to serious, usually fatal, conditions, such as chronic bronchitis and lung cancer.

Chronic bronchitis—a persistent cough producing sputum—increases susceptibility to other chest infections. It may also lead to emphysema, in which lung tissue loses its normal elasticity and oxygen-uptake is reduced, causing breathlessness. Complications of chronic bronchitis can lead easily to respiratory failure. Treatment is with antibiotics and possibly oxygen therapy until the infection is controlled.

The most common infections of the lungs are lobar pneumonia, usually caused by pneumococci, and bronchial pneumonia. If an infection reaches the lining of the lung (pleura), pleurisy can result. The chief symptom is painful breathing, which is also a symptom of viral pneumonia. The bacteria causing a similar infection, Legionnaire's disease, has been identified recently as *Legionella pneumophila*.

The occurrence of lung cancer is almost entirely a result of smoking and is closely linked to total numbers of cigarettes smoked and their tar content. Although this is the commonest type of cancer in Western countries, the incidence has begun to approach a leveling-off as the public becomes more conscious of the dangers of smoking. Lower tar content and filtered cigarettes may also be beneficial. There are three main methods of treatment—surgery, radiation therapy, and cytotoxic chemotherapy, used alone or in combination. Surgery is most useful if the disease has not spread outside the lung, and may be curative. Radiation therapy is valuable in controlling more advanced disease, especially secondary deposits in the bones or brain, but it rarely provides a cure. Chemotherapy shows great promise, especially when combined with radiation therapy, in controlling and possibly even curing one particular kind of lung cancer, called oat-

cell carcinoma.

Asthma

The symptoms of asthma are a combination of wheezing and a sensation of shortness of breath, caused by constrictions of the bronchial tubes and thickening of their walls by fluid. It is a common disease, affecting approximately 3.8 per cent of the total population and is thought to be an allergic reaction to inhaled dust particles.

In most cases, the allergen is unknown and treatment is directed toward relieving the airway constriction. Depending on the severity and frequency of the attacks, this may mean taking bronchodilators by an inhaler or may require powerful steroids and, occasionally, hospitalization. Recently developed drugs that patients inhale show great promise in preventing asthmatic attacks, especially in children. Treatment by desensitization injections and by special exercise programs have not been shown to alter the frequency or severity of attacks.

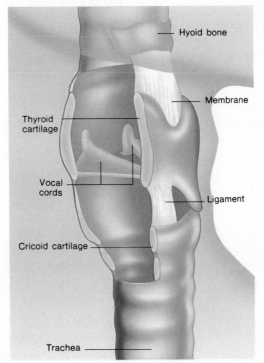

The larynx, or voice box, is an enlargement of the trachea (windpipe), partly closed by the vocal cords. Inflammation of the larynx—laryngitis—often spreads from the throat and causes the vocal cords to become swollen, usually resulting in hoarseness or even complete loss of voice. In an emergency, blockage of the upper larynx by swollen membranes in diphtheria or moniliasis (thrush) may be relieved by a tracheostomy, in which a small surgical incision is made in the windpipe below the voice box.

Hyoid bone

Membrane

Thyroid cartilage

Vocal cords

Ligament

Cricoid cartilage

Trachea

Heart, blood, and circulatory disorders

Arterial disease, and in particular arteriosclerosis, causes more deaths than any other disease in Western countries. The most common heart disease is actually due to diseased coronary arteries rather than to heart tissue itself. Damage or degeneration of these arteries reduces the blood supply to heart muscle, which ceases to function as a result. Other disorders can affect the rhythm of the heart, the valves, or the muscle directly. The heart can also be affected by general infections such as rheumatic fever, by cancer, usually as a secondary rather than a primary site, and by disorders such as high blood pressure (hypertension), which in turn may result from external factors such as smoking, lack of exercise, and fatty diet.

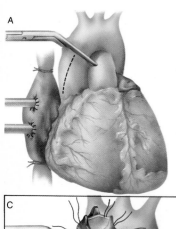
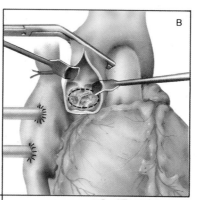
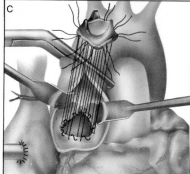
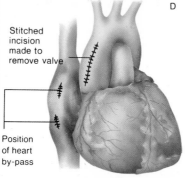

Stitched incision made to remove valve

Position of heart by-pass

Valvular heart disease may be treated by an operation to replace the disordered valve with an artificial one. First the patient's heart is by-passed by a heart-lung machine (A), the aorta clamped, and an incision made (B) to expose the diseased valve, which is removed. The replacement is lined up with long stitches (C), which are then drawn tight. Finally all incisions are closed (D). The photograph *(right)* shows an artificial heart valve stitched into its final position.

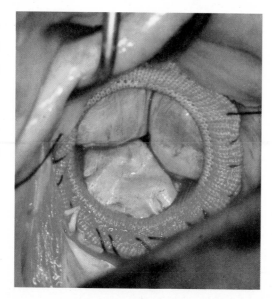

Over the past 30 years, the treatment of heart disease by surgery has advanced astonishingly. The use of heart-lung machines has enabled the heart to be stopped during operations. Implantation of artificial pacemakers and valves is now routine. Even heart transplant operations are becoming more successful, although all the problems have not yet been solved.

Arteriosclerosis

Arterial disorders are particularly dangerous because they affect the blood flow and so can cause damage to the heart, brain, and other parts of the body. With advancing years arteries and their walls become thickened (arteriosclerosis), and fatty material is laid down in the lining (atheroma), narrowing the vessel. Symptoms are unusual before middle age, though studies on American soldiers killed in Vietnam showed the presence of the disease as early as the late teens.

Several factors significantly increase the risk of developing arterial disease: smoking, high blood pressure, the amount of fats (lipids) in the bloodstream, diabetes, and aging. Diet can also affect blood pressure and blood lipid content.

If the surface of an atheromatous plaque is ulcerated, continuous healing and scarring tends to produce an ever-constricting arterial "bottleneck." Partial blockage in the flow of blood causes symptoms of ischemia (reduced local circulation) in the part of the body supplied by the affected arteries. Symptoms vary accordingly, but in the leg, for example, calf muscle pain may be caused by brief exercise and relieved by resting. If coronary arteries are affected, the symptom is chest pain (angina pectoris), which is particularly likely to occur when walking uphill in cold weather. An atheroma that causes ischemia in a kidney, in contrast, results in increased blood pressure.

Thrombosis

As the ulcerated plaque heals, local blood clotting may occur. If the clot (thrombus) blocks the artery completely, the effects are likely to be immediate and dramatic. In the heart, such blockage (occlusion) prevents blood reaching heart muscles, causing a heart attack (myocardial infarction). Unless the blood flow can be restarted quickly, the muscle dies. In the brain, arterial occlusion results in a type of stroke known as a cerebral infarct. In the legs, total loss of blood supply causes gangrene as tissue dies.

Even if such a clot does not block the artery completely, part of it (an embolus) may break off, travel in the circulation, and lodge in smaller arteries. Blockage may last for a short time only before the clot is broken down. If such a vessel is one of the network supplying the brain, short-lived symptoms, such as loss of consciousness, limb weakness, or difficulty with speech, may occur. This is described as a transient ischemic attack (TIA).

Aneurysms

Progressive damage to an artery wall can lead to weak points where the vessel wall bulges, producing an aneurysm. The aorta is commonly affected, and if so, may rupture, causing catastrophic hemorrhage. Aneurysms in cerebral vessels compress the surrounding brain tissue, producing various symptoms according to the part of the brain that is affected.

Treatment of arterial disease

The treatment of arterial disease is divided into prevention of clinical symptoms by slowing the progress of the disease, and repair of damaged vessels after symptoms have developed. Arterial damage can probably be minimized if the risk factors can be controlled by not smoking; by avoiding certain fats (particularly animal fats) in the diet; by treating hypertension; through weight loss; and by reduced salt content in the diet. Psychodynamic methods such as biofeedback, meditation, or other means of reducing stress may also be useful, or drug treatment may be necessary.

Exercise, for instance jogging, cycling, or cross-country skiing, improves the blood supply to the heart and muscles, reducing the risk of damage from occlusion of a single artery. People who exercise regularly tend to reduce or avoid smoking and lose excess weight, thereby lowering blood lipid levels and blood pressure.

Because many of the adverse effects of arterial diseases are related to thrombosis, there is great interest in the possibility that agents that inhibit clotting may reduce the progression of the disease. For instance, aspirin in low doses can inhibit platelet aggregation (stickiness), which is part of the clotting process.

Primarily, however, treatment for arterial disease is surgical. Usually, an occluded artery is opened and the atheromatous area is removed. The arteries commonly treated in this way are the carotid arteries in the neck, which supply the brain, and the femoral arteries, which supply the legs.

Diseases of the coronary arteries may be treated either by surgery or with drugs, de-

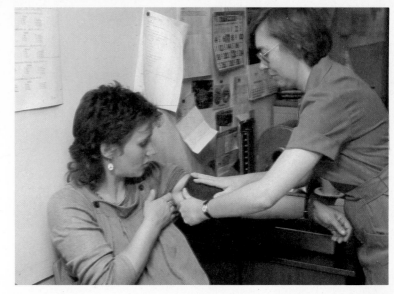

pending on the exact sites of obstruction and the individual patient's symptoms. The most common surgical procedure is the coronary artery by-pass graft, in which segments of vein taken from the legs are connected to the aorta and the coronary artery to by-pass the area of occlusion. Surgery is also sometimes required to repair areas of dead muscle after myocardial infarction, especially when the muscular wall (septum) between left and right ventricles has ruptured, or when the muscle controlling the mitral valve is torn.

Two new forms of therapy for coronary artery disease have been developed recently. One employs a thin tube (catheter), which is passed along a coronary artery until a narrowed segment is reached; a balloon on the end of the catheter is then inflated to dilate the constriction. In the other, used if a coronary artery has been obstructed very recently by thrombosis, a clot-dissolving enzyme can be injected into the arteries using a catheter. If this is done within a few hours of coronary thrombosis, heart muscle death can be prevented.

Blood pressure—or, more precisely, the pressure in an artery when the heart muscle contracts (the systolic pressure) and the pressure when it relaxes (the diastolic pressure)—is a useful diagnostic measurement for a physician, shown here measuring the blood pressure of a pregnant woman. High blood pressure, above $\frac{145}{90}$, is called hypertension and generally requires treatment. Low blood pressure (hypotension), below $\frac{100}{60}$, may be a symptom of shock or some other underlying disorder of the circulation.

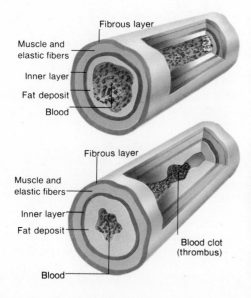

Fibrous layer
Muscle and elastic fibers
Inner layer
Fat deposit
Blood

Fibrous layer
Muscle and elastic fibers
Inner layer
Fat deposit
Blood clot (thrombus)
Blood

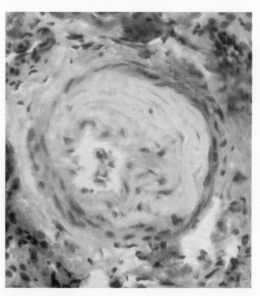

Arteriosclerosis is a disorder in which fatty deposits accumulate in an artery, narrowing it and restricting the flow of blood. The artery also loses its elasticity and suppleness. The diagram shows sections of normal and sclerotic arteries. Severe arteriosclerosis may so narrow a vessel that a blood clot forms. The photograph shows a section of an affected coronary artery that carries blood to the muscles of the heart itself.

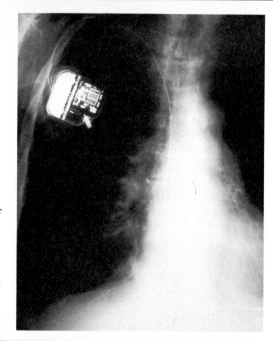

An artificial pacemaker can be connected to the heart of a patient to restore correct rhythmic beating when the natural pacemaker is deficient. The X ray *(right)* shows a pacemaker implanted near the shoulder and connected to the heart along a vein. The child *(below)* has a rechargeable pacemaker that can be reactivated externally, without the need for regular operations to replace the pacemaker's batteries.

Fast-growing and malignant, leukemia cells are stained purple here so that they show up in a sample of blood from a patient with this pervasive form of cancer, which can spread through the circulatory system. There are various types of leukemia, most of which originate in the bone marrow and other blood-forming tissues. Some respond to chemotherapy using drugs that selectively destroy the cancerous cells. Exposure to radioactivity or X rays has been identified as a possible cause.

Venous thrombosis

Blood may clot in veins because of damage to the vein wall, poor blood flow, or abnormally thick blood. It is more common in women than men, and particularly in those taking the contraceptive pill. The vein affected is almost always in a leg, which becomes red, swollen, and painful. Treatment is with anticoagulants, especially heparin. In some cases, part of the clot breaks loose and travels to the lungs, where it obstructs the blood flow. This is called pulmonary embolus and is also treated with anticoagulants. If the clot is large enough to block the main pulmonary vessels, the condition can be fatal.

Varicose veins

Varicose veins also occur most commonly in the legs. They are dilated veins that form when the valves that normally control the pressure in the vessel are damaged. This may be due to obstruction of the veins during pregnancy, trauma, or gradual deterioration through aging. In the elderly, damaged veins may lead to the formation of varicose ulcers, especially around the ankles.

Treatment may be with elastic stockings, which help compress the vessels; with injections to thrombose small veins leading into the varicosed ones, in order to reduce the blood flow through them; or by surgical removal (stripping) of the affected vessels.

Heart diseases and disorders

Congestive heart failure occurs when the heart muscle cannot pump enough blood for the body's needs. This is usually caused by the gradual replacement of heart muscle tissue by fibrosis. The condition can be partially relieved by drugs, such as digitalis, which strengthen the remaining muscle fibers, and by diuretics, which reduce the accumulation of blood.

The rhythm of the heart may be abnormal in many ways. The most extreme occurs when

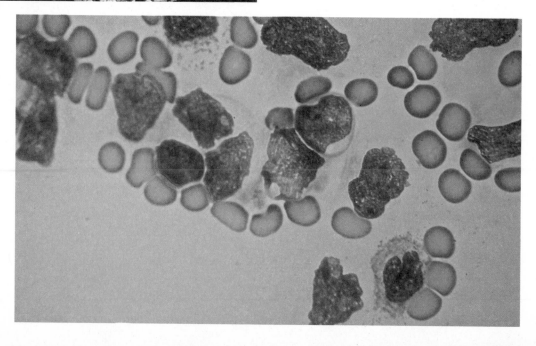

the muscle contracts in a completely uncoordinated way (fibrillation). The patient will die within minutes unless cardiac massage or electric shock (cardioversion) is applied. Pacemakers implanted surgically and a variety of drugs may control other arrhythmias.

Heart valves may be damaged by rheumatic fever or by a process similar to arteriosclerosis that affects them directly. In either case, the valve may become too small (stenosis) or leaky (regurgitant). Treatment is to replace the diseased valve with an artificial one by surgery. Some congenital abnormalities may also need surgical treatment.

Blood diseases and disorders

The red cells in the blood carry oxygen; a deficiency of red cells (anemia) produces symptoms such as fatigue and lethargy because insufficient oxygen reaches the tissues. Dietary deficiencies of iron, vitamin B_{12}, or folic acid are the commonest causes. Anemia is especially common during pregnancy, because the fetus uses the mother's reserves. It can also occur as a result of prolonged blood loss, commonly a result of a stomach ulcer or very heavy menstruation, or as a symptom of certain cancers of the digestive tract. Treatment is to replace the missing dietary factor or to treat the cause of blood loss.

An excess of red blood cells (polycythemia) makes the blood thicker than normal and therefore less able to flow through smaller blood vessels. The disease, particularly common in smokers, increases susceptibility to strokes, transient ischemic attacks, and venous thrombosis.

White blood cells are part of the body's defense mechanism and increase in number during infections. White-cell deficiency is rare, but is found in patients treated with cytotoxic drugs against cancer, or following adverse drug reactions. Abnormal white cell production occurs in leukemia, a form of cancer affecting white blood cells.

Infection of the blood is called septicemia, and generally spreads from a local infection such as an abscess or a wound. Treatment is with antibiotics.

Although blood required for transfusion is kept sterile, certain viral or viruslike infections are transmitted by transfused blood nevertheless. At least two types of hepatitis can be transmitted in this way. So can AIDS (acquired immune deficiency syndrome), which can also be transmitted by means of body fluids, such as semen. In AIDS, the balance of different types of white cells in the body is altered, leaving the individual susceptible to unusual infec-

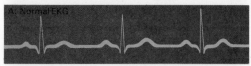

A: Normal EKG

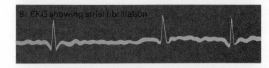

B: EKG showing atrial fibrillation

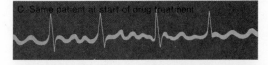

C: Same patient at start of drug treatment

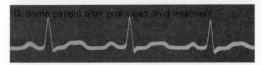

D: Same patient after prolonged drug treatment

An electrocardiogram (EKG), generated as a graph by a chart recorder or displayed on a cathode-ray tube, is a simple, painless but extremely useful diagnostic device for a cardiologist. Its purpose is to record the electrical activity of the heart, which produces a characteristic trace on the EKG; the instrument above is monitoring the heartbeats of a premature baby. The four EKG traces illustrated *(left)* show (A) a normal heartbeat; (B) that of a patient with a fluttering beat (atrial fibrillation); (C) the same person's EKG after beginning drug treatment; and (D) after prolonged treatment, with a nearly normal EKG.

tions and certain rare cancers.

Once very rare in America, malaria is now becoming more common as increasing numbers of people travel abroad. It is a blood disorder caused by a parasite that enters the blood from a mosquito bite. The parasite breeds in red blood cells, which then burst to release the offspring, causing symptoms of fever, shivering, and aches. Various drugs are used to prevent the disease but resistant forms are becoming more common.

Fact entries

Leukemia is a cancer affecting white cells in blood or bone marrow. There are many different types, broadly categorized into acute and chronic forms. Probable causes include exposure to radiation, although no actual causes have been established.

Acute lymphoblastic leukemia is the commonest form of cancer in children. It responds well to chemotherapy and at least 50 per cent of cases are curable. Treatment always includes irradiation of the head and spine to kill tumor cells in the nervous system. If che-

motherapy fails, bone marrow transplantation may be beneficial. Symptoms of acute lymphoblastic leukemia are high fever with a severe throat infection; there may also be nosebleeds, pain in the joints, lethargy, and increasing weakness.

Acute myeloid leukemia usually affects adults and is less responsive to chemotherapy than acute lymphoblastic leukemia. Bone marrow transplantation, aided by the drug cyclosporin A, is now an important treatment.

Chronic myeloid leukemia can occur at any time in adult life. The development of the disease is generally slow and controllable, though ultimately, in two out of three patients, this is followed by a rapid and fatal crisis.

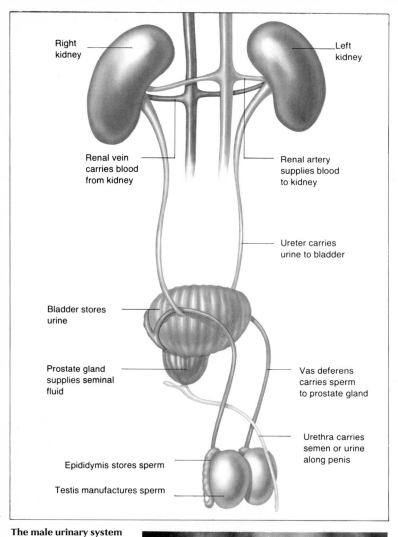

Right kidney

Left kidney

Renal vein carries blood from kidney

Renal artery supplies blood to kidney

Ureter carries urine to bladder

Bladder stores urine

Prostate gland supplies seminal fluid

Vas deferens carries sperm to prostate gland

Urethra carries semen or urine along penis

Epididymis stores sperm

Testis manufactures sperm

Urogenital disorders

The urinary and reproductive systems develop in parallel in the fetus; the genitalia also have both reproductive and urinary functions. For these reasons, diseases of both systems are treated as urogenital disorders.

Kidney disorders

Kidneys may fail for many reasons, the commonest being complications of nephritis, infection, hypertension, and diabetes. Early diagnosis and treatment are important to prevent the development of renal failure. Infection is particularly common in children and pregnant women and must be treated vigorously with antibiotics.

Renal failure may be either acute or chronic. Acute renal failure is a temporary condition that can result from shock, poisoning, or infection. While the cause is being treated, the patient may need dialysis to remove toxic waste. Chronic renal failure requires regular dialysis with an artificial kidney machine or the surgical insertion of a donated transplant.

Stones (calculi) in the kidney may block the urine flow and cause acute pain. Their presence may be indicated by blood in the urine (hematuria). Stones can be removed from the kidney by surgery (lithectomy) or, once they move into the bladder, by crushing. Once done by physically using an endoscope, modern technology has now introduced lithotripsy, which shatters a calculus by focusing ultrasound on it from outside the body.

Renal insufficiency is usually investigated by ultrasonic scanning and by injecting a radiopaque substance such as iodine into the bloodstream. An X ray taken when the substance is passing through the kidneys reveals their internal silhouette and shows how well they are working. Dietary measures are important in the treatment of kidney disorders—particularly to limit the intake of water, salts, and protein. It is also important to treat hypertension, which may cause either renal failure or be caused by it.

Bladder disorders

Infection of the bladder is particularly likely to affect women, because the female urethra is short. The main symptoms of bladder inflammation (cystitis) are frequent and painful urination. Treatment involves drinking large quantities of fluid to flush out the bladder and following a course of antibiotics.

A particularly troublesome form of cystitis, often called "honeymoon cystitis," is caused by the bacteria introduced into the urethra during intercourse.

Bladder cancer is one of the best-documented examples of an environmental cause of cancer. The disease is much more common in petrochemical and rubber workers than in the rest of the population. It is also more common in cigarette smokers. The main symptom

The male urinary system is more complicated than that of a female because of its conjunction below the bladder with the ducts that carry sperm and semen. In the photograph the system has been made opaque to X rays by injecting an iodine compound into the bloodstream. From where blood is filtered by the kidneys at the top, urine flows down the two ureters to be stored in the bladder. From there it should flow along the urethra, but this man has an enlarged prostate gland (immediately below the bladder) which constricts the urethra and blocks the passage of urine. The condition requires urgent treatment, which usually takes the form of surgery to remove the prostate.

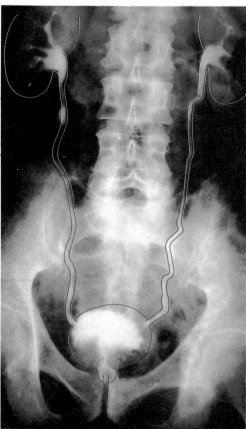

is blood in the urine (hematuria). Bladder cancer often takes a very slow course and may be controlled for years if monitored by regular cystoscopic examinations.

Prostate disorders

Enlargement (hyperplasia) of the prostate is part of the male aging process. Surgical treatment may be required if the enlarged gland prevents the normal passage of urine.

Cancer of the prostate, which is common among elderly men, is now generally treated by the oral administration of estrogen, combined with surgery as necessary. Treatment may alter the body's hormonal balance but effectively prohibits further cancerous growth.

Sexually transmitted disease (STD)

STD, or venereal disease (VD), describes a large and diverse group of disorders with little in common except the way in which they are spread and the parts of the body affected. Increased sexual freedom over the past 50 years has led to an increase of the three major forms: nonspecific urethritis, gonorrhea, and syphilis.

Nonspecific urethritis (NSU) is an infection caused by a variety of organisms. One increasingly common form (chlamydia) is smaller than a bacterium, but larger than a virus. The disease causes pain on urination and, in men, a discharge from the penis. It may be difficult to treat because it does not always respond to antibiotics.

The main symptoms of gonorrhea are genital irritation and discharge. Treatment is with antibiotics, although resistant strains of the infection are an increasing problem.

Gonorrhea and NSU often produce no symptoms in women, so contact tracing is important both for their treatment and to prevent further spread.

Syphilis is a more serious disease, with a number of specific stages; the first is a sort of ulcer (a chancre), and the last can affect all parts of the body and may cause death. In the early stages, the development of the disease may be prevented by the use of antibiotics, normally penicillin.

Two other diseases associated with sexual intercourse—though neither is exclusively transmitted by this means—are herpes and acquired immune deficiency syndrome (AIDS).

Herpes is caused by a virus almost identical to the one that causes cold sores, *Herpes simplex.* In both cold sores and genital herpes, the symptoms—small painful blisters at the affected site—appear periodically, and are diffi-

cult to treat definitively, although some new antiviral drugs seem to show signs of being successful.

AIDS is a condition that occurs particularly among bisexuals, intravenous drug users, and homosexual men and appears to be spread by blood and body fluids such as semen. In AIDS, the body's defense mechanisms are destroyed so that other infections and certain cancers find no natural resistance. At present, there is no consistently successful form of treatment.

STD's affect homosexuals as readily as heterosexuals, although the lesions occur in different places. Both AIDS and hepatitis B can be transmitted as STD's by homosexuals, although neither is exclusively a sexually transmitted disease.

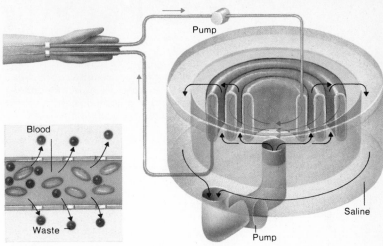

A dialysis machine removes waste products from a patient's blood and so acts as an artificial kidney. In this design, blood from an artery is pumped through a coil of thin plastic membrane, which is bathed in a saline fluid. The waste materials pass through microscopic holes in the membrane, and the "cleaned" blood returns to the patient via a vein.

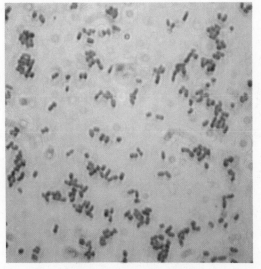

Gonorrhea is a highly infectious disease transmitted by sexual contact. It is caused by the gonococcus bacterium *Neisseria gonorrhoeae,* shown stained red in this photograph. It responds to prompt treatment with antibiotic drugs, but may remain undetected in females, in whom it produces few symptoms. Untreated, it can lead to sterility, and blindness in babies born to an infected mother.

Fact entries

Renal failure, if complete, is fatal unless treated either by artificial dialysis or by transplantation of a healthy kidney from a donor.

A kidney dialysis machine washes toxic substances from the body by bringing a chemical solu-

tion (dialysate) into close contact with body fluids so that excretory products pass from the latter into the former. There are two types of dialysis. In hemodialysis, blood is diverted from the body through a machine (artificial kidney), which contains dialyzing fluid sepa-

rated from the blood by a membrane that acts as a filter. Excretory products cross this membrane and are removed. In peritoneal dialysis, the dialysate is washed in and out of the peritoneal cavity.

Transplantation is the surgical insertion of a kidney donated by another person. The tissue types of the donor must be matched with those of the recipient as closely as possible, and drugs given after the transplant to prevent the donated kidney from being re-

jected by the recipient's immune system. Such immunosuppressive treatment may have to be continued for several years after transplantation, until the patient may be advised that rejection has become extremely unlikely.

Obstetrics and gynecology

Obstetrics is the branch of medicine concerned with pregnancy and childbirth. Because most pregnancies are not problematic, the main role of an obstetrician is to monitor the progress of mother and fetus and to assist at the birth. Gynecology is concerned with treatment of disorders of the female sex and reproductive organs.

Gynecological disorders

Abnormalities of the menstrual cycle include amenorrhea (absence of periods); dysmenorrhea (painful periods); menorrhagia (heavy bleeding); irregular periods; and premenstrual syndrome (PMS), also known as premenstrual tension (PMT).

A pelvic examination reveals most abnormalities of vagina, uterus, and ovaries. Blood tests reveal hormonal abnormalities. In some cases, an operation called dilatation and curettage (D and C) is performed under general anesthetic: the cervix is dilated and scrapings of the womb lining are taken for examination to detect any abnormalities, such as tumor, fibroids, or polyps. Polyps can be removed in the same operation.

A hysterectomy (surgical removal of the uterus) may be performed if the womb is the site of a cancerous growth, if fibroids (benign tumors) are growing in the uterine muscle, or to treat otherwise uncontrollably heavy periods.

Cancer of the cervix of the uterus is among the easiest neoplasm (tumor) to detect, by means of a cervical smear test. This involves examining microscopic cells scraped from the cervix for precancerous cells. If present, precancerous tissue can be removed—in some operations the affected site is cauterized using a laser—to prevent its development into malignant cancerous tissue.

The commonest malignant tumor in women affects the breast. Usually breast cancer is first evident as a small, hard, painless lump. To treat it, the lump and the surrounding tissue must be removed. In certain cases, this extends to removal of the whole breast (mastectomy). Because the spread of the disease can be rapid and extensive, surgery may be followed by drug and radiation therapy. Eighty per cent of women in whom the disease is treated early are perfectly well five years after treatment. Cysts are another common cause of breast lumps. These are harmless, but must be distinguished from potentially dangerous growths by medical examination.

Infertility

Male infertility is usually caused by absent or decreased numbers of sperm in the semen, or by abnormalities in the sperm. Infertility in a woman may be hormonal or physical. The most common cause of the latter occurs if the Fallopian tubes are scarred or blocked, usually as a result of infection, which prevents the ovum passing to the uterus. Polyps or fibroids in the womb may also cause infertility by preventing implantation. The use of "fertility drugs," which stimulate ovulation, may cure infertility. Alternatively, some cases of infertility

A common complication of pregnancy is a breech birth (A), in which the baby is born buttocks first, rather than head first. About 1 in 80 pregnancies results in twins, of which there are two types. In identical, or maternal, twins (B and *right*) both babies derive from a single egg and share the same placenta in the mother's womb. Nonidentical, or fraternal, twins (C) originate from two separate eggs and each has its own placenta. Nearly all twins are born normally.

A

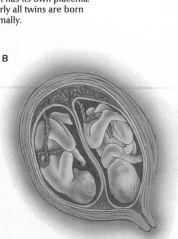

B

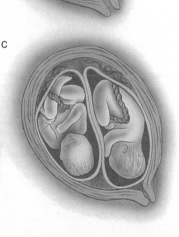

C

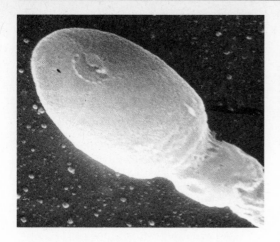

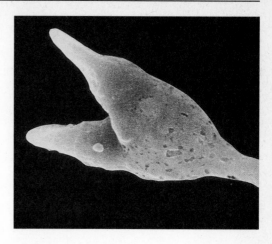

Infertility is a problem that faces many couples who want to have children. Usually it is caused by faulty ovulation or imbalances in the complex cycle of hormonal changes in the woman. It can also occur if the man produces dead, unhealthy, or insufficient sperm. These two photographs show a healthy *(left)* and an unhealthy sperm.

can be treated by removing an ovum and fertilizing it outside the body, then implanting it when the developing embryo is viable. This is the technique described popularly as creating "test-tube babies."

Prenatal screening

During pregnancy, regular visits to a prenatal clinic monitor weight gain, blood pressure, and ankle edema (swelling). Urine is tested for sugar, which may indicate diabetes, and for protein, which may suggest infection or preeclampsia. The top of the uterus (fundal height) is regularly checked against the expected size, and if there is a rapid increase, an examination using ultrasound may detect twins or an excess of fluid. This technique is harmless to mother and baby.

Blood is tested for Rhesus factor incompatibility and immunity to various viral infections, including rubella (German measles). The latter is ordinarily a mild infection, but if a woman contracts it in the first four months of pregnancy, fetal abnormalities, such as deafness or blindness, can occur. Further monitoring includes tests for anemia and syphilis. A test for the presence of alphafetoprotein is usually also carried out to detect spina bifida. Amniocentesis—in which a small amount of amniotic fluid is taken from the sac surrounding the fetus—may be carried out whether or not there are signs of fetal abnormality. Cells in the fluid may indicate the possibility of hemolytic disease (from an untreated Rhesus negative mother), and chromosomal abnormalities such as Down's syndrome (mongolism).

Other aspects of pregnancy

Iron and folate tablets are commonly pre-

scribed for the mother, but other drugs should not be taken without medical supervision. Sometimes a miscarriage (spontaneous abortion) occurs for no apparent reason, although it may be a reaction to fetal abnormality or placental insufficiency.

An ectopic pregnancy occurs when a fertilized ovum implants outside the uterus, usually in a Fallopian tube. At about 10 weeks, the tube ruptures and an emergency operation must be performed.

Complications of childbirth

During labor, the child is at risk from hypoxia (shortage of oxygen), and the baby's heart rate is usually monitored to assess this risk. If there is severe fetal distress, or for certain other reasons, such as a misplaced placenta, or if the mother is ill, a Caesarean section may be performed as an emergency. In this, an incision is made in the abdomen and the baby is delivered through the lower section of the womb. Fortunately, however, such complications are rare.

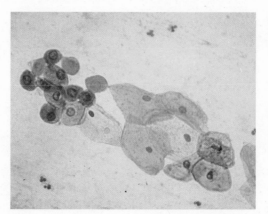

A cervical smear test to detect the possible presence of precancerous cells is carried out on a sample of tissue from the neck of the womb. The cells in the sample are stained and examined using a microscope; a healthy sample has the appearance shown here. The presence of abnormal but precancerous cells allows the physician to begin treatment—with drugs or minor surgery—before the onset of a malignant cancer.

Fact entries

Rhesus factor incompatibility occurs if a woman with Rhesus negative (Rh−) blood with a Rhesus positive (Rh+) partner conceives a Rh+ baby. In this circumstance, the mother's blood creates antibodies to kill the alien red blood cells that enter the bloodstream across the placenta toward the end of the pregnancy. No problem affects the first Rh+ child, but if another Rh+ child is conceived, maternal antibodies crossing into the fetal blood react against fetal blood cells and destroy them, causing hemolytic disease. To prevent this happening, antibodies are injected immediately after the first child is born, so that these antibodies destroy any fetal Rh+ blood cells before the mother can produce antibodies of her own.

Preeclampsia is a complication of pregnancy in which the mother's body retains fluid. The cause is unknown. If unchecked, it can lead to the death of the fetus. Treatment consists of bed rest and diuretics. If ineffective, labor is generally induced.

Gastrointestinal and liver disorders

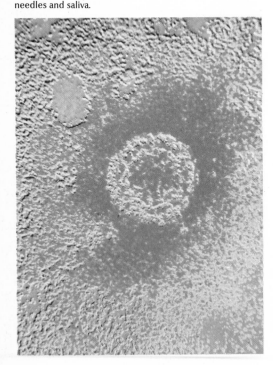

Most of the gastrointestinal tract is packed in the abdomen like convoluted plumbing. For clarity, it has been separated and extended in the diagram *(below right)*.

Hepatitis B, which results in inflammation of the liver and symptoms of jaundice, is caused by a virus, shown here in a false-color electron micrograph. It is highly infectious and is spread by various means, including contaminated hypodermic needles and saliva.

In present-day Western society, diet and the consumption of alcohol are the commonest direct or indirect causes of most disorders of the gastrointestinal tract and the liver. Almost all gastrointestinal infections are acquired in this way, as are some forms of hepatitis.

The esophagus, stomach, and duodenum

Many disorders of the upper gastrointestinal tract are caused by acids produced by the stomach in abnormal amounts or locations. These disorders often share a common symptom: a burning pain in the lower chest (heartburn).

Duodenal ulcers are thought to be at least partly caused by excess acid. They and stomach ulcers may require surgery, especially if erosion reaches an artery and causes hemorrhage. Cancer of the stomach is becoming less common in the U.S., possibly due to changes in diet. Surgical removal provides the only possibility of cure, but unfortunately this cancer has often spread by the time symptoms appear.

Virus infections and the bacterial contamination of food cause inflammation of the stomach and small intestine (gastritis). Symptoms include vomiting and diarrhea, both of which

are urgent attempts by the body to expel the noxious agent. Serious bacterial infections include cholera, typhoid, and some forms of dysentery, which are treated with antibiotics. Dehydration due to fluid loss and nonabsorption of fluids by the inflamed intestines must also be treated, sometimes by an intravenous saline drip. Drugs—which the gastrointestinal tract may not be able to absorb in these diseases—are sometimes administered intravenously too.

Celiac disease is an abnormal reaction to the protein gluten, present in wheat; individuals affected have to follow a strict diet avoiding all wheat and wheat-flour products.

Intestinal disorders

Disorders affecting the intestines usually cause either diarrhea, constipation, or failure to absorb nutrients such as vitamins and iron, although a low-fiber diet (such as one low in fresh vegetables) may also be a cause of constipation.

Appendicitis occurs when inflammation develops in the wormlike appendix. Treatment is by surgical removal of the appendix, which is usually necessary to prevent it from bursting and so contaminating the membrane that lines

The whole digestive tract *(right)* from esophagus to rectum is susceptible to various disorders, particularly inflammation, resulting in such disorders as gastritis, appendicitis, and colitis. Ulceration and tumors are more serious conditions that can affect the tract.

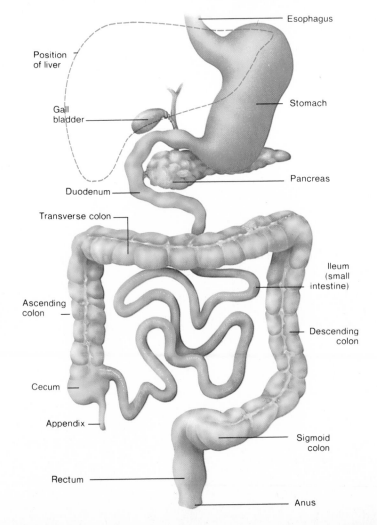

the abdominal cavity and other abdominal organs.

Crohn's disease and ulcerative colitis are conditions in which parts of the bowel become inflamed and ulcerated. The cause is unknown. Symptoms such as cramping pain and severe diarrhea are treated with drugs, but occasionally surgery is necessary. Irritable bowel syndrome (spastic colon) produces the same symptoms without organic disease.

Hemorrhoids (piles) are dilated veins in the wall of the rectum and anal canal. These may descend through the anus and become trapped there. They are strongly associated with constipation. If the disorder becomes persistent, thrombosing the dilated vein (blocking it, entirely sealing it off) by injection may relieve the symptoms. Surgery may be required. Cancer of the lower bowel (colon and rectum) is common, but can be cured if the growth is removed in its early stages. In some cases, this treatment requires an artificial opening (colostomy) to be made from the colon through the abdominal wall.

The pancreas and gall bladder

These organs produce and store digestive enzymes and bile required for the digestion of fats. The commonest disorder of the pancreas affects the endocrine cells secreting insulin and glucagon, and causes a type of diabetes that is treated as a specialized glandular disorder. Abnormalities in the bile result in gallstones, which in turn may cause inflammation of the gall bladder. The symptoms (abdominal pain and flatulence) are worse after fatty meals. If gallstones block the flow of pancreatic secretions, the pancreas may become inflamed, causing pancreatitis. This can also occur as a result of alcohol abuse. If cancer affects the pancreas, it is usually fatal.

Liver disorders

The liver converts nutrients absorbed from the gastrointestinal tract into products the tissues can use and excretes breakdown products in bile. Any disorder interfering with bile production or excretion may cause jaundice.

At least three major types of viral hepatitis are known. Hepatitis A virus is contracted through contaminated water or food, and the disease is normally self-limiting. Hepatitis B virus and non-A/non-B virus are transmitted in blood or body fluids; they present a small risk of rapid and fatal liver failure, and also a slightly greater risk of persistent infection, which may lead to liver degeneration over several years. Hepatitis may result from alcohol

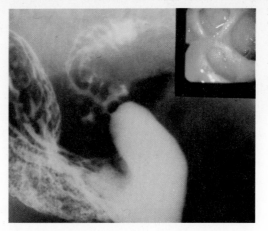

abuse or, rarely, is a complication of drug treatment. Vaccines against hepatitis B virus are also becoming available. Protection against hepatitis B virus, which is particularly common in the tropics, can be achieved by injections of immune globulin, although the effect is only temporary.

Cirrhosis of the liver—in which nodules form on areas of the liver already affected by fibrosis—is generally progressive and results in eventual death, unless the cause can be eliminated. A major cause is alcoholism; others are chronic viral hepatitis and some autoimmune disorders.

Liver cancer is rare in Europe, except in patients with cirrhosis, but is very common in countries where many people suffer chronic hepatitis B infection. The close link between the virus and liver cancer makes possible the prevention of the latter by immunization against hepatitis B.

X-ray photography and endoscopy (see diagram below) are important diagnostic techniques for examining the gastrointestinal tract. The barium-meal X ray (left) and endoscope photograph (inset) show fibrosis in the duodenum.

Endoscopy allows a physician to observe directly internal parts of the body—in this illustration an ulcer in the stomach—without cutting through external layers. In some cases, endoscopic surgery can also be performed or tissue samples taken using minute instruments attached to the head of the endoscope.

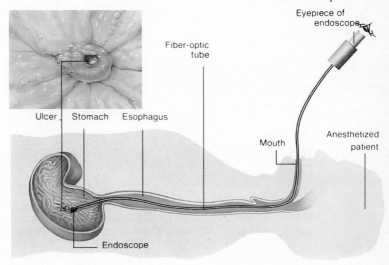

Ulcer   Stomach   Esophagus

Fiber-optic tube

Eyepiece of endoscope

Mouth

Anesthetized patient

Endoscope

Fact entries

Jaundice is the yellow coloration of the skin and eyes, which is a common symptom of liver or gall bladder disorders. It is caused by the accumulation in the blood of the yellow bile pigment called bilirubin, which is produced by the liver as one of the products of me-tabolism. Obstructive jaundice is usually caused by stones in the biliary system or cancer of the pancreas and is treated by removal of the cause, normally by surgery. Hepatocellular jaundice is generally due to a virus infection or an adverse reaction to a drug.

Yellow fever is an acute, infectious, potentially fatal tropical disease that takes its name from the symptoms of jaundice it produces. The disease is caused by a virus transmitted by mosquitoes. Symptoms include fever, vomiting, and hemorrhages, in addition to jaundice. Treatment concentrates on preventing death from dehydration as the disease runs its course. Yellow fever can be prevented by vaccination with a mild form of the virus; protection lasts for ten years. Such immunization is not advised for pregnant women.

Bone, joint, and muscle disorders

Bones and muscles give the body its strength and shape; with joints, they also allow the body to move. Disorders affecting them are usually treated by an orthopedic specialist, though other specialties, such as neurology for neuromuscular disorders, rheumatology for joints, physiotherapy to aid recovery, and alternative treatments, such as osteopathy, may also be used.

Fractures and dislocations

The commonest bone, joint, and muscle disorders are fractures, dislocations, and sprains. In most cases, they are relatively easy to treat, although complications can occur.

Dislocation occurs when the bones at a joint are separated or violently misaligned. Muscles, ligaments, and tendons can be stretched or torn in a dislocation, as well as in injuries such as sprains, where dislocation does not occur.

In all fractures and dislocations, the first treatment is to reset ("reduce") the broken bone or the misaligned joint so that all elements are correctly repositioned. This can be checked by means of X rays. The affected parts are then immobilized while bones, tendons, and ligaments mend. Fractures are usually immobilized by splints, bandages, or plaster of Paris casts. Traction—a way of gently keeping an affected limb extended, using a balanced system of pulleys and weights—may also help to maintain the straightness of a reset bone. In certain cases, internal support is provided by fixing metal pins or plates to the bone. This has the advantage of allowing muscles to be used again as soon as possible, which is important for their healing. Sometimes the pins or plates are removed again at a later date. Some fractures are slow to heal and may be helped by the application of mild electric current to the fractured site. Ultrasound may also be used to speed healing of traumatic damage. It is not known why these last two treatments are effective, however.

Other bone disorders

Bone diseases are uncommon, because bone tissue is well protected from primary infections and because degenerative and deficiency disorders are rare in Western countries.

If bone becomes infected, the most likely disease is osteomyelitis, a bacterial infection of the actual substance of the bone. The infection usually enters through an open fracture or through the bloodstream. The disease most commonly attacks the ends of the long bones of the arm or leg, and is especially likely to affect children. Prompt treatment with antibiotics is almost always effective. Tuberculosis of the bone is a special form of osteomyelitis. It can affect any bone tissue but often involves the spine.

In older people, and especially in women, the bones become more brittle in a disorder called osteoporosis. Hormonal factors—causing bone calcium levels to be reduced—or some deficiency in dietary intake may contribute to the condition, and hormone, vitamin, or calcium supplements may be prescribed in treatment.

A lack of vitamin D, normally obtained in the diet or made by the skin in response to sunlight, disrupts calcium and phosphorus metabolism and causes the bone disease called rickets in children or osteomalacia in adults. It is now rare in developed countries. Treatment consists of adding vitamin D to the diet.

Although a variety of bone tumors occur, statistically they are rare. More commonly, bone cancers result from the spread of cancer cells from elsewhere in the body to form secondary tumors in bones. Of primary bone tumors, the form called an osteosarcoma is most

Broken bones are the most frequent condition treated by an orthopedic surgeon. The most common types include (A) a simple or closed fracture; (B) a compound or open fracture, in which the broken bone punctures the skin; (C) a comminuted fracture, in which the bone at the site of the break is in several fragments; and (D) a greenstick fracture, common in children, in which the bone bends and breaks on one side only. Broken limb bones are usually set and kept in a plaster of Paris cast while they heal.

Types of fracture

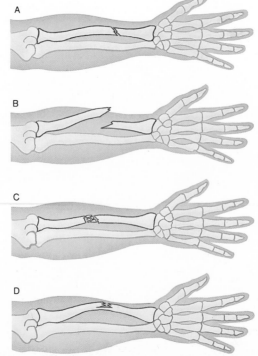

A

B

C

D

Awkward fractures may require special orthopedic techniques *(far right)*. Here, a broken olecranon bone at the elbow has been fixed back into position with a long metal pin. More sophisticated techniques include the total replacement of a joint, such as the hip or knee, with a metal or plastic substitute.

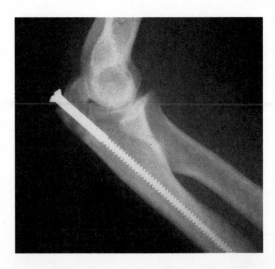

feared. Commonly occurring in young adults, this requires radical treatment involving drugs, irradiation, or even amputation to prevent its spread.

Disorders of the joints and muscles

Clubfoot, muscular dystrophy, and congenital hip dislocation are all disorders present at birth. Clubfoot, caused by muscular anomalies, can be treated by splinting, physiotherapy or, in some cases, surgery to lengthen tendons that are too short. Muscular dystrophies form a group of inherited, progressive diseases that inhibit muscle function. They affect men more often than women. Congenitally dislocated hips can be treated with splints if diagnosed early enough.

Arthritis is the most common joint disorder. The term—meaning joint inflammation—is applied to rheumatoid arthritis, osteoarthritis, and infective arthritis.

Rheumatoid arthritis is a chronic inflammation of the joints, especially the small ones in the hands and feet. The cause is unknown but may be due to an autoimmune reaction or to an unidentified infection. Symptomatic relief may be achieved with heat treatment, but usually anti-inflammatory drugs such as aspirin are required. Steroids may be necessary in very severe cases. If the disease progresses to permanent joint destruction, the damaged bone ends can be removed and replaced by artificial joints, restoring movements to an otherwise uselessly stiff or deformed hand. Physiotherapy works well in less severe cases.

Osteoarthritis is a degenerative disorder that tends to affect the elderly, usually in the larger joints, such as those of the hip and spine; it may also affect younger patients after trauma.

Treatment for all forms of arthritis involves the use of drugs such as aspirin, which helps to relieve pain and reduce inflammation. In severe cases, surgery may be necessary—for example, to replace an osteoarthritic hip.

Backache is probably the single most common source of discomfort in Western countries. Causes range from minor muscle or ligament strain to serious problems, such as a slipped disk (properly known as a herniated or prolapsed intervertebral disk) or secondary deposits of cancer. Serious disorders may need surgical correction to prevent permanent damage to the spinal cord and nerves. Less dangerous causes of backache can be relieved by relaxation, ultrasound treatment, acupuncture, or osteopathy (spinal manipulation). Since a significant component of pain is psychological, any therapy that concentrates on providing mental relaxation is also likely to relieve symptoms.

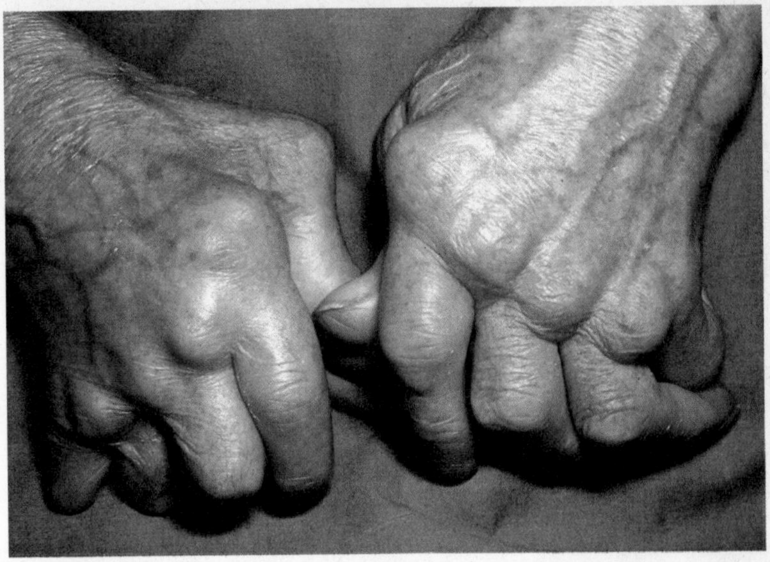

Osteoarthritis is a degenerative disorder of the joints often accompanied by inflammation and swelling.

Artificial limbs

Some amputated limbs can be repaired using microsurgical techniques to re-implant severed muscles, ligaments, blood vessels, and nerves. In other cases, it is necessary to replace a limb with an artificial one (prosthesis). The simplest (such as the traditional wooden leg) provide balance but little else. More sophisticated prostheses aim to replace the limb's function, and some now available have all the appearance of normal flesh. Furthermore, recent advances in microelectronics make it possible to build artificial hands that respond to the nerve impulses and muscle contractions of the remaining forearm, facilitating movements such as grasping.

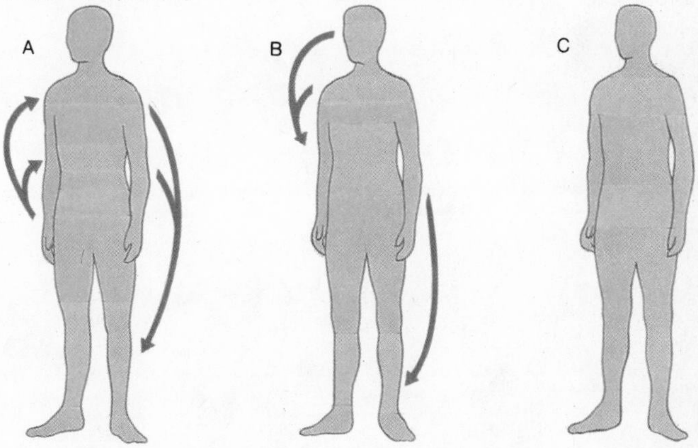

Muscular dystrophy involves progressive degeneration of the muscles. The Duchenne type (A) affects the pelvis first, then the trunk, shoulders, and limbs. The facio-scapulo-humeral type (B) progresses from the face and shoulders to the trunk and limbs. The limb-girdle type (C) affects the muscles of the hip and shoulder first.

Fact entries

Fractures are of various types. Complete breaks can be straight across the bone (transverse fracture), at an angle (oblique fracture), or twisted (spiral fracture). If the bone breaks or splinters with more than one fracture line, it is called a comminuted fracture. And an injury that bends the bone without breaking right through it is called a greenstick fracture. This is particularly likely to affect the pliable bones of children. In a hairline fracture, a bone cracks without breaking completely. A bone may also be indented or crushed. When a bone breaks, the sharp, broken edge may damage nearby tissues, particularly nerves or blood vessels, and when this occurs, it is described as a complicated fracture. It may, alternatively, pierce the skin, in which case it is called a compound fracture. Or it may be forced into another bone, which creates an impacted fracture. Usually, however, none of these occurs, and the commonest fractures are called simple, or closed.

Glandular disorders

Glands are organs, or collections of cells, which manufacture chemical compounds essential to the body's functioning. There are two kinds—the ductless, or endocrine glands, which release hormones directly into the bloodstream, and the exocrine glands, which release their secretions via ducts or tubes to a particular part of the body, such as the hair, skin, eyes, or alimentary canal.

There are countless exocrine glands throughout the body, from the mucosal glands of the nose to the digestive glands of the alimentary canal and the sweat glands of the skin. There are also several larger, complete collections of exocrine glands—the salivary glands, the thymus, the pancreas, and the prostate among them. The ones most commonly affected by illness are the salivary glands, for example in mumps, which primarily affects the parotid gland, and the prostate, a gland found at the base of the bladder in men that can become inflamed, particularly in older adults.

There are six main endocrine glands—the pituitary, thyroid, parathyroid, pancreas, adrenal, and sex glands (ovaries or testes)—and the term glandular disorders refers most commonly to these.

Pituitary disorders

The activity of several endocrine glands is controlled by the pituitary gland. Specifically, the anterior pituitary gland, stimulated by the hypothalamus, produces trophic hormones that act upon the thyroid gland, adrenal glands, and sex glands. It also produces the growth hormones.

Overproduction of growth hormones may cause gigantism or acromegaly (enlargement and distortion of the bones); underproduction may result in dwarfism, or restricted growth. Excessive secretion of the hormone adreno-corticotropin (ACTH) affects the adrenal glands, causing excessive steroid production. This may cause disorders such as Cushing's syndrome, which is characterized by abnormal fat deposits, high blood pressure, wasting of the muscles, fullness of the face, and various abnormalities of the body chemistry.

Panhypopituitarism, or overall loss of anterior pituitary function—usually the result of a tumor, a cyst, or necrosis of the gland—will be followed by failure of all glands under anterior pituitary control. It can be treated by substitution of the various hormones produced by the target glands.

The posterior pituitary gland produces antidiuretic hormone (ADH), which is responsible for maintaining the correct water balance in the body. Deficiency results in diabetes insipidus. This rare disorder is characterized by the production of excessive, extremely dilute urine, with corresponding dehydration and thirst.

Diabetes

Diabetes mellitus, or sugar diabetes, is the most common endocrine disorder. There are two major types. Type I (juvenile type) is due to deficient insulin production; Type II (Matu-

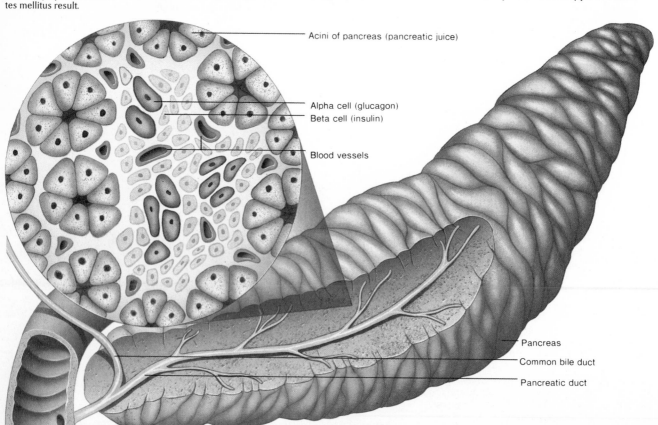

Acini of pancreas (pancreatic juice)

Alpha cell (glucagon)
Beta cell (insulin)

Blood vessels

Pancreas

Common bile duct

Pancreatic duct

Duodenum

rity onset) is usually due to insensitivity of the body to normal levels of insulin. Insulin itself is produced by clumps of cells called the islets of Langerhans situated within the pancreas. If they fail to produce insulin, the body cannot make proper use of sugar and starch in the diet. Instead of being used by the body to produce energy, glucose and other sugars accumulate in the blood and are excreted as waste in urine. This is associated with severe thirst and weight loss, while the high blood sugar level encourages infection. If untreated, diabetes can produce a number of other symptoms, such as drowsiness, and can lead eventually to coma and cardiac failure.

Diabetes is a common disorder, affecting some two per cent of the population. All diabetics need treatment to reduce the sugar content of their blood and urine and reduce the risk of associated disorders, such as cataracts or arteriosclerosis. Type II diabetes can sometimes be treated by a special diet or by tablets taken orally. Type I diabetes is usually treated only by daily injections of insulin, combined with a controlled diet.

Overproduction of insulin, in contrast, is quite rare and is caused by an insulinoma, or insulin-producing tumor, of the pancreas.

Thyroid disorders

The thyroid gland affects the metabolism of practically all the body tissues. It is unique among the glands in that it requires iodine obtained from the diet to make its principal hormone, thyroxine, in a process controlled by the pituitary. Healthy thyroid function therefore requires an adequate supply of iodine, a normal pituitary gland, and normal pathways of hormone synthesis and release from the thyroid.

Hyperthyroidism, or excessive production of thyroid hormones, also known as thyrotoxicosis, or Graves' disease, may be caused by a benign tumor (adenoma). More commonly, it is a result of an overactive thyroid. Symptoms include weight loss, flushed skin, thirst, tension, and anxiety. Body processes speed up, the thyroid enlarges, and the eyes protrude. Treatment may involve drugs or surgical removal of part of the thyroid.

Hypothyroidism (thyroid deficiency) may develop for a number of reasons, or it may be congenital. Once known as cretinism, the congenital form occurs when a child is born with a deficient thyroid or with no thyroid at all. Or it may develop in adulthood if the pituitary ceases to function normally. Most commonly, the thyroid is attacked by an autoimmune process that slowly destroys the gland and so causes hormone levels to drop, leading to progressive illness. Thyroid deficiency produces a low metabolic rate, giving symptoms such as fatigue, lethargy, depression, slurred speech, and a changed physical appearance as the skin becomes dry and puffy, and the weight increases. Treatment depends on early diagnosis and involves replacement doses of thyroxine.

An enlarged thyroid is known as a goiter. It may be caused by iodine deficiency or excessive production by the pituitary of thyroid-stimulating hormone (TSH).

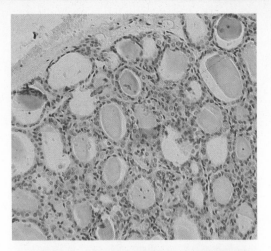

The thyroid gland contains cells that produce thyroxine, which collects in follicles between the cells. This microscopic section of thyroid tissue shows normal cells and follicles.

Goiter is a glandular disorder in which the thyroid gland, situated at the front of the neck, is abnormally enlarged.

Mumps *(below)* is an infection of the salivary glands, particularly the parotid gland, which causes them to swell. The salivary glands are paired, one of each pair being on either side of the face. All secrete salivary juices into the mouth cavity.

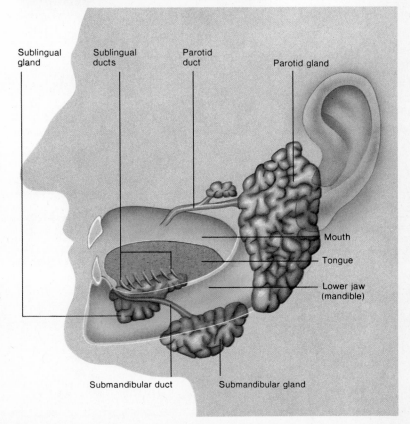

Sublingual gland · Sublingual ducts · Parotid duct · Parotid gland · Mouth · Tongue · Lower jaw (mandible) · Submandibular duct · Submandibular gland

Ophthalmics

The eyes are complex and delicate organs. They have their own external and internal muscles to move the eyeball and change the shape of the lens, and they are supplied by several cranial nerves—the optic nerve for sight, and the oculomotor, trochlear, and abducens nerves for eye movement. They also make use of several specialized types of tissue, notably in the cornea, lens, and retina.

We rely on good eyesight for most of our waking lives. It is the primary sense for perception of events and is important in almost all physical coordination. For most people, even a slight problem with their sight can cause considerable irritation or distress—although in fact it is also true that people adapt to small defects remarkably quickly.

Some babies are born with minor eyesight disorders, such as color blindness (which is hereditary) or a squint (strabismus). The former cannot be cured but the latter can usually be corrected by an operation. Other defects develop through later life, and by about the age of 40 or 50, many adults need to wear corrective lenses for some minor or major problem concerning their eyes.

Focusing problems

The most common eyesight defects involve a difficulty in focusing on objects sharply. Myopia (nearsightedness) occurs when the eyeball is elongated from front to back. Instead of forming precisely on the fovea of the retina, focal images form slightly in front of it, causing distant objects to appear blurred. Near objects, however, can be seen distinctly.

Hyperopia (farsightedness) is the opposite problem. In this condition, the eyeball is shorter than normal from front to back. The focal point of images is beyond the retina, so near objects appear blurred, whereas distant objects can be seen clearly.

Presbyopia is an age-related disorder in which the lens of the eye gradually loses some of its elasticity, making focusing more difficult.

Astigmatism is a condition in which the cornea, at the front of the eyeball, is unevenly curved. Images are slightly distorted in particular regions, because some of the incoming rays of light are bent more than others.

All these focusing defects can tire and strain the eyes, because the eyes adjust constantly in an attempt to refocus and correct the problem. Eyestrain and headaches are common symptoms of focusing problems that need treatment.

Other eyesight problems

Many other difficulties, not related to focusing, can also affect the eyesight. Problems occasionally occur with the retina of the eye, for example, if it becomes partly or completely detached from the underlying tissue, perhaps as a result of an accident. This damage can repair itself in some cases, but in others must be repaired by surgery. Techniques using a laser to fix the retina back in place are used increasingly in this operation.

A cataract is a disorder in which the lens of the eye gradually becomes more and more opaque, eventually causing almost total loss of detailed vision. Surgery can often provide effective treatment of this disorder, especially cryosurgery, in which the lens is frozen so that the cataract can be removed. The disorder may also require the lens to be removed totally, in which case artificial lenses must be worn after the operation to compensate for

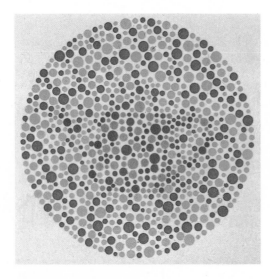

Color blindness can be assessed by a series of tests, one of which is a confusion chart, shown here. Under controlled lighting, a person with normal color vision sees a teapot in the pattern of dots. A person with color-defective vision sees only a cup.

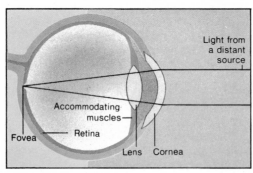

Normal eyes focus light from a distant source precisely on to the fovea of the retina.

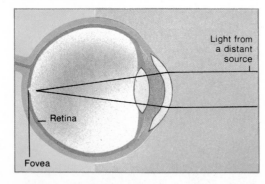

Nearsighted (myopic) eyes cannot focus light precisely from a distant source because the focal point is in front of the retina. They can focus light from a near source, however. The eyeball of a nearsighted person is slightly elongated.

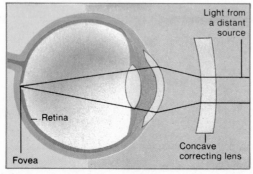

Correction of nearsightedness requires a concave (diverging) lens to be placed between a distant light source and the eye.

the loss of the natural lens.

Other conditions that can affect the eyesight include migraine headaches, which often produce blurred, narrowed, or distorted vision; albinism, an inherited condition in which the normal pigment of the eye is missing (often associated with photophobia, an excessive sensitivity to light); glaucoma, when increased pressure within the eyeball causes objects to appear slightly blurred, as if they have halos around them (this can permanently damage the optic nerve if untreated); and color blindness, or color-deficient vision, an inherited disorder affecting roughly 8 per cent of men and 5 per cent of women, which is characterized by an inability—to a greater or lesser degree—to identify one or more of the primary colors. Some infections, such as conjunctivitis, can also have an adverse effect on eyesight.

Testing the sight

Problems such as defective vision, a squint, or color blindness are noticed most often in childhood. Accurate diagnosis of these and other defects usually requires a full eye test with an optician or ophthalmologist, who tests each eye separately to see if it has any focusing problems. The eyes are also examined with an ophthalmoscope for any possible damage to the retina. The patient is asked whether he or she feels any strain, headaches, or pain associated with the eyesight, in normal or unusual light conditions. The ophthalmologist then tries several different sample lenses in front of each eye to see which one produces the sharpest image. From these experiments, most eyesight disorders can be identified, and corrective lenses can be prescribed.

Corrective lenses

Corrective lenses can be worn either as glasses or as contact lenses. Glasses can be more comfortable to wear because the lenses do not come into contact with the eyes; they also carry less risk of infection. In addition, bifocal or trifocal lenses can be fitted in glasses to avoid the need to use different lenses for different activities.

Contact lenses give a more accurate image of objects, however, because they work closer to the natural eye lens than do glasses. They also tend to be preferred by people who find glasses embarrassing or inconvenient. New users have to accustom themselves gradually to wearing contact lenses all day, because at first they feel like any other foreign body in the eye; however, once they are in place, accustomed wearers find them almost unnoticeable.

Many types of contact lenses are made: some are small and hard and have to be taken out before sleeping; others are large and soft and can be left in at night. All types have to be cleaned regularly and scrupulously. The ophthalmologist usually gives advice on the best kind of lenses to suit an individual's needs, preferences, and life style.

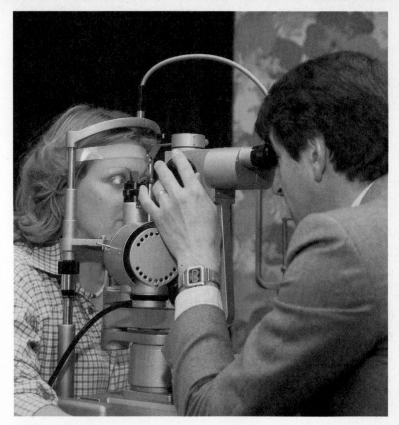

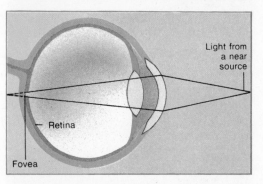

An ophthalmoscope is used by an optician or ophthalmologist to examine the eyes during an eye test.

Normal eyes focus light from a nearby source onto the fovea by changing the shape of the lens.

Farsighted (hyperopic) eyes can focus light from a distant source but cannot focus light from a near source, because the focal point of the latter is behind the retina. The eyeball of a farsighted person is slightly shortened.

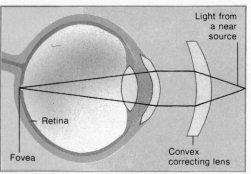

Correction of farsightedness requires a convex (converging) lens to be placed between the nearby light source and the eye.

Dentistry

Dental caries (decay) and gum disease are among the most common disorders of developed societies, and research shows that poor dental hygiene is the prime factor in tooth decay.

Techniques of dentistry are becoming more and more sophisticated, but prevention is both better and cheaper than cure. Habits that encourage good dental hygiene, from attention to diet to regular brushing of the teeth, improve the likelihood of retaining healthy teeth—particularly if these habits are taught to children as the first permanent teeth emerge at about the age of seven.

The teeth

The growth of the 20 first teeth, or milk teeth, begins when a baby is in the womb. Calcium for the formation of the baby's bones and teeth is taken from the mother's own supply, so if her diet contains insufficient calcium, the baby's requirements may cause the condition of her own teeth to deteriorate.

Generally, the milk teeth begin to emerge from the gums at about six months after birth, first the front teeth, then those at the sides and the back. Gradually through childhood, these teeth are replaced by a set of 32 permanent teeth. The back molars, known as the wisdom teeth, are the last to emerge.

Each tooth consists of a crown (the visible part) and the root, which anchors it in sockets in the jaw. A tooth consists mainly of hard dentin. The crown is coated with even harder enamel, while the root is covered with cementum to help anchor it in the jaw. Inside each tooth is a cavity full of pulp, carrying nerves and the tooth's blood and lymph supply. Decay usually begins at the enamel and eats through the dentin to the pulp. When decay reaches the pulp, pain and inflammation follow, and the tooth may die.

Treating decay

Decay is caused by the corrosive action of the acid in plaque, a sticky substance that forms from minute food particles and adheres to the enamel surface of the teeth. The first step in treating early decay is to drill out the decayed matter and to replace it with a hard substance so that decay does not recur.

The usual technique is to create a clean cavity with a high-speed drill, then to fill this cavity with amalgam (a mixture of silver, tin, copper, zinc, and mercury) in the back teeth, or a white resin for the front teeth. Each cavity is first lined with an insulating material to protect the sensitive pulp from temperature changes that are easily transmitted by the metallic amalgam. Cement is put into the cavity to ensure that the amalgam remains in place. If the decay has reached the pulp, the pulp cavity can be cleaned out and then filled with a sterile substance to save the tooth. Badly decayed teeth, once they have been repaired, can be capped (rebuilt) with gold or porcelain crowns to restore the tooth's function.

Extraction

Badly decayed teeth can cause extremely pain-

A tooth consists mainly of hard dentin, which is covered on the tooth's crown and neck by even harder enamel. At the center of a tooth is the pulp cavity, which contains the tooth's blood, nerve, and lymph supply. The root of a tooth, covered by cementum, is embedded in a socket in the jaw. The peridontal membrane, an extension of the gum, lies between the cementum and the bone.

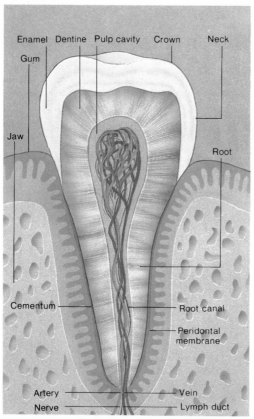

Enamel Dentine Pulp cavity Crown Neck
Gum
Jaw
Root
Cementum
Root canal
Peridontal membrane
Artery — Vein
Nerve — Lymph duct

Tooth decay usually starts (A) at the chewing surface. Serious decay (B) occurs if initial decay is not prevented. A dentist stops decay by drilling out the decayed part of the tooth (C), sterilizing the pulp cavity if decay has reached so far, then filling the cavity (D) with adhesive cement lining and a durable filling, usually of a metallic amalgam.

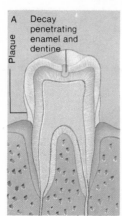

A Decay penetrating enamel and dentine
Plaque

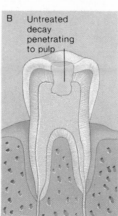

B Untreated decay penetrating to pulp

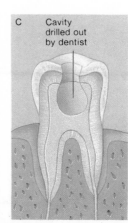

C Cavity drilled out by dentist

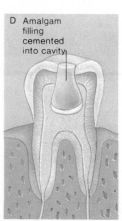

D Amalgam filling cemented into cavity

ful abscesses in the gums, and to cure this the tooth may have to be removed. But extraction may be necessary even when teeth are healthy. The usual reason for this is over-crowding in the mouth. Wisdom teeth that do not emerge normally should also be removed to allow the other teeth to grow properly. If plaque is allowed to remain around the parts where the teeth join the gums, advanced gum disease may also make it necessary to remove otherwise healthy teeth.

Extractions can be done under local anes-thetic, which blocks the nerves of the teeth and jaw, or under general anesthesia, which causes temporary unconsciousness.

Replacement

False teeth are made to fit the gap left by an extraction. A single false tooth can be screwed into the jaw or attached to adjacent teeth. Two or a group of several false teeth can be at-tached to a plastic plate which fits in the mouth. A full set of false teeth is held in place on the empty gums by suction.

Orthodontics

Orthodontics is the branch of dentistry that is involved in correcting faults in the positioning of the teeth. Many people's permanent teeth emerge crooked or too crowded, often look-ing unsightly and also making good dental hy-giene difficult.

Some teeth may need to be removed in order to reduce overcrowding in a growing jaw. If this is done, the remaining teeth can then be repositioned gradually with the aid of an adjustable brace, which is either clipped over the teeth or cemented temporarily to their surfaces. A child's teeth can also be pushed out of alignment by habits such as constant thumbsucking or chewing on pencils. In such cases, the habit needs to be stopped before the orthodontic treatment can be effec-tive. Orthodontics also includes cosmetic work that can be carried out on the teeth. The most usual form of cosmetic dentistry is the provi-sion of new crowns for teeth that are damaged or discolored.

Preventive measures

The importance of the prevention of decay is constantly emphasized by dentists. Plaque is formed most readily by sticky, sugary food particles, so it can be minimized by avoiding excess sugar in the diet, and also by avoiding snacks between meals. Cleaning the teeth thoroughly after every meal, using a good-quality brush and proper brushing technique, is also advised by dentists. Dental floss can be used for cleaning between the teeth. Also, some public health authorities add fluoride to the water supplies because it has been found that this helps reduce the occurrence of tooth decay.

Regular visits to the dentist are essential, so that the teeth can be cleaned and polished, any decay can be detected at the earliest op-portunity, and specific advice can be given if necessary. Some dentists also use fissure seal-ants to smooth out the cracks where plaque can lodge.

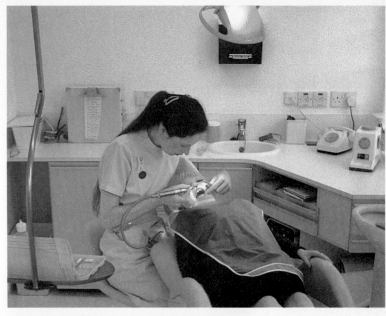

Dental care from an early age helps to ensure that the teeth remain healthy throughout a person's life-time.

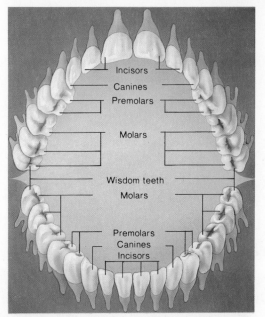

Incisors
Canines
Premolars
Molars
Wisdom teeth
Molars
Premolars
Canines
Incisors

An adult's mouth contains 32 teeth, 16 in the upper jaw and 16 in the lower jaw. The rear molars are also known as wisdom teeth.

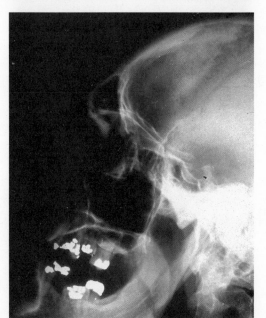

Extensive dental work has been required by the per-son whose skull and jaws are shown in this X-ray pho-tograph. Each of the solid white patches in the teeth is a filling.

Nervous system and skin disorders

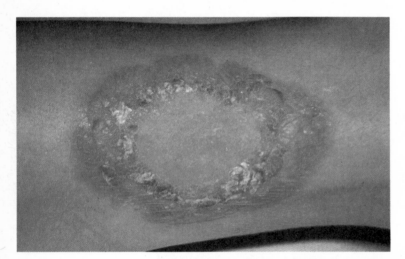

Herpes simplex virus, shown here in an electron micrograph, causes cold sores, watery blisters that affect the lips. A similar virus, *Herpes zoster,* attacks nerve endings in the skin, causing the acutely painful disorder called shingles.

The brain, central nervous system (CNS), and autonomic nervous system control most body functions. The skin is the body's largest sensory organ and is supplied with local pain and temperature receptors as well as parasympathetic fibers to hair follicles, sweat glands, and blood vessels.

The brain and spinal cord

In order to function, the brain must be supplied with blood. If this supply ceases because of a blood clot (thrombus) blocking a vessel, a stroke occurs. The symptoms may include partial paralysis, numbness, or loss of speech. After a stroke, these usually diminish gradually as other areas of the brain take over some functions of the damaged part. Factors that increase the likelihood of a stroke are constriction in a blood vessel (atheroma), high blood pressure, heart disease, and shock.

Investigation of any brain damage is essential after a stroke. Modern technology utilizes angiograms, ultrasound, and computerized axial tomography (CAT scans, involving computer-enhanced X-ray photography); treatment varies according to the diagnosis. Where muscles and coordination are affected, physiotherapy is almost always necessary.

Symptoms resembling those of a stroke may be caused by accidents to the head, particularly if there is any bleeding in or around the brain. The most obvious symptom is loss of consciousness, though whether this occurs or not, more profound symptoms—loss of memory, disorientation, fainting attacks, and speech or motor defects—may occur later, even after apparent recovery.

The second most common neurological disease is epilepsy, caused by abnormal electrical activity in the brain. Symptoms vary in character and severity and can include twitching, hallucinations, unconsciousness, and convulsions. Treatment is normally by drugs, though these control symptoms rather than cure the condition.

Spinal nerves are susceptible to damage if the bone or cartilage surrounding them shifts awkwardly. This occurs in a herniated disk, in which a damaged intervertebral cartilage disk presses on a spinal nerve. If the sciatic nerve is so trapped, this causes sciatica.

Infections of the brain or spinal cord, such as meningitis or encephalitis, which affect the protective covering membranes (meninges) or the brain itself, are extremely dangerous. Treatment is with antibiotics and must be both rapid and vigorous, as both conditions can cause long-term damage and may be fatal. Poliomyelitis is a virus infection that affects the

Eczema is inflammation of the skin characterized by an itching red rash, often symptomatic of an allergic reaction. The photograph *(above)* shows a spreading patch of eczema on a child's leg, below the knee. Antihistamines and corticosteroid drugs may be used in treatment, while an attempt is made to eliminate the cause of the allergy.

Permanent paralysis is a possible outcome of some disorders of the nervous system, such as poliomyelitis. These archers suffer from paraplegia (paralysis of the lower half of the body), but ably demonstrate their ability to lead a full and active life.

gray matter of the spinal cord and can cause paralysis. Children can be immunized against the disease, and it is now rare.

Damage to the brain in an accident may cause concussion, or symptoms similar to those of a stroke. Spinal cord damage usually results in paralysis of parts of the body supplied by nerves originating below the point of injury. Peripheral nerves can be cut or crushed, but can grow again. New microsurgical techniques endeavor to join severed nerve sheaths to help this regeneration.

Degeneration of the nervous system

Like other parts of the body, the brain degenerates with increasing age. Ultimately, this may cause senile dementia, which is marked particularly by deterioration in intellectual functions. One form of dementia, called Alzheimer's disease, can occur in middle-aged people as well as in the elderly.

Multiple sclerosis is a degenerative disease of the white matter of the brain and spinal cord. The cause is not known. Symptoms vary according to the parts of the CNS that are affected, but are characterized by various forms of uncoordination. There is no specific treatment, although steroids and ACTH (adrenocorticotropic hormone) may sometimes help.

Infections of the skin

Skin is exposed to a wide variety of damaging agents, including viruses, bacteria, parasites, carcinogens, and even the sun.

Viral infections of the skin include warts and cold sores and are extremely common. Treatment concentrates on alleviating the symptoms, though some antiviral drugs are available. Boils and impetigo, caused by bacteria, are treated with antibiotics. Fungal infections include ringworm, thrush (moniliasis), and athlete's foot, treated with antifungal drugs. The skin may also be attacked by scabies mites, fleas, or lice.

Other skin conditions

Eczema is a type of allergic reaction in which the skin is itchy and inflamed and may flake at the affected patch. Treatment is with soothing creams or, in more serious cases, with ointments containing steroids. Dermatitis is a similar condition, generally caused by a substance such as a metal or a chemical compound, for example, soap that has been in contact with the skin.

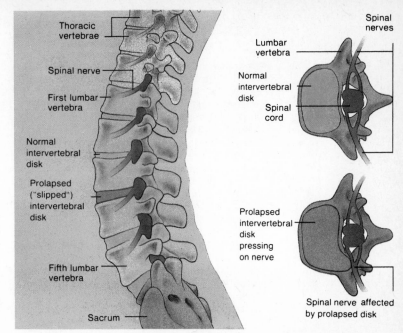

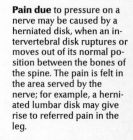

Pain due to pressure on a nerve may be caused by a herniated disk, when an intervertebral disk ruptures or moves out of its normal position between the bones of the spine. The pain is felt in the area served by the nerve; for example, a herniated lumbar disk may give rise to referred pain in the leg.

The cause of acne remains unknown, although hormonal factors appear to be important. In most cases, the condition improves spontaneously. Recently, high doses of vitamin A have been found to be effective in prevention or treatment. Exposure to sunlight may also help.

Psoriasis produces red, scaly lesions, especially over the elbows and knees. Treatment involves the use of ointments that improve the skin's ability to absorb sunlight.

Sunlight has beneficial effects on the skin, notably the production of vitamin D and the reduction of acne. But sunlight is potentially harmful, too. It damages the underlying connective tissue, reducing elasticity, and is a potential cause of all types of skin cancer.

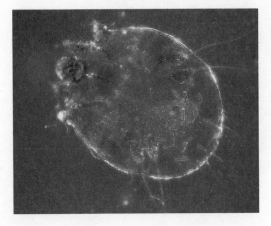

The scabies mite *Sarcoptes scabiei,* a microscopic arachnid animal, burrows into the skin and causes an itching, contagious skin condition that is an allergic reaction to the mite and its eggs. The hands and feet are most usually affected, and treatment is to paint the patient's body with scabicidal chemicals.

Fact entries

Epilepsy is a general term covering several different types of seizures. Seizures used to be described as *petit mal, grand mal,* and psychomotor. But the International Seizure Classification groups and describes seizures according to the area of the brain involved. The two major classes are generalized seizures, which involve all of the brain, and partial seizures, which involve only a part of the brain. Both types are the result of an involuntary discharge of electricity by brain cells. Epilepsy may develop at any age.
Generalized seizures are characterized by momentary periods of unconsciousness, or absence attacks, in which the person appears totally unaware of his or her surroundings. They are most common in children, and tend to disappear in adolescence or early adulthood. Seizures apparently rarely cause any permanent damage.
Generalized tonic-clonic seizures are usually characterized by major convulsions. A seizure is often preceded by a combination of sensations called an aura. These culminate in sudden unconsciousness and often convulsions. Following the seizure, the patient may feel disoriented, and is likely to wish to sleep.
Partial seizures with simple symptoms produce twitching movements of specific muscle groups and sometimes brief visual or auditory hallucinations. With complex symptoms, partial seizures involve impairment of consciousness and may be characterized by purposeless activities or aimless wandering.

Mental disorders

Until the end of the last century, most people thought mental disorder was the same as insanity. This view changed following the careful observations of the German psychiatrist Kraepelin, who established the classification of psychoses and differentiated depression into two categories: endogenous (coming from within) and reactive (having an external or social cause). During this century, a great deal of thought has been devoted to such classification and definition.

Definition of mental disorders

The definition and diagnosis of mental disorders and what is considered to lie within the bounds of normality varies, inevitably, with different cultures. In many non-European cultures in all parts of the world, states of "possession" by spirits, involving trances and hallucinations, are considered normal, while in our society such behavior would almost certainly be seen to indicate some form of mental disorder. Even among Western societies, there is disagreement about the details of what constitutes mental disorder and how it should be classified. The diagnosis of schizophrenia, for instance, is made more frequently in the United States and Canada than in Western Europe, although research indicates that

the incidence of the disease is fairly uniform throughout the world.

Despite these arguments about the borderlines between normality and abnormality, there are certain disorders of mind and behavior about which there is general agreement. These include altered states of mind such as abnormal anxiety, depression, or phobias, in which the individual is subject to considerable personal suffering, and aspects of individual behavior that are clearly regarded as disordered by the community as a whole.

Basic concepts

The development of ideas about mental disorder reflects the history of society itself. In the Middle Ages, disordered behavior was usually attributed to witchcraft; in the late nineteenth century, to brain disorder or heredity; and today, there is disagreement between social or psychodynamic and biological psychiatrists about causes of mental disorder, particularly about what is socially or environmentally determined.

One of the major contributions of Sigmund Freud was to show that unconscious factors play a crucial part in determining an individual's behavior. In particular, he established the idea that the unconscious is a reservoir of wishes and fantasies, basically sexual and aggressive (love and hate), and showed how unconscious conflict can give rise to psychopathology. He also supplied the method (psychoanalysis) for further study of the unconscious by later investigators.

In developing his theories about unconscious mental processes, Freud used three concepts termed id, ego, and superego, to denote interacting forces in human behavior. The id is the sum of primitive instinctive forces in an individual, which seek expression constantly through the search for pleasure and the avoidance of pain. The ego is the conscious self that mediates between the primitive id and the third aspect of the mind, the superego, and through this mediation controls behavior. The superego is perhaps best described as the "conscience." It is developed through upbringing and experience, and often conflicts with the instinctual drives of the id. Such conflict is normally resolved by the ego, but if it remains unresolved, neuroses can develop. Freud thought that much neurosis was

Freud and Jung, seated left and right of G. Stanley Hall, their host, visited Clark University, Worcester, Massachusetts in 1909 during their visit to the United States, where their ideas were received with great interest. Their colleagues A. A. Brill, Ernest Jones, and Sandor Ferenczi (left to right) stand behind them in this photograph.

Early schools of psychoanalysis, such as those of Jung and Adler, and the Neo-Freudian analysts, such as Klein and Horney, can trace their origins to the work of Freud. The links between Freud and other psychotherapies are more tenuous.

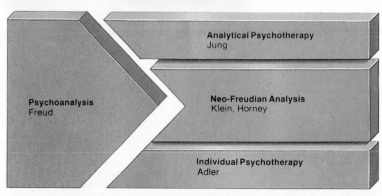

Psychoanalysis
Freud

Analytical Psychotherapy
Jung

Neo-Freudian Analysis
Klein, Horney

Individual Psychotherapy
Adler

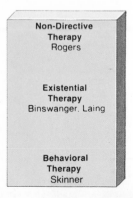

Non-Directive Therapy
Rogers

Existential Therapy
Binswanger, Laing

Behavioral Therapy
Skinner

caused by the suppression of the knowledge of sexual events in childhood. Not everyone accepted this emphasis, however. Carl Jung, for example, broke away from Freud's teachings because he was unable to accept that suppression of sexual memories was the primary cause of neurosis. He believed in the notion of a collective unconscious and dwelt more on the psychological present and future (stressing what people were capable of becoming) than on the past. Melanie Klein, who studied under Freud's pupil Sandor Ferenczi, placed the origins of neurosis and mental disturbance earlier in a child's psychic life than Freud proposed, maintaining that the significant period is in the first months and the first two years of childhood.

Classification

Neuroses are distinguished from psychoses because, in the former, contact is maintained with reality, whereas in the latter this contact is lost. The classification of neuroses is somewhat arbitrary, because most patients suffer from more than one classic type. The types serve to identify symptoms, however, and include a form of anxiety, phobias, obsessive or compulsive behavior, hypochondria, hysteria, a form of depression, and neurasthenia or excessive fatigue (which often accompanies depression).

Psychosis, in contrast, describes a mental state with no evident physical cause, in which a person's mental disorder is so great that contact with reality is lost, and delusions and possibly hallucinations occur. Manic-depressive psychosis, paranoia, and schizophrenia are the best-known psychotic syndromes.

Personality disorder, a loose classification, is usually regarded as the third major area of mental disorder. Such disorders range from minor disturbances, such as excessive shyness, irrational mood changes, and mild paranoia, none of which need be debilitating, to compulsive personality traits, often with a deviant sexual focus and extreme antisocial psychopathic behavior.

Superficial similarities between some minor personality disorders—irrational mood changes (cyclothymia) for instance—and psychoses, such as manic-depressive psychosis, emphasize the difficulty of classification. Other difficulties are posed by the question of whether minor sexual disorders, such as impotence or frigidity, and the states of mind associated with alcoholism, drug addiction, and even suicide are mental disorders as such or merely unfortunate aspects of the human condition.

Psychiatric syndromes

In the psychiatric treatment of mental illness, several specific syndromes are of particular concern. Anxiety and depression are prominent among these, because they are the two most common symptoms the psychiatrist is called upon to treat. Anxiety may be neurotic or psychotic. Neurotic anxiety is, perhaps, the commonest neurosis. Psychotic anxiety accompanies schizophrenia or manic-depressive states.

Mental subnormality, or deficiency, de-

Group therapy, with its informal atmosphere, is a valuable form of psychotherapy for people who share a common problem, such as a personality disorder or psychological dependence on drugs or alcohol. Professional organizations that help people to overcome alcoholism or compulsive gambling, for example, commonly use group therapeutic techniques. The therapist may initiate the discussion, but then often takes a more passive role, allowing the group members to talk among themselves.

Art therapy encourages people to express their inner thoughts and feelings through drawings and paintings, and may help to reveal repressed or unconscious aspects that contribute to a mental disorder.

Manic-depressive psychosis is a severe mental disorder that affects up to one person in every hundred, and is more common in women than in men. It is characterized by extreme swings of mood. In the manic phase *(left)*, the person is overactive and excited, often to the extent of lacking all self-control. In the depressive phase *(right)*, there is a prolonged period of deep depression and melancholia that may be severe enough to be suicidal.

scribes a condition of retarded, incomplete, or abnormal mental development at birth or in early childhood. Treatment is more commonly the concern of educational psychologists than psychiatrists, though where medical therapy is required the responsibilities may overlap.

The most common psychiatric illness in old age, senile dementia, is commonly manifest in childlike, perverse, or destructive behavior. The cause is unknown, but current research suggests it may be related to the pathology of Alzheimer's disease. There is no effective treatment, though research into Alzheimer's disease has recently made some advances.

Other disorders

Alcohol and drug abuse are difficult to classify in psychiatric terms, though both can be seen as attempts to allay or avoid anxiety. There is a possibility that those who become addicted to either have a psychological propensity toward addiction, which may be a neurotic compulsion, a personality disorder, or an indefinable urge toward self-neglect or self-destruction. However, both alcohol and addictive drugs

are severely harmful in themselves, and mental disturbance is a frequent result of alcohol or drug abuse.

It is believed that suicide reflects a person's feeling that he or she can no longer go on living with profound and long-standing depression. A distinction is usually made between successful and attempted suicide on the assumption that the latter is a dramatic "cry for help" rather than a serious attempt to die. Treatment of an attempted suicide concentrates on the underlying cause.

Minor sexual disorders can sometimes be treated by psychotherapy or psychoanalysis. More direct or interactive methods, usually described as sex therapy, may be successful.

Disorders in which the mind unconsciously affects the body are termed psychosomatic. In fact, many disorders may have a psychological component, and the term psychosomatic could describe conditions as varied as stress-related eczema and impotence. One serious psychosomatic condition is anorexia nervosa, in which an excessive desire to lose weight results in emaciation; typically, this affects teenage girls.

Drug and other medical treatments

Although many mental disorders do not seem to have an obvious physical cause, physical methods seem to be the only successful way to treat them. Drugs in particular are used extensively. Because there is no physical disorder to attack, however, drug treatment tends to concentrate on relieving and controlling symptoms. The main types of drugs used are tranquilizers and antidepressants. Antischizophrenic drugs are powerful tranquillizers, but are regarded as a separate category because of their specific uses in the treatment of schizophrenia. The use of lithium, usually in the form of lithium carbonate, in conjunction with an antidepressant, is sometimes valuable in reducing the mood changes in manic-depressive psychosis.

Two other treatments, electroconvulsive therapy (ECT) and psychosurgery, are sometimes (though ever more rarely) used. ECT induces a modified epileptic seizure in an

Modern mental hospitals include a whole range of recreational facilities, many of which acknowledge the therapeutic role of exercise and normal activities in the treatment of mental disorders. The hospital illustrated below has a nine-hole golf course laid out in relaxing country surroundings.

anesthetized patient by means of electric current, in an attempt to treat severe depression. Psychosurgery involves surgery on part of the brain to prevent the symptoms of chronically depressed or obsessive patients. Both are controversial and are questioned by many psychiatrists on moral and ethical grounds.

The talking cures

Adjuncts to medical treatment are the forms of therapy that attempt to treat the psychological causes rather than the symptoms of mental disorders. Collectively, these forms of treatment are called psychotherapy.

The original "talking cure" was developed by Freud, who gave it the name psychoanalysis to stress its scientific foundation. The science of psychoanalysis has been developed by Freud's successors into a variety of analytic techniques based on the principle of developing a close relationship between patient and analyst, which allows undesirable or abnormal aspects of the patient's mental state to manifest themselves. The origin, nature, and effects of these can then be made clear to the patient by the analyst's explanation.

In an alternative, more specific sense, the term psychotherapy describes modified forms of psychoanalysis in which the patient is seen only once or twice a week, and not necessarily for such an extended period as in psychoanalysis.

There is also a wealth of alternative therapies with different approaches and methods. These include behavior therapy, family therapy, group therapy, and psychodrama. Behavior therapy attempts to modify behavior by psychological conditioning. The technique does not require the patient to understand the cause of his condition. The others use a psychodynamic approach, aiming to involve patients in the process of understanding themselves and coming to terms with their problems, with the guidance of an experienced therapist who directs the course of the treatment.

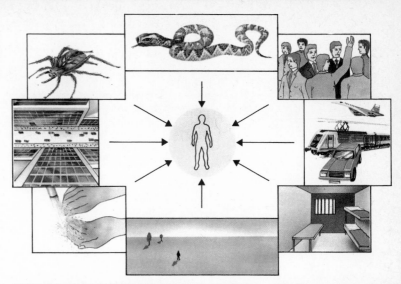

Phobias can be caused by many things, some of which—for instance, modes of transport, crowds of people, or open spaces—give little or no cause for fear in most people. The diagram *(above)* illustrates these and other common phobias.

Anorexia nervosa is a disorder that occurs most frequently in teen-age girls. Their refusal to eat can cause extreme loss of weight and cessation of menstruation. The condition usually needs prolonged psychiatric treatment.

Fact entries

Hall, G. Stanley (1884-1924), American psychologist and teacher who was among the first to link the results of investigations into child psychology with theories about the education of children.

Freud, Sigmund (1856-1939), Austrian physician whose study of mental disorders, particularly neuroses, led him to formulate theories of the unconscious and subconscious mind, which became the basis of the therapeutic technique known as psychoanalysis.

Kraepelin, Emil (1856-1926), German psychiatrist who established the classification of psychoses into schizophrenia (dementia praecox) and manic-depressive psychosis.

Adler, Alfred (1870-1937), Austrian psychiatrist who disputed the Freudian emphasis on sexuality and formulated an alternative theory that the desire for power or success is fundamental in human motivation.

Jung, Carl Gustav (1875-1961), Swiss psychologist and psychiatrist who founded his own school of analytical psychology after disagreement with Freud. Jung's theories centered on the unconscious and spiritual nature of the mind, and emphasized the need for self-discovery in the growth of the personality.

Binswanger, Ludwig (1881-1966), Swiss psychiatrist whose modification of psychotherapy, based on existentialist philosophy, explains certain mental disorders in terms of the patient's distorted image of the self and its relation to the world.

Klein, Melanie (1882-1960), Austrian psychoanalyst whose work on child psychology, particularly in terms of the psychological significance of play in anxiety situations, extended understanding of the processes of childhood development far beyond the Freudian model.

Horney, Karen (1885-1952), American psychoanalyst whose modifications of Freudian theory stress the importance of social and environmental factors in determining personality.

Rogers, Carl Ransom (1902-   ), American psychotherapist whose "client-centered" therapy stresses the mind's "actualizing tendency" to heal and fulfill its own potential.

Bettelheim, Bruno (1903-   ), American psychiatrist and educator, renowned for his studies of the psychology and treatment of emotionally disturbed children, with particular regard to social factors.

Skinner, Burrhus Frederic (1904-   ), American psychologist whose views have had great influence on the techniques of behavior therapy.

Laing, Ronald David (1927-   ), British psychiatrist whose interpretation and treatment of psychosis, particularly schizophrenia, emphasizes that the stresses in many "normal" social relationships are great enough to be a prime cause of psychotic illness.

Drugs

A physician's task in treating various kinds of ailments and their symptoms has been made much easier in recent years by the availability of a vast armory of drugs. At the same time, the manufacture of drugs has become a full-scale industry with its own research, testing, packaging, marketing, and promotion divisions. Constant research, refinement, and experimentation by the pharmaceutical companies is continually resulting in the production of new or improved drugs. As an overall consequence, drug treatment is becoming more effective all the time.

Although treatment is undoubtedly improving, drugs are also becoming increasingly expensive, and questions about the cost of producing drugs are of great concern to many people. Research and development is often a long and costly process, and even when a new drug is discovered it can be both difficult and expensive to produce. On the other hand, enormous sums are spent in packaging and advertising drug products, so arguments about costs and waste are difficult to resolve.

One point often used to explain the cost of drugs is that every care must be taken to ensure that they are safe to use. Indeed, it has even been argued that so much attention is paid to safety requirements that this actually inhibits research.

Despite such stringent precautions, however, mistakes do occur, and the question of where responsibility lies is also controversial. Some mistakes are particularly horrifying, as in the cases of malformed children born to women who took the drug thalidomide as a sedative while pregnant. Many drugs are extremely potent agents and most can be dangerous if misused. In any case, drugs should be considered only as temporary solutions even to permanent problems. The fact remains, however, that most drugs are taken on prescription to combat pain or disease, and few are abused.

Drugs and the physician

A physician, faced with a patient who has described all the perceived symptoms, may decide to prescribe drug treatment. Most physicians are inundated with leaflets, brochures, and free samples from pharmaceutical companies advertising their drugs, and from these and other sources of information the physician has to choose a drug that provides the maximum help. The treatment might have to be effective in more than one way—treating both pain and infection, for example, as well as any other localized or general condition. Alternatively, a combination of drugs might be indicated—and the compatibility of the prescribed drugs has to be ensured. For information on this subject, the physician generally consults one of the large reference works on drugs, commonly known as a *Physician's Desk Reference*. But a physician may use a "trial and error" approach with certain drugs if the symptoms displayed indicate one of several possible causes.

The physician has also to consider possible side effects of drug treatment. A number of useful drugs have known side effects, and a patient should be warned about these in advance. They can vary from comparatively minor effects, such as the tendency of the painkilling drug codeine to cause constipation, to potentially hazardous ones, such as the drowsiness induced by some drugs prescribed to combat travel sickness. The occurrence of side effects is especially serious in some chemotherapy techniques for treating cancer, in which internal tumors are virtually overwhelmed with drugs. The treatment can be very effective, but there may be visible side effects (such as alopecia) that may depress the patient's morale. The physician must therefore

Some antibiotics can be prepared from organic sources, such as mold (one type of which is a source of penicillin) or bacteria—for example, this culture of *Streptomyces lividans*.

Thalidomide is a sedative drug used originally in the 1950's and 1960's, which caused pregnant women who took it to give birth to physically malformed children. These children were not mentally defective, however, and many live normal lives.

consider whether such possible side effects balance or even outweigh the potential benefit derived from the use of the drug, and careful monitoring of a patient's reactions to a drug is therefore essential.

Before contemplating the type of drug to prescribe, the physician must be certain the patient's condition has been diagnosed correctly. Diagnosis must take into account the patient's possible inability to explain exactly what and where the symptoms are, the fact that pain can be "referred" from one location in the body to another, and the fact that to a patient a secondary side effect may assume greater importance than that of a primary symptom. There is also the possibility that the patient really needs no medical treatment at all—that attending the clinic or office is essentially either a cry for social rather than medical help, or the result of genuine hypochondria.

In the latter case, a physician must prescribe a course of "dummy" pills (placebos), which are realistic fakes that may fool the patient but which have no clinical effect. In fact, it is now believed they may have some slight effect—possibly by encouraging the release of the peptides known as endorphins in the body. Unfortunately, however, the introverted personality of a hypochondriac is usually of the type least likely to be affected by such treatment, and placebos seem to work most effectively with stable, extrovert personalities. One survey on the use of placebos provided the interesting statistic that one in three patients who are unaware of being prescribed placebos comes back for more.

Such subtle analysis requires the physician's personal knowledge of the patient. And although such a close acquaintance with every patient may be difficult, particularly in an urban area, a physician has to be quite certain before completing a prescription for a drug that the prescribed drug will produce no allergic effects, nor any side effects with which the patient might be unable to cope satisfactorily. A physician has to be especially vigilant in diagnosis when prescribing drugs that could be abused because extended usage of certain drugs could encourage addiction. This is particularly likely with some stimulants and depressants.

The various forms of prescribed drugs

The form in which pharmaceutical compounds are presented—solid, liquid, or gaseous—depends on the nature of their ingredients and what they are designed to do.

Solid forms include granules, tablets, capsules, and even a type of chewing gum (for

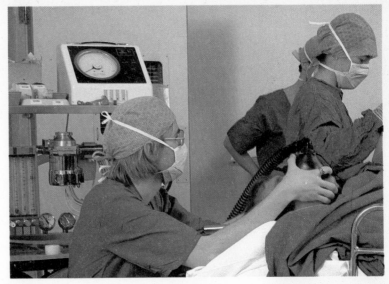

Modern surgery relies to a considerable extent on anesthetic drugs and on the skill of the anesthetist to select the appropriate drug and technique of administration, depending on the type of operation and the patient's age and condition.

weaning smokers off cigarettes). Powders, creams, and ointments are generally designed for external (topical) application. Pessaries and suppositories, which consist of a drug in a soluble base that dissolves in moist conditions and at body temperatures, deliver drugs directly into the vagina and rectum, respectively. Some drugs are designed to be dissolved in water first for easier internal absorption, particularly the proprietary drugs sold as fast-acting painkillers.

Liquid drugs include remedies such as

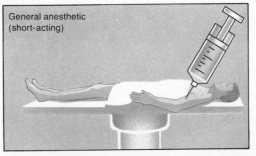

General anesthetic (short-acting)

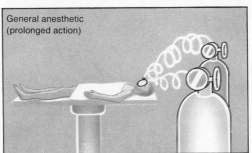

General anesthetic (prolonged action)

Anesthetics can be classified as general or local, according to their action. General anesthetics affect the whole body and cause complete unconsciousness. Short-acting ones are usually administered by injection; long-acting ones by inhalation. Local anesthetics are intended to anesthetize a specific area of the body. They can be administered by a spray, often used to relieve the pain of a burn, or by injection, which a dentist uses to block nerves to the teeth. A special type of local anesthetic (called epidural) is injected into the fluid around the spinal cord. This anesthetizes parts of the body supplied by lower spinal nerves and is sometimes used to relieve the pain of childbirth.

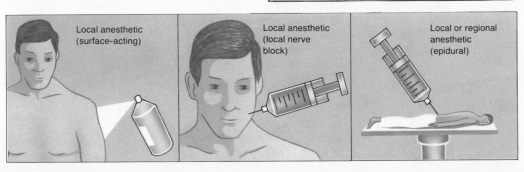

Local anesthetic (surface-acting)

Local anesthetic (local nerve block)

Local or regional anesthetic (epidural)

Drugs can be administered in various forms. The main ones are illustrated here. The symbols below relate to the table of drugs on this and the facing page. The forms illustrated are, in clockwise direction, liquid, spray, liquid for injection, suppositories, hypodermic syringe for injection, tube for cream or lotion, capsules, and tablets.

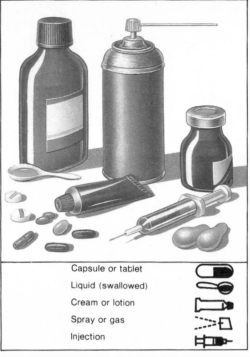

Capsule or tablet
Liquid (swallowed)
Cream or lotion
Spray or gas
Injection

cough mixtures; antibiotic preparations for babies, young children, and elderly people; drugs to counteract gastrointestinal infections; some laxatives; and ulcer-healing preparations. Other liquid drugs are given by injection: under the skin (subcutaneously), into muscle (intramuscularly), or into veins (intravenously). Large volumes of liquid-containing drugs can be administered directly into veins from an intravenous infusion set.

Gaseous drugs include some general anesthetics, inhalations for catarrh and sinusitis, drugs for the heart condition angina pectoris, and some old-fashioned cures, such as smelling salts for fainting attacks. Drugs that relax constricted bronchial passages (bronchodilators) are commonly supplied to a patient in an inhaler (an aerosol or mechanical spray).

Types of drugs

Most types of drugs—including some that occur naturally in the body (such as hormones)—are represented in the table on this page.

Generally, they are intended either to give

Drug group and description	Usual forms	Examples
Analgesics relieve pain (without affecting other sensations)		aspirin, acetaminophen
Anesthetics numb sensation, either generally or locally		halothane, sodium pentathol, nitrous oxide (general); procaine (local)
Antacids neutralize stomach acid (to relieve indigestion)		sodium bicarbonate, aluminum hydroxide
Antiarrhythmics steady irregular and/or fast heartbeat		digoxin
Antibacterial drugs prevent or treat bacterial infection		sulfadiazine
Antibiotics counteract bacterial or fungal infections by preventing the growth of microorganisms		penicillin, ampicillin, tetracyclines, chloramphenicol, griseofulvin
Anticoagulants inhibit the blood-clotting mechanism		heparin, warfarin
Anticonvulsants control epileptic or other seizures		phenobarbital, diazepam, ACTH
Antidepressants treat depression		imipramine, phenelzine
Antihistamines counteract allergic and traumatic reactions to histamine release in the body; also used as sedatives and antinauseants		brompheniramine maleate, promethazine
Antimalarial drugs prevent or treat malaria		quinine, mepacrine, chloroquine
Antinauseants counter vomiting (as in travel sickness)		meclizine, prochlorperazine, trimethobenzamide
Anti-Parkinsonism drugs treat Parkinson's disease		levodopa (l-dopa)
Antipyretics relieve or prevent fever		indomethacin, aspirin
Antirheumatic drugs relieve rheumatic pain		phenylbutazone
Antiserums are used in vaccinations to prevent certain specific disease (and contain antibodies against them)		diphtheria vaccine
Antispasmodics relax intestinal and bronchial smooth muscle (when they are bronchodilators), to relieve diarrhea or lung congestion		ephedrine, theophylline
Antitussives suppress coughing		noscarpine, codeine
Antivenins treat bites from venomous animals (such as snakes and spiders)		specific to animal
Antiviral drugs treat certain virus infections (such as shingles and cold sores)		idoxuridine
Chelating agents treat heavy metal poisoning		penicillamine
Contraceptive drugs prevent ovulation in a woman		estrogen-progestogen hormone combinations

protection against disease, as do immunization and vaccination, or to cope with a disease once it is diagnosed, as do antibiotics, for example. In the latter case, drugs may be prescribed to treat the condition either by eradicating the underlying cause, or by suppressing the symptoms. Usually it is the underlying cause that the physician prescribes the drug to attack, but there are certain conditions (such as peptic ulceration and arteriosclerosis) in which the best treatment is to alleviate the symptoms. There are, in any case, many more symptom-suppressing drugs than there are those that attack root causes.

Moreover, some medical conditions caused by environmental circumstances require treatment with chemicals and substances that are not usually considered drugs. Deficiency diseases, for instance, endemic in some parts of the world, are often only temporarily "cured" by administering proteins, vitamins, or any other substances that make up the deficiency. Proteins and vitamins could then quite legitimately be termed drugs.

Ampicillin crystals photographed with polarized light testify to the purity of this synthetic antibiotic drug. All drugs have to be produced in a clinically pure form as either a solid or a liquid of known concentration, so that dosages and formulations can be made up accurately.

Drug group and description	Usual forms	Examples
Corticosteroids reduce inflammation and relieve allergic or rheumatic symptoms		hydrocortisone
Cytotoxic drugs destroy or prevent the growth of cancerous cells (also called anticancer or antitumor drugs)		fluorouracil, l-asparaginase
Decongestants relieve wheezing or clear nasal passages		antispasmodics, antihistamines
Diuretics increase the output of urine from the kidneys (to treat edema or glaucoma)		thiazides, caffeine
Emetics promote vomiting		salt solution, ipecac
Globulins (proteins in blood plasma) are used in transfusions and sometimes to confer immunity		fibrinogen
Hallucinogens (psychedelics) produce perceptual distortions and mood changes		LSD, mescaline, phencyclidine
Hormones are natural glandular secretions or synthetic equivalents used to treat a lack or deficiency of the hormone in the body or to moderate hormone balance		anabolic steroids, male sex hormones, female sex hormones
Hypnotics induce sleep or unconsciousness		chloral hydrate, barbiturates
Hypotensives reduce blood pressure or slow heartbeat		thiazides, beta-blockers
Immunosuppressants suppress the body's immune system (generally to avoid rejection of grafts or transplants)		azathioprine, cyclophosphamide, prednisone
Laxatives promote evacuation of the bowels		cascara sagrada, mineral oil
MAO inhibitors are antidepressants, often used to treat mental illness		phenelzine, isocarboxazid
Muscle relaxants relax certain muscles		atropine, scopolamine
Narcotics suppress pain and, in larger doses, produce stupor		morphine, codeine
Sedatives depress brain function and promote sleep; mild sedatives are called tranquilizers		barbiturates
Stimulants raise blood pressure, increase heartbeat and may increase the sense of alertness and/or well-being		amphetamines, caffeine
Vaccines confer immunity from certain specific diseases (and contain weak or dead pathogens that stimulate antibody formation in the body)		measles vaccine
Vasoconstrictors make blood vessels contract		(epinephrine) adrenaline
Vasodilators expand blood vessels		azapetine

Surgery

Surgery is one of the fields of medicine in which great advances are continually being made—stimulated as often by misfortunes, such as accidents and war, as by advances in other areas of medicine and science. New techniques and equipment enable surgeons to undertake remarkable treatments, from transplanting organs, such as the heart or kidney, to replacing a severed limb and restoring its function.

Diagnosis has also been considerably improved, both by refinements in slightly older techniques—such as the electroencephalograph (EEG) and the electrocardiograph (EKG)—and by the invention of new ones—such as the use of ultrasound, or of a computer to interpret X rays in the process known as computerized axial tomography (CAT) scanning.

Surgery itself has undergone remarkable refinement, with the result that many seriously ill or injured people can now be successfully treated, whereas perhaps only ten years ago little or nothing could have been done for them.

New surgical techniques

Among the most important new instruments and techniques available to the surgeon are endoscopy, microsurgery, cryosurgery, laser surgery, and patient monitoring devices.

An endoscope is a device for looking inside a patient's body. Most modern endoscopes employ fiber optics, in which strands of fiber packed together in a long, thin, flexible tube carry light (or an image) from one end of the tube to the other. The tube thus becomes an excellent diagnostic aid if inserted through a bodily orifice (or small surgical incision) to the

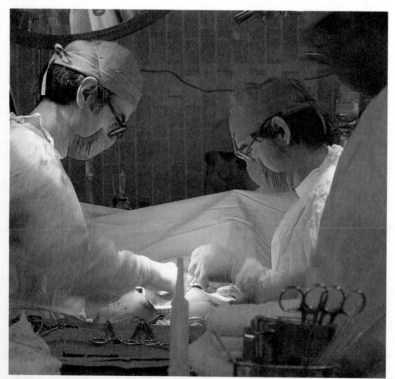

An operation is conducted in aseptic conditions. All instruments are sterilized and the surgical team wear sterile clothes.

site of whatever the physician wants to examine. It can also be used as a surgical instrument when the internal end of the tube is fitted with a wire loop or blades, which can cut or cauterize tissue. Stones in the bladder, for instance, can be easily crushed and washed out using this method (litholapaxy), with no need for abdominal surgery. In parts of the body that are particularly difficult to reach, a computer-enhanced image intensifier and a visual display unit (VDU, a television screen) may be used in conjunction with the endoscope so that its pictures are made quite clear.

A VDU attached to a microscope is now commonly used for microsurgery, which deals with the smallest and most sensitive parts of the body, such as individual nerve endings and blood vessels. Using microsurgery, it is possible not only to reattach an accidentally amputated limb, but to reconnect many of the neural pathways and thus enable the patient eventually to regain movement—and even some feeling—in the limb. This is an exceptional use, however; more common areas for microsurgery are the larynx and the ear.

Another modern technique is that of using localized but extreme cold (below $-4°$ F., $-20°$ C) to freeze and thus destroy tissue. This method—called cryosurgery—is not in common use, but is nevertheless occasionally employed in brain surgery, in ophthalmology, and in treating some skin disorders.

Probably the field in which most advances have been made recently uses lasers, which have various surgical applications. Pulsed laser beams can be produced either as an extremely narrow, concentrated ray with a diameter of only a fraction of a millimeter (used as a scalpel), or as a wider, diffuse ray (used to "vaporize" tissue over an area). The laser's main advantages are that it is totally aseptic and that—particularly when it is used as a scalpel—the heat produced cauterizes smaller blood vessels instantly, so that blood loss (and therefore shock) is greatly reduced. Moreover, a laser beam can be used in combination with an endoscope. The overall power of a beam depends on the type of laser. Carbon-dioxide lasers are extremely powerful (and are used mainly for the vaporization of unhealthy tissue). But they need a marker beam from a second laser (usually an argon or neon type) projected along the same path, because they are otherwise invisible. Probably the most common application for lasers in medical practice is to remove unhealthy tissue in a condition known as precancer of the cervix. The best-known use, however, is in "welding" back a detached part of the retina of the eye.

New and improved drugs for use as anesthetics during operations are constantly being discovered. At the same time, refinements are also being made in the equipment used for monitoring the patient's condition during an operation—also the responsibility of the anesthetist. Most operating theaters now have an array of automatic electronic monitoring devices.

Modern surgery

Nearly all parts of the body can be treated surgically; some organs and body systems, however, present the surgeon with special prob-

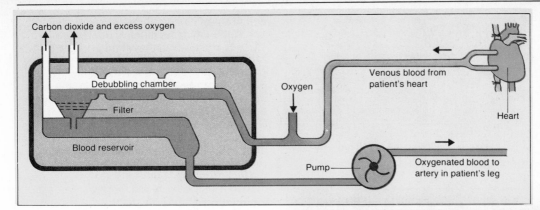

A cardiopulmonary bypass, commonly known as a heart-lung machine, makes it possible for a surgeon to maintain the blood circulation while a patient's heart is stopped. Venous blood from the patient's heart is oxygenated, displaced carbon dioxide and excess oxygen are removed, and the filtered blood is pumped back into the patient's circulation via an artery in the leg.

lems. Until quite recently, most operations were performed by general surgeons. Even today, although specialization is increasingly important, a general surgeon is the most likely person to deal with appendectomies, gallbladder operations, breast operations, and surgery on the gastrointestinal tract. In some cases, the general surgeon may also be concerned with the removal of benign or malignant growths. In this context, a surgeon may have to decide, during the operation, how much tissue to remove to prevent further spread of cancerous growth.

Specialist surgeons are concerned not only with the appropriate surgical techniques but also with all other aspects of medical care relating to their speciality.

A neurosurgeon, for example, is concerned with operations on the nervous system: the brain, spinal cord, spine, and nerves. Injuries to the brain through accidents are all too frequent; tumors of the brain and spinal cord, and congenital disorders, such as hydrocephalus, are other common problems. Technical advances that have been of particular benefit to neurosurgeons include cryosurgery and laser surgery, both of which may be used in highly specific operations on the brain.

An orthopedic surgeon deals with disorders of the bones and joints. Common operations include the correction of congenital defects, such as clubfoot or scoliosis (curvature of the spine), and the insertion of metal or plastic artificial joints, for example, in the hip. Treatment of fractures is important too, and usually involves returning broken bones to their correct position and fixing them there—using splints or traction—until they have healed. Other orthopedic operations include the treatment of people with herniated disks,

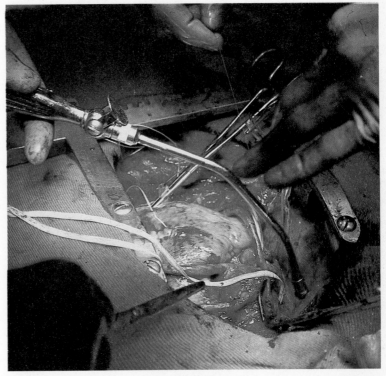

accident victims, and patients with bone cancer.

Urological surgeons deal with disorders affecting the urinary tract and male reproductive organs. Common problems include prostate disorders, kidney stones and kidney disease, and cancer of the kidneys, bladder, prostate, or testicles.

Obstetricians and gynecologists are concerned with pregnancy, childbirth, and female reproductive problems. Careful monitoring

Open-heart surgery, shown below, has become a common technique since the development of the heart-lung machine, which takes over the functions of the patient's heart and lungs so that the operation can be performed with the heart stopped.

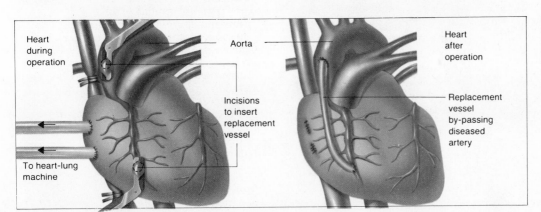

Coronary artery disease can be treated surgically by rerouting the blood through a by-pass. In this operation, a section of saphenous vein from the patient's leg is used as the replacement blood vessel.

A kidney transplant is one of the most successful types of transplant operations. The new kidney, from a donor, is positioned at the top of the pelvic girdle and turned upside down to facilitate connections with the renal blood supply and the ureter. The adrenal glands are left in their original positions.

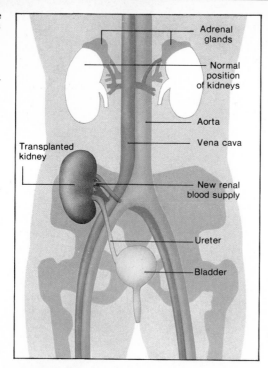

Adrenal glands

Normal position of kidneys

Aorta

Vena cava

Transplanted kidney

New renal blood supply

Ureter

Bladder

An artificial heart valve is stitched into position using many small sutures (stitches), which have to be strong enough to withstand the pressure inside a pumping heart.

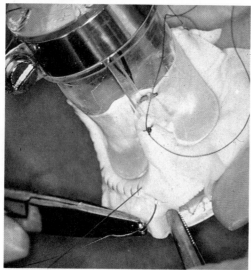

Specialized surgery on the eye includes cornea transplants. This photograph shows the donor's cornea being removed.

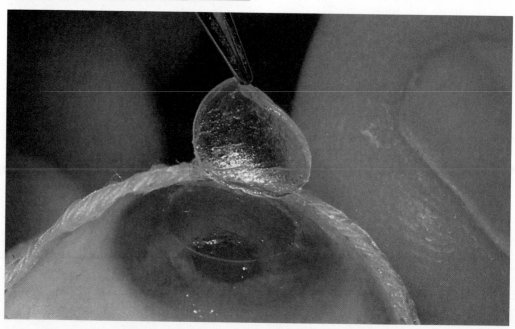

and prenatal care minimize obstetric difficulties. Common gynecological operations include D and C (dilatation of the cervix and curettage of the uterus) for diagnostic or screening purposes, or for the removal of small growths (polyps) in the uterus; the removal of fibroids; removal of the uterus (hysterectomy); and surgery to treat cancer of the uterus or cervix.

The cardiac (heart) surgeon has derived particular benefit from technological advances, especially in the development of the heart-lung machine, which takes over the functions of the heart and lungs of a patient undergoing surgery so that the heart can be operated on while stopped; in the use of computers to aid monitoring; and in techniques that involve cooling the patient to slow down metabolism during an operation.

Transplant surgery involves the replacement of a diseased or failed organ (such as kidneys or the heart) with a healthy one, usually taken from a donor who has just died. By the early 1980's, heart transplants were still comparatively rare, although there had been some remarkable successes. Kidneys and bone marrow can, however, be transplanted from a living donor. The chief difficulty in transplant surgery is ensuring that the new tissue is not rejected by the recipient, whose natural immune response to foreign tissue can be as acute as it is to agents that cause allergy or disease. This difficulty can be largely overcome by careful matching of the tissue types of donor and patient, and by using special drugs that suppress the patient's immune response. (The use of these drugs is itself dangerous, however, in that the patient is thus left without any natural defenses against infection.)

Replacement (or "spare part") surgery avoids the problem of rejection by using inert plastic or metal devices to replace or strengthen natural ones. Some arteries, veins, heart valves, and joints can be replaced with artificial equivalents. Replacement of limbs or parts of limbs has been possible for a long time, but the sophistication of artificial limbs has reached such a degree nowadays that it is possible to use the nervous impulses in the remaining portion of the damaged limb to control the battery-operated replacement (prosthesis).

A plastic surgeon is concerned with the reconstruction and cosmetic repair of damaged surface tissue and bone, whether for aesthetic or psychological reasons, or after damage caused by burns or other injury.

An ophthalmic surgeon deals with the eyes, especially with the removal of cataracts (opaque patches in the lens), replacement of a damaged or diseased cornea by a corneal graft, or with the repair of a damaged or detached retina. Microsurgical techniques and advances, such as the medical use of lasers, particularly benefit ophthalmic surgery. They are also important for operations on the minute and delicate organs of the ear.

Removal of the tonsils and adenoids is a common ear, nose, and throat (ENT) operation, as is surgery to treat certain inner ear infections. Specialists in ENT surgery also remove tumors in the sinuses, mouth, larynx, and throat.

Common major operations

Most major operations are abdominal, and the most common of these include appendectomy (removal of the appendix); removal of ulcerated parts of the digestive tract, all or part of diseased organs, and benign or malignant growths; and the repair of hernias.

Accidents—particularly road accidents—are another common reason for major surgery. Further types of major surgery include urinary tract, cardiovascular, thoracic, and neurosurgical operations.

Preparations for surgery

Before an operation, the patient is tested for any condition that might complicate the operation, such as high blood pressure. Solid food is restricted for a period before any operation that requires a general anesthetic, in case the patient vomits while anesthetized. Finally, premedication is given to relax the patient before the anesthetic itself is administered. Preoperative antibiotics may also be given to minimize the risk of internal infection, particularly if surgery is to be carried out on or near the gastrointestinal tract.

Meanwhile, sterile conditions are established in the operating theater, and sterile instruments and clothing are obtained. Members of the surgical team "scrub up" by washing their hands extremely thoroughly and wear sterile clothing, which includes gloves, face masks, hats, and overgarments.

The patient is anesthetized before entering the operating theater, usually by an intravenous injection of barbiturate. Anesthesia is usually maintained during the operation by means of inhaled gas and monitored throughout the operation by an anesthetist or anesthesiologist.

Operations are performed by a skilled and specialized team consisting of the surgeon (or surgeons), various assistants, an anesthetist or anesthesiologist, and, where special apparatus is being used, a technician to operate it. A surgeon may also require the presence of one or

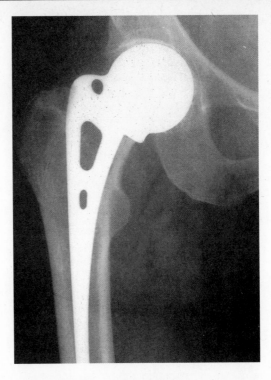

Orthopedic surgery includes the replacement of damaged or diseased joints. This X ray shows an "artificial hip," which comprises a metal pin fixed in the neck and body of the femur and a ball-and-socket joint that replaces the hip joint itself. The ball joint fits into the socket as the head of a normal femur fits into the acetabulum.

more specialists, from radiologists to pathologists.

Postoperative care is very important. After surgery, the patient is taken to a recovery room until the effects of the anesthesia wear off and he or she regains consciousness. If recovery is satisfactory, the patient is returned to the ward. If there are postoperative complications, however, the patient may need to be kept temporarily in an intensive care unit.

An intensive care unit monitors a patient's condition and helps to keep him or her alive during the recovery period after a serious operation.

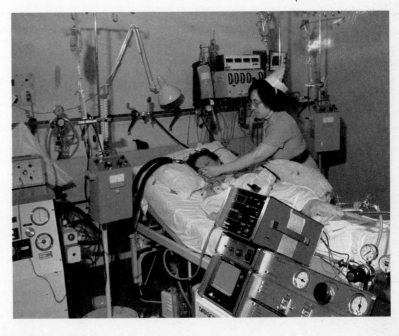

Alternatives

The iris of the eye is studied by the technique called iridology, as explained in the chart below.

Alternative therapies are, for the most part, still suspect in conventional medical eyes; indeed, several of them are commonly regarded as no more than quackery—except by the patients who seem to benefit from them. The medical profession, however, is properly cautious, secure in the knowledge that it has science and proven safety records behind it; physicians' reservations are deeply felt. Yet overall, in both physicians and public, there is a growing awareness that conventional medicine does not hold all the answers, and techniques such as osteopathy have become recognized medical practices.

Drug treatment in particular has contributed to this disquiet because—although drugs are a strong weapon in the fight against disease and pain—many have harmful side effects.

Furthermore, drugs are often used to control symptoms rather than to prevent or cure disease. Drug treatment, however, like surgery, has the advantage that it can be understood in conventional scientific terms, and this is crucially important to those trained in that tradition, because the mysticism and ritual that seems to surround some alternatives makes them unacceptable to a scientist from the start.

Iridology claims to interpret the color and condition of segments of the iris in terms of the state of health of various parts of the body. This simplified chart is for the right eye (the left-eye chart is basically a mirror image of this one). For example, by studying the right-hand sector of the eye at the four o'clock position, an iridologist can possibly diagnose ill health in a person's back or spine.

The alternative approach

There are so many different alternatives that to regard them as a whole can be of only limited value. One characteristic many share, however, is that the interrelationship, or coordination, between the healer, the patient, and the method used is much closer than is usual in orthodox medicine. Although the variety of alternatives is vast, their modes of action can be broken down into three major categories.

The first category includes techniques that manipulate the body's "energy"—a characteristic that is difficult to understand, but which certainly seems to exist. It has been effectively excluded from Western medical concepts, but in some Oriental philosophies it is known as "prana" or "chi," which translates best as "life force."

The second category works on the physical body as conventional drugs and other treatments do. These therapies either alter the structure of the body—as does osteopathy, for instance—or alter the chemicals within the body, as occurs in orthomolecular therapy or herbalism.

The third category has a mental or psychological approach. Examples include biofeedback, or—on a paranormal or psychic level—faith healing.

Acupuncture

Acupuncture is one of the oldest forms of medical treatment and has been practiced in China for centuries. Classical acupuncturists believe that the body remains healthy so long as its energy or life force *(chi)* flows freely along well-defined channels known as meridians. Blockages in these channels are the cause of ill health, and the insertion of needles into points along these channels or the application of heat at these points (moxibustion), allows the energy to flow once more, encouraging the restoration of health.

Acupuncturists decide where to insert needles either by assessing the qualities of six pulses felt at each wrist, which represent the major organs of the body or, if they are treating pain, by needling points lying along the meridians that cross the painful area. Pain is often successfully treated by acupuncture but many other conditions can be helped too—notably hay fever and depression. Belief in acupuncture is not needed for it to be effective, although some people—for unknown reasons—do not respond to treatment. Techniques are still developing and recent advances include electrical stimulation of needles, ear acupuncture, and the use of acupuncture in anesthesia.

Homeopathy

Homeopathy originated in the 1750's when a German doctor, Samuel Hahnemann, noticed that if the effects produced by a substance taken by a healthy person corresponded to the sufferings of a sick person then this substance, homeopathically prepared, could provide a useful cure. His homeopathic preparations were made by repeatedly diluting and shaking the substance.

Why does this system work, even when the degree of dilution may be so great that the physical presence of the original substance is virtually undetectable? Many homeopaths believe that every substance has both physical properties and a characteristic "vibrational en-

Iridology chart (right eye)

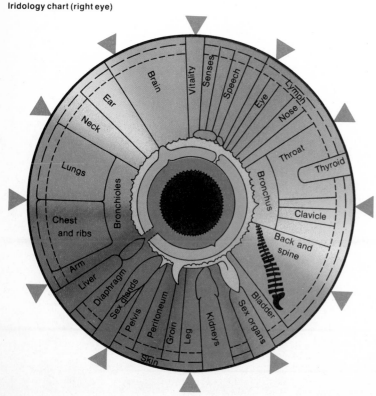

ergy," which is enhanced by homeopathic preparation. Treatment is effected by a substance with a vibrational energy that corrects the distorted vibrational energy of the patient. The substance is usually chosen as a result of investigating both the symptoms and character of the patient, though some practitioners attempt to match up the vibrational energy of the remedy to the patient directly. This can be done using radionics or electrohomeopathy. Homeopathy has been used to treat all forms of illness and tends to work either very well or not at all.

Osteopathy

Osteopathy was developed in the 1870's by the American doctor Andrew Taylor Still, who felt that the physical integrity of the spinal column was essential for good health. Today, this is no longer generally believed, although osteopathic techniques are widely and usefully practiced. Osteopathic medicine emphasizes the importance of the muscles and bones of the body and their connecting tendons and ligaments. These parts of the body make up the musculoskeletal system, which osteopathic physicians believe has important interrelationships with all other body systems. Osteopathic physicians are specially trained in the detection and treatment of musculoskeletal disturbances. They use massages and other types of osteopathic manipulation to treat these disturbances. This form of therapy is a distinctly osteopathic approach to the problems of health and disease. However, osteopathic physicians also use all the medical, surgical, immunological, pharmacological, psychological, and hygienic procedures of modern medicine.

Orthomolecular medicine

Orthomolecular medicine was developed in the 1950's, with the aim of supplying patients with quantities of all the forty or so nutrients the body needs, on the assumption that a lack of any of these prevents the body from either working or healing itself effectively.

As well as adequate amounts of protein, fats and carbohydrates, minor nutrients, including vitamins and minerals, are also neces-

sary for health. All of the substances used in orthomolecular medicine are found naturally in foods. The nutrients are either supplied by alterations to the diet or by dietary supplements. A range of methods, including blood and urine tests, hair analysis, and the use of questionnaires, together with information obtained directly from the patient by questioning or examination, help the practitioner to formulate the treatment. How much of any nutrient is required is difficult to decide. However, as the majority of nutrients used are harmless and without side effects—unless given in extremely large doses—there is a tendency for practitioners to err on the side of excess. Although this form of treatment can be used on its own, it is often even more useful when combined with other treatments, whether orthodox or not.

Curative properties of mud and hot sand have been advocated for hundreds of years. Here, a group of people, completely buried except for their heads and feet, relax in the warm volcanic sands at the hot springs near Ibusuki in Japan.

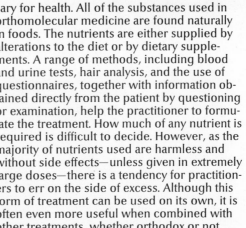

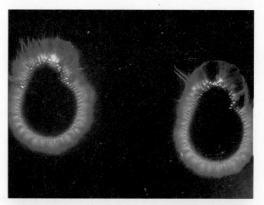

Healing by touch, or "laying on of hands," has been regarded with skepticism by some orthodox practitioners, who challenge its scientific basis. That physical changes do occur is demonstrated in these remarkable photographs, taken by Kirlian photography using an electrostatic field. The upper illustration shows the fingertips of a healer in their normal state; in the lower photograph, the fingers are in a state of healing.

Acupuncture is an ancient discipline that finds increasing use today as a method of inducing anesthesia. Here, a fully conscious patient obviously feels no pain while undergoing abdominal surgery. Some dentists fill or extract teeth using acupuncture anesthesia.

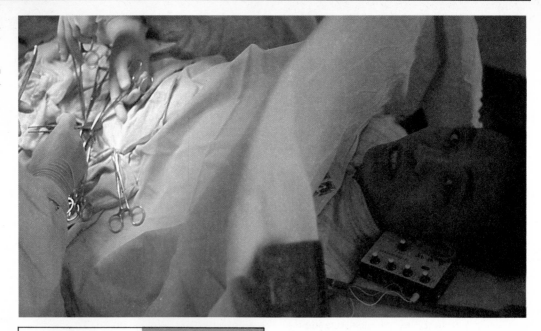

Medicinal plants have been used to treat illness, relieve symptoms, and affect the body or mind since ancient times, in societies at all levels of sophistication and in all parts of the world. In Western countries, refined pharmaceutical preparations tend to be favored, but some of these are, in fact, the active ingredients of traditional "herbal" remedies. For example, distillations of deadly nightshade (belladonna) were used as sedatives or antispasmodics; one modern drug obtained from belladonna is atropine, which has various medical uses, including the treatment of the spasms of asthma. Preparations of foxglove (digitalis) were employed as heart stimulants, and one derivative, digitoxin, is used for this purpose today. Peyote is still taken for its hallucinogenic properties by some North American Indians, and its derivative—mescaline—is also used as a psychedelic drug. Willow bark was employed in ancient times—for instance, by the Romans—as a dressing for wounds because it relieved pain and inflammation; its active ingredient resembles aspirin, which is widely used for pain relief today.

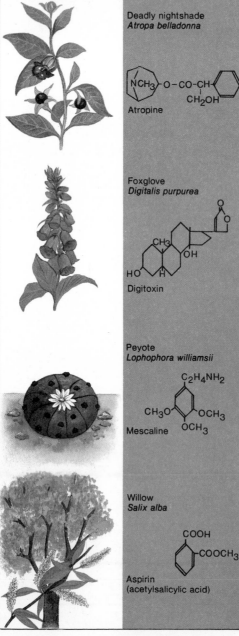

Deadly nightshade
Atropa belladonna

Atropine

Foxglove
Digitalis purpurea

Digitoxin

Peyote
Lophophora williamsii

Mescaline

Willow
Salix alba

Aspirin
(acetylsalicylic acid)

Hypnosis

Hypnosis is now an accepted part of medical practice, although it has passed in and out of fashion since it was first used clinically in the 1820's. A hypnotic state can be invoked in a variety of ways, but all aim to suppress the activity of the conscious mind. This relaxes the patient deeply, allowing the subconscious part of the mind to become more accessible. Through this access, the hypnotherapist can discover, explore, and remove forgotten mental or physical traumas that may be the root of the patient's disorder. The high degree of relaxation also allows the patient's body to heal itself, which is especially valuable in cases where relaxation is normally hampered by an overactive conscious mind.

Hypnosis can also be used in a form of behavior therapy. An idea, such as stopping smoking, is suggested to the patient under hypnosis, so that it continues to work through the patient's subconscious mind once the session is over and full consciousness is restored. Not everyone can be hypnotized, and there is great variety in the depths of hypnotic state that can be achieved in different people.

Most people experience an enhanced sensation during hypnosis—being hypnotized is not like being sent to sleep—although they respond automatically to the hypnotherapist's suggestions. A hypnotized subject would break from the hypnotic state, however, if an attempt was made to override the conscious will. Hypnosis is particularly useful if mental or emotional factors are important in a condition—for example, in an illness that is psychosomatic or induced by stress. It is also of value in the treatment of addictions.

Faith healing

Faith healing is as old as civilization and appears under many guises. As a general term, it is used (by uninformed observers) to cover any means of healing that claims to work by unknown forces that only certain people are able to utilize. It can be argued that such methods work by psychological suggestion based on confidence, beliefs, and receptivity of the patient and healer. However, this does not explain why such methods seem to work even when the patient has no faith.

Many healers work by lightly stroking or touching the patient, often while the healer enters a meditative or trancelike state. The healer's thoughts are directed toward the health and love of the person, and this seems to encourage the healing phenomenon—even when "projected" from a distance. It is possible for any illness to be helped by faith healing but in no specific case can success be guaranteed.

Alternatives evaluated

Contrary to many people's beliefs, alternative therapies are not without their dangers, because almost any treatment that is of value can do both good and harm. In alternative therapies, the most common unwanted effect (often termed a "flare-up") is the worsening of symptoms after treatment. Nevertheless, despite its temporary unpleasantness, this is a measure of the patient's sensitivity and usually indicates that treatment will succeed.

One fear shared by many regarding alternative therapies is that they are practiced by charlatans or quacks. Unlike conventional physicians, alternative therapists are not subject by law to a strict code of therapeutic practice. Uniform standards of training and practice are not established, although membership in a recognized organization goes some way toward providing this.

The future

As interest in alternatives grows, among conventional medical practitioners as much as the general public, the clear distinction between the two camps is disappearing. When drugs fail or surgery seems inappropriate, alternatives such as osteopathy may be suggested. And conversely, a homeopath or acupuncturist would recommend antibiotics to treat an abscess or an infected wound. Fair evaluation by each of the other techniques can only serve to advance medical knowledge, and this view is gaining favor in what is loosely called "the holistic approach." This involves all forms of treatment, according to what is thought likely to benefit the patient most.

Fact entries

Alternative therapies fall into three major categories, each with two subdivisions. The categories are concerned with energy, physical techniques, and psychological techniques, respectively. Acupuncture is based on principles of energy flow, as are techniques such as Reflexology, Shiatzu, and Acupressure. Vibrational energy is important in Homeopathy, and also in Radionics and Bach Flower Remedies. Physical techniques affecting the structure of the body include Osteopathy, Chiropractic, Massage, Alexander Technique, Yoga, and Rolfing. Physical techniques affecting body chemistry include Orthomolecular Therapy, Herbalism, Naturopathy, Special Diets, and Fasting. Hypnosis, Biofeedback, Meditation, and Encounter Therapy are psychological techniques based on normal mental processes. Paranormal psychology, in contrast, seems to be the basis of Faith Healing and variants such as Spiritual Healing, Therapeutic Touch, and Healing Pilgrimages. Many so-called "alternative" treatments are attractive because of their novelty or their "personal" style. It must always be remembered, however, that few offer any genuine scientific evidence for their effects, and most are suspect in conventional medical eyes.

Glossary

In the following glossary, small capital letters (for example, HORMONE) indicate terms that have their own entries in the glossary.

A

abscess An infected, often painful area in which pus forms. An abscess is most commonly caused by BACTERIA entering the body through a break in the skin or a cavity in a tooth.

acute An acute disease is one in which onset is sudden, and duration is comparatively short. A CHRONIC disorder, by contrast, lasts for a long time.

adenoma A BENIGN (noncancerous) TUMOR of a GLAND or similar tissue. An adenoma can occur almost anywhere in the body.

adipose tissue Fatty connective tissue; that part of the body where fat is stored.

albumin A PROTEIN present in blood PLASMA. As serum albumin, it helps to regulate water distribution in the body.

allergen Any substance that causes ALLERGY.

allergy An abnormal reaction to specific substances (ALLERGENS), such as pollen or certain foods.

amino acid Any of about 20 nitrogen-containing organic acids that constitute the building blocks of PROTEIN. When food is digested, the protein in it is broken down into amino acids that are then reassembled to form the particular types of protein required for the manufacture of muscles, red blood cells, and other body tissues. Most amino acids can be manufactured by the body, but eight "essential" amino acids are not synthesized by the body and must be obtained directly from protein in the diet.

amniocentesis The process by which a specimen of amniotic fluid is obtained through a small tube for analysis. Performed early in pregnancy, it is valuable in detecting fetal abnormalities such as SPINA BIFIDA.

amnion The thin membranous sac that encloses the fetus in the uterus. It is filled with amniotic fluid.

anaerobic Without oxygen; usually used to describe BACTERIA that live or function without free air or oxygen, such as the tetanus bacterium. It is the opposite of aerobic, which means living in or using oxygen.

analgesic A drug such as aspirin, acetaminophen, or codeine that relieves pain without loss of consciousness.

androgen A male sex HORMONE.

anesthesia Loss of feeling in part or all of the body either from natural processes or accidents, or deliberately by use of anesthetic drugs.

angina Spasmodic pain, sometimes producing feelings of suffocation. Angina pectoris, for instance, is a painful symptom of a heart disorder.

antibiotic An antibacterial drug made synthetically or obtained from living organisms, such as fungus or mold, that inhibits the growth of, or destroys, BACTERIA. Specific antibiotics can be used to combat specific PATHOGENIC bacteria.

antibody A PROTEIN in the blood that combines with an ANTIGEN so that it destroys or neutralizes that specific substance. Antibodies are key elements in the body's IMMUNE system.

antigen A foreign substance that stimulates the production of ANTIBODIES.

antitoxin A type of ANTIBODY that works against a specific TOXIN entering the body. Some are produced naturally in response to a disease; others are manufactured artificially from SERUM obtained from immunized horses or other mammals. Antitoxins are used to treat diphtheria and tetanus.

auscultation Listening with the ear or a stethoscope to sounds within the body to determine the condition of various organs, particularly the heart and lungs.

autoimmune disease A disease caused by excessive functioning of the IMMUNE mechanism so that sensitivity is created to certain of the body's own tissues.

axon A single, thin, long fiber that conducts nerve impulses away from a nerve cell. Most axons are covered with MYELIN.

B

bacterium A tiny, single-celled organism that may be shaped like a rod, sphere, or spiral. Most bacteria are harmless; those that cause disease are described as PATHOGENIC.

barium meal A preparation of barium sulfate in water swallowed by a patient to be X-rayed for intestinal disorders, such as ULCERS or TUMORS. X RAYS cannot pass through the barium, so the relevant organ—usually the stomach or intestine—shows up clearly on the developed X ray. A barium enema may be given to X-ray the rectum or lower intestine.

benign A term used to indicate a disorder that is neither recurrent nor progressive. It is the opposite of MALIGNANT and is usually applied to noncancerous TUMORS.

biopsy Removal of a small piece of tissue from the living body for examination and diagnosis, often in cases of suspected CANCER. A biopsy may be performed during an operation or during a preliminary investigation. For example, a section of a lump in the breast—which may be a CYST or a TUMOR—may be removed under anesthetic. The specimen is then frozen, cut into slices, stained and studied under a microscope. If the lump is BENIGN, the operational incision is sutured; if it is MALIGNANT, an operation to remove it may be carried out immediately.

blastocyst A stage in embryonic development following the stage of CLEAVAGE that forms the MORULA. The blastocyst is a small cluster of cells that forms within the morula, from which the fetus, amniotic sac, and placenta develop.

blind spot A small area in the retina of the eye, where the optic nerve enters, which is insensitive to light.

blood count A laboratory procedure by which the concentrations of red and white blood cells and platelets are determined. The concentration of hemoglobin (the oxygen-carrying chemical of the blood) is also obtained.

blood pressure Usually refers to the pressure of blood in the main arteries. A sphygmomanometer—an instrument consisting of a dial or column of mercury and a hollow rubber cuff—is usually used to measure blood pressure. The cuff is wrapped around the upper arm and inflated to stop the blood flow. Air is slowly released until a tapping sound can be heard (with the aid of a stethoscope). This is caused by a spurt of blood being forced through the artery. A reading at this point indicates SYSTOLIC pressure. The cuff is further deflated until sounds disappear, the reading at this point indicating DIASTOLIC blood pressure. Normal pressure for young adults is about 120/80mm of mercury (systolic/diastolic) or less.

bowels A general name for the intestines.

bronchoscope A tubelike instrument inserted, under anesthetic, through the mouth and down the trachea. A light and system of lenses and mirrors enable examination of the trachea and bronchi; alternatively, the bronchoscope may be used to remove secretions or tissue samples.

C

Caesarean section Surgical delivery of a baby through an incision in the abdomen and uterus.

calculus An abnormal stonelike deposit, which may consist of mineral salts, especially calcium, CHOLESTEROL, PROTEIN, or urea. Calculi, or stones, form most commonly in the urinary bladder. If they obstruct the normal flow of body fluids, they can cause pain and malfunction of the parts affected by the blockage. Treatment is usually by surgical removal.

calorie Equivalent to one kilocalorie, a calorie is a unit of heat used in measuring body METABOLISM. A calorie is the amount of heat required to raise the temperature of one kilogram of water one degree Celsius.

cancer A disease that results when cell division gets out of control, leading to the development of MALIGNANT CELLS. Cancer cells multiply in an uncoordinated fashion to form a TUMOR. By the process of METASTASIS, cells may then travel from the primary (original) site via the bloodstream or lymph vessels to form secondary cancers elsewhere in the body.

candidiasis A fungal infection caused by *Candida albicans.* Also known as thrush, candidiasis commonly occurs on nails, skin, and in the mouth, vagina, and gastrointestinal tract.

carbohydrate With PROTEINS and fats, carbohydrates are one of the three main constituents of food. Carbohydrates occur as sugars and starches, the latter being converted to sugars during digestion. Carbohydrate-rich foods include bread, potatoes, rice, and all sweet foods. If more carbohydrates are consumed than are used as energy, the excess is stored as fat.

carcinogen Any substance that contributes to the development of CANCER.

carcinoma A CANCER originating in the epithelium, the tissue of the skin, MUCOUS MEMBRANES, and organs or glands, such as the lung, breast, prostate, or thyroid.

Carcinomas are the most common form of MALIGNANT TUMOR.

cardiac Of the heart.

cardiovascular Of the heart and blood vessels.

cauterize To destroy damaged or abnormal tissue by burning.

cell The basic unit from which all living tissues are built. Some simple microscopic organisms, such as amebas, are single-celled; the human body consists of about one hundred million million cells. Each cell consists of a variety of specialized structures, the largest of which is the cell NUCLEUS, which contains 23 pairs of GENE-carrying CHROMOSOMES. Sex cells (sperm or ova) have only half the number of chromosomes in their nuclei but combine at fertilization to create a new cell with the full complement. Body cells replicate by a process called MITOSIS, which is the basis of cell division.

cerebral palsy A form of paralysis characterized by jerky or spasmodic movements, resulting from damage to MOTOR control centers in the brain. It may result from birth injury or damage to the fetal brain before birth. The degree of disability varies considerably.

cholesterol An organic compound chemically related to vitamin D and the sex hormones, found in all body tissues, particularly the brain and spinal cord. A key element in the body's chemical processes, cholesterol regulates the passage of substances through cell walls, maintains water balance, and performs other functions not yet understood. Cholesterol is manufactured principally in the liver and is also found in various foods, such as egg yolk, meat, and milk. Excess cholesterol is thought to be a contributory cause of heart and blood vessel diseases.

chromosomes Threadlike bodies contained within the NUCLEUS of every CELL. Usually occurring in pairs, chromosomes consist mainly of nucleoprotein, a combination of protein with DEOXYRIBONUCLEIC ACID (DNA), and are the sites for GENES.

chronic A chronic disorder is one which lasts for a long time without any marked change. It is the opposite of an ACUTE disorder.

cilia Minute hairlike threads that beat or lash rhythmically to keep mucous fluids flowing in a constant direction, for instance, out of the lungs.

cleavage A stage in embryonic development when the ZYGOTE undergoes repeated MITOTIC division to form the MORULA.

collagen Fibrous PROTEIN that forms the fibers of connective or supporting tissues of the body. Collagen is found in cartilage, bone, the inelastic material of tendons, and the elastic part of skin. Collagen (or connective tissue) diseases are a group of diseases, such as rheumatoid arthritis, characterized by inflammation of the connective tissues.

colostrum A milky fluid produced by a mother's breasts during the few days just before and after the birth of a baby. Colostrum is not true milk but is rich in PROTEINS and ANTIBODIES, which protect against infection.

cone A specialized cell of the central part of the eye's retina, responsible for color distinction and detailed vision.

congenital Present at birth.

corpus luteum The yellow body that develops from an ovarian FOLLICLE after a ripened ovum has been released. The corpus luteum produces the HORMONE progesterone to prepare the uterine lining for a fertilized egg. If FERTILIZATION occurs, the corpus luteum enlarges and continues to produce progesterone for several months; otherwise, the corpus luteum shrinks and gradually degenerates.

cortex The outer layer of an organ, such as the brain,

kidney, or adrenal gland.

culture medium A substance, such as agar jelly or gelatin, on which microorganisms, such as bacteria, are allowed to grow for identification or analysis.

cyst A lump consisting of a liquid- or semiliquid-filled sac without an opening. Cysts occur most commonly in the breast, ovary, and skin. Most are BENIGN, but because some may become MALIGNANT or interfere with the body's functioning, their removal may be advised.

D

dementia A general term for mental disorder involving deterioration of the brain and its functions.

dendrite A thin, branched fiber that receives and conveys impulses to the nerve cell of a NEURON.

deoxyribonucleic acid (DNA) A long-chain compound found in the NUCLEUS of all CELLS. In humans, the DNA molecule is made up of four basic building blocks, called nucleotides, joined together in two long intertwining helices. DNA contains a set of "instructions" for reproducing other cells of the same kind as the original cell. It also contains the genetic information required for sexual reproduction.

desensitization Removal or reduction of a person's sensitivity to a specific substance, most commonly in the treatment of ALLERGY.

diagnosis The process of identifying a disease or diseases. Many factors must be taken into account when making a diagnosis—for instance, the findings of physical examination, previous medical history, and perhaps the health of other members of the family.

dialysis A method of separating substances in solution by passing them through a semipermeable membrane. This process is carried out naturally by the kidneys, and artificially by a kidney dialysis machine.

diastole The relaxation and dilatation of the heart after each contraction or SYSTOLE. It is during the diastole stage that the chambers of the heart fill with blood. In BLOOD PRESSURE readings, the diastolic pressure is the lower of the two figures.

differentiation Changes in structure or function of CELLS, tissue, or organs during embryonic development. Cell differentiation may manifest itself by the appearance of particular visible structures, such as muscle striations, or the production of chemical substances, such as enzymes. Tissue differentiation usually involves the grouping of cells of various types to form different tissues, which in turn may develop into a specialized organ.

dilatation (or dilation) Widening of an organ or part of it. The term is commonly used with reference to the pupil of the eye or to the neck (cervix) of the uterus.

Down's syndrome Also known as mongolism or trisomy 21, Down's syndrome is a CONGENITAL abnormality resulting from a chromosomal defect called trisomy, in which a Down's syndrome child has 47 chromosomes rather than the normal 46.

E

electrocardiograph (EKG) A machine that records electrical activity in the heart, producing a recording (electrocardiogram) in the form of a trace on paper or on an oscilloscope.

electroencephalograph (EEG) A machine that amplifies and records electrical activity in the brain. The resulting trace is called an electroencephalogram.

embolism Obstruction of a blood vessel by foreign material (embolus). The embolus may be a blood clot, clump of BACTERIA, air bubble (air embolus), or similar obstruction that is carried through the blood until it lodges in a blood vessel and blocks the blood flow. The consequences vary, depending on the size of the embolus and the part of the body deprived of blood. Embolism is one cause of STROKE, in which a part of a blood clot lodges in an artery supplying the brain. Deprived of their blood supply, brain cells starve and die (infarction), and a stroke results. Other areas that may be affected include the heart, lungs, and arteries of the legs.

endorphins Peptides with a relatively low molecular weight that occur naturally in the body and bind to the same receptor sites in the brain as do morphine compounds. Their name derives from the original description of them as endogenous morphines. They are believed to be part of the body's natural protection against pain, and it is postulated that their action may explain the fact that some pains can be temporarily ignored if a person is distracted, for instance, by another pain. They may also be involved in the apparent "addiction" of some people to certain activities, such as long-distance running, which may encourage the body's production of endorphins, producing the so-called "runner's high."

endoscopy Examination of parts of the body by means of inserting a lighted instrument through one of the body's natural orifices or through a small surgical incision. Instruments include a BRONCHOSCOPE and sigmoidoscope. Endoscopes may incorporate lens systems for viewing or photography, or devices for tissue sample removal (BIOPSY).

endothelium A membrane consisting of narrow, flattened cells that line the blood vessels, heart, and lymph vessels.

enzymes A large group of naturally-produced PROTEINS that act as catalysts in specific biochemical reactions, particularly in METABOLISM.

epinephrine A HORMONE produced by the adrenal GLANDS. It stimulates heart action, constricts certain blood vessels, and relaxes bronchial tubes and other smooth muscle. When the body is under stress, production is stimulated, thus preparing the body for emergency "flight or fight" action. Epinephrine obtained from animals or produced synthetically can be used to treat bronchial asthma and some allergic conditions.

epithelium A layer of tissue that covers external and internal body surfaces.

F

fertilization The union of sperm cell and egg cell. Although many million sperm are released into the vagina at ejaculation, only one penetrates and fertilizes the ovum. Once fertilized, the ovum's membrane is reinforced and the ovum becomes impenetrable to further sperm.

fibrinogen A PROTEIN manufactured in the liver and released into the blood, where it acts as a clotting agent when a blood vessel is damaged. Together with another substance—thrombin—fibrinogen produces long threads of fibrin that create a mesh that traps blood corpuscles to form a blood clot.

fibroid A normally benign TUMOR that grows in the muscle and connective tissues of the uterus or vagina. One single large tumor or several smaller ones may develop. A large fibroid may cause the uterus to press on neighboring organs, particularly the bladder, or may interfere with normal menstrual functioning. In such cases, surgical removal of the fibroid(s) may be required.

fimbria A fringelike projection, particularly the one at the opening of each Fallopian tube, close to each ovary. Fimbriae are covered with CILIA, which lash backward and forward, sweeping a matured ovum released by the ovary into the Fallopian tube.

fluoride A compound of the chemical element fluorine. Fluorides help to maintain calcium deposits in hard tissues of the body. The addition of fluorides to water supplies seems to help prevent tooth decay. Fluorides may also play a role in the prevention and treatment of osteoporosis.

follicle A small cavity or sac that produces secretions. Follicles have various forms. Hair follicles are tiny cylindrical depressions from which single hairs grow; they are linked to sebaceous GLANDS. In the ovary, each ovum, or egg cell, is contained within a membrane, which with the ovum constitutes an ovarian or Graafian follicle.

G

ganglion In the nervous system, a ganglion is a cluster of NERVE cells where nerve fibers connect to create a center of nervous activity. Ganglion also describes a type of swelling or CYST that contains fluid. Most ganglia of this type are connected to a tendon or membrane at a joint, usually at the wrist. Usually painless, a ganglion may be removed by surgery if it is troublesome.

gangrene Death of tissue caused by lack of oxygen, usually because the blood supply has been stopped. It may be caused by burns, frostbite, injury, obstruction of blood vessels, or vascular disease. Wet gangrene is characterized by an offensive, watery discharge and is easily infected. In dry gangrene, infection does not occur, instead, circulation is cut off gradually, the affected part becoming dry and mummified. Amputation may be necessary as a result of either type.

gastrulation An embryological term referring to the complex rearrangement of CELLS that occurs within the BLASTOCYST following CLEAVAGE. This rearrangement involves the migration of cells whose descendants will form future internal organs in their approximately final positions within the embryo. The pattern of movement varies among different animals, but in human beings, cells either migrate inward to form the mesoderm and endoderm layers or they remain on the outside to form the ectoderm layer.

gene The basic unit of inheritance, composed of molecules of DEOXYRIBONUCLEIC ACID (DNA) and located on the CHROMOSOMES of each CELL. The genes determine and pass on all the characteristics an individual inherits, for example, color of eyes and hair and shape of facial features.

gland A CELL or organ that produces and releases substances needed for the normal functioning of the body. There are two kinds—those with ducts (exocrine glands), which carry their secretions to specific regions inside or outside the body (examples being salivary glands, mammary glands, and sweat glands); and those without ducts (endocrine glands), which release their secretions (called HORMONES) directly into the bloodstream, an example being the thyroid gland.

H

hematoma An accumulation or clotted lump of blood in tissue, usually associated with bruising after an injury. Some are quite minor and may be reabsorbed by the body; others may be serious. A subdural hematoma is one that occurs under the skull following a head injury. This type may press on the brain and require surgical treatment.

hemorrhage Bleeding. Where blood loss is rapid and large, shock results and may be fatal unless blood is replaced by means of a transfusion. Hemorrhage may result from injury, complications of childbirth, from an ULCER or TUMOR, the rupturing of a blood vessel, or from bloodclotting abnormalities.

hemostat An instrument that stops bleeding by clamping a blood vessel.

hereditary Inherited genetically from one or both parents.

herpes Inflammation of the skin accompanied by the formation of small blisters, caused especially by two types of virus: *Herpes zoster* (chickenpox and shingles) and *Herpes simplex* (cold sores). An unusual feature of this condition is that although ANTIBODIES are produced after the primary infection, so that there should be no recurrence, the virus lies dormant and may reemerge in response to some strong stimulus. The process is not fully understood, nor is it clear what the stimulus might be.

hormone Any of several substances present in very small amounts in the blood and producing specific effects in the body. For instance, the hormone insulin controls the way in which the body uses glucose. The endocrine GLANDS produce most of the hormones essential for normal body functioning, their activity being governed by the action of the nervous system under the control of the hypothalamus and by the pituitary gland. Some hormones are produced by other tissues: for instance, the placenta produces sex hormones during pregnancy, and the stomach and intestines produce hormones that aid digestion.

hydrocephalus A rare condition usually present at birth, in which there is abnormal enlargement of the head due to the accumulation of cerebrospinal fluid in the brain cavities. Often found in babies suffering from SPINA BIFIDA, it may also occur as a result of brain TUMOR or meningitis. Mild cases may clear by themselves; more severe cases require surgery to drain the fluid and pass it into the bloodstream.

hypertension Abnormally high BLOOD PRESSURE.

I

immunity The ability to resist infectious disease. Immunity to certain human diseases varies according to individual inherited differences in antibody output. The chief source of natural immunity is the lymphatic system, which manufactures ANTIBODIES in response to specific alien proteins (ANTIGENS). Interferons—proteins that curb the spread of viruses—also provide natural immunity. Immunity may be active or passive. Natural active immunity is the immunity that the body creates by the production of antibodies so that one attack by a disease may produce lifelong immunity against that disease thereafter, artificial active immunity is that conferred by vaccination or immunization. Passive immunity is temporary. It occurs in the case of a newborn infant who acquires antibodies from the mother before birth, which provide a natural immunity that lasts only a few months. Or it can be provided artificially by the use of SERUM.

immunization The procedure by which acquired IMMUNITY to disease is induced in a person.

induction (of labor) Artificial stimulation of labor before it begins naturally, usually by rupturing the amniotic sac or by the use of drugs, such as OXYTOCIN.

inoculation The introduction into the body of live, weakened, or dead germs to produce IMMUNITY against infectious diseases, such as diphtheria, measles, poliomyelitis, or smallpox; a type of IMMUNIZATION.

insulin A HORMONE produced by the small groups of cells in the pancreas known as the islets of Langerhans. Insulin controls the metabolism of sugar (glucose). Insufficient production of insulin results in diabetes mellitus.

J

joint The point where two bones articulate or fuse. Joints may be immobile, as in the skull, or movable, as in the limbs.

K

keratin A tough fibrous PROTEIN that makes up the horny tissues of the body, such as fingernails, hair, and skin.

kilocalorie *See* calorie

Krebs cycle (citric acid cycle) A complex cycle of enzyme-controlled natural biochemical reactions by which pyruvic acid is broken down in the presence of oxygen to carbon dioxide. It is the final stage in the oxidation of CARBOHYDRATES.

L

lacrimal Of or relating to tears, which are produced by the lacrimal GLANDS sited just above the eye.

lanugo Fine, downy hair that covers the fetus. Most of it disappears before birth.

ligament A band of tough, flexible tissue that supports body organs or keeps bones in place. Damage to a ligament causes a sprain—the overstretching of a ligament attached to the bones of a joint. Ligaments can also be torn in an accident.

lipids Fatty substances, one example of which is CHOLESTEROL, stored in the body. They are needed as sources of available energy, but an excess is associated with obesity and tissue disorders, such as arteriosclerosis.

lipoma A fatty benign TUMOR occurring most commonly in the armpit, or on the forearm, back of the neck, or trunk.

lymph The colorless fluid of the lymphatic system. It contains white blood cells known as LYMPHOCYTES, stored in the LYMPH NODES. At the base of the neck, the two main branches of the lymphatic system merge with two veins so that lymph becomes incorporated in the bloodstream.

lymph nodes Small masses of spongy tissue found throughout the lymphatic system, especially in the armpit, neck, and groin. The lymph nodes contain LYMPHOCYTES, act as filters for BACTERIA and waste debris, and produce ANTIBODIES. Lymph nodes are stimulated by infection, and, in such circumstances, may become swollen and painful.

lymphocyte A type of white blood cell formed in the thymus and bone marrow and found in the lymphatic system. Lymphocytes are concerned with the production of ANTIBODIES and IMMUNITY.

lymphoma A general term for new tissue, which may be MALIGNANT, growing in the lymphatic system.

M

malignant Tending to grow progressively worse; potentially life-threatening. Malignant usually refers to cancerous TUMORS as opposed to BENIGN tumors. A malignant tumor, or CANCER, invades surrounding tissue and must be removed surgically or treated with radiotherapy or drugs at the earliest possible stage.

medulla The inside of certain organs, such as bones and GLANDS, as opposed to the surface CORTEX.

melanin The brown or black pigment that occurs naturally in the lowest layer of the epidermis. It gives coloring to parts of the body such as the hair, skin, and iris of the eye. It is derived from an AMINO ACID, tyrosine, through ENZYME action. If the enzyme is absent, the person has no melanin pigment and is described as an albino.

meninges Three membranes that cover the brain and spinal cord. They are the pia mater (internal), the arachnoid, and the dura mater (external).

metabolism All the chemical processes by which life systems are organized and maintained, involving the breakdown (catabolism) and building up (anabolism) of complex substances, the assimilation of nutrients, and the release of energy. Metabolic rate describes an individual's energy output. Basal metabolic rate describes this output in an individual at rest.

metastasis The movement of CANCER cells from one part of the body to another.

micturition An alternative term for urination.

mitosis The process by which a CELL replicates to produce two daughter cells, each identical to the parent. This is the method by which the body grows, and is also the way it generates new cells to replace those lost as a result of injury or normal cell death. During mitosis, each CHROMOSOME is duplicated, then the resulting duplicates separate and migrate to opposite sides of the parent cell. A new nuclear membrane develops around each set of chromosomes, and a new cell wall forms between the NUCLEI. In this way, mitosis produces two daughter cells with the same chromosome constitution as the parent cell. Meiosis is a similar but more complex process of cell division in which the daughter cells end up with only half the total number of chromosomes of the parent cell and so become gametes (sex cells), either sperm or ova.

mole A small, pigmented area of skin, sometimes raised above the level of the surrounding skin. A mole present at birth is usually called a birthmark.

morula A stage of embryonic development following CLEAVAGE. After fertilization, the ZYGOTE undergoes continuous cell division to produce a small bundle of cells—the morula. In turn, the cells of the morula become separated to form an outer wall (the trophoblast) and a cluster of cells (the BLASTOCYST).

motor Having to do with, or causing, motion. Motor NERVES carry impulses from the central nervous system to muscles to make the latter contract.

mucous membrane Mucus-secreting tissue that lines most of the inner cavities and passages of the body, such as the digestive tract, the respiratory tract, the urinary tract, and reproductive tract. Although similar in structure, mucous membranes perform different functions. Those of the nose warm and moisten air; those of the trachea (windpipe) trap dust and dirt; while those of the stomach contain special GLANDS concerned with digestion and prevent stomach acids from harming body tissues.

myelin A white, fatty material that covers most AXONS, or impulse-carrying fibers, of NEURONS. Diseases such as multiple sclerosis result from myelin abnormalities.

N

narcolepsy An irresistible tendency to fall asleep at any time or place, not caused by normal tiredness. It is most usually the result of brain damage in the region of the hypothalamus, perhaps as a consequence of infection, brain tumor, or head injury.

narcotic Any substance that produces stupor, sleep, and relieves pain. Narcotics include opium and opium-derivatives such as morphine. Popularly and legally, the term also refers to an addictive drug used illegally.

necrosis Death of CELLS, tissues, or part of an organ in an otherwise living body. Necrosis may occur after severe burns or other injuries, or because the blood supply is cut off for a long period, as in GANGRENE.

neoplasm A new and abnormal growth or TUMOR that may be BENIGN or MALIGNANT.

nerve Any of the cordlike bundles of sensory fibers or NEURONS along which nerve impulses travel.

neuron A NERVE cell, including the cell body. DENDRITES carry incoming impulses to the nerve cell; the AXON carries impulses away.

nucleus The central body of a CELL. Surrounded by cytoplasm, the nucleus contains CHROMOSOMES and the materials required for cell division and heredity.

O

occlusion Closing or shutting off—a blockage anywhere in the body. In coronary occlusion, one of the arteries supplying blood to the heart is blocked by a blood clot or similar obstruction. The term also applies to the mouth's "bite"—the way in which the teeth of the upper and lower jaws fit together.

optic chiasma The arrangement of nerve fibers where the optic nerves of both eyes join and cross, in front of the limbic system.

ossification The process of bone formation.

oxytocin A HORMONE produced by the pituitary gland that stimulates uterine contractions. Synthetic oxytocin is sometimes used to stimulate labor (INDUCTION).

P

pacemaker A small knot of tissue in the right atrium of the heart that triggers the heartbeat. If this natural pacemaker fails to function properly, however, its function can be taken over by an artificial electronic device known as a cardiac pacemaker, which may be inserted surgically. It acts by stimulating the heart with tiny electrical impulses.

pathogen The scientific name given to any microorganism that causes disease.

percussion A method of physical examination that involves tapping the body surface with quick, sharp blows of the fingertips to cause vibration in internal organs, particularly the heart and lungs. Unusual sounds may indicate the need for further investigation.

peristalsis Slow, wavelike motions of organs of the body, such as the esophagus, intestines, and Fallopian tubes, which push along the contents of the tube or duct. It is affected by coordinated, sequential involuntary contractions of smooth muscle.

phagocytosis The process by which a specialized cell (phagocyte) engulfs or ingests other small particles, particularly bits of foreign matter, such as dust, or pathogenic BACTERIA. It is an important mechanism in the body's defenses against infection.

phenotype The outward physical appearance of an organism determined by genetic and environmental factors.

physiotherapy The treatment—usually to assist recovery from accidents or surgery—of bone, joint, and muscle disorders by physical means, such as massage and aided exercise, or other techniques, such as heat treatment (diathermy), ultrasound, or electrical stimulation.

plasma The liquid part of blood, without the blood cells.

platelet A minute, colorless blood cell that helps blood to clot.

polyp A TUMOR of the MUCOUS MEMBRANES, usually occurring in the nose, uterus, or colon. Polyps are seldom MALIGNANT but may cause obstruction.

prolactin A hormone of the pituitary gland that stimulates milk production in the female breasts.

prostaglandins A group of hormonelike substances in the body that perform a variety of actions. Not all their functions are fully understood, but they stimulate or relax smooth muscle, may regulate CELL behavior and the blood flow in the kidneys, and contribute to the action of HORMONES. Following medical studies, some prostaglandins may become valuable drugs to be used, for example, in induction of labor, treatment of peptic ULCERS, and relief of inflammation.

protein A complex chemical compound built of long chains of AMINO ACIDS that forms an essential part of every living CELL. Hair, muscles, and skin are largely protein, and protein also makes up part of CHROMOSOMES, ENZYMES, blood PLASMA, and hemoglobin. Synthe-

sis of protein by the body is essential not only for the growth and repair of tissues but also for the continuation of life processes.

psychoanalysis A technique of investigating and treating certain mental disorders, which was developed by Sigmund Freud and is practiced now by Freudian, neo-Freudian, and other psychoanalysts.

psychotherapy A general term for all forms of non-medical treatment of mental illness, typified as the "talking cures." At its most general, the term can mean simply treatment of the mind. More specific usage, however, tends to restrict it to non-Freudian (that is, non-psychoanalytical) techniques.

R

rabies A lethal VIRAL disease transmitted to humans by the bite of an infected (rabid) animal. Dogs, although the best known, are not the only source. The virus travels from the bite along the NERVE fibers to the brain. Symptoms include muscle spasms, convulsions, and extreme excitement, as well as a fear of drinking—which gave the disease its original name: hydrophobia. Although usually fatal, rabies has an incubation period of one month to a year, and treatment with injections of rabies vaccine at an early stage usually prevents the disease from developing.

ribonucleic acid (RNA) A substance found in all living cells that directs the CELL to manufacture specific ENZYMES and other PROTEINS by regulating the assembly of AMINO ACIDS.

rod A cylindrical structure in the retina of the eye. Rods distinguish only shades of gray but are sensitive to faint light, enabling us to see in dim surroundings.

rubella Also known as German measles, a mild VIRAL infection characterized by a pink rash spreading all over the body, sometimes accompanied by headache and mild fever. Although not normally a problem, rubella contracted by a woman during the first three months of pregnancy can cause serious birth defects, such as cataracts of the eyes.

S

saline A solution containing salt. In medical usage, this refers to a weak solution of salt, at approximately the same concentration as body fluids.

sarcoma A MALIGNANT TUMOR in connective tissue.

septicemia Blood poisoning in which BACTERIA or other germs are present in the blood and cause illness. Since the introduction of ANTIBIOTICS to treat infection, septicemia has become far less common.

septum A wall or division between two cavities, as in the nasal septum, which divides the nostrils.

serum The clear, yellowish fluid that separates from blood after clotting. Serum is PLASMA without FIBRINOGEN, and contains ANTIBODIES. The term is also used to describe blood fluid containing antibodies that is used to provide temporary immunity. Examples are antivenins, used to counteract the venom of a snake bite, and ANTITOXINS.

shock An emotional or physical reaction to a traumatic event. The term is used most commonly to describe emotional shock. More serious, and potentially fatal, is clinical shock, which is a common consequence of physical TRAUMA, such as can occur in an accident or major surgery. Clinical shock can cause death from reduced blood supply to the brain and vital organs.

sinus A hollow space or cavity, generally in bone. The term commonly refers to the paranasal sinuses, the membrane-lined cavities in bones around the nose. Sinusitis refers to inflammation of these sinuses.

spina bifida A CONGENITAL malformation of the spine in which some of the vertebrae fail to fuse correctly to create the channel that normally protects the spinal cord. As a result, the cord may be malformed and lack certain nerves. Complications of the most severe cases include HYDROCEPHALUS and meningitis (inflammation of the MENINGES).

steroids Naturally occurring or synthetic HORMONES. Natural steroids include the sex hormones—progesterone and estrogen.

stroke A THROMBOSIS affecting the brain. The term can also describe the result of any injury that blocks the blood supply to part of the brain, causing symptoms such as paralysis.

symptom An obvious change in the body's appearance, feelings, or functions, indicating an underlying disorder.

synapse A junction between NERVE cells where nervous impulses are transmitted from one cell to another.

syndrome A collection of SYMPTOMS or other signs that characterize an illness.

systole The rhythmic contraction of the heart that pumps blood through the circulatory system. Relaxation of the heart is called DIASTOLE.

T

thrombosis The OCCLUSION or blockage of a blood vessel by a blood clot (thrombus). If thrombosis occurs in an artery leading to an arm or leg, tissue NECROSIS or GANGRENE may result. Thrombosis in an artery of the brain or in a neck artery leading to the brain causes a STROKE. A coronary thrombosis is a thrombosis in an artery that supplies the heart.

toxemia A condition caused by the absorption into the blood of poisonous (toxic) substances. Toxemia of pregnancy, however, refers to a metabolic disturbance which, if left untreated, may develop into eclampsia.

toxin A poisonous substance that can be produced in the body by PATHOGENIC microorganisms, such as BACTERIA. An ANTITOXIN may be produced naturally by the body to neutralize their effects, or prepared synthetically for the same purpose.

trauma In psychological terms, an emotional SHOCK that leads to disordered thoughts or behavior. The term is also used for a physical injury, such as an accidental or surgical wound.

tumor A swelling on or in a part of the body, caused either by abnormal tissue growth or from a collection of fluid. Tumors may be BENIGN or MALIGNANT.

typhus A group of infectious diseases caused by various *Rickettsia* microorganisms and spread by infected lice, fleas, rats, and mice. The disease is endemic in parts of the Third World.

U

ulcer An inflamed open sore on the skin or on the MUCOUS MEMBRANES lining a body cavity. Ulcers may be caused by infection, injury, disturbances of the nerve or blood supply, or by acid (as in peptic ulcers).

unconscious A term used in Freudian PSYCHOANALYSIS to describe the aspect of personality of which the conscious mind is unaware. C. G. Jung developed the separate concept of the collective unconscious, which describes the part of the personality that is influenced by "collective" memories and instincts common to all mankind, probably through cultural and social upbringing. The patterns of these influences are reflected in Jungian "archetypes," usually represented as pairs of symbols with opposing characteristics, such as good and evil. In the relationship between the conscious mind and the unconscious, Freud identified three divisions, which he called id, ego, and superego. Jung, in contrast, saw the relationship as having four modes—thinking, feeling, sensation, and intuition—cut across by two tendencies, also opposed, called introversion and extroversion.

urine test One of the oldest and still most valuable DIAGNOSTIC tests available to doctors. The examination of urine is used to detect diseases such as diabetes, diseases of the bladder and kidneys, jaundice, and other disorders of body chemistry, that cause specific changes to urine composition.

V

vaccination A means of making an individual immune to an infectious disease, such as smallpox, by injecting (or, in some cases, by swallowing) a VACCINE. The vaccine stimulates the immune system of the body to produce ANTIBODIES that neutralize the ANTIGENS, so producing IMMUNITY.

vaccine A preparation containing weakened or killed viruses introduced into the body to produce IMMUNITY against a specific disease by causing the formation of ANTIBODIES. Vaccine may be prepared in various ways. VIRUSES may be killed by heat, sound waves, or chemical treatments. Alternatively, a living—but weakened—germ can be used.

vasopressin A HORMONE secreted by the pituitary gland and having the function of regulating the water content in the body. Medically, its chief use is the control of excessive urination that occurs in diabetes.

vernix A greasy substance that covers and makes waterproof the skin of the fetus in the uterus.

villus A microscopic, threadlike projection from an internal body surface. The small intestine is lined with thousands of villi.

virus Any of a group of minute PATHOGENIC agents that occupy the borderline between living and nonliving organisms. They can survive only by penetrating the living cells of another organism. Viruses show no lifelike activity unless introduced into a living CELL; once this has occurred, however, they control the processes of the invaded cell. Viruses are responsible for numerous diseases, including HERPES and RABIES.

W

wart A harmless but unattractive growth formed on and rooted in the skin. Common warts tend to occur on hands, fingers, knees, and face, and are most common among children. They are caused by a VIRUS and are contagious but easily removed.

weal A temporarily swollen area on the skin that may result from ALLERGY, drugs, or minor injury.

X

X-chromosome One of the two sex CHROMOSOMES in the cells of human beings (the other is the Y-chromosome). A person with two X-chromosomes in each pair is female.

X rays A form of electromagnetic radiation with high energy and short wavelength and with the ability to penetrate soft tissues. X rays are invisible, but they affect photographic film and so can be used to "photograph" the interior of the body and its structures.

Y

Y-chromosome One of the two sex CHROMOSOMES in the cells of human beings. A person with one Y-chromosome and one X-chromosome in each pair is male.

Z

zona pellucida The membrane that surrounds a fertilized egg cell; it disappears before the egg becomes implanted in the lining of the uterus.

zygote The fertilized egg CELL formed from the union of a female egg cell (ovum) and a male sex cell (sperm). It is the first stage in the development of an embryo, and is followed immediately by CLEAVAGE as the cells start to divide.

Index

Credits